Papers on

PLANT
SYSTEMATICS

Flowering heads of Tragopogon. *See page 130.*

CONTENTS

v

SECTION III

Biochemical Systematics

SECTION IV

Field and Garden Studies

CONTENTS

*Pagination of the papers in this collection is indicated by the bold-
face number centered at the bottom of the page. Other page numbers appearing on certain papers refer to original publication.*

INTRODUCTION

Modern plant systematists are concerned with the taxonomic application of facts concerning plants, but they also function as active researchers who obtain these facts. Much fundamental knowledge in such diverse fields as cytogenetics, ecology, morphology, anatomy, and some areas of biochemistry owes its existence directly or indirectly to systematics. In this book of readings I have included papers that serve to illustrate the diversity of problems investigated by plant systematists and the variety of techniques used in investigating these problems.

This book of readings is aimed at advanced undergraduate students or graduate students interested in the research methods of systematic botany. The group of papers included here will, I hope, present research giving students some insight into the diversity of systematics and the vigor of the field. Students in taxonomy courses often (if not usually) receive little introduction to the nature of the information taxonomists use in arriving at their taxonomic decisions. Consequently they have little exposure to the actual research methods that systematists, in their role as the "fact finders," use in getting information of taxonomic use.

Approximately half the papers reproduced here have been published since 1960 and all but four have appeared since 1950. They are taken from fourteen journals, many of foreign origin and, for the most part, are available in the libraries of moderate-sized institutions. However, since many institutional libraries do not place journals or periodicals on reserve, papers are not always easily and reliably accessible to students. Although various methods of duplicating printed material on a large scale are now available, these methods usually do not reproduce photographs faithfully, are expensive, and in some cases are in violation of copyrights. The chief virtue of reprinting papers in a collection such as this is its convenience.

The papers included in this collection have met certain qualifications. First, they must present original research work that was done to solve a systematic problem. Second, the kinds of problems investigated must be those involving the relationships among taxa, the mode of origin and adaptive significance of certain kinds of variation patterns, the nature of isolating mechanisms, characterization of groups by anatomical, chemical, or other criteria, and so on. The results of most of these investigations are of immediate taxonomic importance. Some of the information obtained, however, is of less direct taxonomic importance, although it may help to give taxonomists some understanding of the basis of certain variation patterns. I have not included any papers dealing with typification of a plant name, with determining the correct name for a taxon, or other items of strictly nomenclatural interest.

This book has been divided into four sections which broadly represent different methodological categories: (1) "Anatomy and Morphology," (2) "Cytology, Embryology, and Genetics," (3) "Biochemical Systematics," and (4) "Field and Garden Studies." Papers in each of these sections have been selected to give a sample of the problems that exist at different taxonomic levels, ranging from the interfamily level to the intraspecific level. I have included papers illustrating some of the different approaches used to solve these problems. For the convenience of students in this country, the selection was made only from papers written in English; for the most part, they are by American workers currently contributing to systematic research. Each of the papers selected has its own bibliography; a short list of general works is also included at the back of the book to guide students interested in further reading.

Some readers will be puzzled by the omission of papers on numerical taxonomy from this collection. This interesting field was a casualty of space considerations, although its elimination is perhaps justified on the grounds that it is not primarily concerned with the research techniques associated with obtaining systematic information. The choice of papers in numerical taxonomy would be especially difficult since the field is experiencing many rapid theoretical and conceptual changes; consequently, many recently published papers are already out of date.

The papers presented in this collection reflect my own biases and interests and give only a fragmentary survey of the variety of available approaches to systematic problems. I hope, however, that this collection serves to emphasize the eclecticism and continuing vigor of systematics, wherein lies its survival value.

I am indebted to Ralph Alston, Sherwin Carlquist, Arthur Kruckeberg, Robert Sokal, and P. B. Tomlinson for their suggestions concerning portions of this work, and to Peter H. Raven and Grady L. Webster for their useful comments on the entire selection of papers.

Papers on

PLANT
SYSTEMATICS

SECTION I

Anatomy and Morphology

BAILEY, I. W., and A. C. SMITH. 1942. Degeneriaceae, a new family of flowering plants from Fiji. J. Arnold Arboretum 23: 356–365.

CARLQUIST, S. 1958. Anatomy and systematic position of *Centaurodendron* and *Yunquea* (Compositae). Brittonia 10: 78–93.

HAGERUP, O. 1953. The morphology and systematics of the leaves in Ericales. Phytomorph. 3: 459–464.

STERN, W. L. 1952. The comparative anatomy of the xylem and the phylogeny of the Julianiaceae. Amer. J. Bot. 39: 220–229.

REEDER, J. R. 1957. The embryo in grass systematics. Amer. J. Bot. 44: 756–768.

REEDER, J. R. 1962. The bambusoid embryo: A reappraisal. Amer. J. Bot. 49: 639–641.

HEINTZELMAN, C. E., JR., and R. A. HOWARD. 1948. The comparative morphology of the Icacinaceae. V. The pubescence and the crystals. Amer. J. Bot. 35: 42–52.

LEWIS, W. H. 1965. Pollen morphology and evolution in *Hedyotis* subgenus Edrisia (Rubiaceae). Amer. J. Bot. 52: 257–264.

SKVARLA, J. J., and B. L. TURNER. 1966. Pollen wall ultrastructure and its bearing on the systematic position of *Blennosperma* and *Crocidium* (Compositae). Amer. J. Bot. 53: 555–563.

Anatomical and morphological studies of plants have traditionally provided the keystone for systematic investigations; consequently, the number of papers in these fields is formidable. In this section I have included papers which illustrate a variety of techniques as well as levels of morphological and anatomical study. The first two papers represent systematic studies which integrate information obtained from the examination of a number of structures or tissues, such as carpels, stamens, and wood. Next are papers presenting the results of study of single organs or tissues, followed by papers dealing with individual cell types or cellular inclusions.

The paper by Bailey and Smith describes Degeneriaceae, a family of ranalian plants of exceptional phylogenetic interest because of the many primitive features of its sole member, *D. vitiensis* from Fiji. In view of the prominence given *Degeneria* in many recent taxonomic and morphological texts, students may be interested to read the paper in which the family made its taxonomic debut.

Carlquist deals with the unusual arborescent composite genera *Centaurodendron* and *Yunquea*, both endemic to the Juan Fernandez Islands off the coast of Chile. These odd plants have been referred to the Cynareae, the thistle tribe of Compositae, but they bear little superficial resemblance to other thistles. Nevertheless, a survey of the vegetative and floral anatomy of these genera suggested to Carlquist that they are indeed "good" members of the Cynareae.

Hagerup's paper serves as an example of the use of simple, rather gross vegetative characters of a single organ in taxonomic studies. Hagerup studied various features of the leaves of Ericales (mostly Ericaceae) and constructed a simple leaf typology in this order to which ericalean leaves can be assigned. There is little disagreement between relationships of Ericales based on foliar characters and those based on floral and other characters except that Hagerup argues for a closer affinity between *Cassiope* and *Calluna* than seems generally acknowledged. In view of the diverse opinions concerning the relationships of Empetraceae, it is interesting to see that in foliar characters this family is definitely ericalean. It is unfortunate that greater consideration of Epacridaceae was not given in this study.

At the tissue level, Stern's paper concerns the wood anatomy of Julianiaceae, a family of trees which some workers have suggested is related to Anacardiaceae and others have allied with Juglandaceae. Stern's study of various cellular and anatomical features of Julianiaceae shows that there are many characters shared with Anacardiaceae, but that there are few shared with Juglandaceae. These findings suggest that the relationships lie with the first rather than the second family. Stern's study emphasizes the value of anatomical evidence in shedding light on controversies which seem insoluble by other means.

Reeder's papers on the use of embryo characters in grass systematics represent an extensive survey of a neglected structure which provides characters for grouping grass genera into large clusters immediately below the family level. The suggested tribal rearrangements are based on information derived from embryo morphology integrated with that from cytological and anatomical surveys made by a number of other workers. The second of the two papers completes the story presented in the first one by reinterpreting the bambusoid embryo and adding another embryo type to those discussed in the first paper.

The next paper by Heintzelman and Howard on hairs and crystals of Icacinaceae illustrates the utility of cellular and intracellular features in characterizing genera of this family and confirming their relationships.

Also at the cellular level, Lewis' study of several species of the rubiaceous genus *Hedyotis* (*Houstonia*) is an example of the use of pollen characters in working out interspecific relationships. Lewis found five pollen types in this group of species and postulated a pollen-character phylogeny which in general agreed with suggestions of phyletic affinities that had been based on other kinds of evidence.

The last paper by Skvarla and Turner is an interesting one which applies data from an investigation of pollen ultrastructure to a problem of systematic affinities. The relationships of *Blennosperma* and *Crocidium* to each other and to other Compositae have been the subject of controversy. The evidence presented in this study suggests some answers to these questions of affinity and further suggests that studies at the ultrastructural level are of potentially great value in systematic research.

DEGENERIACEAE, A NEW FAMILY OF FLOWERING PLANTS FROM FIJI

I. W. Bailey and A. C. Smith

With five plates

In 1934 the junior author collected specimens of a fruiting tree on the Fijian island of Vanua Levu, but efforts to place the plant in a family failed. Neither fruit nor foliage suggested any plant previously known from the Pacific. Although wood from the trunk was available, no definite suggestion of a family could be made by those who examined the specimen. Recently, a re-examination of the wood and a study of the internal structure of the twigs and leaves indicated that the plant is related to the Magnoliaceae, and it has subsequently been ascertained that the plant is conspecific with a tree collected in flowering condition in the interior of Viti Levu by Mr. Otto Degener in 1941.

This Fijian plant, which is now represented by ample foliage, flowers, fruits, and wood, is definitely a member of the ranalian complex. It exhibits close similarities to the Magnoliaceae, particularly in the internal structure of its vegetative organs, in its pollen, and in the vascularization of its stamens. However, we cannot place it in the Magnoliaceae, for reasons to be discussed on succeeding pages, without expanding the current concept of that family to an unwarranted degree and certainly far beyond the limits proposed by Dandy (in Kew Bull. **1927**: 257–264. 1927) and Hutchinson (Fam. Fl. Pl. Dicot. 81. 1926). Another comparatively close relative of the new plant is the genus *Himantandra* F. v. Muell.,[1] originally believed to be a member of the Annonaceae, but since — and we believe correctly — established as representing the unigeneric family Himantandraceae (Diels in Bot. Jahrb. **55**: 126. 1917).

These three families, Magnoliaceae (sensu stricto),[2] Himantandraceae, and the proposed Degeneriaceae, form a group with salient morphological similarities. They are differentiated from more remotely related families such as the Eupomatiaceae, Annonaceae, Winteraceae, Trochodendraceae, etc. by fundamentally significant differences which we shall consider in future detailed treatments of these groups. For the purposes of the present paper, the relationships of the new plant need not be considered beyond the Magnoliaceae, Himantandraceae, and Winteraceae. Following the

[1] The use of the name *Himantandra* F. v. Muell. rather than *Galbulimima* F. M. Bailey is discussed in detail in the following article in this Journal.

[2] Whenever mentioned in the following pages, the family Magnoliaceae is intended in the restricted sense, as interpreted by Dandy, Hutchinson, and many other recent students.

Reprinted by permission of the authors and publisher from the Journal of the Arnold Arboretum, **23**, 356–365 (1942).

technical description of the new genus and species, we shall discuss the salient internal morphological features of the plant. The remarkable stamens and carpel of *Degeneria* deserve special consideration, since they are likely to prove of some significance in future discussions of the floral morphology of the angiosperms.

It is a privilege to associate the name of the new plant with that of Mr. Otto Degener, collector of the type specimen and author of Flora Hawaiiensis and numerous other works on Pacific botany. We are indebted to Dr. J. Hutchinson, of the Royal Botanic Gardens, Kew, for his kindness in sending us floral material of *Himantandra,* and to Dr. A. O. Dahl for verifying our interpretation of the pollen morphology of *Degeneria.* Figures 1–11 were drawn by Mr. Gordon W. Dillon and figures 12–14 by Dr. Charlotte G. Nast. We are further indebted to Dr. Nast for the preparation of serial sections of the vegetative and floral organs of our plant.

Degeneriaceae fam. nov.

Familia characteribus generis unici.

Degeneria gen. nov.

Arbor, stipulis nullis, foliis alternatis simplicibus pinnatinerviis. Flores solitarii supra-axillares hermaphroditi. Sepala et petala disparia, calyce rotato, sepalis quam petalis multo minoribus, petalis pluriseriatis carnosis imbricatis, toro coriaceo subgloboso vel convexo, centro sub ovario depresso. Stamina hypogyna pluria carnosa complanata, loculis 4 binis parallelis extrorsis immersis rimis 2 longitudinalibus dehiscentibus. Staminodia intra stamina et quam stamina pauciores, textura similia. Carpellum unicum inaequilateraliter ellipsoideum, partibus ventralibus approximatis diffuse stigmatiferis, loculo unico, ovulis numerosis biseriatis, placentis 2 sutura ventrali parallelis. Fructus indehiscens, seminibus numerosis biseriatis, alteris sessilibus, alteris funiculo filiformi suspensis.

Degeneria vitiensis sp. nov.

Arbor ubique glabra, ramulis subrectis teretibus crassis (apicem versus 3–8 mm. diametro) fusco-nigrescentibus rugulosis saepe fistulosis; petiolis gracilibus (1.5–3 mm. diametro) rugulosis supra canaliculatis 2–6.5 cm. longis basi incrassatis; laminis chartaceis vel subcoriaceis siccitate utrinque fuscis ellipticis vel obovato-ellipticis, 9–27 cm. longis, 3.5–13.5 cm. latis, basi gradatim angustatis et in petiolum decurrentibus, apice rotundatis vel leviter emarginatis, margine integris et leviter revolutis, supra subnitidis, costa supra subplana vel interdum leviter canaliculata subtus prominente et rugulosa, nervis secundariis utrinsecus 10–18 cum aliis debilioribus interspersis divergentibus marginem versus anastomosantibus et rete venularum intricato utrinque conspicue prominulis; pedicellis sub anthesi 2–3 cm. longis gracilibus nigrescentibus rugulosis apicem versus gradatim incrassatis, bracteas 2 vel 3 coriaceas ovatas obtusas 1–1.5 mm. longas gerentibus vel cicatricibus ornatis; calyce coriaceo sub anthesi 8–9 mm. diametro profunde lobato, sepalis 3 ovato-deltoideis 3.5–5 mm. longis et latis ubique obscure luteo-glandulosis, apice obtusis, margine anguste scariosis subintegris (vel obscure erosulis) inconspicue ciliatis (pilis circiter 0.15 mm. longis); petalis 12 vel 13 ut videtur 3–4-seriatis concavis apicem versus plus minusve cohaerentibus, elliptico-oblongis (vel interioribus obovatis), apice et basi rotundatis, ubique obscure luteo-glandulosis, margine pilis simplicibus ad 0.6 mm. longis decidue ciliatis, exterioribus maximis 18–19 mm. longis et 10–12 mm. latis, interioribus crassissimis et minimis circiter 12 mm. longis et 6 mm. latis; staminibus circiter 20 congestis plus minusve 3-seriatis oblongis vel obovato-oblongis, 4.5–6 mm. longis, 1.5–2.5 mm. latis (interioribus angustissimis), apice rotundatis vel subtruncatis et ibi ut petalis ciliatis, obscure luteo-glandulosis, loculis 2–3.5 mm. longis; staminodiis 11 vel 12 spathulato-oblongis, circiter 6 mm. longis et apicem versus 1.5–2.5 mm. latis, apice rotundatis et conspicue introrse cucullatis; carpello sub anthesi circiter 5.5 mm. longo, 3 mm. lato, et 2 mm. crasso, basi obtuso, apice subrotundato, marginibus stigmatiferis 3–4 mm. longis undulatis, ovario crasse carnoso luteo-glanduloso, loculo lineari-oblongo circiter 4 mm. longo parti ventrali oblique parallelo, ovulis 24 vel 26 oblongis sub anthesi circiter 0.5 mm. longis utrinque rotundatis; pedicellis sub fructu crassis (2–3 mm. diametro) ad 4 cm. longis, cicatricibus persistentibus infra medium, sepalis persistentibus; fructibus oblongo-ellipsoideis maturitate ad 5 cm. longis et 3 cm. latis et crassis, leviter inaequilateralibus, dorso basim versus affixis, ventre stigmatum carina ornatis, pericarpio coriaceo demum ad 2 mm. crasso; endocarpio inter semina carinato et appendiculas ceriferas irregulariter lobatas 2–3 mm. longas basi seminum vel funiculorum subpersistentes saepe gerente; seminibus obovoideis, 8–11 mm. longis, 5–8 mm. latis, valde complanatis, grosse scrobiculatis, basi obtusis vel breviter stipitatis, apice rotundatis.

FIJI. Viti Levu: T h o l o   N o r t h : Nauwanga, vicinity of Nandarivatu, alt. 750 m., *Degener 14537* (TYPE, Arn. Arb.), Feb. 24, 1941 (tree, in forest). Vanua Levu: M b u a : Lower Wainunu River valley, alt. 0–200 m., *Smith 1754* (Gray Herb., N. Y. Bot. Gard., etc.), May 7, 1934 (tree 14 m. high, in open forest; native name: *yaranggele*).

The type collection bears flowers and a single detached immature fruit, while *Smith 1754* bears mature fruits. In foliage the two specimens show slight differences, which appear to us of an individual nature.

STEM. In *Degeneria* the primary vascular cylinder is a much dissected dictyostele, being composed of numerous discrete bundles that are separated by conspicuous gaps. Each bundle is capped externally by slender thick-walled fibers and is subtended internally by slender, vertically elongated strands of parenchyma. The bulk of the pith is composed of large, relatively thin-walled medullary cells, but transversely oriented plates or diaphragms of stone cells are formed, particularly at the nodal and subnodal levels of the stem. Large spherical oil cells and irregular, often branched sclereids are conspicuous features of the cortex.

In the secondary xylem of the young stem, narrow multiseriate rays extend outward from the gaps in the dictyostele. These rays flare outward through the secondary phloem (*fig. 24*), which is stratified into alternating strands of hard and soft bast. The thin-walled, angular vessels (*fig. 25*) of the secondary xylem occur singly or in small, usually radially oriented clusters. The vessel-members have numerous scalariform perforations and the pitting between vessels, and between vessels and parenchymatous elements, is typically scalariform. The thin-walled imperforate tracheary cells have

7

pits with minute borders. The parenchyma distribution is dominantly banded apotracheal with a low percentage of scanty paratracheal. The multiseriate rays in the later-formed secondary xylem (*fig. 26*) are of typically fusiform outline as seen in tangential longitudinal sections. The infrequently occurring uniseriate rays are low and are composed of upright cells, such as are present on the margins of the multiseriate rays. Oil cells are of sporadic occurrence in the rays of the secondary xylem. In the stem, the periderm develops in a superficial position.

Each of the salient structural features enumerated in the two preceding paragraphs occurs in the Magnoliaceae, and similar combinations of these structural characters are formed in tropical representatives of that family. In fact, the similarities are so close that it is difficult to differentiate the stems of the two families without a detailed study of their nodal anatomy. On the contrary, the stems of *Himantandra,* although of the same general structural type as in *Degeneria* and the Magnoliaceae, may be differentiated by the occurrence of alternate multiseriate pitting in the vessels of the secondary xylem and by a less conspicuous stratification of the phloem into alternating strands of hard and soft bast.

LEAF AND NODAL ANATOMY. In *Degeneria* five traces enter the base of the petiole, leaving five gaps in the cauline vascular cylinder, i.e. the plant has a penta-lacunar node. The traces divide in their outward course, forming numerous vascular bundles that become oriented into a cylindrical foliar stele. This medullated foliar stele (*fig. 27*), which tends to have a more or less flattened adaxial surface, extends through the petiole and the midrib of the leaf.

The vascularization of the leaf exhibits fundamental similarities to that which occurs in *Himantandra* and the Magnoliaceae, but differs markedly from that which characterizes the Winteraceae, Eupomatiaceae, Annonaceae, Schizandraceae, etc. In *Degeneria,* as in *Himantandra* and the Magnoliaceae, the vascular bundles that branch outward from the median trace are segregated into two groupings on opposite sides of the foliar vascular cylinder. In other words, one or more of them retain a normal orientation of xylem and phloem and form part of the abaxial surface of the foliar stele, whereas the remaining ones develop an inverted orientation of xylem and phloem and form part of the adaxial surface of the foliar vascular cylinder.

Himantandra is characterized by having a tri-lacunar node instead of a penta-lacunar one as *Degeneria.* Although the number of traces that pass outward into the petiole of the Magnoliaceae fluctuates from three to five to many, the nodes of these plants may be distinguished from those of *Himantandra* and *Degeneria* by the fact that they have an additional trace which is concerned primarily in the vascularization of the stipules. This trace occurs on the opposite side of the cauline stele from the median trace of the leaf.

The leaves of *Degeneria,* like those of *Himantandra,* have no stipules, but the leaf-blades of the former genus resemble those of the Magnoliaceae in having stomata with conspicuous subsidiary cells oriented parallel to the

8

guard cells, numerous large spherical oil cells, etc. The leaves of *Himan-tandra* are characterized by having their stomata arranged in circles under each of the peltate scales which cover the lower surface of the lamina.

FLOWERS. Solitary supra-axillary flowers characterize *Degeneria*. In the Magnoliaceae the only genera with axillary bisexual flowers are *Elmerrillia* Dandy and *Michelia* L., and here solitary flowers are unusual. The axillary flowers of *Himantandra* are sometimes solitary. The fact that the pedicels of *Degeneria* are bracteate near the middle may indicate that the inflorescence is reduced from a more complex structure and that the supposed pedicel is partially peduncular in origin.

The floral axis of *Degeneria,* unlike that of most Magnoliaceae, is short (*fig. 4*), and the solitary indehiscent carpel is attached in a depression on the apex of the torus (*fig. 28*); this annular apex of the torus is formed at least in part by the fused bases of the stamens and staminodes. A similar apical depression of the torus occurs in *Himantandra*. The vascularization of the floral axis of *Degeneria* and *Himantandra* is of a type commonly encountered in dicotyledons. On the contrary, that of the Magnoliaceae is characterized by its complexity. In addition to a normal dictyostele, the floral axis commonly exhibits a system of anastomosing and dichotomizing cortical bundles. The median vein of the sporophylls is attached to the inner dictyostele, whereas the lateral veins frequently connect with the outer cortical vascular cylinder.

The floral envelope of *Degeneria* is clearly differentiated at maturity into calyx and corolla, but, although the petals differ from the sepals in size and form (*fig. 3*), they resemble them in texture and in their internal cellular composition. In the Magnoliaceae the sepals and petals are usually sub-similar, all of the tepals commonly having a more typically petaloid form, texture, and internal structure. Most early descriptions of the perianth-arrangement in *Himantandra* mention the calyx as composed of two closed calyptrate sepals, one within the other. Diels (in Bot. Jahrb. 55: 126. 1917) describes these organs as calyptriform bracts and states that sepals and petals are lacking. As the flower of *Himantandra* matures, first one and then the other of these calyptriform organs is lost, leaving closely approximated circular scars at the base of the floral axis. In this connec-tion, however, it should be noted that serial transverse sections of young flower-buds suggest that the calyptriform organs are not single modified appendages, but rather represent fused parts of a perianth. Their internal cellular structure closely resembles that of the sepals and petals of *Degeneria*. Therefore it seems likely that they should be interpreted as a calyptra of fused petals enclosed within a calyptra of fused sepals, just as the single calyptra of *Eupomatia* is regarded as having arisen from fused parts of a perianth.

STAMENS AND STAMINODES. The stamens of *Degeneria* are not differen-tiated into filament, anther, and connective, and are best described as broad micro-sporophylls (*figs. 15* and *18*) having four slender elongated sporangia that are immersed beneath the abaxial surface of the sporophyll. The

9

stamens have a conspicuous median vein that dichotomizes at its apex and two lateral veins situated near the margins of the sporophyll (*fig. 15*). The paired sporangia are not located in close relationship to either the median or the lateral veins and thus are not in direct contact with vascular tissue. The staminodes, formed at a higher level of the floral axis, are hooded and have three parallel veins (*fig. 17*). Occasionally one of these hooded organs bears rudimentary micro-sporophylls (*fig. 16*).

The stamens of *Himantandra* are of a fundamentally similar morphological type, but they are much longer and have shorter basally disposed sporangia. Three veins enter the base of the stamens and staminodes, as in *Degeneria,* but the lateral veins frequently do not extend beyond the lower third of the micro-sporophylls. The veins of unusually large stamens may form short lateral veinlets, but these vascular branches are not oriented in relation to the sporangia. In *Himantandra* staminodes occur both below and above the fertile micro-sporophylls.

Although the stamens of the Magnoliaceae differ markedly in having large, protuberant, usually marginally placed pairs of elongated sporangia, they are characterized by having a similar type of vascularization. Many representatives of the family, in addition to a conspicuous median vein, exhibit two lateral veins at the base of the stamen which extend outward for varying distances. Here again, neither the lateral veins nor their branches are related in distribution to the sporangia. In certain of the Magnoliaceae, e. g. species of *Michelia,* the lateral veins are much reduced or are entirely eliminated.

POLLEN. The pollen grains of *Degeneria* are broadly ellipsoid in form, 45 to 55 μ long and 37 to 42 μ broad, their dimensions fluctuating considerably during varying degrees of re-expansion of the grains. They are typically of the so-called monocolpate type, having a single narrow furrow (*fig. 12*), which broadens markedly at both poles of the grain. The outer exine is smooth except in the region of the furrow, where it is finely and irregularly pitted. During the later stages of the re-expansion of the pollen grains, this layer tends to split in the broader polar parts of the furrow and thus to allow the contents of the grain to bulge outward. In pollen that has been re-expanded by a brief treatment in dilute NaOH, the furrow of the outer exine is subtended by a broad band of much swollen, finely and uniformly pitted material (*figs. 13* and *14*). This porous layer dissolves along with the contents of the grain during more prolonged treatments with NaOH, leaving the outer exine as the only residue.

Monocolpate pollen grains of similar size and form, having similar polar extensions of the furrow, occur in various representatives of the Magnoliaceae. Our colleague, Dr. A. O. Dahl, has demonstrated experimentally that even in the pollen grains of *Magnolia stellata* (Sieb. & Zucc.) Maxim., *M. denudata* Desr., and M. *salicifolia* (Sieb. & Zucc.) Maxim. the pollen tubes frequently emerge at the poles, rather than at the sides, of the grains. The pollen grains of *Himantandra* are smaller and of more nearly spherical form. They have a thin, smooth outer surface, but are provided with a single furrow and thus are also of the monocolpate type.

10

CARPEL. *Degeneria* is characterized by having a single indehiscent carpel (*figs. 4, 30*). In *Himantandra* the carpels are several, usually more or less coherent at the base, at length concrescent and indehiscent. The Magnoliaceae usually have numerous carpels, which frequently are coherent at the base; the carpels commonly are dehiscent, but in some cases are indehiscent and then concrescent. Reduction in the number of carpels is infrequent in the Magnoliaceae, but in certain cases, such as *Pachylarnax* Dandy, these organs may be reduced to two. It should be noted in this connection that reduction to a single carpel occurs in several species of the Winteraceae.

The carpel of *Degeneria,* preceding and during anthesis, resembles an adaxially folded, 3-veined sporophyll (*fig. 22*), in which the lateral veins, the narrow linear placentas, and the two rows of numerous ovules are quite remote from the margins of the macro-sporophyll. Furthermore, the margins of the carpel are not infolded or coherent during ontogeny, but tend to flare apart externally (*figs. 22* and *23*). The placentation is clearly laminar and adaxial. At anthesis, broad areas (between the margins and the placentas) of the adaxial surface of the macro-sporophyll are closely approximated, but are not actually coherent except in the basal part of the carpel. The epidermal layers of the two adjacent adaxial surfaces are separated by numerous, loosely interlocking, short, glandular hairs. Thus the stigmatic areas of the carpel of *Degeneria* are not localized externally upon the recurved margin of the sporophyll, but extend inward along the adaxial surfaces of the carpel into close proximity to the placentas. During the development of the fruit, the contiguous adaxial surfaces of the carpel become concrescent, the outwardly recurved margins of the sporophyll persisting as parallel corky ridges. The ovules of *Degeneria* are of the anatropous type illustrated in *figs. 20* and *21*. The vascular bundle of the ovule is conspicuously coiled in its course through the funicle.

FRUIT. The mature fruit of *Degeneria* is inequilaterally oblong-ellipsoid, marked on the ventral side by the elongated stigmatic ridges described above. The coriaceous pericarp is smooth without, while the endocarp is irregularly ridged, possibly due to the pressure of the developing seeds (although even when the seeds are abortive, these ridges are discernible). In addition to these subcoriaceous ridges, the endocarp bears small irregular waxy appendages, these being especially apparent in the placental regions. Often these appendages appear somewhat cupuliform about the bases of seeds, with which they are frequently detached (*fig. 11*); however, the appendages have no attachment to the seeds and are strictly endocarpic in origin. Having no fresh fruits to study, we cannot be sure of the significance of these appendages nor of the inner consistency of the fruit.

The seeds are in two rows and the attachment is still apparent in nearly mature fruits (*fig. 10*). Those of one row are strictly sessile, while those of the other row are borne on slender elongated funicles. Apparently there is a substantial proportion of sterility in the seeds of *Degeneria* (as not infrequently in the Magnoliaceae and related groups), for none of our seeds contain embryos. Attempts to germinate some of them, in order to obtain a chromosome count, having failed, we dissected others and failed to find any embryos or any endosperm which could be interpreted. The external coarse reticulation of the seeds is characteristic. The single fruit accompanying the type collection is not quite mature but bears a full complement of seeds (*fig. 10*). The fruits of the Smith specimen (*fig. 2*), however, although essentially similar externally, have only a few seeds developed (and these sterile), the majority of the ovules being atrophied and dried upon the walls of the large cavity.

The fruits of the Himantandraceae and Magnoliaceae are so different from those of *Degeneria* as to make comparison unnecessary for the time being. However, the presence of a slender elongated funicle in *Degeneria* and in many Magnoliaceae is noteworthy; such a funicle is not found in *Himantandra*. Superficially, the fruit of *Degeneria* suggests that of certain species of Winteraceae, although these as a rule are much smaller. However, an undescribed New Guinea species of *Bubbia* v. Tiegh. has a large fruit remarkably similar to that of *Degeneria*, differing, however, in its small several-seriate seeds without funicles and in various other details.

CONCLUSIONS. The various families of the ranalian complex exhibit similarities and differences in their vegetative and floral organs that are indicative of reticulate rather than linear relationships. Certain of the morphological similarities may be, and probably are, due to parallel specialization from a common ancestry, whereas others represent retentions of structures that characterized the primitive ranalian stock. Therefore, in discussing the relationships of the various families of the Ranales, it is essential to consider and carefully to weigh evidence from *all* organs and parts of the plants.

The salient morphological features of the vegetative organs of *Degeneria* closely resemble those of the Magnoliaceae, plants of the latter family differing chiefly in the presence of stipules and a correspondingly more complex type of vascularization of the leaf. The absence of stipules in *Degeneria*, in itself, is not sufficient grounds for excluding the genus from the Magnoliaceae, particularly as the petioles are provided with marginal expansions (*fig. 29*) that envelop the "growing point" during early stages of their ontogeny. The successively formed leaves of magnoliaceous seedlings not infrequently exhibit transitions between such foliar structures and leaves with conspicuous stipules. At the same time, the vascularization of the seedling leaves becomes increasingly complex. Thus, the chief justifications for excluding *Degeneria* from the Magnoliaceae are to be found in its reproductive rather than in its vegetative organs. Here the morphological differences are numerous and extensive, significant similarities occurring, however, particularly in the pollen and in the vascularization of the stamens.

Although the flowers of *Degeneria* resemble those of *Himantandra* in their remarkable stamens, in their compressed floral axes, and in the presence of numerous staminodes, the morphology of the carpels and the

12

calyptriform perianth-parts of the latter genus present serious obstacles to the inclusion of *Degeneria* in the Himantandraceae. Furthermore, although the vascularization of the stem and leaf is of a fundamentally similar type in *Degeneria* and *Himantandra*, the xylem and phloem of *Degeneria* are indicative of a closer structural relationship to the Magnoliaceae than to the Himantandraceae. Of course, the peculiar distribution of the stomata and the peltate scales of *Himantandra* have no counterparts in either the Degeneriaceae or Magnoliaceae.

The reproductive organs of *Degeneria* exhibit similarities to those of certain representatives of the Winteraceae (exclusive of *Illicium*). Such similarities occur at times in the form and texture of the perianth, in the reduction of the carpels to one, in the morphology of the carpel, in the formation of numerous ovules, and in the gross appearance of the fruit. However, the stamens—as regards both their form and their vascularization—are of a fundamentally different type throughout the Winteraceae. The pollen grains differ profoundly in their salient morphological features and no staminodes are formed in the Winteraceae. In addition, the internal structure of the vegetative organs of *Drimys* and its segregates is entirely unlike that of *Degeneria*. The vascularization of the leaf is of a fundamentally different type, and the structure of the vesselless xylem and of the phloem is indicative of a rather remote relationship of the Winteraceae to the Degeneriaceae, Himantandraceae, and Magnoliaceae.

In conclusion, it should be emphasized that extensive comparative investigations of the stamens and carpels of the Ranales are needed, since the remarkable sporophylls of *Degeneria* may afford clues for visualizing diverse trends of morphological specialization in these organs.

In the following analyses we point out the salient features of the Degeneriaceae and its closest allies:

Stipules none; sepals much smaller than petals and very distinct from them; floral axis short, broader than long, depressed at apex; anthers dehiscing extrorsely, the pollen-sacs not protuberant; staminodes present within the stamens, cucullate; carpel solitary, open along the ventral suture when young; ovules numerous (24–26); carpel indehiscent, the seeds biseriate, those of one series sessile, of the other series conspicuously funiculate..........................Degeneriaceae.

Stipules present; sepals usually subsimilar to petals; floral axis usually elongated; anthers dehiscing introrsely or laterally (extrorsely in *Liriodendron*), the pollen-sacs protuberant; staminodes none; carpels numerous, very rarely as few as 2 (in *Pachylarnax*), never solitary, closed along the ventral suture; ovules few or several, seldom more than 10; carpels usually dehiscent, concrescent if indehiscent; funicle often elongate......................................Magnoliaceae.

Stipules none; copious peltate scales present on branchlets, lower leaf-surfaces, and inflorescence-parts; perianth composed of a calyptra of fused petals within a calyptra of fused sepals; floral axis short, depressed at apex; anthers dehiscing extrorsely, the pollen-sacs not protuberant; staminodes present both without and within the stamens, not cucullate; carpels several, closed along the ventral suture; ovules 1 or 2; fruit composed of coalesced carpels; funicle not elongate.........
.... Himantandraceae.

Stipules none; sepals often much smaller than petals, sometimes (in *Drimys*) calyptriform; floral axis short, not depressed at apex; anthers dehiscing apically, subapically, or laterally, the pollen-sacs protuberant; staminodes none; carpels many to few, sometimes solitary, closed along the ventral or apical stigmatic suture; ovules few to many; carpels indehiscent, the seeds without elongated funicles.........
.... Winteraceae.

EXPLANATION OF PLATES

All plates illustrate *Degeneria vitiensis* I. W. Bailey and A. C. Smith. All figures are drawn or photographed from *Degener 14537* except *figs. 2, 25,* and *26,* which are from *Smith 1754.*

PLATE I

Fig. 1. Flowering branchlet, × ½; 2. Fruiting branchlet, × ½; 3. Flower at anthesis, × 1; 4. Floral axis, with petals, stamens, and staminodes removed, slightly after anthesis, × 2; 5. Side view of carpel, slightly after anthesis, × 4; 6. Longitudinal section of carpel, × 4; 7. Petal, inner surface, × 2; 8. Stamens, extrorse and lateral views, × 2; 9. Staminodes, introrse and lateral views, × 2; 10. Fruit, nearly mature, with a portion of wall removed to show seeds, funicles, and ridges and appendages of the endocarp, × 1; 11. Seed and portion of the endocarpic appendages, × 3; 12. Pollen grain re-expanded and mounted in lactic acid, × 300; 13. Pollen grain after brief treatment in NaOH, mounted in lactic acid, × 300; 14. Pollen grain after similar treatment, optical section, × 300.

PLATE II

Fig. 15. Stamen re-expanded and cleared in dilute NaOH, showing sporangia and median and lateral veins, × 24; 16. Hooded staminode with rudimentary sporangia, × 24; 17. Hooded, 3-veined, typical staminode, × 24; 18. Transverse section of re-expanded and cleared stamen, showing four sporangia and four short arcs of endothecium, × 107; 19. Part of *fig. 18* more highly magnified, × 260.

PLATE III

Fig. 20. Transverse section of carpel just after anthesis, showing ovules, × 31; 21. Sagittal section of ovule, × 260; 22. Transverse section of young carpel at level of locule, × 31; 23. Transverse section of young carpel above level of locule, × 64.

PLATE IV

Fig. 24. Transverse section of young secondary phloem, showing flaring rays and strands of hard and soft bast, × 107; 25. Transverse section of mature secondary xylem, × 50; 26. Tangential longitudinal section of mature secondary xylem, × 50.

PLATE V

Fig. 27. Transverse section of petiole, showing foliar vascular cylinder, × 27; 28. Transverse section at base of flower-bud, showing carpel in apical depression and surrounded by ring-shaped crown of torus, × 8; 29. Transverse section at apex of vegetative shoot, showing clasping bases of young leaves, × 39; 30. Transverse section of flower bud, showing petals, stamens, staminodes and carpel, × 8.

BIOLOGICAL LABORATORIES AND ARNOLD ARBORETUM,
HARVARD UNIVERSITY.

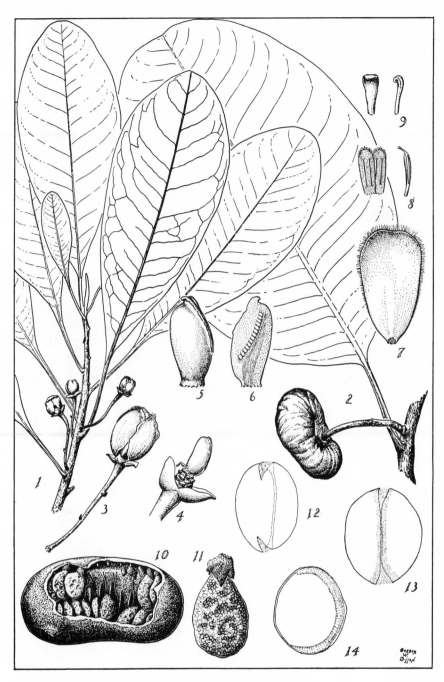

Degeneria vitiensis Bailey and Smith

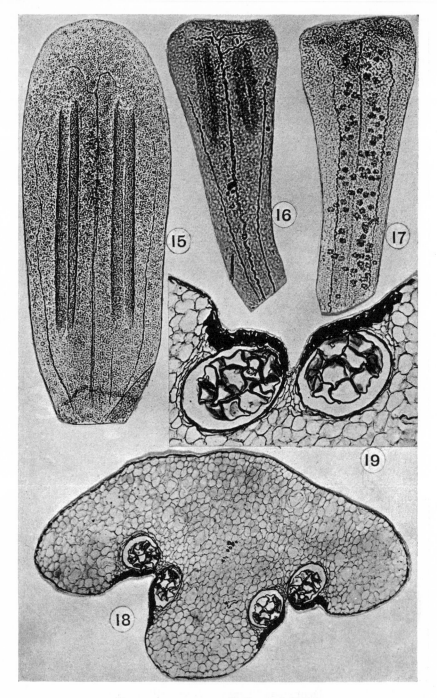

Degeneria vitiensis Bailey and Smith

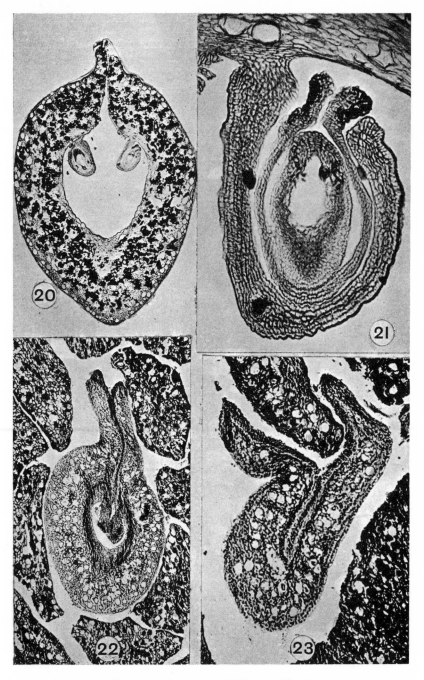

Degeneria vitiensis Bailey and Smith

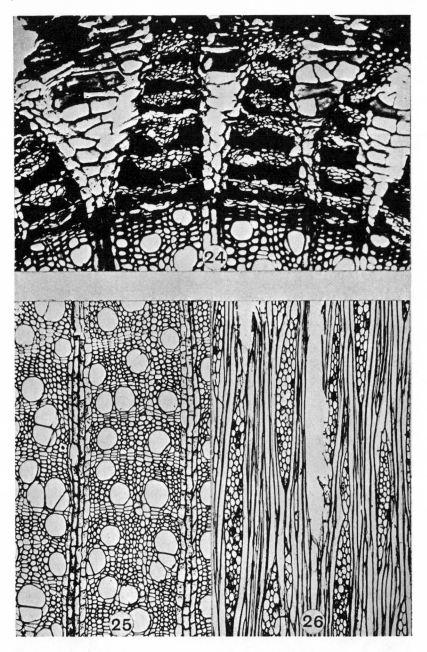

DEGENERIA VITIENSIS Bailey and Smith

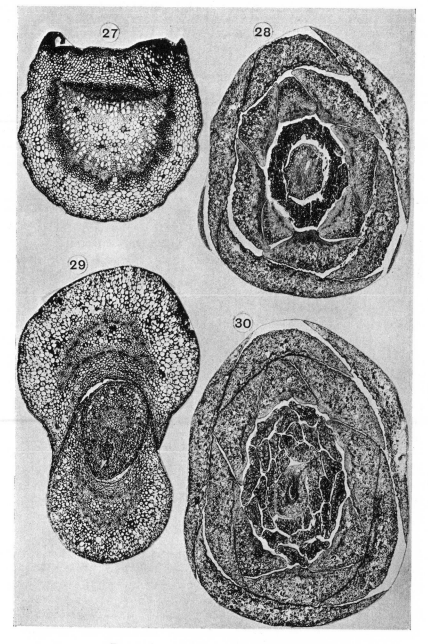

Degeneria vitiensis Bailey and Smith

ANATOMY AND SYSTEMATIC POSITION OF
CENTAURODENDRON AND YUNQUEA (COMPOSITAE)

SHERWIN CARLQUIST

Claremont Graduate School, Rancho Santa Ana Botanic Garden
Claremont, California

The genera *Centaurodendron* and *Yunquea* are remarkable in that they are both "rosette trees" which have been interpreted as belonging to the tribe Cynareae (Skottsberg 1938) and are endemic to the island Masatierra in the Juan Fernandez Islands. *Centaurodendron* consists of two species, *C. dracaenoides* Johow and *C. palmiforme* Skottsberg, whereas *Yunquea tenzii* Skottsberg is the single species of its genus. The main purpose of the present study is to show how anatomical evidence bears on the systematic relationships which have been proposed on the basis of gross morphology. Because *Centaurodendron* and *Yunquea* are the only arborescent genera referred to Cynareae, and because they show little superficial similarity to other Cynareae in vegetative characters, a study of their anatomy is desirable in determining if this is, indeed, the correct disposition of these genera.

A secondary problem is created by the genus *Yunquea*, which Skottsberg (1929) erected on the basis of scanty vegetative material. Although subsequent collections have furnished no flowers of this plant, which evidently flowers with extreme infrequency, anatomical data from the vegetative portions of the plant and from recently collected mature achenes appear to be decisive in assessing Skottsberg's (1929) suggestion that it should be regarded as a genus closely related to *Centaurodendron*. Individuals of *Yunquea* are rare, and the localities in which they grow are difficult of access (Kunkel 1957; Skottsberg 1953). It may become extinct, as has so much of the autochthonous Juan Fernandez vegetation, without having been collected in the flowering state.

The recent discovery (Skottsberg 1957) of *Centaurodendron palmiforme* is significant, for this species shows greater similarity to *Yunquea* than does *C. dracaenoides*. Moreover, anatomical characters can be used in contrasting the two species of *Centaurodendron*.

MATERIALS AND METHODS

Centaurodendron dracaenoides is only slightly more abundant than *C. palmiforme* or *Yunquea*, but has been collected, at rare intervals, in flower. Therefore, the writer was able to use herbarium material for studies of the anatomy of inflorescence parts. Except for this material, listed below, the present study was based entirely on material collected by Dr. Skottsberg or collectors who assisted him during his visit to the islands in 1955. Skottsberg's own collections were preserved in dilute ethyl alcohol, and consisted of stems, leaves, and shoot tips. Wood samples were also collected and dried. Although no herbarium specimens were prepared to document these collections, which in a sense are documented by Dr. Skottsberg's intensive knowledge of the Juan Fernandez flora, the writer is retaining the liquid-preserved samples on which the studies were based. The specimens are as follows:

Reprinted by permission of the author and publisher from
BRITTONIA, **10,** 78–93 (1958).

Centaurodendron dracaenoides. Vegetative. Coll. C. Skottsberg, Sept. 3, 1955. Portezuelo de Villagra, Masatierra. Liquid.

Same. Flowering. Coll. H. Weber, without data, 1937 (University of California Herbarium, Berkeley.

Centaurodendron palmiforme. Vegetative. Coll. C. Kunkel, Sept. 3, 1955. Masatierra. Dried.

Same. Weathered inflorescence. Coll. B. Sparre, Jan. 10, 1955. Masatierra. Dried.

Same. Old stem. Coll. B. Sparre, March 5, 1955. Masatierra. Dried.

Yunquea tenzii. Vegetative. Coll. C. Skottsberg, June 3, 1955. El Yunque, Masatierra. Liquid.

Same. Achenes. Coll. G. Kunkel, June 3, 1955. El Yunque, Masatierra. Dried.

The writer wishes to express sincerest appreciation to Dr Skottsberg for the material mentioned, and to Dr T. H. Goodspeed, through whose good offices arrangements for these collections were made. The cooperation of the University of California Herbarium in allowing use of the specimen listed above is gratefully acknowledged.

Herbarium material was prepared by treatment with 2.5 per cent NaOH in a 60° C oven. When material was sufficiently cleared and expanded by this method, it was washed and stored in 50 per cent ethyl alcohol. Both the alcohol-fixed material and the "revived" herbarium specimen portions were dehydrated according to Johansen's (1940) tertiary butyl alcohol series, and embedded and sectioned according to the usual techniques. Treatment with hydrofluoric acid for several weeks was found necessary for softening the rather sclerotic stems of *Centaurodendron dracaenoides* before dehydration. Sections were stained by means of tannic acid and ferric chloride, followed by a safranin-fast green combination. In addition to sectioned material, whole mounts of leaves, involucral bracts, flowers, and pollen were prepared by the NaOH technique mentioned above, followed by dehydration and staining with safranin.

The wood samples were sectioned on a sliding microtome after boiling in water, followed by immersion for about six weeks in 36 per cent hydrofluoric acid. Stems of *C. palmiforme* were sectioned without such treatment. Safranin in absolute ethyl alcohol was employed as a stain.

VEGETATIVE ANATOMY

Leaves of *Centaurodendron* differ markedly from those of *Yunquea* in gross morphology. *Yunquea* has petiolate, toothed leaves with prominent ribs (corresponding to the major veins) on the lower surface; the ribs and petiole have a light covering of uniseriate, non-glandular hairs. *Centaurodendron* leaves are sessile (rarely somewhat petiolate), nearly emarginate (the teeth obscure, although more obvious in *C. palmiforme*), and smooth and glabrous on both surfaces.

Study of foliar ontogeny demonstrates that leaves of the two genera are basically more alike than these differences would suggest, although study of their mature anatomy reveals additional characters which distinguish the genera. The shoot apex of *Yunquea* shown in Figure 1 serves to demonstrate the leaf origin in both of these genera. Leaf primordia originate in a spiral around the dome-shaped apical meristem. The meristem itself is rather clearly zonate. Three layers of tunica are discernible, and the corpus contains a central mother-cell zone which has abundant pectic accumulations at cell interstices. Prominent rib-meristem action is initiated a short distance below the mother-cell zone. These clearly defined files of cells are not responsible for the formation of the entire pith, however, but only the central portion of it. The shoot apex of *Centaurodendron dracaenoides* shows the same features except that the groups of cells destined to become pith sclereids are demarcated at an early stage, as mentioned below.

Figure 2 shows the presence of two types of hairs on an immature petiole of *Yunquea*. These trichomes may be classified as uniseriate non-glandular (top of photograph) and biseriate glandular (near top and bottom of photograph). Despite the glabrous nature of leaves in *Centaurodendron,* the uniseriate non-glandular hairs are present on immature portions of herbage in that genus, just as they are in *Yunquea*. On mature *Yunquea* leaves, uniseriate hairs are preserved only along the ribs on the lower surfaces of leaves, in the leaf axils, and on petioles. They appear to be wholly lacking on mature leaves of *Centaurodendron*. Degeneration of such uniseriate trichomes is evident in the stage shown in Figure 2, which is prior to the formation of pockets surrounding glandular hairs. The difference in vesture of leaves between *Centaurodendron* and *Yunquea,* then, is a matter of relative preservation of uniseriate hairs, which are present on young leaves in both genera.

For the most part, the biseriate glandular hairs do not degenerate soon. Rather, they become sunken into pockets (Figs. 4, 5) on both surfaces of the leaves, both in *Centaurodendron* and *Yunquea*. Glandular hairs on mature leaves, however, appear to be non-functional and collapsed. Although sunken biseriate glandular trichomes have been demonstrated for Compositae only in a member of Mutisieae, *Hesperomannia* (Carlquist 1957a), they probably occur also in Cynareae, as Skottsberg's reports (1929, 1938) of similar "glandular dots" in *Centaurea* suggest.

The mature lamina of *Centaurodendron dracaenoides* (Fig. 4) differs from that of *Yunquea* (Fig. 5) in a number of respects. As noted by Skottsberg (1938), two layers of palisade are characteristically present in *C. dracaenoides,* whereas a single layer occurs in *Yunquea*. Moreover, the total number of mesophyll layers is greater in both species of *Centaurodendron,* which have nine cell-layers, than in *Yunquea,* which has six. Where veins occur, of course, layers are more numerous. Bundle sheaths are well developed in *Centaurodendron,* and larger veins have conspicuous bundle-sheath extensions (Fig. 4, right). In addition, fibers are abundant around the larger veins (Fig. 4, right) and even some of the smaller veins (Fig. 4, left). In *Yunquea,* bundle sheaths are also present; veins with sheath extensions are those associated with a prominent rib on the lower surface of the leaf (Fig. 5, left). Fibers are present within the bundle sheaths of the larger veins, although they are less abundant and do not completely jacket a vein as they often do in *Centaurodendron*. The prominent teeth on the margins of *Yunquea* leaves are hydathodic in construction. The relatively obscure teeth of *Centaurodendron* leaves also have such a structure. Aside from the points mentioned above, structure of the lamina in the two genera is quite alike. Lamina structure of *C. palmiforme* was observed to be identical to that of *C. dracaenoides* in all respects.

Petiole and Node. *Centaurodendron* lacks a clearly defined petiole. The narrowed portion of the leaf base subtending the lamina is shown for *C. dracaenoides* in Figure 3. This section corresponds to that illustrated diagrammatically in Figure 12. The leaf base of *C. dracaenoides* differs anatomically from the lamina in that more numerous layers are present, with no differentiation into palisade and spongy tissue. Smaller intercellular spaces are present in the abaxial portion, although large lacunae occur on the adaxial side. A

22

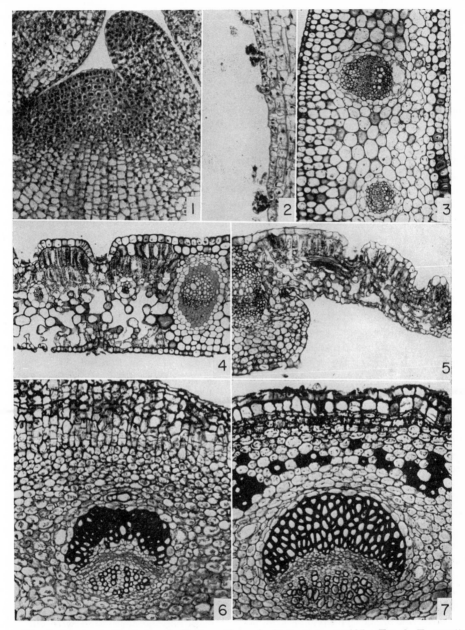

FIG. 1. *Yunquea tenzii*, longitudinal section of shoot apex; × 135. FIG. 2. *Y. tenzii*, portion of longitudinal section of young petiole; × 170. FIG. 3. *Centaurodendron dracaenoides*, transection of sheathing leaf base, adaxial face at right: × 60. FIG. 4. *C. dracaenoides*, portion of lamina transection, adaxial face above; × 78. FIG. 5. *Y. tenzii*, portion of lamina transection, adaxial face above; × 115. FIGS. 6, 7. Portions of transections from stems with some secondary growth, × 108. FIG. 6, *C. dracaenoides*. FIG. 7, *Y. tenzii*.

sclerified hypodermis is prominently differentiated in the adaxial face (Fig. 3, right). Collenchyma is present in the abaxial layers. Around the bundles, fibers differentiate tardily in comparison with the rapid sclerification of the adaxial hypodermis. Several secretory canals surround each bundle in the leaf base (Fig. 3); five or more are present around the larger veins. These canals are continuous with those associated with leaf traces in the cortex (Fig. 6). The leaf base of *C. palmiforme* differs from that of *C. dracaenoides* only in lacking a sclerified hypodermis (collenchyma is present on both faces) and in possessing fewer (usually two) secretory canals around the larger veins.

Comparison of the leaf base of *C. dracaenoides* (Fig. 12) with the leaf traces in the cortex of a given node (Fig. 11, below) reveals that more numerous bundles are present in the leaf base. This condition results from repeated branching of the most lateral pair of leaf traces in the leaf base. Each of these laterals may branch several times. Other leaf traces are unbranched. Figure 12 shows larger and smaller veins alternating in the leaf base. The larger veins depart from the vascular cylinder at a lower level than the smaller veins. Approximately sixteen traces, associated with sixteen gaps, were characteristically present in each node of the *C. dracaenoides* material examined.

The petiolate nature of the leaf in *Yunquea* results in certain anatomical differences in comparison with *Centaurodendron*. Although the sheathing basal portion of the leaf (Fig. 9) is not unlike that of *Centaurodendron* (Fig. 12), the distal portion of the petiole (Fig. 10) has a central group of bundles in addition to the outer arc of large and small bundles. This central group of bundles is further distinguished by the orientation of xylem and phloem, an orientation at variance with that of the outer arc. These bundles do not originate from an adaxial meristem. Study of successive sections indicates that they branch from the larger bundles of the outer arc. As in *Centaurodendron*, numerous small secretory canals surround each of the larger veins, both at the level shown in Figure 9 and that in Figure 10. As in *Centaurodendron*, they are continuous with secretory canals of the leaf traces in the cortex below a node, although they fade out near the lamina base and are not present in the lamina. At the level shown in Figure 10, secretory canals are present only around the bundles of the outer arc. The course of secretory canals in the cortex adjacent to leaf traces, and their extension into leaf bases, where they terminate below the lamina, has been reported by Van Tieghem (1872) in *Xeranthemum cylindraceum*, *Cirsium arvense*, and *Lappa grandiflora*. The petiole of *Yunquea* shows resemblance to the leaf base of *Centaurodendron* in that collenchyma is present exterior to the outer arc of bundles in the petiole.

The nodal venation of *Yunquea* differs from that of *Centaurodendron* in its greater abundance of veins. The number of traces which supply a leaf of *Yunquea* is approximately twenty; each of these is associated with a gap in the vascular cylinder. The larger number of traces may be correlated with the fact that the leaf base extends more nearly around the circumference of the stem than it does in *Centaurodendron*. As in *Centaurodendron* the most lateral pair of leaf traces in each leaf base of *Yunquea* branch toward the margin, increasing the number of veins. Other veins throughout the leaf base branch; some are formed de novo in the leaf base (i.e. without downward connection to leaf traces). Thus a much greater number of veins is present in the leaf base of *Yunquea* than in that of *Centaurodendron*.

Precise data on nodal venation in other Cynareae is not available. The type illustrated here, however, is that which one would expect to be associated with the broad, sheathing leaf bases typical of many Cynareae.

Stem. Figures 6 and 7 illustrate comparable portions of the cortex of *Centaurodendron dracaenoides* and *Yunquea tenzii* respectively. In both of these stems an accumulation of secondary growth was present. Cork formation, initiated in the hypodermal layer, is seen in both. In *C. dracaenoides* and *C. palmiforme,* a few layers of collenchyma are formed in the outer cortex, whereas none is present in *Yunquea. Yunquea,* however, characteristically develops numerous sclereids in the outer cortex, whereas no sclereids were observed in cortex of stems of either *Centaurodendron* species. In both Figures 6 and 7, a leaf trace is shown. The prominent cap of fibers is similar in both genera. Surrounding the bundle cap, various numbers of secretory canals are present. The number of secretory canals around leaf traces of *Centaurodendron* varies from one to three, whereas from three to five are characteristically present in such leaf traces of *Yunquea.* These canals are never present near the xylem face of the bundle. Some secretory canals are adjacent to vascular bundles of the vascular cylinder proper in both genera. These secretory canals are usually one per bundle; this number increases at a higher level in the stem for any given bundle, as the bundle becomes demarcated as a leaf trace. In addition, a few secretory canals arranged without reference to leaf traces were observed in the cortex of *Yunquea.*

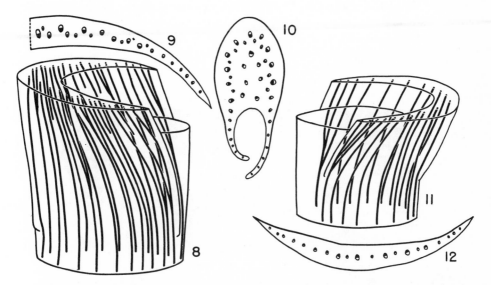

FIGS. 8–10. *Yunquea tenzii.* FIG. 8. Reconstruction (based on serial sections) of a node, showing veins to a single leaf only; × 3.3 FIG. 9. Diagrammatic transection of leaf base at the level at which the leaf is cut in Figure 8; × 3.3. FIG. 10. Diagrammatic transection of petiole; × 4.8. FIGS. 11, 12. *Centaurodendron dracaenoides.* FIG. 11. Reconstruction of a node, showing veins to a single leaf only; × 6. FIG. 12. Diagrammatic transection of leaf base at the level at which the leaf is cut in Figure 11; × 4. Black portions of bundles in Figures 9, 10, and 12 are xylem.

The presence of secretory canals in Compositae has been the subject of several surveys, such as those of Van Tieghem (1872) and Col (1903). A particular feature of interest, however, is the presence of more than one or two canals per leaf trace in Cynareae, whereas in other tribes of the family they are, if present, only one or two per trace. Although some Cynareae have only a pair, such as *Cynara scolymus* (Jeffrey 1917) or have a large number abaxial to a trace, as in *Arctium* (Jeffery, op. cit.), certain examples which resemble the condition in *Centaurodendron* and *Yunquea* may be cited. Such an example is *Serratula centauroides* (Van Tieghem 1872); several others, also from the subtribe Centaurinae, are offered by Col (1903).

Distinctive conditions of sclerification are found in the pith of *Centaurodendron* and *Yunquea*. In *Yunquea* (Fig. 14) and *C. palmiforme* the inner margins of bundles have prominent caps of fibers which extend for considerable distances into the pith; in the pith of these, however, no isolated sclereid groups occur, and the parenchyma is thin-walled. In *Centaurodendron dracaenoides* (Fig. 13), on the contrary, numerous large nests of sclereids are scattered throughout the pith. Sclerenchymatous inner margins of bundles also occur in *C. dracaenoides*, and some of the sclereid nests, which consist of similar cells, are connected with these. The sclereid nests of *C. dracaenoides* are clearly foreshadowed in the apical regions of the shoot before sclerification takes place. Cells destined to become sclereids are much smaller in diameter than cells which will develop into thin-walled parenchyma.

The presence of sclerenchyma as inward extensions of bundles in *Centaurodendron* and *Yunquea,* and as sclereid nests in *C. dracaenoides* pith, may have some relation to the arborescent growth-form of these genera. If the accumulation of secondary xylem is slow (as compared with that in truly arboreal plants), additional sclerenchyma may be of value in providing mechanical support for an arborescent form. It is interesting to note that such arborescent Compositae

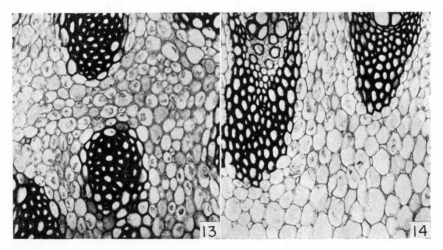

FIG. 13. *Centaurodendron dracaenoides,* portion of pith transection; ✕ 95. FIG. 14. *Yunquea tenzii,* portion of pith transection, showing inner margins of vascular bundles; ✕ 95.

as *Hesperomannia* (Carlquist 1957a) and certain Guayana Mutisieae (Carlquist 1958a) have conditions quite similar to *C. dracaenoides.* Likewise, the less woody species of *Fitchia,* an arborescent genus of Heliantheae, demonstrate a wide variety of pith sclerification (Carlquist 1957c). Herbaceous or shrubby members of these tribes at large seem mostly to lack such sclerenchyma. If such sclerification were a secondary acquisition, as it appears to be in *Centaurodendron,* rather than primitively present, it might be interpreted as a partial indication that a truly arboreal form is derived in Compositae. Such a suggestion would certainly not rule out the possibility of woody forms among primitive Compositae, however. The lack of pith sclereids in *Centaurodendron palmiforme* and *Yunquea* may be related to the life-form of these two species. They are monocarpic, whereas *C. dracaenoides* is hapaxanthic (Skottsberg, personal communication).

Wood. Because *Centaurodendron* and *Yunquea* are the only arborescent genera assigned to Cynareae, study of anatomy of their secondary xylem seems desirable. The oldest stem samples of *Yunquea* and *C. palmiforme* had a radial width of approximately 3 mm of secondary xylem. The stem of the longer-lived *C. dracaenoides* collected by Skottsberg, however, came from "the last mature generation of branches" and had a thick cylinder of xylem. Despite this difference in wood samples—probably related to the life form of the plants— differences in the structure of the secondary xylem in the two genera can be demonstrated. These differences were verified by comparison of younger stem samples of *C. dracaenoides* with the stems of *C. palmiforme* and *Yunquea,* which had a similar accumulation of xylem.

The measurements in Table I are presented as a means of comparing the species and genera with each other, and of comparing the two genera with other woody Compositae.

TABLE 1. Wood measurements of *Centaurodendron* and *Yunquea.*

	Range in vessel element diameter, μ	Diameter vessel elements, average, μ	Length vessel elements, average, μ	Vessels per vessel group, average	Length libriform wood fibers, average, μ	Length apotracheal parenchyma cells, average, μ	Greatest outside diameter of fibers average, μ	Height multiseriate rays, average, mm.
C. dracaenoides	26–90	53	244	1.86	396	198	21	.9
C. palmiforme	23–82	48	270	1.60	262	—	23	1.1
Y. tenzii	13–66	40	335	1.36	462	—	15	1.5

Comparison of *C. dracaenoides* with *Yunquea* reveals an overall tendency toward longer, narrower elements in *Yunquea. Centaurodendron palmiforme* is intermediate between the two taxa in this regard. Detailed comparisons involving qualitative characters also may be arranged as follows:

VESSELS. Vessel element dimensions illustrate the tendency toward longer, narrower elements in *Yunquea.* A further difference occurs in respect to vessel grouping. In *Yunquea,* vessels are more often solitary or in more limited groups

than those of *C. dracaenoides*. *Centaurodendron palmiforme* is intermediate in
this respect. Lateral wall pitting on vessels consists of numerous alternate circular bordered pits in both genera. Prominent resin deposits occur in vessels of
C. dracaenoides (Figs. 15, 16) although none were observed in vessels of
C. palmiforme or *Yunquea*.

LIBRIFORM FIBERS; WOOD PARENCHYMA. Wood fibers in *Yunquea* are narrow
(Fig. 19) and long (Fig. 20) compared with those in *Centaurodendron*. In
C. palmiforme, fibers are uniformly wide (Fig. 17) and short (Fig. 18). In
C. dracaenoides, however, one may say that fibers are dimorphic. In addition
to long, thick-walled fibers with tapered ends (Fig. 16, extreme right), there are
shorter, thinner-walled elements with rounded or blunt ends; these elements occur
in a somewhat storied pattern (Fig. 16, center). These latter cells occur in
tangential bands which extend around the stem (one such band is clearly visible
across the center of Figure 15). On account of their characteristics and mode of
occurrence, these cells must be called apotracheal parenchyma. Their similarity
to fibers is evident, and it may be, as appeared to be the case in *Dubautia*
(Carlquist 1958b), that such apotracheal parenchyma cells are in fact a phylo-
genetically derived form of libriform wood fibers. No such parenchyma bands
were observed in *Yunquea* or *C. palmiforme*, although the stems examined may
not have been old enough to exhibit them. Apotracheal parenchyma bands have
been reported in the wood of certain Mutisieae (Carlquist 1957b). As is typical
in Compositae, vasicentric parenchyma is present in *Centaurodendron* and
Yunquea in the form of a scanty incomplete sheath, never more than a single
cell-layer wide, surrounding vessels or vessel groups. Fewer such cells are
present in wood of *Yunquea* (Fig. 19) than in that of *Centaurodendron* (Figs.
15, 17).

RAYS. The two species of *Centaurodendron* show much more limited ray
height than *Yunquea*, in which some rays may be over a centimeter in vertical
height. In both genera, however, rays which are narrowed along some parts of
their vertical extent, and appear to be two superposed rays connected by
prominently erect ray cells, may be seen. There are some fiber-like erect cells
along the margins of the rays in both genera (Figs. 16, 18, 20). A conspicuous
difference between the two genera occurs in the presence of narrow procumbent
cells chiefly in the central portion of rays of *Centaurodendron* (Figs. 16, 18).
Such procumbent cells are almost completely lacking in rays of *Yunquea* (Fig.
20). Uniseriate rays are infrequent in wood of *Centaurodendron dracaenoides;*
none were observed in wood of *C. palmiforme* or *Yunquea*. Some rather narrow
(two or three cells maximum width) rays are present in wood of both *Centaurodendron* species. In the wood of *Yunquea*, all the multiseriate rays appear at
least four cells wide. Resin deposits fill some ray cells in *C. dracaenoides;* occasional resin droplets were noted in ray cells of *Yunquea* (Fig. 19). No resins at
all were observed in wood of *C. palmiforme*.

In summary, the wood of *C. palmiforme* may be said to be intermediate
between that of *C. drancaenoides* and that of *Yunquea*. The presence of procumbent cells in the rays of *C. palmiforme*, and the wide, short fibers clearly ally

---

Explanation of Figures 15-20

Sections of secondary xylem. FIGS. 15, 17, 19, transections. FIGS. 16, 18, 20, tangential sections. FIGS. 15, 16, *Centaurodendron dracaenoides*. FIGS. 17, 18, *C. palmiforme*.
FIGS. 19, 20, *Yunquea tenzii*. All × 120.

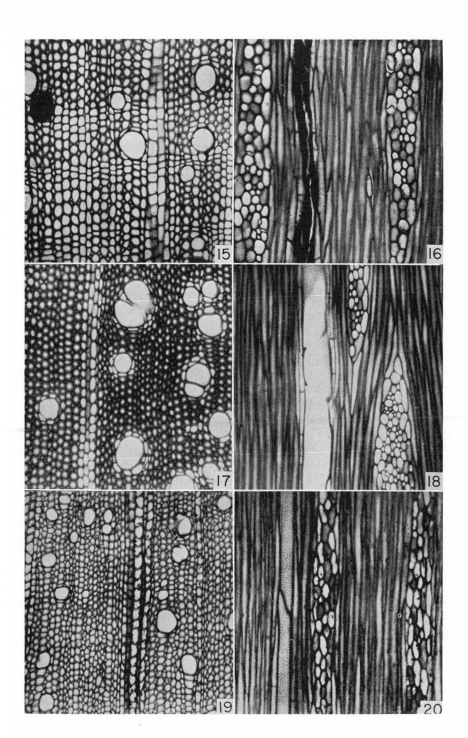

this species to *C. dracaenoides*. The lack of apotracheal parenchyma in *C. palmiforme*, as in *Yunquea*, may be a reflection of the monocarpic life form of these species, as opposed to the hapaxanthic habit of *C. dracaenoides*.

INFLORESCENCE ANATOMY

The vascular cylinder of the inflorescence axis and its branches in *Centaurodendron dracaenoides* is much like that of the vegetative stem, although these branches are narrower in diameter. Some of the bundles occupy a position slightly exterior to the vascular cylinder proper; these supply the outer involucral bracts, whereas the remaining bundles supply the inner involucral bracts and flowers. Several secretory canals are present around the phloem pole of bundles in the inflorescence axis. Pith and pith rays of the infloresence branches consist of thin-walled parenchyma. In the material of *C. palmiforme* examined, pith and pith rays were composed of thin-walled sclereids which were connected with the fibers of prominent bundle caps. This difference in sclerification, however, may be due to the more advanced age of the *C. palmiforme* inflorescence as compared to that of *C. dracaenoides* which was studied.

Involucres of *C. palmiforme* were too weathered to permit anatomical study. Consequently, only the involucre of *C. dracaenoides* could be studied. The structure of an outer involucral bract is illustrated in Figure 21. The outer face of the bract at the level indicated consists of several layers of sclerenchyma, whereas on the inner face, only the epidermis and a few cells of the layer beneath it are sclerified. The remainder of the bract consists of thin-walled parenchyma. Vascular bundles occur in a single arc in the parenchyma, and are not jacketed by fibers. A secretory canal is usually present at the phloem face of each bundle. A transection near the apex of an outer involucral bract shows a marked alteration of this pattern (Fig. 22). Several layers of sclerenchyma are present on the inner, rather than the outer, face of the bract; the outer face shows sclerification only on the epidermal cells. The mesophyll of the bract at this level, rather than consisting exclusively of thin-walled parenchyma, contains bands of sclereids between the bundles. At the phloem pole of each bundle, a secretory canal is present. Inner involucral bracts show a structure similar to that of the outer bracts, differing only in that fewer layers of sclerenchyma and mesophyll parenchyma are present. Receptacular bristles (Fig. 23) are quite simple in structure. They consist of a sclerified epidermis, on which biseriate glandular hairs occur, overlying a ground tissue of thin-walled parenchyma. No vascular bundles were observed in receptacular bristles.

Among studies on anatomy of involucral bracts in Cynareae, closest similarity to the condition observed in *Centaurodendron dracaenoides* is found in Daniel's (1890) descriptions and illustrations of *Centaurea cineraria* and *Serratula tinctoria*. Distribution of sclerenchyma and occurrence of secretory canals in bracts of these species are reminiscent of, although not identical with, the situation in *Centaurodendron dracaenoides*. Involucral bracts of other taxa differ more markedly. Although sclerenchyma and secretory canals have been reported for bracts of Astereae (Napp-Zinn 1956) and Heliantheae (Napp-Zinn 1956; Carlquist 1957c), they have a different pattern in these tribes. The Mutisieae which have been studied lack secretory canals in involucral bracts (Carlquist 1958a), and the Cynareae for which bract structure has been described, other than those mentioned above (Daniel 1890; Napp-Zinn 1956), do not by any means agree in this respect with *Centaurodendron dracaenoides*.

FLORAL ANATOMY

The careful descriptions of floral morphology of *Centaurodendron dracae-noides* given by Skottsberg (1938) are quite detailed, and few data need to be added. The floral venation of *C. dracaenoides* is of a simplified type found widely in Compositae, and corresponds exactly to the illustration given by the writer (1956) for *Eriophyllum lanatum*. Short segments of median veins appear to be present at the corolla-lobe tips. Examination of these, however, proves them to be composed of fibers, not tracheary elements. No secretory canals were observed in the corolla of *C. dracaenoides*. The trichomes illustrated by Skotts-berg on inner involucral bracts, receptacular bristles (shown here, Fig. 23), and

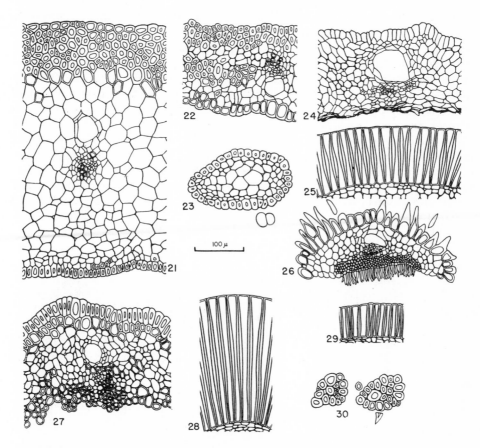

FIGS. 21–26, *Centaurodendron dracaenoides*. FIG. 21. Portion of transection taken mid-way along the length of an outer involucral bract; adaxial face below. FIG. 22. Portion of transection taken near apex of an outer involucral bract, adaxial face above. FIG. 23. Transection of receptacular bristle; biseriate hair in section, below. FIG. 24. Portion of transection of wall of fertile mature achene. FIG. 25. Portion of transection of outer surface of ovule from the same achene. FIG. 26. Transection of stigmatic branch. FIGS. 27–30, *Yunquea tenzii*. FIG. 27. Portion of transection of mature achene. FIG. 28. Portion of transection of dorsal face of ovule. FIG. 29. Portion of transection of lateral face of same ovule. FIG. 30. Transection of two pappus setae. Scale for all figures indicated.

pappus setae are biseriate glandular hairs like those of the herbage, although they are more elongate and not sunken into pockets.

A transection of a stigmatic branch of *C. dracaenoides* (Fig. 26) is presented to show the presence of a secretory canal. Occurrence of secretory canals in styles of Cynareae may be frequent, although mention of this is lacking in the literature. Secretory canals are common in styles of Heliantheae (Carlquist 1957c) and have been reported in a single genus of Mutisieae (Gueguen 1902), although they appear to be lacking in the majority of Compositae which have been examined.

The achene wall of *Centaurodendron dracaenoides* (Fig. 24) consists of thin-walled parenchyma at maturity, and is of interest only in the presence of a secretory canal opposite the phloem pole of each of the four veins of the achene. The achene wall of *Yunquea* (Fig. 27), on the contrary, is more complicated in structure. The outer epidermis, and two or three layers beneath it, consist of thick-walled sclerenchyma. Cells lining the achene cavity are also sclerified, although less markedly; they are also smaller than those on the outer face. Some of these sclereids are scattered through the soft-walled parenchyma of the achene wall. Prominent ridges are present on the achene wall of *Yunquea*. These differ anatomically from other portions of the wall by a greater thickness of the layer of thin-walled parenchyma. Some parenchyma, however, is present between the outer and inner sclerenchyma at all points on the achene wall. Four bundles, each with an associated secretory canal, were observed in the achenes of *Yunquea* studied. Studies of the achene wall of Compositae reveal few which contain secretory canals. Those which possess canals are members of Cynareae (Lavialle 1912), in which canals are external to the bundles, and Heliantheae (Carlquist 1957c), in which they are internal to the bundles. Of

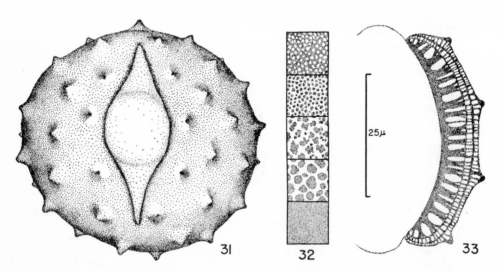

FIGS. 31–33. *Centaurodendron dracaenoides.* FIG. 31. Entire pollen grain, showing one of the furrows. FIG. 32. Successive optical transections of exine; outermost above, innermost below. FIG. 33. Optical equatorial transection of one third of a pollen grain, showing details of exine structure. Scale for all figures indicated.

the examples given by Lavialle, an achene wall identical to that of *Centaurodendron dracaenoides* is shown for *Serratula tinctoria*. Presence of sclerenchyma in the achene wall, such as that of *Yunquea*, is found in certain species of *Centaurea*, such as *C. cirrhata* (Lavialle, op. cit.). Lavialle also lists a number of species of *Centaurea* in which secretory canals are charcteristically present.

Peculiar thickenings of the ovule epidermis are found in *Centaurodendron dracaenoides* (Fig. 25). In *C. dracaenoides*, the epidermis is of approximately the same thickness at all points around the circumference of the ovule. In *Yunquea*, however, epidermal cells on the dorsiventral faces of the ovule (Fig. 28) are much longer than those on the lateral faces of the ovule (Fig. 29). The characteristic thickenings of the epidermis walls in both of these genera are identical with those reported by Lavialle (1912) in a number of Cynareae, including *Serratula*, *Centaurea*, and *Cynara*. This type of ovule epidermis is not found in certain other groups of Compositae.

The pappus setae of *Yunquea* (Fig. 30) are identical to those of *Centaurodendron dracaenoides* as seen in transection. They consist of a small number of cells, similar in wall thickness, with no differentiation between the epidermis and center of the seta.

Pollen. The pollen of *Centaurodendron dracaenoides* (Figs. 31–33) is of unusual interest in its highly complicated exine. The exine has three sculptured layers. The inner of these consists of numerous large bacula (Fig. 31; see also sectional views in Figure 32). The outer layers consist of fine rods. Although he does not illustrate it, Wagenitz (1955) gives some data concerning the pollen grain of *C. dracaenoides*. The writer's observations agree with those of Wagenitz, except that fully turgid grains appear to be more nearly oblate, as shown in Figure 31. The polar to equatorial axis ratio given by Wagenitz is .98, indicating a virtually spherical form. The systematic importance of Wagenitz' study on pollen of the subtribe Centaurinae seems to be considerable, because of the distinctive types of exine morphology which he describes and finds referable to the taxonomic system. The writer agrees with Wagenitz' placement of *C. dracaenoides* pollen in the ''*Serratula*-type'' which includes *Centaurea* (sections *Plectocephalus* and *Cheirolophus* only), *Acroptilon*, *Amberboa*, *Callicephalis*, *Crupina*, *Leuzea*, *Mantisalca*, *Plagiobasis*, *Rhaponticum*, and *Serratula*, but excludes all other members of the subtribe Centaurinae.

SYSTEMATIC CONCLUSIONS

The relatively precise and distinctive data concerning pollen offered by Wagenitz (1955) are perhaps most decisive in suggesting what the closest relatives of *Centaurodendron* and *Yunquea* may be. Data from secretory canal distribution, involucral bract anatomy, and achene anatomy indicate clearly that these genera belong within the tribe Cynareae, and that the closest comparisons are with the genera *Centaurea* and *Serratula*, in agreement with the data from pollen. The occurrence of pollen identical with that of *Centaurodendron* in *Centaurea* sect. *Plectocephalus* is of considerable interest, because Skottsberg (1938) considers this group in his discussion of the affinities of *Centaurodendron*, but rejects it on account of certain details of pappus and stigmatic branch morphology. These characters are often quite variable in Compositae, and the fact that *Centaurea* sect. *Plectocephalus* is represented by several species in Chile, the nearest land mass to the Juan Fernandez Islands, as well as the resemblance in pollen morphology, suggests that the possibility of relationship between *Centaurodendron* and *Plectocephalus* should remain open. The specialized sexual conditions in the head of *Centaurodendron* as compared to that of *Centaurea* do not seem so impressive to the writer as they did to Skottsberg (1938). In another group of Juan Fernandez Compositae, the closely related genera *Robinsonia, Rhetinodendron,* and *Symphochaeta,* the latter two genera appear to have evolved a dioecious condition from the monoecious condition found in *Robinsonia.* Probably no species of Centaurinae clearly illustrates a desired ancestral type from which the highly distinctive genera *Centaurodendron* and *Yunquea* can be derived, but the extreme closeness to this subtribe in respect to the anatomical characters reviewed above suggest that the two genera have considerable affinity to some members of Centaurinae: a more discrete affinity, in fact than one can usually postulate between insular endemic genera and their putative mainland relatives.

Data from vegetative anatomy also permit a relatively decisive outlook on relationships among the three species considered in this paper. The writer believes that closeness in such features as glandular trichomes, leaf anatomy, node anatomy, distribution and number of secretory canals, and wood anatomy confirm Skottsberg's (1929) contention that *Yunquea* must be related to *Centaurodendron.* The coincidence of these anatomical features could hardly be explained in any other way. Similarly, Skottsberg's decision to erect a new genus from the rather fragmentary material of *Yunquea* he received seems well justified in terms of anatomical data. The differences in leaf, cortex, and node anatomy are minor. The divergences in wood anatomy are somewhat greater. These differences, taken as a whole, are approximately what one would expect of plants which are generically different.

On account of virtual identity in leaf, leaf base, node, and cortex anatomy, the new species *Centaurodendron palmiforme* is correctly placed in that genus rather than in *Yunquea.* In some anatomical characters, however, it resembles *Yunquea* more closely than does *C. dracaenoides.* The lack of pith sclereids, absence of apotracheal parenchyma, and intermediacy in certain dimensions of tracheary cells between *Yunquea* and *C. dracaenoides* indicate this tendency. Other wood characters, such as the ray anatomy and fiber width, clearly mark it as referable to *Centaurodendron.*

LITERATURE CITED

Carlquist, S. 1956. On the generic limits of *Eriophyllum* (Compositae) and related genera. Madroño 13:227–239.

———. 1957a. Systematic anatomy of *Hesperomannia.* Pacif. Sci. 11:207–215.

———. 1957b. Wood anatomy of Mutisieae (Compositae). Trop. Woods 106:29–45.

———. 1957c. The genus *Fitchia* (Compositae). Univ. Calif. Publ. Bot. 29:1–144.

———. 1958a. Anatomy of Guayana Mutisieae. Part II. Mem. N. Y. Bot. Gard. 10:00–00.

———. 1958b. Wood anatomy of Heliantheae (Compositae). Trop. Woods 108:00–00.

Col, M. A. 1903. Recherches sur l'appareil sécréteur interne des composées. Jour. de Bot. 17:252–318.

Daniel, L. 1890. Recherches anatomiques et physiologiques sur les bractées de l'involucre des composées. Thesis, G. Masson, Paris.

Gueguen, F. 1902. Anatomie du style et du stigmate des phanerogames. Jour. de Bot. 16: 300–313.

Jeffrey, E. C. 1917. The anatomy of woody plants. University of Chicago Press, Chicago.

Johansen, D. A. 1940. Plant microtechnique. McGraw Hill, New York.

Kunkel, G. 1957. Beobachtungen über die Vegetation auf dem Yunque-Massiv. Bot. Jahrb. 77:149–157.

Lavialle, P. 1912. Recherches sur le développement de l'ovaire en fruit chez les composées. Ann. Sci. Nat. Bot. sér. IX. 15:39–149.

Napp-Zinn, K. 1956. Beiträge zur Anatomie und Morphologie der Involucral- und Spreublätter der Compositen. Bot. Studien 6:1–116.

Skottsberg, C. 1929. Notes on some recent collections made in the islands of Juan Fernandez. Medd. Göteborgs Bot. Trädg. 4:155-171.

————. 1938. On Mr. C. Bock's collection of plants from Masatierra (Juan Fernandez), with remarks on the flowers of *Centaurodendron*. Medd. Göteborgs Bot. Trädg. 12: 361–373.

————. 1953. The vegetation of the Juan Fernandez Islands. Nat. Hist. Juan Fernandez and Easter Isl. 2:793–960.

————. 1957. Une seconde espèce de *Centaurodendron* Johow. Bull. Jard. Bot. Bruxelles 27:585–589.

Van Tieghem, P. 1872. Mémoire sur les canaux sécréteurs des plantes. Ann. Sci. Nat. Bot. sér. V. 16:96–201.

Wagenitz, G. 1955. Pollenmorphologie und Systematik in der Gattung *Centaurea* L. s. l. Flora 142:213–279.

THE MORPHOLOGY AND SYSTEMATICS OF
THE LEAVES IN ERICALES

O. HAGERUP

Botanical Museum, Copenhagen, Denmark

From his researches on the morphology of the floral organs Nordhagen (1937-38) concluded that *Calluna* has such an isolated position within the Ericaceae as to make it difficult to make out the nearest relations of this genus.

However, there is a whole series of investigations dating from the last century to recent times which obviously show that the vegetative organs of the Ericales, particularly the leaves, are the most remarkable found within the flowering plants. Certain peculiar features are quite characteristic of large taxonomic units, and many plants (e.g. *Rhododendron*) can even be identified up to the specific level by the characters of the hairs on the leaves (Cowan, 1950).

It, therefore, occurred to me to find out whether the form and structure of the leaf of *Calluna* could possibly give any information as to where the nearest relations are to be found.

I soon realized, however, that the form of leaf in the Ericaceae had not been sufficiently utilized in taxonomic literature, although generally such observations are easily made. This defect is particularly glaring in *Calluna* — a plant whose leaves are almost unique both regarding their external form and anatomical structure.

These defects originate in the fact that some of the earliest studies on the leaf anatomy of *Calluna* are completely incorrect and even deceptive. When some of the cross-sections in manuals and text-books were examined, it was found (Schroeter, 1904-1908; p. 101, Fig. 4) that they do not belong to *Calluna*, but, as

Reprinted by permission of the publisher from PHYTOMOR-
PHOLOGY, 3, 459–464 (1953).

far as I am able to decide, to *Erica carnea*. Actually the anatomy of the leaf of *Calluna* remained almost unknown, until Beijerinck (1940) examined it a few years ago.

In order to make a fuller survey, the leaves of not only *Calluna* but also many other members of the Ericales in the copious collection at the Botanical Museum of the University of Copenhagen were examined. It appeared then that according to the form and structure the leaves of the order can be divided into the following 5 fundamental types (Ljungström, 1883, p. 3). Generally they are so well marked out that for taxonomic investigations they ought to be utilized to a higher extent than has been the case till now.

The Rhododendron Leaf

This is flat, generally broad, less frequently narrow (Figs. 1, 2); stomata on the lower side; palisade towards the upper. Margins are often flat; if they are recurved, the history of evolution shows (Hagerup, 1946) that the margins of the true " Rollblätter " are revolute; as will be seen below, they are on principle different from the leaves of *Erica*. This form of leaf, which is also very common in other phanerogams, is found in numerous Ericales, and especially within the Pyrolaceae, Rhodoraceae, Vacciniaceae, and some Ericaceae, e.g. *Andromeda*, *Arctostaphylos*, *Arbutus*, etc.

The Needle-shaped Leaf

This is narrow and pointed with flat margins (Figs. 3, 4). The section shown in Fig. 3 shows stomata as well as an assimilating tissue both on the upper and the lower side. This form of leaf is rare within Ericales, but is common in the Epacridaceae and in certain species of *Cassiope*, *Erica* and *Harrimanella*. The evolution (Hagerup, 1946) does not show anything of fundamental interest.

The Ericoid Leaves

Of these there are 3 different fundamental types (Figs. 5-13), all of which are small and linear and provided on the lower side with a hairy groove containing the stomata. How this groove arose is enigmatic. Although Ljungström solved this problem as early as 1883, his work was overlooked, and modern manuals and text-books still incorrectly regard the ericoid leaf as " Rollblätter " from the wrong conception that the groove should be limited by the revolute margins of the leaves. But if a developmental study is made from a series of sections, it appears that the various ericoid leaves are unique, not only among the Ericales, but also among the phanerogams as a whole. As the origin of the groove has already been thoroughly examined (Hagerup, 1946), the point may be illustrated here only with Fig. 7 of *Phyllodoce coerulea*, which may serve as a typical example.

When very young, the ericoid leaf is plainly needle-shaped. But at an early stage some subepidermal cells (dotted in Fig. 7) on the lower side of the leaf start dividing, so that they form 2 coherent pads along the margin of the lamina. During the further growth of the leaf these pads become ever higher, at the same time bending from both sides towards the midrib, until the lower side of the leaf is completely locked up into a cavity, being connected with the surroundings by only a narrow, hairy groove (Figs. 5, 9, 11, 13). Anatomically, too, these pads are peculiar, for the palisade tissue found on the outer side is similar to that on the upper side. Besides, stomata are found on the interior side. Thus it was clear that the leaf margins are really situated at the extreme ends along the sides (Figs. 11-13), and do not limit the groove on the lower side. On principle ericoid leaves are, therefore, different from " Rollblätter ", whose margins are recurved towards the lower side (Fig. 2).

Ericoid leaves can, as mentioned, be divided into the following fundamental types according to the length of the stalk, the formation of the pads and the position of the palisade tissue.

THE TETRALIX LEAF (Figs. 5, 6) — It has a short stalk; the groove on the lower side *is open at the base* because the two pads limiting the groove do not continue across the base of the lamina

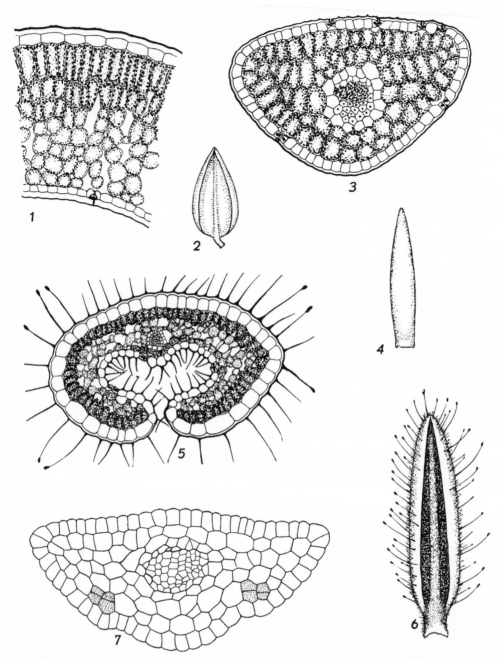

FIGS. 1-7 — Fig. 1. *Oxycoccus palustris*, c.s. leaf. × 150. Fig. 2. *Oxycoccus microcarpus;* leaf. × 6. Fig. 3. *Harrimanella hypnoides;* c.s. leaf. × 225. Fig. 4. *Harrimanella hypnoides;* entire leaf. × 18. Fig. 5. *Erica tetralix;* c.s. leaf. × 150. Fig. 6. *Erica tetralix,* entire leaf. × 15. Fig. 7. *Phyllodoce coerulea,* c.s. young leaf. The dotted cells are the first initials of the pads which will limit the ventral groove of the leaf. × 500.

(cf. Figs. 6 and 8). Palisade tissue is found on the upper side of the leaf (Fig. 5). This form of leaf is the commonest among the ericoid types. Out of 85 species of *Erica* examined, 70 possessed the same open groove as in *Erica tetralix* and this is also the condition in numerous species belonging to the majority of other genera having ericoid leaves.

THE EMPETRUM-LEAF (Fig. 8) — This resembles the leaf of *Tetralix* in form and size; it also has a short stalk and a palisade tissue at the upper side. However, it differs in the groove at bottom being *closed*, because the 2 pads are reciprocally connected by a bridge across the base of lamina. The Empetrum type of leaf is less common than the Tetralix type. These 2 leaf forms are often found in species belonging to the same genus. Among the species of *Erica* examined by me, 20 per cent had a closed groove, e.g. *E. cinerea*, *E. carnea*, *E. mediterranea*, and *E. gracilis*. The Empetrum type of leaf is also found in other genera of Ericaceae (*Blaeria, Philippia*) as in the whole family Empetraceae.

THE CALLUNA-LEAF (Figs. 10-13) — This queer leaf differs in several essential respects from other ericoid leaves. Here a stalk is lacking; and the 2 pads of the lower side of the leaf continue into 2 arrow-shaped prolongations which are turned downwards. In transection the outline of the lamina is triangular, resembling the leaves of certain Araceae. The internal structure of the leaf is just as peculiar. In its middle lies a strikingly large intercellular space. The cells lying immediately below the upper epidermis do not form a palisade tissue, nor is it a typical spongy tissue. They form instead long cellular filaments, poor in chlorophyll, which run along the length of the leaf and are parallel to each other. This lining of cellular filaments is better developed in *Cassiope* than in *Calluna*.

This form of leaf is the rarest of the 5 mentioned above, occurring only in some species of *Cassiope* and *Erica* in addition to *Calluna*. Its anatomical structure is related to the fact that the leaves are directed slopingly upwards and pressed in towards the stem, so that the morphological upper side is illuminated to a smaller extent than the lower side.

Taxonomic Results

As is well known, vegetative characters of plants are generally not of much systematic significances. However, the Ericales must in this respect be regarded as an exception as was already conceded by the classic authors (e.g. Drude, 1897, p. 18) long ago. As indicated above both the form and anatomy of the leaf are quite characteristic in some cases for larger taxonomic units (families), and in some cases for smaller units (species). From this point of view it is, therefore, interesting to find out whether there exist elsewhere in the plant kingdom similar unique types of leaf as found in the ericoid:

(a) Besides many Ericaceae the Empetrum-leaf is found only in the family Empetraceae. That this is an expression of a real relationship is already shown by Samuelsson (1913) and Hagerup (1922).

(b) To the Rhododendroideae, which generally has the large and broad *Rhododendron* type of leaf mentioned above, is also reckoned the genus *Phyllodoce* (Drude, 1897), although the latter has, indeed, typical Tetralix-like leaves as in many Ericaceae. The actual reason for this assignment (Drude) is that in *Phyllodoce* the so-called anther horns are absent. This lack is, however, also seen in numerous species of *Erica*, which indeed, for that reason, were not removed from their natural circles of relationship. The leaf form suggests that *Phyllodoce* belongs to the Ericaceae, which is also confirmed by a study of the corolla.

(c) A comparison of Figs. 10-13 shows that the leaf of *Calluna* is in the main constructed just as in *Cassiope tetragona*. Still these leaves are quite different from those of most other ericoids (Figs. 1-9) as well as from all other leaves on the whole. That these remarkable conformities between the unique leaves of *Calluna* and *Cassiope* are an expression of a close relationship between them is confirmed by the fact that several other characters are common to them. Thus they have similar hibernacles without any specially formed bud-scales and are both naked, which is a very rare phenomenon within woody plants from northern regions.

Further, both genera possess more than 2 bracteoles on the floral stalk, a phenomenon not common in Bicornes, although,

however, a similar arrangement is found in *Empetrum, Erica* and the Epacridaceae.

The annual shoots (Fig. 14) are also very remarkable in having 3 different

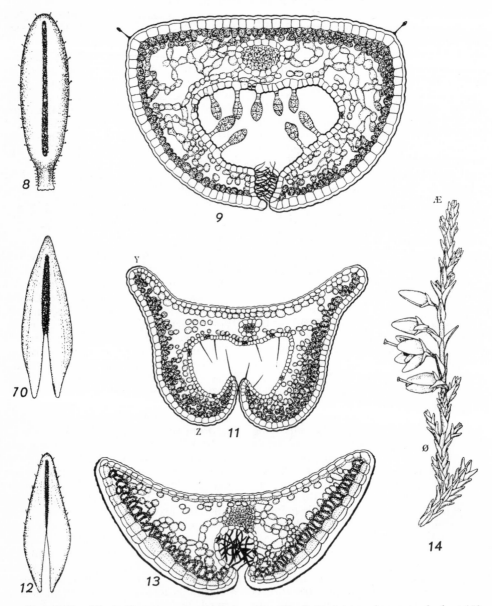

FIGS. 8-14 — Fig. 8. *Empetrum nigrum*, leaf. × 12.   Fig. 9. *Empetrum nigrum*, c.s. leaf. × 150. Fig. 10. *Cassiope tetragona*, entire leaf. × 11.   Fig. 11. *Cassiope tetragona*, c.s. leaf (*y*, margin of leaf; *z*, one of the pads). × 12.   Fig. 12. *Calluna vulgaris*, entire leaf. × 15.   Fig. 13. *Calluna vulgaris*, c.s. leaf. × 150.   Fig. 14. *Calluna vulgaris*, annual shoot, consisting of 3 parts, of which only the middle is flowering and the upper (Æ) and lower (Ø) are vegetative. × 2½.

parts, only the middle of which produces flowers, whereas both the bottom and the top parts are completely vegetative. These circumstances were investigated in detail in *Empetrum* (Hagerup, 1922) and *Calluna* (Nordhagen, 1937-38). The resemblances in the vegetative organs are so remarkable that I consider these an expression of a close relationship between *Cassiope* and *Calluna*. *Cassiope* has no doubt been placed in a wrong way in the Ericaceae. Drude (1889, p. 41) classes it with Andromedeae, which indeed differs much in having large leaves of the Rhododendron type. The structure of the leaf seems to show that the nearest relatives of *Cassiope*, too, are to be found within the Ericaceae with ericoid leaves.

On the whole, the ericoid forms of leaf are so characteristic and remarkable that a decisive weight is to be laid upon them at the high taxonomic division of the Ericales. It is my opinion that all the genera with ericoid leaves ought to be grouped into an independent family, the Ericaceae proper, and within this the genera *Calluna* and *Cassiope* should form a special subfamily of their own.

Summary

According to their form and structure the leaves of Ericales may be classified as follows:

1. THE RHODODENDRON TYPE — Lamina dorsiventral, often large and broad, margins flat or revolute (Figs. 1-2).

2. THE NEEDLE TYPE — Lamina needle-shaped or subulate, small with flat margins, stomata and assimilating tissue, often both, on the upper and lower sides (Figs. 3-4).

3. THE ERICOID TYPE which are small and narrow with a ventral groove which conceals stomata. The groove is not enclosed by revolute margins, but by 2 pads which are initiated along the margins on the lower side of the leaf, a phylogenetic neoformation.

4. THE ERICOID TYPE is further subdivided as follows:
   (a) Groove *open* at base of lamina; leaf petiolate with a palisade tissue on the lower and upper sides. Examples: *Tetralix* (Figs. 5-6).
   (b) Groove *closed* at base of lamina; leaf petiolate with a palisade tissue on the lower and upper side. Example: *Empetrum* (Figs. 8-9).
   (c) Groove open at base; leaf not petiolate, with 2 arrow-shaped auricles at base, a palisade tissue found only on the lower side; large air space in the middle of the leaf. Example: *Calluna* (Figs. 10-13).

In the higher taxonomic division of the Ericales much more consideration is to be given in future to leaf structure than was the case up till now. Forms with Ericoid leaves ought to be placed together in a group of their own into a special family (or subfamily), in which *Calluna* and *Cassiope* are to be assigned to a particular group, isolated from others, owing to their unique leaves.

Literature Cited

BEIJERINCK, W. 1940. *Calluna*. Verh. d. Kon. Nederl. Akademie van Wetenschappen, Afd. Naturkunde, II, **38**: 1-180.

COWAN, J. M. 1950. " The Rhododendron Leaf." London.

DRUDE, O. 1889. Ericaceae. (In Engler and Prantl: Natürlichen Pflanzenfamilien **4**: 1-80).

HAGERUP, O. 1922. On *Empetrum nigrum* L. Bot. Tidsskr. **37**: 253-304.

— 1946. Studies on the Empetraceae. Det Kgl. Danske Videnskabernes Selskab. Biolog. Meddelelser **20** (5): 1-49.

LJUNGSTRÖM, E. 1883. Bladets byggnad inom familien Ericaceae. Lunds Univ. Årsskrift. **19**: 1-47.

NORDHAGEN, R. 1937-38. Studien über die monotypische Gattung *Calluna* Salisb. Bergens Mus. Årbok. Naturv. rekke No. 4/1.

PETERSEN, H. E. 1908. Ericineae. Medd. Grönland. **36**: 73-138.

SAMUELSSON, G. 1913. Studien über die Entwicklungsgeschichte der Blüten einiger Bicornes-Typen. Svensk. bot. Tidskr. **7**: 97-188.

SCHROETER, C. 1904-8. " Das Pflanzenleben der Alpen etc." Zürich.

41

THE COMPARATIVE ANATOMY OF THE XYLEM AND THE PHYLOGENY OF THE JULIANIACEAE [1]

William L. Stern

THE NATURAL AFFINITIES of the Julianiaceae have been debated ever since the description of the genus *Juliania* (then *Hypopterygium*) by von Schlechtendal in 1843. Most workers who have investigated the internal anatomy of the group are inclined to place the family close to the Anacardiaceae. Thus Fritsch (1908) suggested that one of the chief points of resemblance between Julianiaceae and Anacardiaceae lies in the occurrence of large resin-containing canals in the phloem and pith of both families. Both *Rhus simulata* and *Spondias mangifera* were found ". . . to possess such resin-canals in the leaf in exactly the same position . . ." as in Julianiaceae. Copeland and Doyel (1940), in their study of the anatomy of *Toxicodendron diversiloba*, give several points which in their opinion indicate a close relationship between Julianiaceae and Anacardiaceae. Copeland and Doyel, referring to Boodle's work which is included in Hemsley's (1908) paper, show that *Toxicodendron* and julianiaceous ovules agree in orientation, vascular supply, and the presence of a hypostase. The embryos are also similar in the peculiarly oriented radicle, and in the shape of the margins of the cotyledons. I. W. Bailey (as quoted in Copeland and Doyel) is of the opinion that the secondary xylem of Julianiaceae and Anacardiaceae is so alike that the two might be grouped in a single family. In his study of the secondary xylem of Wettstein's Gruinales and Terebinthales, Heimsch (1942) agrees that the Julianiaceae are closely related to the Anacardiaceae. Standley (1923), and Standley and Steyermark (1949), in writing of *Juliania adstringens*, state that the simple-leaved form, reduced from compound, sometimes found here, indicates a

relationship with Anacardiaceae and Burseraceae for similar kinds of compound leaves are found in certain species of *Bursera* and *Rhus*. In these species, leaves on the same branch may vary from unifoliolate to trifoliolate, and even 5–7 leaflets.

In direct contrast to this theory, Rose, in a letter quoted in Hemsley (1908), states that he does not believe that the group has any relationship with either Burseraceae or Anacardiaceae and ". . . that it must be closely related to the Juglandaceae . . .". Macbride (1936) believes the resemblances of the Julianiaceae with Juglandaceae may be more fundamental than those with Anacardiaceae. He points to the presence of unisexual flowers which are common to both Juglandaceae and Julianiaceae. The Julianiaceae are placed in a distinct order, the Julianiales, by Johnson (1931), Engler and Diels (1936), and Rendle (1938). Each of these workers places the order in close proximity to the Juglandales. Hutchinson (1926), and Wettstein (1935), place the family Julianiaceae under the order Juglandales with the family Juglandaceae. Hallier (1905) treats the genera of Julianiaceae as a tribe (?) under the family Juglandaceae co-existent with Juglandeae. However, in 1908, he revised this conception and said that *Juliania* had arisen from *Pistacia* through the reduction of the pistillate flowers. Therefore, he placed *Juliania* in the family Terebinthaceae. Hemsley (1908), after considering other possible affinities of the Julianiaceae, came to the conclusion that the family was most closely related to the "Cupuliferae." He based his opinion on the common possession of a closed involucre in *Juliania*, *Fagus*, *Castanea*, and *Castanopsis*; the similarity of the male flowers, inflorescences, and pollen in *Juliania adstringens* and certain species of *Quercus*; the "collateral" flowers and nuts in *Castanea* and *Juliania*; the exendospermous seeds of *Juliania* and the "Cupuliferae"; and the fact that the cotyledons of *Juliania* and the "Cupuliferae" are epigeal in germination. On these bases he suggested that the family be placed between the Juglandaceae and the "Cupuliferae." According to Kershaw (1909), additional evidence for Hems-

[1] Received for publication October 9, 1951.

Grateful acknowledgment is made to Professor Oswald Tippo for his assistance with the problem; to Mr. Theodore Delevoryas for his skill in photography; to Professor G. Neville Jones for his help with the taxonomic portions of the work; to Dr. Theodor Just for making herbarium facilities available; to Mrs. Martha Leavenworth for gift of materials; to Professor Charles Heimsch for loan of slides; to Dr. G. Erdtman for his analysis of pollen; and to my wife who typed the manuscript.

Reprinted by permission of the author and publisher from the AMERICAN JOURNAL OF BOTANY, 39, 220–229 (1952).

ley's views might be derived by a more detailed comparison of the ovules of *Juglans* and *Juliania*. Both have a nucellus which is free from the vascularized integument. *Juliania* and *Juglans* also possess a peculiar outgrowth (the obturator) at the base of the ovule. Kershaw mentions the occurrence of a vascular supply in the single integument of *Mangifera* but he states that ". . . there is no clear indication of the obturator." Copeland and Doyel (1940) say that in *Toxicodendron*, the funiculus bears a projection which might be called an obturator, but it does not extend across the micropyle (as does the obturator in Julianiaceae). Bessey (1915) places Julianiaceae between Myricaceae and Proteaceae.

Thus, in general, there appear to be two main points of view with regard to the affinities of the Julianiaceae: (1) that they are closely related to Anacardiaceae, (2) that their closest affinities lie with Juglandaceae. A third suggestion has been offered, namely that their vegetative form sometimes resembles Burseraceae and, therefore, they belong with that group. The present study of the secondary xylem of Julianiaceae was undertaken in the hope that the knowledge here gained, coupled with that from other fields of botany, will serve to elucidate the phylogeny of the family.

The Julianiaceae (Hemsley, 1908) consist of two genera, *Juliania* Schlechtendal and *Orthopterygium* Hemsley, and four, possibly five, species: *J. adstringens* Schlechtendal (*Amphipterygium adstringens* Schiede), *J. mollis* Hemsley (*Amphipterygium molle* Hemsley & Rose), *J. amplifolia* Hemsley & Rose (*Amphipterygium amplifolium* Hemsley & Rose), *J. glauca* Hemsley & Rose (*Amphipterygium glaucum* Hemsley & Rose), and *Orthopterygium huaucui* Hemsley (*Juliania huaucui* A. Gray, *Amphipterygium huaucui* Hemsley & Rose). The species of *Juliania* are found in Mexico; however, *J. adstringens* has also been collected in Guatemala (Standley and Steyermark, 1949) and in Honduras.[2] *O. huaucui* has been collected only in Peru (Macbride, 1936).

The plants are small trees or large shrubs. The leaves are alternate, exstipulate, deciduous, usually pinnately compound, and clustered at the ends of branchlets. The plants are dioecious, the staminate flowers being borne in pendent, axillary panicles. The male flowers have a simple, 3–9 parted perianth with linear, acute segments. Stamens are as many as the perianth segments, and are borne alternately with them. Female inflorescences are inconspicuous at anthesis, being crowded in among the newly-developing leaves. Female flowers number 3–4 in each inflorescence and are situated within the globose expansion of a peculiar shortened inflores-

cence axis. Usually only one flower matures. The unilocular ovary contains one ovule; however, the style is branched to form three, exserted, hairy lobes. The fruit is samaroid. At maturity the flattened peduncle of the inflorescence in *Juliania* forms a wing-shaped structure, narrow at its point of attachment and widening distally to the seed. The involucre may completely or partially surround the seed. In *Orthopterygium*, the wing margins are more or less parallel. Mature fruits are often clustered and pendent. The bark, when cut, exudes a thick, milky sap. According to Standley (1923), the bark of *Juliania adstringens* possesses tannin which has astringent properties. It is used by the natives to ". . . harden the gums, cure old wounds, and it is said to be employed also as a remedy for malaria." The bark is also known to produce a red dye.

MATERIALS AND METHODS.—Of the nine wood samples available for this study, only one was mature (*Juliania adstringens*, collected by W. C. Leavenworth, 1946). Twig specimens used are as follows: *Juliania adstringens*, collected by Ferris (No. 6175), and *Orthopterygium huaucui*, collected by Weberbauer (No. 5691), were supplied by the United States National Herbarium; *Juliania amplifolia*, collected by Pringle (No. 8769), came from Harvard University, and *Juliania amplifolia*, also collected by Pringle (No. 6871), was obtained from the Chicago Natural History Museum Herbarium; *Orthopterygium huaucui*, collected by Macbride (No. 2866), was sent from Harvard. Prepared slides of *Juliania adstringens* and *Orthopterygium huaucui*, No. 19461 and 19681 respectively, were obtained from the Harvard University slide collection.

The microtechnical procedures used are essentially those outlined by Wetmore (1932). Dried wood samples were boiled to remove the air, cooled, dehydrated, infiltrated with celloidin, and stored in glycerin-alcohol. Transverse, radial and tangential sections were cut on a Reichert sliding microtome. These sections were stained with Heidenhain's iron-alum haemotoxylin and safranin, cleared in xylol, and mounted on slides in Canada balsam. Macerations were made following Jeffrey's technique as outlined by Johansen (1940). Due to the scarcity of material, macerations could only be made of *J. adstringens* (Leavenworth, No. 1497a).

The diagnostic features believed most significant and appropriate to the woods under investigation were selected from among those listed by Tippo (1941). Measurements of macerated fibers and vessel elements were taken from only one specimen as mentioned above. In measuring the lengths of vessel elements, the suggestions of Chalk and Chattaway (1934) were followed: that is, "total lengths" (from tip to tip) were gauged. These figures have perhaps more phylogenetic significance than mea-

---

[2] No published record has been found, but herbarium specimens from Honduras housed in the Chicago Natural History Museum, collected by Standley in 1949 (No. 24674), were observed.

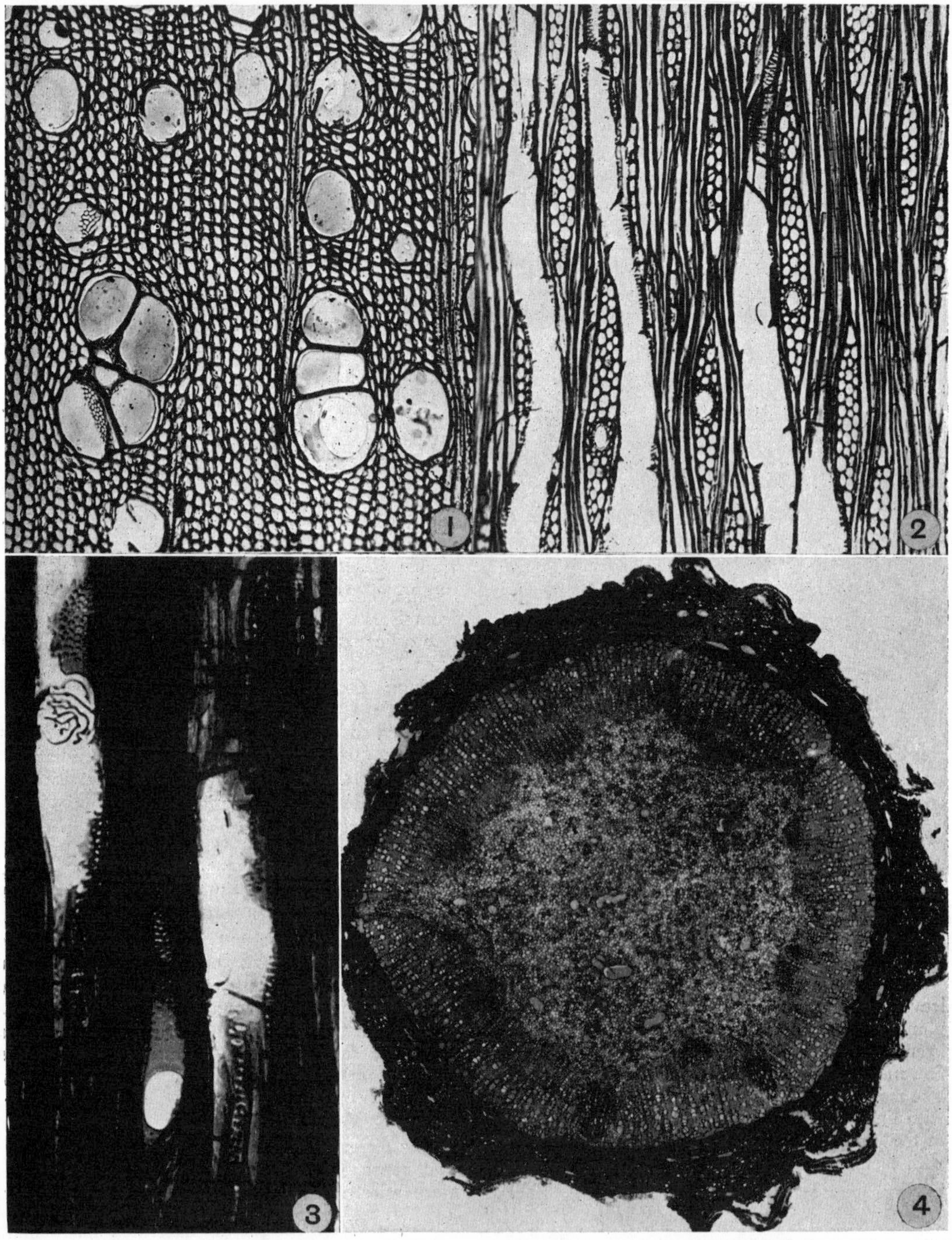

Fig. 1–4.—Fig. 1. *Juliania adstringens*, cross-section with weakly defined growth rings showing solitary pores, pore multiples and clusters. ×97.—Fig. 2. *J. adstringens*, tangential section depicting uni- and multiseriate vascular rays and intercellular canals. ×97.—Fig. 3. *J. glauca*, radial section showing simple and reticulate perforation plates. ×200.— Fig. 4. *Orthopterygium huaucui*, cross-section with intercellular canals in the pith and bark and showing resin-filled pith cells. ×14.

surements obtained by any alternative methods, since they more nearly approximate the lengths of the fusiform cambial initials from which the vessel elements are derived. Unfortunately, vessel element lengths had to be measured from sections in all but the one case mentioned above. For these measurements "extreme body length" (from the top of the upper perforation to the bottom of the lower) was chosen as a "second best" to "total length." The lengths of 100 vessel elements were obtained on all samples. The tangential diameters of 100 vessel cross-sections were also gauged.

Fibrous tracheary elements were not measured from sectioned material, for as Tippo (1938) has noted, these measurements are too inaccurate. Only in the case of the macerated wood were the lengths of 100 fibrous tracheary elements measured.

Calculations following Rendle and Clarke's (1934a,b) suggestions were made and are included in table 1. Kribs' (1935, 1937) classifications, for vertical xylem parenchyma and for vascular rays, were followed. General terms referring to the size of vessel diameters are those suggested by Chattaway (1932). Chalk's (1936) values are utilized to describe vessel element lengths. Other descriptive terms are those listed in the International Association of Wood Anatomists' Glossary of Terms Used in Describing Woods (1933).

Many of the observations and determinations included here must be qualified in those cases where young wood had to be utilized. As mentioned by Rendle and Clarke (1934a), measurements on young wood often vary from those on mature wood in the same species or plant. Barghoorn (1940, 1941), in his studies on vascular rays, has shown that the structure of rays in plants is very variable. He states that "The height and width of rays in the identification of woods should, therefore be used with great care, if at all. Such criteria may vary more in different portions of the individual than in corresponding woody portions of closely related species." ". . . in phylogenetic studies ray type designations should be used with considerable caution as an aid for determining the degree of specialization of the xylem. This is true because of the more or less extensive variations in ray structure which occur during successive stages of secondary growth. Thus ontogenetic stages in the same individual may represent different levels of phylogenetic modification . . .".

ANATOMICAL DESCRIPTION OF THE XYLEM.—Some of the specimens under observation exhibit weakly defined growth rings (fig. 1). Since pores do not vary markedly in size and number in these growth rings, the woods are diffuse-porous. Pore arrangement is summarized in table 2. It can be seen that solitary pores are most abundant and clusters least numerous, with the number of multiples falling between these two categories. No pore chains were observed. Large pores are round, with smaller

pores tending to be somewhat angular. The numbers of pores in the aggregate types (multiples or clusters) is given in table 2.

The ground-mass of the wood is composed of fibrous elements whose pits range in form from fairly well-defined bordered types to simple pits. Thus both fiber-tracheids and libriform wood fibers are present and in approximately the same numbers. Practically all fibers are septate, there being two or three septa to an element. The walls of these fibers are thin, the diameter of the lumen being wider than the thickness of the walls. Fiber length (table 1) ranges from 400–1250μ, the mean centering about 838μ.

Vessel element end walls vary from transverse to oblique (30°–45°). Perforation plates are mostly simple (fig. 3); however, in each species a few reticulate plates were observed (fig. 3). Vessel element lengths, in the material under study, were "moderately short" (table 1), the mean being about 248μ for the family. In computing these figures, measurements derived from the sectioned material of J. adstringens (Leavenworth No. 1497a) were not included. They are placed in table 1 to indicate the difference in measurements as performed on sectioned material as contrasted with those on macerated material. Thin vessel walls (1–4μ) are evident in all samples. Vessel diameters are "small." The intervascular pitting consists of three types: transitional, opposite, and alternate. The pitting of very few vessel elements appears to be solely of either the transitional or opposite types. Alternate pitting is the most common type. All bordered pits have elongated or elliptical apertures. Alternate pits are crowded, the outlines of their borders are polygonal often having as many as six angles. Tyloses are abundant in the mature wood, and have been seen in some twig specimens as well.

Vascular ray width (fig. 2, table 2) varies from uniseriate to pentaseriate. No rays over five cells in width were observed in the samples under investigation. Ray height (table 2) is from 1–40 cells. All rays correspond to Kribs' heterogeneous type IIB. Vertical xylem parenchyma is scanty, vasicentric. Ray-vessel pitting appears "gash-like" as does parenchyma-vessel pitting.

Intercellular canals are a constant feature of mature wood, but they were not observed in the wood of any twig specimens. These canals (fig. 2) occur singly in rays scattered throughout the wood. Only radial intercellular canals have been seen in the wood, although both vertical and horizontal canals occur in the pith (fig. 4), and at least vertical canals in the bark (fig. 4). The canals are lined with a uniseriate (usually) epithelium (fig. 2) composed of cells smaller than ordinary ray cells. No tylosoids were seen in any of the canals. The cells in the pith are often seen to be filled with what appears to be a resinous material (fig. 4).

TABLE 1. *Dimensions of tracheary elements in Julianiaceae.*

Species and specimen number	Range in μ	Most frequent range in μ	Mean and standard error in μ	Standard deviation and standard error in μ
Juliania adstringens				
Fibrous element lengths				
Leavenworth No. 1497a	400–1250	674–1002	838±16.4	164±11.6
Vessel element lengths				
Leavenworth No. 1497a (macer.)	250–630	337–485	411±7.4	74±5.2
Leavenworth No. 1497a (sect.)	40–470	179–375	277±9.8	98±6.9
Hinton No. 4812	50–320	119–237	178±5.9	59±4.2
Harvard No. 19461	100–570	202–378	290±8.8	88±6.2
Mean for species			293±7.4	74±5.2
Vessel diameters				
Leavenworth No. 1497a	28–126	55–99	77±2.2	22±1.5
Hinton No. 4812	21–80	34–56	45±1.1	11±0.8
Harvard No. 19461	11–74	29–57	43±1.4	14±1.0
Mean for species			55±1.6	16±1.1
Juliania amplifolia				
Vessel element lengths				
Pringle No. 6871	120–460	229–371	300±7.1	71±5.0
Pringle No. 8769	80–500	158–366	262±10.4	104±7.3
Mean for species			281±8.7	87±6.1
Vessel diameters				
Pringle No. 6871	25–92	38–72	55±1.7	17±1.2
Pringle No. 8769	21–92	33–65	49±1.6	16±1.1
Mean for species			52±1.6	16±1.1
Juliania glauca				
Vessel element lengths				
Ferris No. 6175	90–500	185–343	264±7.9	79±5.6
Vessel diameters				
Ferris No. 6175	11–89	33–60	46±1.4	14±1.0
Vessel element length, mean for the genus			226±8.0	80±5.6
Vessel diameter, mean for the genus			51±1.5	15±1.1
Orthopterygium huaucui				
Vessel element lengths				
Harvard No. 19681	50–300	109–221	165±5.6	56±3.9
Weberbauer No. 5681	50–290	126–232	179±5.3	53±3.7
Macbride No. 2866	20–300	70–184	127±5.7	57±4.0
Mean for species			157±5.5	55±3.8
Vessel diameters				
Harvard No. 19681	18–110	25–67	46±2.1	21±1.4
Weberbauer No. 5681	21–108	40–82	61±2.1	21±1.4
Macbride No. 2866	23–99	32–62	47±1.5	15±1.1
Mean for species			51±1.9	19±1.3
Vessel element length, mean for the family			248±6.7	67±4.7
Vessel diameter, mean for the family			51±1.7	17±1.2

TABLE 2. *Pore arrangement and ray size in Julianiaceae.*

	Juliania	Orthopterygium	Julianiaceae
Pore distribution			
% solitary	75	53	64
% multiples	19	28	23
% clusters	6	19	12
Average number of pores in each grouping			
Multiples	2	3	
Clusters	4	5	
Vascular rays			
Range in width (number of cells)			
	1–4	1–5	
Range in height (number of cells)			
Uniseriate rays	1–33	1–15	
Multiseriate rays	4–40	3–32	

DISCUSSION.—The anatomy of the xylem of Julianiaceae as seen in the material at hand, does not present any obvious bases for separation of the family into two genera as was done by Hemsley (1908). Moreover, no significant differences were found among the woods of the different species (table 1, 2).

Hemsley (1908) has listed the following characteristics for the two genera:

Juliania	*Orthopterygium*
1. Mature leaves large	Mature leaves small
2. Male inflorescence pendulous	Male inflorescence erect
3. Male perianth segments exceeding stamens	Male perianth segments shorter than stamens
4. Male perianth 5–8 parted	Male perianth often 4–parted
5. Female inflorescences often 4–flowered	Female inflorescences often 3–flowered
6. Fruiting peduncles much dilated with tapering margins	Fruiting peduncles little dilated with parallel margins
7. Style strongly exserted from the involucre	Style hardly exserted from the involucre

Hemsley says that mature fruits of *Orthopterygium* were not observed by him, and he expresses doubt regarding the length of the style branches in this genus. Apparently Hemsley only supposed that they were "hardly exserted," since he places a (?) after the statement. On the basis of what has been observed on the wood anatomy of the Julianiaceae, and because of the fact that Hemsley never saw mature fruiting peduncles (nor apparently satisfactory female inflorescences), it is suggested that the taxonomy of this group needs further study. Regarding this last statement, it may be added that Asa Gray (1854) described, though somewhat incompletely, *Juliania huaucui* as a new species. He placed the species under the Anacardiaceae, probably following Bentham and Hooker (1862-1867),

and expressed doubt as to whether this Peruvian species was the same one as that in the Hooker herbarium (*Juliania adstringens*). He described the fruit as having a wing which is "straight and equal-sided" and an inch longer than the Mexican species. Gray's description of the fruit corresponds with that of Hemsley's *Orthopterygium huaucui* and is probably the same species. Thus, the description of *Juliania huaucui* A. Gray precedes *Orthopterygium huaucui* Hemsley by a period of 54 years.

As previously mentioned, it is believed by some workers that Julianiaceae are more closely allied to Juglandaceae than to any other group. Study of the wood of the two groups cannot support this viewpoint. Several distinct anatomical features serve to distinguish Julianiaceae from the walnut family. Among these characters are: septate fibers in all species, a ground-mass consisting of both fiber-tracheids and libriform wood fibers, presence of conspicuous intercellular canals, intervascular pitting which in all species consists of three types, i.e., transitional, opposite, and alternate; presence of reticulate perforation plates, and vertical xylem parenchyma that is exclusively scanty, vasicentric. For comparisons with juglandaceous woods, publications by Tippo (1938), Heimsch and Wetmore (1939), Heimsch (1942), and Kribs (1927) were consulted. Septate fibers, distinct libriform wood fibers, intercellular canals and reticulate perforation plates have not been reported by these authors as being present in juglandaceous woods. Most, if not all the intervascular pitting in Juglandaceae is alternate. Xylem parenchyma distribution varies in the family, the banded types predominating. Vasicentric and scanty paratracheal distributions have been reported in various species. Often, more than one type of parenchyma arrangement is exhibited by a single species. Scalariform perforation plates are present in a few juglandaceous genera, while none has been observed or reported in Julianiaceae.

Several other types of evidence can be cited to support the contention that Julianiaceae and Juglandaceae are not closely related. The insertion of the gynoecium in Juglandaceae has been reported as being inferior (Hutchinson, 1926). Hutchinson, placing Julianiaceae under Juglandales, asserts that the ovary here is also inferior. However, Johnson (1931), Willis (1948), and Gunderson (1950) describe the gynoecium of Julianiaceae as superior. In Hemsley's (1908) drawings of the sectioned pistils and involucres, the pistils appear to be superior, since they are free from, and not imbedded in the cushion upon which they are situated. As is evidenced by the trifid style in Julianiaceae, the ovary is probably tricarpellate. The Juglandaceae, however, usually have two carpels. Of doubtful import is the fact, that in Julianiaceae the cotyledons are epigeal in germination (Hemsley, 1908), while those of Juglandaceae are usually hypogeal (Rendle, 1938).

Works by Berry, Chaney, Jongmans (1931), and Knowlton were consulted for possible julianiaceous fossil evidence. However, no record was found. A search made in Darlington and Ammal (1945), Gaiser (1926, 1930a,b), Tischler (1927, 1931, 1950), and Wanscher (1934) proved fruitless as far as chromosome numbers in the Julianiaceae are concerned.

Most wood anatomists who have studied the Julianiaceae have concluded that the family has close anacardiaceous affinities. This is also the opinion of the writer. More than a few wood characteristics are common to both of these families. In comparing these two groups, papers on the Anacardiaceae by Heimsch (1940, 1942), Record (1939), and Dadswell and Ingle (1948) were consulted. Septate fibers are common in Anacardiaceae, both those with bordered pits (fiber-tracheids) and simple pits (libriform wood fibers). Pore distribution compares favorably in the two groups, solitary pores being most common. Perforation plates are mostly simple with reticulate plates occurring in Anacardiaceae as well as in Julianiaceae. As in Julianiaceae, vessel end walls are oblique or transverse. Intervascular pitting in both groups has been shown to be of three types, crowded-alternate predominating, with some transitional and opposite. The pit apertures are slit-like in both families. In Julianiaceae, the pit borders are almost invariably angular, while in the cashew family, pit borders may be either rounded or angular. Vascular rays are mostly heterogeneous type IIB in Anacardiaceae, as in Julianiaceae. Intercellular canals are a constant feature in the rays of many species of the Anacardiaceae. Vertical xylem parenchyma is described as abundant or scanty paratracheal by Heimsch (1942), as sparingly vasicentric or occasionally "finely" terminal and diffuse by Record (1939), and as vasicentric by Dadswell and Ingle (1948). In general, it can be seen that the parenchyma distribution in Julianiaceae is more nearly like that of Anacardiaceae, than the parenchyma of Juglandaceae.

The paniculate inflorescences of Anacardiaceae compare favorably with those in Julianiaceae. Unisexual flowers occur through reduction of bisexual flowers in Anacardiaceae (Rendle, 1938), and some species are dioecious. The insertion of the gynoecium is superior in Anacardiaceae as is suspected in Julianiaceae. The plates in Hemsley's (1908) work show that the pinnately compound leaves in the Julianiaceae are often reduced to the trifoliolate or unifoliolate (a compound leaf reduced to a single leaflet) condition in all species.[3] The leaves of anacardiaceous species also show a pinnate, trifoliolate, and (rarely) unifoliolate condition. Carpel number in Anacardiaceae is variable (1–5), 3 being a common number.

[3] Also verified by the author from specimens in the herbarium of the Chicago Natural History Museum.

The many similarities listed above between Julianiaceae and Anacardiaceae suggest that a close relationship exists between the two families. Of course the presence of single or a few common morphological characteristics in groups is insufficient to warrant the inference of close relationship. However when two families show a number of similarities, in different characteristics (wood anatomy, floral morphology, vegetative characters, etc.) some affinity may be assumed.

Manning (1938) suggests that the inflorescences of some of the Anacardiaceae fulfill the ancestral requirements of the juglandaceous inflorescence (a terminal, highly-branched panicle). He mentions other features in common between these two groups as pinnately compound leaves, absence of stipules, a tendency to imperfect flowers, etc. The Julianiaceae, according to Manning, also resemble the Juglandaceae in their paniculate inflorescences, and compound leaves. It is not possible to state here whether or not the Juglandaceae have ancestral affinities with either the Anacardiaceae or the Julianiaceae. However, it can be said, that the evidence from wood anatomy does not favor such an assumption.

The pollen of *Juliania adstringens* (Pringle No. 7243) has been described by G. Erdtman in correspondence with the author (September, 1951).[4] This description was compared with the diagnoses of the few anacardiaceous pollen grains delineated in Wodehouse (1935), Heimsch (1940), and Erdtman (1943), and juglandaceous pollen grains in Wodehouse and Erdtman. Hardly any similarities between the pollen of the Julianiaceae and either that of Anacardiaceae or Juglandaceae could be found. In fact, several differences appear. The texture of the indument in pollen grains of *Rhus typhina* is finely reticulate as it is in *J. adstringens*. Germ pores while varying from 3–7 in *J. adstringens*, are usually three in Anacardiaceae and number up to 15 in at least some species of *Juglans*. The grains of *Rhus typhina* are elongated (prolate), those of *Juglans, Engelhardtia*, and *Pterocarya* are flattened, and those of *J. adstringens* are suboblate to oblate spheroidal. Julianiaceous pollen grains are similar to those of Juglandaceae in that multiple germ pores are present in both groups. More complete information on anacardiaceous pollen grains will be necessary in order to evaluate adequately the significance of pollen characteristics among these families.

Webber (1941), in her work on the anatomy of the Burseraceae, noted that certain similarities exist between the xylem of this family and the woods of

[4] The description of the pollen of *J. adstringens* (Pringle No. 7243), as diagnosed by Erdtman, is as follows: "Grains (3–) 5 (–7)– colporate (brevicolpate), suboblate-oblate spheroidal (27×30μ). Sexine slightly thinner than nexine, finely reticulate (muri simplibaculate). Colpi narrow, about 8μ long. Ora lalongate (meridional diameter 3μ)."

Anacardiaceae, Rutaceae, Simarubaceae and Meliaceae. Heimsch (1942), also, describes this complex as possessing some similar xylem characteristics. In tabulating the xylem characteristics of the above mentioned families, works consulted other than those previously listed herein are as follows: Dadswell and Ellis (1939) and Kribs (1930) on Meliaceae, Dadswell and Eckersley (1938), and Record and Hess (1940) on Rutaceae, and Webber (1936) on Simarubaceae.

Structural features of the xylem possessed in common by at least some members of all families in this complex are: (1) heterogeneous IIB or homogeneous vascular rays, (2) libriform wood fibers which form the major part of the ground-mass of the xylem, (3) fibers which are septate, (4) pores which are solitary, in short, radial multiples, and in small clusters, (5) vessels with simple perforation plates, (6) intercellular canals, (7) paratracheal parenchyma, and (8) vascular rays, multi- and uniseriate.

By referring to the previous description of the xylem of Julianiaceae, it can be seen that this family also possesses the same xylem features as those listed above, with the exception of (2), since Julianiaceae are also rich in fiber-tracheids. Thus, from the standpoint of wood anatomy, the Julianiaceae might be considered as a member of Webber's complex.

Within this complex, certain families tend to possess more xylem characteristics in common with some families than with others. The woods of Anacardiaceae, Burseraceae and Julianiaceae are alike in that some members have normal intercellular canals, ray-vessel and parenchyma-vessel pit pairs are long and gash-like, vascular rays are chiefly heterogeneous IIB, septate fibrous elements are present in many Anacardiaceae, practically all Burseraceae, and in all Julianiaceae, vertical intercellular canals are present in the pholem and cortex, and the vessel end walls may be oblique and transverse in the same species. The Burseraceae and Julianiaceae differ from Anacardiaceae in that all the members are diffuse-porous. The Burseraceae are distinguished from Julianiaceae and Anacardiaceae, in that the intervascular pitting is strictly alternate and all perforation plates are of the simple type.

In the Simarubaceae, Rutaceae and Meliaceae, all intercellular canals are traumatic (Webber, 1938), some of the members show storied structure, spiral thickenings on vessel walls, distinct growth rings, and ray-vessel and parenchyma-vessel pit pairs which are not elongated.

Certain other characters are held in common among these six families. Some of these are: mostly actinomorphic flowers, compound leaves which may be reduced to the tri- or unifoliolate state, superior ovaries, predominantly near equatorial distributions, and mostly woody members.

Regarding the foregoing generalizations, it must be remembered, that very few if any of the preceding characters are possessed by all members of all the families. They are listed merely to indicate similarities among the larger groupings (families). As Heimsch (1942) has stated in discussing the general trends among the woods of the families Anacardiaceae, Rutaceae, Meliaceae, Burseraceae and Simarubaceae, ". . . they are not absolute and do not serve to delimit one group from another without exceptions."

Among the six families under discussion, the Julianiaceae, Anacardiaceae and Burseraceae appear to be more closely related to each other than to Rutaceae, Simarubaceae or Meliaceae. Both Heimsch (1942) and Webber (1941) agree that the Rutaceae and Simarubaceae resemble each other rather closely. Perhaps the wood structure of the Meliaceae represents somewhat greater specialization than that occurring in Rutaceae or Simarubaceae.

By virtue of the common features listed above, it is the opinion of the author that Julianiaceae, Anacardiaceae, Burseraceae, Rutaceae, Simarubaceae, Meliaceae and possibly other families constitute a closely-related group of plants stemming from a common progenitor.

SUMMARY

The wood shows little variation from species to species in Julianiaceae. All members possess intercellular canals in the pith and bark and probably in the wood, septate fiber-tracheids and libriform wood fibers are present in all species, rays are all heterogeneous IIB, vertical parenchyma is vasicentric and sparse, woods are diffuse-porous, simple and reticulate perforation plates are present, and intervascular pitting is transitional, opposite and alternate. The evidence from wood anatomy does not support Hemsley's contention that the Julianiaceae should be separated into two genera. It is suggested that the family as conceived by Hemsley needs to be revised taxonomically. Some botanists consider Julianiaceae to have close affinity with Juglandaceae, while others have concluded that the former are related to Anacardiaceae. This study of the secondary xylem of Julianiaceae suggests that this group is most closely allied to Anacardiaceae and its relatives. Among the xylem features common to both of these families are: septate fibrous elements, intercellular canals, heterogeneous IIB rays, some reticulate perforation plates, and transitional, opposite and alternate intervascular pitting. Other characteristics such as reduction in leaf compoundedness, dioecious species, paniculate inflorescences, and the superior insertion of the floral parts are also similar in the two groups. Manning suggests that anacardiaceous or julianiaceous inflorescences possibly satisfy the conditions for his prejuglandaceous inflorescence. Evidence from wood anatomy does not support this suggested affinity. Cytological and fossil evidence are apparently lacking for Julianiaceae, and thus no conclusions can be drawn from these fields. Certain xylem characteristics are common to the families Anacardiaceae, Burseraceae, Rutaceae, Simarubaceae, and Meliaceae. Some of these are: intercellular canals, heterogeneous IIB vascular rays, vessels with simple perforation plates, septate fibrous elements, and paratracheal parenchyma. The members of Julianiaceae also possess these characters. It is, therefore, suggested that Julianiaceae be included in this complex which consists of two groups of families, one more highly evolved as based on wood characters, and a more primitive group. To the first group belong Meliaceae, Simarubaceae, and Rutaceae; to the second group, Burseraceae, Anacardiaceae, and Julianiaceae. The more highly evolved group has some members showing storied structure and only traumatic intercellular canals. The more primitive group does not show storying, and normal intercellular canals are present.

DEPARTMENT OF BOTANY,
UNIVERSITY OF ILLINOIS,
URBANA, ILLINOIS

LITERATURE CITED

BARGHOORN, E. S., JR. 1940. The ontogenetic development and phylogenetic specialization of rays in the xylem of dicotyledons. I. The primitive ray structure. Amer. Jour. Bot. 27: 918-928.

——. 1941. The ontogenetic development and phylogenetic specialization of rays in the xylem of dicotyledons. II. Modification of the multiseriate and uniseriate rays. Amer. Jour. Bot. 28: 272-282.

BENTHAM, G., AND J. D. HOOKER. 1862-1867. Genera plantarum. Vol. 1. L. Reeve and Co. London.

BESSEY, C. E. 1915. The phylogenetic taxonomy of flowering plants. Annals Missouri Bot. Gard. 2: 109-164.

CHALK, L. 1936. The distribution of the lengths of fibers and vessel members and the definition of terms of size. Imp. Forestry Inst. Paper 2: 1-12.

——, AND M. MARGARET CHATTAWAY. 1934. Measuring the length of vessel members. Trop. Woods 40: 19-26.

CHATTAWAY, M. MARGARET. 1932. Proposed standards for numerical values used in describing woods. Trop. Woods 29: 20-28.

COMMITTEE ON NOMENCLATURE. International Association of Wood Anatomists. 1933. Glossary of terms used in describing woods. Trop. Woods. 36: 1-13.

COPELAND, H. F., AND B. E. DOYEL. 1940. Some features of the structure of Toxicodendron diversiloba. Amer. Jour. Bot. 27: 932-939.

DADSWELL, H. E., AND A. M. ECKERSLEY. 1938. The wood structure of some Australian Rutaceae with methods for their identification. Council Sci. Ind. Research, Australia, Bull. No. 114.

——, AND D. J. ELLIS. 1939. The wood anatomy of some Australian Meliaceae with methods for their identification. Council Sci. Ind. Research, Australia, Bull. No. 124.

——, AND H. D. INGLE. 1948. The anatomy of timbers of the southwest Pacific area. I. Anacardiaceae. Australian Jour. Sci. Research, Ser. B 1: 4: 391-415.

DARLINGTON, C. D., AND E. K. J. AMMAL. 1945. Chromosome atlas of cultivated plants. Geo. Allen and Unwin Ltd. London.

ENGLER, A., AND L. DIELS. 1936. Syllabus der Pflanzenfamilien. Elfte Aufgabe. Geb. Borntraeger. Berlin.

ERDTMAN, G. 1943. An introduction to pollen analysis. Chronica Botanica Co. Waltham, Mass.

FRITSCH, F. E. 1908. The anatomy of the Julianiaceae considered from the taxonomic point of view. Trans. Linn. Soc. Lond. 27: 129-151.

GAISER, LULU O. 1926. A list of chromosome numbers in angiosperms. Genetica 8: 402-484.

——. 1930a. Chromosome numbers in angiosperms II. Bibliog. Genetica 6: 171-466.

——. 1930b. Chromosome numbers in angiosperms III. Genetica 12: 162-260.

GRAY, A. 1854. Botany phanerogamia. Vol. 1. George Putnam and Co. New York. (also Botany of the United States exploring expedition. United States National Museum. Phanerogamia Vol. 15).

GUNDERSON, A. 1950. Families of dicotyledons. Chronica Botanica Co. Waltham, Mass.

HALLIER, H. 1905. Provisional scheme of the natural (phylogenetic) system of flowering plants. New Phytol. 4: 151-162.

——. 1908. Ueber Juliania, eine Terebinthaceen-Gattung mit Cupula und die wahren Stammeltern der Katzchenblutler. Beih. Bot. Centralblatt 23: 81-256.

HEIMSCH, C., JR. 1940. Wood anatomy and pollen morphology of Rhus and allied genera. Jour. Arnold Arboretum 21: 279-291.

——. 1942. Comparative anatomy of the secondary xylem of the "Gruinales" and "Terebinthales" of Wettstein with reference to taxonomic grouping. Lilloa 8: 82-198.

——, AND R. H. WETMORE. 1939. The significance of wood anatomy in the taxonomy of the Juglandaceae. Amer. Jour. Bot. 26: 651-660.

HEMSLEY, W. B. 1908. On the Julianiaceae: A new natural order of plants. Phil. Trans. Roy. Soc. London Ser. B 199: 169-197.

HUTCHINSON, J. 1926. The families of flowering plants. I. Dicotyledons. Macmillan Co. London.

JOHANSEN, D. A. 1940. Plant microtechnique. McGraw-Hill Book Co. New York.

JOHNSON, A. M. 1931. Taxonomy of the flowering plants. The Century Co. New York.

JONGMANS, W. 1931. Fossilium catalogus II. Plantae: Dicotyledones (Ligna). Junk. Berlin.

KERSHAW, E. M. 1909. A note on the relationship of the Julianiaceae. Ann. Bot. 23: 336-337.

KRIBS, D. A. 1927. Comparative anatomy of the woods of the Juglandaceae. Trop. Woods 12: 16-21.

——. 1930. Comparative anatomy of the woods of the Meliaceae. Amer. Jour. Bot. 17: 724-738.

——. 1935. Salient lines of structural specialization in the wood rays of dicotyledons. Bot. Gaz. 96: 544-557.

——. 1937. Salient lines of structural specialization in the wood parenchyma of dicotyledons. Bull. Torrey Bot. Club 64: 177-186.

caryopses of species repre-
...bes of Gramineae.—a, Poa
...L.—c, Dactylis glomerata L.
... Nevski.—e, Elymus virgini-
...tosa (L.) Beauv.—g, Calama-
..., Anthoxanthum odoratum L.
..., Eriochloa gracilis (Fourn.)
...sgalli (L.) Beauv.—l, Setaria
...ndropogon barbinodis Lag.—n,
...ers.—o, Tripsacum lanceolatum
..., all others ×5. a–h, festucoids.
...ize of the embryo in proportion
...ls. Note that here the embryo is
...or the placement of these genera
...of classification, see table 1.

...ight in a vial of water in the
...der that the embryos might be-
...led. Usually the embryos were
... sometimes the entire seed was
...ration was accomplished by means
...hol series. Serial paraffin sections
... were prepared and stained with
...ast green. Some of the embryos
... transversely and others longitudi-
... being cut in a sagittal plane.

...—When one examines a number of
...different genera, it soon becomes ap-
...ome have relatively large embryos,
...rs the embryos are very small. Little
... been paid to this as a taxonomic char-
...actually it does have some value.[4]
...true festucoids always have rather small
...he seed consisting largely of endosperm.
...e panicoids, on the other hand, the em-
...relatively large and the proportion of
...n is thus correspondingly reduced (fig.
...ome cases, the embryo may be as long as

...the relative size of embryo to endosperm varies
...ifferent species of grasses is mentioned by Martin
...and shown in his figures. He does not indicate,
..., that this character is of taxonomic significance as
...tribes or larger units.
...res of caryopses in Stebbins (1956) show in a gen-
...ay the relative proportion of embryo to endosperm
...e major groups which he recognizes.

the seed and occupy fully half the space inside the seed coat. While some seeds of panicoid species have relatively small embryos, such seeds are rare. With a little experience one can predict the type of embryo (whether panicoid or festucoid) by examining the "seed" under a low power binocular microscope and noting the relative proportion of embryo to endosperm.

Although the relative size of the embryo in relation to the caryopsis has definite taxonomic value, much more important characters are to be observed when thin sections of the embryos are examined under the microscope. A median sagittal section will reveal the course of the vascular tissue which, as mentioned previously, may be one of two types. Among members of the tribes Paniceae, Andropogoneae, and Maydeae the coleoptile is inserted at some distance above the point of divergence of the scutellum bundle, and there is a distinct internode between coleoptile and scutellum. This type of vascularization will be referred to as the panicoid type. Among most members of the tribes Festuceae, Hordeae, Aveneae, Agrostideae, and Phalarideae a different condition is noted with regard to the course of the vascular bundles. Here the coleoptile is inserted at about the point where the scutellum bundle diverges, and no internode is present. This type of vascularization is termed the festucoid type.

A second difference between panicoid and festucoid embryos can be noted with respect to the lower part of the scutellum which may be free, or fused or quite absent. When panicoid embryos are viewed in sagittal section a distinct cleft is visible between the lower part of the scutellum and the coleorhiza. In the festucoids, on the other hand, no cleft is evident, since the lower part of the scutellum is absent, or has become fused to the coleorhiza.

Among the hundreds of embryos examined not a single case has been found in which an embryo with panicoid vascularization lacks this cleft; among embryos with festucoid vascularization, in contrast, the great majority possess no cleft, although there are a few in which it is present. These are special cases, however, and they will be discussed more fully later.

As mentioned previously, both Bruns (1892) and Kennedy (1899) tended to attach undue taxonomic importance to the epiblast, the small organ which, when present, occurs on the side of the embryo opposite the scutellum. Indeed this organ does have some taxonomic significance, especially when used in conjunction with other characters. It can be noted, for example, that it is always absent in grasses belonging to the subfamily Panicoideae.[5] Among members of the Festucoideae,[5] in contrast,

[5] These terms are used here in the traditional sense. See Hitchcock's Manual, ed. 2 (1950).

LEAVENWORTH, W. C. 1946. A preliminary study of the vegetation of the region between Cerro Tacitaro and the Rio Tepalcatepec, Michoacan, Mexico. Amer. Midl. Nat. 36: 137-206.

MACBRIDE, J. F. 1936. Flora of Peru. Field Mus. Nat. Hist. Publ. Bot. Ser. 13: 2: 266.

MANNING, W. E. 1938. The morphology of the flowers of the Juglandaceae. I. The inflorescence. Amer. Jour. Bot. 25: 407-419.

RECORD, S. J. 1939. American woods of the family Anacardiaceae. Trop. Woods 60: 11-45.

————, AND R. W. HESS. 1940. American woods of the family Rutaceae. Trop. Woods 64: 1-28.

RENDLE, A. B. 1938. The classification of flowering plants. Cambridge Univ. Press. London.

RENDLE, B. J., AND S. H. CLARKE. 1934a. The problem of variation in the structure of wood. Trop. Woods 38: 1-8.

————, AND ————. 1934b. The diagnostic value of measurements in wood anatomy. Trop. Woods 40: 27-37.

SCHLECHTENDAL, D. F. L. VON. 1843. Hypopterygium. Linnaea 16: 635-638.

STANDLEY, P. C. 1923. Trees and shrubs of Mexico. Contrib. U. S. National Herb. 23: Part 3: 517-848.

————, AND J. A. STEYERMARK. 1949. Flora of Guatemala. Fieldiana Bot. 24: 176-177.

TIPPO, O. 1938. Comparative anatomy of the Moraceae and their presumed allies. Bot. Gaz. 100: 1-99.

————. 1941. A list of diagnostic characteristics for the description of dicotyledonous woods. Trans. Illinois State Acad. Sci. 34: 105-106.

TISCHLER, G. 1927. Pflanzliche Chromosomen-Zahlen. Tabul. Biol. 4: 1-83.

————. 1931. Pflanzliche Chromosomen-Zahlen. Tabul. Biol. 7: 109-226.

————. 1950. Die Chromosomenzahlen der Gefaesspflanzen Mitteleuropas. Bij Vitgeverij. Junk. Holland.

WANSCHER, J. H. 1934. The basic chromosome numbers of higher plants. New Phytol. 33: 101-126.

WEBBER, IRMA E. 1936. Systematic anatomy of the woods of the Simarubaceae. Amer. Jour. Bot. 23: 577-587.

————. 1938. Intercellular cavities in the rays of dicotyledonous woods. Lilloa 2: 465-469.

————. 1941. Systematic anatomy of the woods of the Burseraceae. Lilloa 6: 441-465.

WETMORE, R. H. 1932. The use of celloidin in botanical technique. Stain Tech. 7: 37-62.

WETTSTEIN, R. 1935. Handbuch der Systematischen Botanik. Vol. 2. 4th ed. Deuticke. Leipzig und Wien.

WILLIS, J. C. 1948. A dictionary of flowering plants and ferns. Cambridge Univ. Press. London.

WODEHOUSE, R. P. 1935. Pollen grains. McGraw-Hill Book Co. New York.

THE EMBRYO IN GRASS SYSTEMATICS[1]

John R. Reeder

THE OBSERVATION that the structure of the caryopsis of grasses, along with the seedling, may have important taxonomic significance dates back more than half a century. Bruns (1892) published the first important paper on this subject and in it he figured the embryos of some 60 species. The character of the embryo which seems to have impressed him most was the epiblast, and he presents a table in which the genera are arranged according to

[1] Received for publication June 12, 1957.
I am indebted to the National Science Foundation for a grant which provided the services of a technical assistant. Thanks also are due the Administration of Yale University for aid in the form of a Blanche Elizabeth MacLeish Billings Memorial Award which made it possible for me to spend some three months in Mexico where many "seeds" used in this investigation were collected.

Hackel's system but with an indication as to whether or not their embryos possess this organ. Unfortunately, however, the most important taxonomic features of the embryo were overlooked. Bruns' paper is more important as a contribution to morphology than to taxonomy, and it includes a thorough review of the literature on the morphology of the embryo and homologies of its various parts.

In contrast to the work of Bruns which contributed but slightly to taxonomy is the paper by van Tieghem (1897) which appeared five years later. The French botanist proved to be much more perceptive than his German colleague, and his work is a classic in the field of the taxonomic significance of the embryo and seedling of grasses. Van Tieghem pointed out the two basic differences

Reprinted by permission of the author and publisher from the
AMERICAN JOURNAL OF BOTANY, 44, 756–768 (1957).

between the panicoid and festu
bryos—differences reveale
examined in longitudinal sa
that in the panicoid type t
the scutellum is free from th
coleoptile is inserted well ab
vergence of the scutellum bund
type, on the other hand, the
scutellum is lacking, or is fused
and the coleoptile is inserted at a
point of divergence of the scutellu
the basis of these criteria, van Tiegl
that the tribe Chlorideae should be r
the Festucoideae and placed with the
He indicated also that the tribes Oryzea
tegineae, which Hackel had placed in
coideae, should be moved to the Festucoide
of these suggestions are quite valid and ha
confirmed by studies reported in the present

In spite of the fact that van Tieghem had a
a new and highly useful tool which could be
in working out the relationships among grass
his work has been neglected almost complete
until very recently.

Two years after the publication of this work by van Tieghem, Kennedy (1899) published a bulletin on the structure of the caryopsis of grasses as an aid in classification. In many respects this paper is very similar to the one by Bruns (1892) and this is especially true with regard to the historical summary, which is essentially a translation from the work of the former author. Like Bruns, Kennedy was much impressed by the presence or absence of an epiblast, and he even reproduced Bruns' table showing the occurrence of this organ among grasses by tribes, although he included a few additional genera. It is not to be inferred, however, that Kennedy's work is merely a translation of Bruns'. Actually there are novel features such as a discussion of the systems of Bentham, Hackel, and Warming. Moreover, there is a discussion of the various tribes in which he mentions not only the usual morphological characters, but those of the caryopsis as well. There are also some pertinent observations regarding relationships of the genera and tribes, and these will be dealt with later in this paper. Although Kennedy cites three of van Tieghem's works, the important paper (1897) on the embryo and seedling of grasses is curiously omitted.

The next paper on the phylogeny of Gramineae which used characters other than the traditional ones of gross morphology was that of the Russian cytologist, Avdulov (1931). In this classical treatise, the first important work on the cytology of grasses, there is presented a system of classification based upon the number and size of chromosomes. The work of van Tieghem on embryos and seedlings, however, was overlooked completely, which is unfortunate in that it would have added support

Fig. 1. Outline drawings of senting various genera and tr pratensis L.—b, Festuca ovina —d, Hordeum brachyantherun cus L.—f, Deschampsia caespi grostis inexpansa A. Gray— —i, Panicum capillare L.— Hitchc.—k, Echinochloa cru glauca (L.) Beauv.—m, Sorghum halepense (L.) Rupr. a, f, g, and h, ×10 Note the relatively small to the seed. i–o, panicoi relatively much larger.

[2] Pilger (1954) has presen
Gramineae which to a certain
newer criteria. In many respe
natural and is scarcely a model

[3] Space does not permit individ
persons who, from time to time
mature grass caryopses. I am deep
and especially to Prof. Dr. W.
Botanique de l'Etat, Brussels, Belgi
Keck, Head Curator of the New Yo
who permitted me to remove "seeds" fro
at that institution; and to my father-i
ding, who collected many seeds for me in

it is usually present. A full discussion of the value of this organ in classification must be delayed until a little later in this paper.

Examination of the embryo in transverse section reveals one more character of taxonomic value. A section through the coleoptile, about midway from base to apex, will reveal the first embryonic leaf which is enclosed. If the embryo is from a member of the Panicoideae, the leaf, in which there are usually a large number of vascular bundles, has overlapping margins. If, on the other hand, the embryo is from a member of the Festucoideae, the embryonic leaf has few bundles and margins which merely meet but do not overlap.

To summarize, four embryo characters were noted as having taxonomic significance: (1) the course of the vascular system (whether the trace to the scutellum and embryonic leaves diverge at approximately the same point, or are separated by a more or less elongated internode), (2) epiblast (whether present or absent), (3) lower part of the scutellum (whether free from the coleorhiza or fused to it), and (4) the cross-section of the embryonic leaf (whether having many bundles and overlapping margins, or few bundles and margins which merely meet). In most cases there was remarkable uniformity among species of a particular genus in respect to these four characters. In *Eragrostis*, for example, no deviation was noted among the 26 species examined. This was true also for the 20 species of *Muhlenbergia* studied. In *Chloris*, however, a slight variation was noted in one species in which the embryonic leaf had overlapping margins, while in the others (3) the margins merely meet. Moreover, in the two species of *Brachypodium* examined, the embryo of *B. mexicanum* had an epiblast, while in *B. pubifolium* it was absent.

In table 1 all genera investigated are listed and scored with respect to each of the four characters mentioned above. Careful study of this chart will reveal that out of the 16 possible combinations of these characters, only 9 were actually found in the material examined. If we express these as formulae using the symbols of the chart, they are $F + F\ F$, $F + F\ P$, $F + P\ P$, $F - F\ F$, $F - P\ P$, $P + P\ P$, $P + P\ F$, $P - P\ P$, and $P - P\ F$.

True festucoids.—Species of the genera listed below were found to have embryos with the formula $F + F\ F$. These are characterized by festucoid vascularization, an epiblast, no cleft between the scutellum and coleorhiza, and in cross-section the primary leaf is seen to have relatively few bundles and margins which do not overlap (fig. 2–10). Included with these genera are *Bromus*, *Elymus*, *Hystrix*, and *Secale*, which actually have the formula $F - F\ F$, and thus differ only in the absence of an epiblast. Since this organ is usually quite small, although its size varies considerably

from genus to genus, its absence among these few genera is considered to be of rather minor significance.

Genera with the embryo formula $F + F\ F$ (typical festucoid):

FESTUCEAE	AVENEAE
Ampelodesmos	*Aira*
Brachypodium	*Arrhenatherum*
Briza	*Avena*
Bromus [6]	*Deschampsia*
Catabrosa	*Holcus*
Cynosurus	*Koeleria*
Dactylis	*Sphenopholis*
Diarrhena	*Trisetum*
Dichelachne	AGROSTIDEAE
Dissanthelium	*Agrostis*
Festuca	*Alopecurus*
Glyceria	*Ammophila*
Hesperochloa	*Apera*
Lamarckia	*Calamagrostis*
Melica	*Cinna*
Poa	*Coleanthus*
Puccinellia	*Gastridium*
Schizachne	*Limnodea*
Sclerochloa	*Milium*
	Oryzopsis
HORDEAE	*Phippsia*
Agropyron	*Phleum*
Elymus [6]	*Piptochaetium*
Hordeum	*Polypogon*
Hystrix [6]	*Stipa*
Lolium	CHLORIDEAE
Nardus	*Beckmannia*
Secale [6]	PHALARIDEAE
Triticum	*Anthoxanthum*
	Hierochloë
	Phalaris

The embryos of all members of these genera are rather small with respect to the seed as a whole, the epidermis and internal anatomy of the leaves is reported to be of the festucoid type (Prat, 1936), and the chromosomes of most members are relatively large and with the basic number of seven.[7] Significantly, too, most are species of temperate regions. These genera, then, are seen to exhibit considerable homogeneity with respect to a large number of characters. They constitute the "true festucoids" and, as a group, may deserve subfamily rank. It will be noted that (with the exception of

[6] no epiblast
[7] Unless otherwise indicated chromosome numbers mentioned in this paper are taken from Darlington and Wylie (1956).

TABLE 1. *List of genera,[a] indicating for each the number of species examined and the four important embryo characters referred to in the text*

Tribes and genera	Number of species studied	Course of vascular system	Embryo characters		X-section Embryonic leaf
			Longitudinal section		
			Epiblast (present or absent)	Scutellum, lower portion	
BAMBUSEAE					
Arundinaria	1	P	+	P	P
Guadua	2	P	+	P	P
Dendrocalamus	1	P	+	P	P
STREPTOCHAETEAE					
Streptochaeta	1	F	—	P	P
FESTUCEAE					
Aeluropus	1	P	+	P	F
Ampelodesmos	1	F	+	F	F
Blepharidachne	1	P	—	P	F
Brachypodium	2	F	±	F	F
Briza	2	F	+	F	F
Bromus	6	F	—	F	F
Catabrosa	1	F	+	F	F
Cortaderia	1	P	—	P	F
Cottea	1	P	+	P	P
Cynosurus	2	F	+	F	F
Dactylis	1	F	+	F	F
Diarrhena	1	F	+	F	F
Dichelachne	1	F	+	F	F
Dissanthelium	1	F	+	F	F
Distichlis	2	P	+	P	F
Ectosperma	1	P	+	P	F
Enneapogon	1	P	+	P	F
Eragrostis	26	P	+	P	F
Festuca	5	F	+	F	F
Glyceria	6	F	+	F	F
Hesperochloa	1	F	+	F	F
Jouvea	1	P	+	P	F
Lamarckia	1	F	+	F	F
Melica	4	F	+	F	F
Monanthochloë	1	P	+	P	F
Orthoclada	1	P	+	P	P
Pappophorum	1	P	+	P	F
Phragmites	1	P	—	P	F
Poa	3	F	+	F	F
Puccinellia	1	F	+	F	F
Schizachne	1	F	+	F	F
Sclerochloa	1	F	+	F	F
Tridens	6	P	+	P	F
Triplasis	1	P	+	P	F
Uniola	1	P	+	P	P
Vaseyochloa	1	P	+	P	F
HORDEAE					
Agropyron	1	F	+	F	F
Elymus	1	F	—	F	F
Hordeum	2	F	+	F	F
Hystrix	1	F	—	F	F
Lolium	1	F	+	F	F
Nardus	1	F	+	F	F
Secale	1	F	—	F	F
Triticum	1	F	+	F	F
AVENEAE					
Aira	1	F	+	F	F
Arrhenatherum	1	F	+	F	F
Avena	2	F	+	F	F
Danthonia	6	P	—	P	F

TABLE 1. *(Continued)*

Tribes and genera	Number of species studied	Course of vascular system	Embryo characters Longitudinal section Epiblast (present or absent)	Scutellum, lower portion	✕-section Embryonic leaf
Deschampsia	3	F	+	F	F
Holcus	1	F	+	F	F
Koeleria	1	F	+	F	F
Lamprothyrsus	1	P	−	P	F
Sieglingia	1	P	−	P	F
Sphenopholis	1	F	+	F	F
Trisetum	3	F	+	F	F
AGROSTIDEAE					
Agrostis	4	F	+	F	F
Alopecurus	1	F	+	F	F
Ammophila	1	F	+	F	F
Apera	1	F	+·	F	F
Aristida	2	P	−	P	F
Blepharoneuron	1	P	+	P	F
Brachyelytrum	1	F	+	F	P
Calamagrostis	3	F	+	F	F
Calamovilfa	2	P	+	P	F
Cinna	1	F	+	F	F
Coleanthus	1	F	+	F	F
Crypsis	1	P	+	P	F
Gastridium	1	F	+	F	F
Heleochloa	1	P	+	P	F
Limnodea	1	F	+	F	F
Lycurus	1	P	+	P	F
Milium	1	F	+	F	F
Muhlenbergia	20	P	+	P	F
Oryzopsis	3	F	+	F	F
Perieilema	1	P	+	P	F
Phaenosperma	1	F	+	P	P
Phippsia	1	F	+	F	F
Phleum	2	F	+	F	F
Piptochaetium	2	F	+	F	F
Polypogon	1	F	+	F	F
Sporobolus	11	P	+	P	F
Stipa	7	F	+	F	F
ZOYSIEAE					
Aegopogon	1	P	+	P	F
Anthephora	1	P	−	P	P
Hilaria	2	P	+	P	F
Perotis	1	P	+	P	F
Tragus	1	P	+	P	F
CHLORIDEAE					
Astrebla	1	P	+	P	F
Beckmannia	2	F	+	F	F
Bouteloua	6	P	+	P	F
Buchloë	1	P	+	P	F
Chloris	4	P	+	P	F(P)
Ctenium	1	P	+	P	F
Cynodon	1	P	+	P	F
Dactyloctenium	1	P	+	P	F
Eleusine	2	P	+	P	F
Gymnopogon	1	P	+	P	F
Leptochloa	4	P	+	P	F
Microchloa	1	P	+	P	F
Munroa	1	P	+	P	F
Schedonnardus	1	P	+	P	F
Spartina	3	P	±	P	F
Trichoneura	1	P	+	P	F

TABLE 1. *(Concluded)*

Tribes and genera	Number of species studied	Course of vascular system	Embryo characters Longitudinal section Epiblast (present or absent)	Scutellum, lower portion	✕-section Embryonic leaf
Tripogon	1	P	+	P	F
Willkommia	1	P	+	P	F
PHALARIDEAE					
Anthoxanthum	2	F	+	F	F
Ehrharta	1	F	—	P	P
Hierochloë	1	F	+	F	F
Phalaris	1	F	+	F	F
ORYZEAE					
Leersia	3	F	+	F	P
Oryza	2	F	+	F	P
ZIZANIEAE					
Pharus	1	F	+	F(P)	P
Zizania	1	F	+	P	P
MELINIDEAE					
Arundinella	1	P	—	P	P
PANICEAE					
Axonopus	1	P	—	P	P
Brachiaria	1	P	—	P	P
Cenchrus	1	P	—	P	P
Digitaria	2	P	—	P	P
Echinochloa	1	P	—	P	P
Eriochloa	2	P	—	P	P
Ixophorus	1	P	—	P	P
Lasiacis	1	P	—	P	P
Leptoloma	1	P	—	P	P
Leptocoryphium	1	P	—	P	P
Lithachne	1	F	+	P	P
Mesosetum	1	P	—	P	P
Olyra	1	F	+	P	P
Panicum	6	P	—	P	P
Paspalum	3	P	—	P	P
Pennisetum	1	P	—	P	P
Sacciolepis	1	P	—	P	P
Setaria	4	P	—	P	P
Rhynchelytrum	1	P	—	P	P
Trichachne	1	P	—	P	P
ANDROPOGONEAE					
Andropogon	3	P	—	P	P
Dimeria	1	P	—	P	P
Erianthus	1	P	—	P	P
Hackelochloa	1	P	—	P	P
Heteropogon	1	P	—	P	P
Miscanthus	1	P	—	P	P
Sorghastrum	1	P	—	P	P
Sorghum	3	P	—	P	P
MAYDEAE (TRIPSACEAE)					
Coix	1	P	—	P	P
Polytoca	1	P	—	P	P
Tripsacum	1	P	—	P	P
Zea	1	P	—	P	P
UNPLACED					
Pariana	1	F	+	P	P

[a] The arrangement of genera into tribes follows that used for the grasses at the United States National Herbarium. A carbon copy of this system, which includes all genera in the family, was presented to me several years ago by Mrs. Agnes Chase. While never published in its entirety, the basic outline of the arrangement is to be found in Hitchcock's Manual (1950) although limited, of course, to those genera which occur in the United States.

58

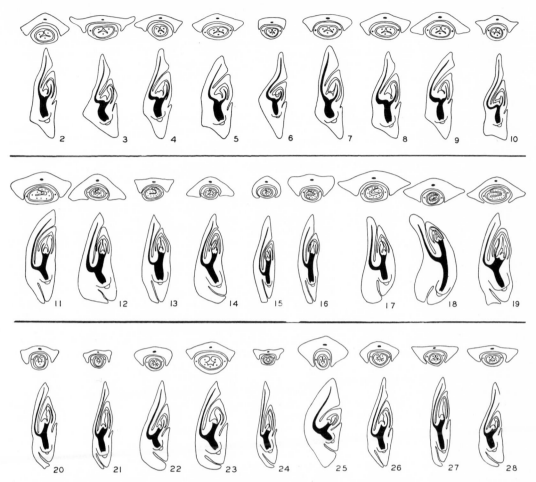

Fig. 2–28. Median sagittal sections and transverse sections through the coleoptile region of embryos of various species of grasses chosen to illustrate three distinct types.—2. *Poa pratensis* L.—3. *Cynosurus echinatus* L.—4. *Agropyron repens* (L.) Beauv.—5. *Hordeum brachyantherum* Nevski.—6. *Koeleria cristata* (L.) Pers.—7. *Deschampsia caespitosa* (L.) Beauv.—8. *Agrostis alba* L.—9. *Gastridium ventricosum* (Gouan) Schinz & Thell.—10. *Phalaris arundinacea* L.—11. *Arundinella Berteroniana* (Schult.) Hitchc. & Chase.—12. *Panicum clandestinum* L.—13. *Rhynchelytrum roseum* (Nees) Stapf & Hubb. ex Bews.—14. *Cenchrus pauciflorus* Benth.—15. *Dimeria falcata* Hack.—16. *Andropogon scoparius* Michx.—17. *Hackelochloa granularis* (L.) Kuntze.—18. *Tripsacum lanceolatum* Rupr.—19. *Anthephora hermaphrodita* (L.) Kuntze.—20. *Chloris cucullata* Bisch.—21. *Schedonnardus paniculatus* (Nutt.) Trel.—22. *Distichlis stricta* (Torr.) Rydb.—23. *Eragrostis pectinacea* (Michx.) Nees.—24. *Pappophorum mucronulatum* Nees. —25. *Calamovilfa gigantea* (Nutt.) Scribn. & Merr.—26. *Muhlenbergia Schreberi* Gmel.—27. *Hilaria mutica* (Buckl.) Benth.—28. *Tragus racemosus* (L.) All. Fig. 2–10, true festucoids, the embryos all having the formula $F + F\ F$. Note in the longitudinal sections that the scutellum bundle diverges directly below the coleoptile, an epiblast is always present and that the lower part of the scutellum is absent or is fused to the coleorhiza. In the transverse section it is seen that the first embryonic leaf has few bundles and the margins of this leaf meet but do not overlap. Fig. 11–19, true panicoids, the embryos all having the formula $P - P\ P$. Note in the longitudinal section that there is a distinct elongation between the point of divergence of the scutellum bundle and the coleoptile, an epiblast is never present, and that the lower part of the scutellum is free from the coleorhiza, there being a distinct cleft between the two. In the transverse section it is seen that the first embryonic leaf has numerous bundles and that the margins of this leaf overlap distinctly. Fig. 20–28, chloridoid or eragrostoid type, the embryos having the formula $P + P\ F$. Note in the longitudinal section that these embryos resemble the true panicoids in respect to the course of the vascular system and the presence of a cleft between the lower part of the scutellum and the coleorhiza. They differ, however, in that an epiblast is always present. In the transverse section it is seen that the embryonic leaf is more like the true festucoids in that there are relatively few bundles and the margins meet but do not overlap. These drawings were made with the aid of a microprojector. They are not all to the same scale. For the placement of these genera in the traditional system of classification, the reader is referred to table 1.

59

Beckmannia[8]) they are all members of five tribes which agrostologists have treated as members of the Festucoideae on gross morphological grounds. In as far as these genera are concerned, this study tends to confirm the validity of the subfamily.

Among those grasses which have embryos of the formula $F + F F$, there are some which differ from the main group with respect to chromosome number, or leaf epidermis and anatomy. Within the traditional Festuceae, *Ampelodesmos* is one of these. Its basic chromosome number is 12 rather than 7 which is usual in this group. In addition to having a festucoid embryo, the epidermis and internal anatomy of the leaves also show festucoid characters (Lohauss, 1905). While its true affinities are still obscure, apparently it is not closely related to *Phragmites* and *Cortaderia*, genera with which it is commonly associated. As will be discussed later in this paper, the embryos of those genera are basically panicoid and have the formula $P - P F$. Four other genera with chromosome numbers other than 7 are: *Catabrosa, Glyceria, Schizachne,* and *Melica*. The first three have a basic number of 5, and for the last, 9 has been reported. Prat (1936) reports a festucoid type of leaf epidermis and anatomy for *Glyceria*, while the figures of Lohauss (1905) indicate a festucoid type for *Catabrosa* and *Melica*, also.

The genus *Nardus*, placed in the Hordeae in the traditional system, is considered by some recent authors to possess combinations of characters which require its placement in a separate tribe, the Nardeae (Hubbard, 1948; Pilger, 1954). Hunter (1934) states that the inclusion of *Nardus* in the Hordeae is absolutely contrary to practically all existing morphological, anatomical and epidermal evidence. He goes on to say that the genus appears to belong naturally to the subfamily Panicoideae. This statement is open to question. It is true that Prat (1931, 1936) reported that the epidermis showed panicoid (chloridoid) characteristics, but the internal anatomy of the leaves was found to be quite festucoid. Hunter himself indicates that the karyotype is *completely lacking* in panicoid characters. I can add that the caryopsis possesses an embryo which is very small in proportion to the size of the seed, and in all respects this embryo is distinctly festucoid. It would appear, then, that the only panicoid character is that of the epidermis —all others are festucoid. It is interesting to note that Avdulov (1931) included *Nardus* in his tribe Festuceae.

Among those members of the traditional Agrostideae in which occur embryos of the formula $F + F F$, *Milium, Oryzopsis, Piptochaetium,* and *Stipa* are considered to be rather closely related by ag-

rostologists and are often treated as members of a distinct tribe, the Stipeae (Hubbard, 1934; Pilger, 1954). The basic chromosome number in *Milium* is reported to be 4, 9, or 14, while in the other genera multiples of 11 or 12 are found. As indicated above, the basic type of embryo is the same among the species of these genera examined, but another character, which is not brought out in the formula, is that the primary root is often bent at a rather sharp angle from the main axis of the embryo. This is especially noticeable in *Stipa* and *Piptochaetium*. It should be pointed out that in these last mentioned genera the epiblast is very large and usually extends to the tip of the coleoptile, while in *Milium* and *Oryzopsis* the epiblast is rather small.

True panicoids.—A second large group of grasses is made up of those genera in which the embryo has the formula $P - P P$. These embryos are characterized by having panicoid vascularization, no epiblast, a distinct cleft between the scutellum and coleorhiza, and in transverse section the primary leaf with its numerous vascular bundles has overlapping margins (fig. 11–19). All members of the tribes Paniceae,[9] Melinideae, Andropogoneae, and Maydeae belong here. Also *Anthephora* of the Zoysieae, has an embryo of this formula, which is not surprising in view of the fact that several authors have included it in the tribe Paniceae (Hubbard, 1934; Pilger, 1940).

It is readily apparent that this group constitutes the subfamily Panicoideae in essentially the form it has been recognized for many years. That this is a very homogeneous and natural group is indicated by many lines of evidence including gross morphology. In this group the embryos are not only of a very distinctive type as regards internal structure, but also are relatively large in proportion to the size of the seed (fig. 1, i–o). The leaf epidermis and internal anatomy have been found to be of a distinctive type (Prat, 1936), and the chromosomes are characteristically rather small and usually have a basic number of 9 or 10. These genera also show similarity in respect to their geographical distribution, being predominantly grasses of tropical regions.

Chloridoid-Eragrostoid type.—Grasses in which the embryo has the formula $P + P F$ constitute a third large and rather homogeneous group. These embryos are basically panicoid in that they are characterized by that type of vascularization, and the lower part of the scutellum is free from the coleorhiza. They resemble festucoids in that they have an epiblast and, when seen in transverse section, the margins of the leaves do not ordinarily

---

[8] Although for many years considered a member of the tribe Chlorideae, this genus has been shown to be quite unrelated to other members of that tribe and to have close affinities with genera in the Agrostideae (Reeder, 1953).

[9] *Olyra* and *Lithachne*, examined in the course of these investigations, were found to have embryos of a different type. As will be discussed later, other lines of evidence likewise indicate that these genera should not be aligned with the Paniceae.

overlap (fig. 20–28). Since the genera of this group are members of several different tribes when classified traditionally, a list of those studied is given below.

CHLORIDEAE	FESTUCEAE
Istrebla	*Aeluropus*
Bouteloua	*Blepharidachne*[10]
Buchloë	*Cottea*[11]
Chloris	*Distichlis*
Ctenium[10]	*Ectosperma*
Cynodon	*Enneapogon*
Dactyloctenium	*Eragrostis*
Eleusine	*Jouvea*
Gymnopogon	*Monanthochloë*
Leptochloa	*Pappophorum*
Microchloa	*Tridens*
Munroa	*Triplasis*
Schedonnardus	*Vaseyochloa*[12]
Spartina	AGROSTIDEAE
Trichoneura	*Blepharoneuron*
Tripogon	*Calamovilfa*
Willkommia	*Crypsis*
ZOYSIEAE	*Heleochloa*
Aegopogon	*Lycurus*
Hilaria	*Muhlenbergia*
Perotis	*Pereilema*
Tragus	*Sporobolus*

For the most part, the embryos among members of this group are relatively large in proportion to the seed as a whole. There is, however, a certain amount of variation in this respect, but in general these embryos tend to be larger than those of festucoids. When considered from the standpoint of anatomy and cytology, as well as from embryo structure, this group exhibits considerable homogeneity. On the basis of these characters also the group shows strong affinities with the panicoids. The chromosomes are usually small and have a basic number of 8, 9, or 10. The epidermis and internal anatomy of the leaf is essentially panicoid, but often with slight differences which led Prat (1936) to consider the group as a subtype of the Panicoideae which he called the Chloridoideae.

[10] In *Ctenium* and *Blepharidachne* the epiblast is rudimentary and represented only by a small hump of tissue. I know of no anatomical or cytological studies of the former genus, but Cáceres (1950), who has studied the leaf epidermis and anatomy of *Blepharidachne* indicates that it should be included in the Eragrosteae.

[11] In transverse section, the edges of the primary leaf in *Cottea* overlap and hence the embryo formula is $P + P P$. In most respects, however, this genus is so similar to the others of the group that there seems little justification for its exclusion.

[12] Darlington and Wylie (1956) give 7 as the basic chromosome number for this genus, citing as authority Brown (1950). In a personal letter dated December 16, 1954, however, Dr. Brown indicates that the small chromosomes in this genus have a basic number of 10.

Like the true panicoids, members of this group are chiefly grasses of tropical regions.

It is apparent that essentially all members of the traditional tribes Chlorideae[13] and Zoysieae[13] are included here. The other genera are all members of the traditional tribes Festuceae and Agrostideae. Certain agrostologists, however, have treated some of them as members of several smaller tribes such as the Eragrosteae, the Pappophoreae, and the Sporoboleae (Hubbard, 1934). Pilger (1954), in his unnatural system, places several of these genera quite logically together in his tribe Eragrosteae. While recognizing the tribe Pappophoreae, he fails however to appreciate its affinities with the Eragrosteae and places it incorrectly under his subfamily Festucoideae. *Aeluropus*, *Distichlis*, *Monanthochloë*, *Ectosperma*, and *Vaseyochloa* are left in the Festuceae, while a separate tribe is created for *Jouvea* under the subfamily Eragrostoideae. He has also moved *Calamovilfa* to a quite unnatural position in the Aveneae. Obviously such a system is so unnatural as to have little to recommend it.

In the opinion of the writer, this group should either be given subfamily status or treated as a single tribe. If the latter suggestion is adopted, one could recognize a number of subtribes, but in light of our present knowledge it seems premature to suggest what these subtribes might be. Certainly any system yet proposed leaves much to be desired.

Bambusoid type.—In the few members of the Bambuseae examined, the embryos all had the formula $P + P P$. These are, of course, basically panicoid, differing principally in the presence of a more or less well-developed epiblast (fig. 29–31). Other differences are the presence of more than one vascular bundle in the scutellum, and sometimes many bundles in the coleoptile (fig. 29), rather than the usual two. The caryopsis in this group resembles that of the festucoids in that the embryo is relatively small in proportion to the endosperm. The cytology of the group is not well known, but in those species which have been examined, the chromosomes are small and appear to have a basic number of 12. Prat (1936) in his study of the epidermis and internal anatomy of the leaves found them to be somewhat intermediate between panicoid and festucoid. He considered that in these respects the bamboos represent a distinct type which he named the "bambusoid." Tateoka (1957) recently examined the leaves of 18 species of Japanese bamboos and reports that in all cases they were bambusoid.[14]

No generalizations are justified on the basis of

[13] It was pointed out earlier in this paper that the genus *Beckmannia* was misplaced in the Chlorideae, and also that *Anthephora* has much closer affinities with genera of the Paniceae than with those of the Zoysieae.

[14] I am indebted to Mr. Shoji Horie, a graduate student at Yale University, for a translation of this Japanese paper.

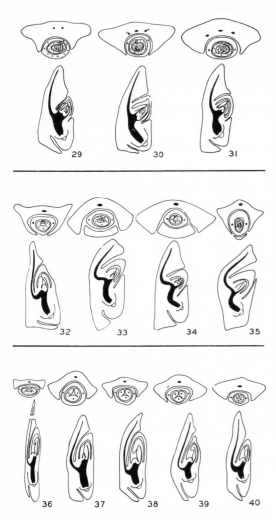

Fig. 29–40. Median sagittal sections and transverse sections through the coleoptile region of embryos of various species of grasses chosen to illustrate three additional types. —29. *Arundinaria tecta* (Walt.) Muhl.—30. *Guadua aculeata* Rupr. ex Fourn.—31. *Dendrocalamus strictus* Nees.—32. *Ehrharta erecta* Lam.—33. *Phaenosperma globosa* Munro.—34. *Olyra latifolia* L.—35. *Oryza sativa* L.—36. *Aristida adscensionis* L.—37. *Phragmites communis* Trin.—38. *Cortaderia Selloana* (Schult.) Aschers. & Graebn.—39. *Danthonia pilosa* R. Br.—40. *Sieglingia decumbens* (L.) Bernh.—Fig. 29–31, Bambuseae, the embryo having the formula $P + P\,P$. The most obvious difference between these embryos and those of the true panicoids is the presence of an epiblast.—Fig. 32–35. Olyroid or oryzoid type, the embryos having usually the formula $F + P\,P$. As seen in longitudinal section, the course of the vascular system is like that of the true festucoids, and epiblast is present (except in *Ehrharta*), and there is a distinct cleft between the coleorhiza and scutellum (except in *Oryza*). The transverse section shows a leaf which resembles the true panicoids in that the margins overlap. Except for the true festucoids, this is the only group in which the

the few bamboo embryos examined. It can be seen, however, that in those genera so far studied the embryos are similar and appear to represent a distinct type. The bamboos, like the two preceding groups, are grasses of tropical regions.

Two other genera in which embryos of the formula $P + P\,P$ occur are *Orthoclada* and *Uniola*. These are both included in the Festuceae in the traditional classification. Prat (1936) indicated that both had a panicoid type of epidermis and that the internal anatomy of the leaf was panicoid in *Uniola* but intermediate in *Orthoclada*. He included these genera among the true panicoids. The basic chromosome number has been found to be 12 in *Uniola*, and while I know of no count for *Orthoclada*, that of *Centotheca*, with which it is usually associated in classificatory systems, has been found to be 12 also. The true affinities of these genera remains obscure, due to lack of sufficient information, but it may be of some significance that in respect to embryo characters, as well as cytology, they seem to resemble bamboos.[*]

Oryzoid-Olyroid type.—When we combine those genera in which embryos of the formulae $F - P\,P$, $F + P\,P$, and $F + F\,P$ occur, the result is an assemblage in which the members appear to be more closely related to each other than to any other genus or group. It will be noted that all have a festucoid type of vascularization and a panicoid embryonic leaf. In most an epiblast is present, and there is usually a cleft between the coleorhiza and scutellum (fig. 32–35). A list of these genera with the embryo formula of each is given below:

Streptochaeta	$F - P\,P$
Ehrharta	$F - P\,P$
Phaenosperma	$F + P\,P$
Pharus	$F + P\,P$
Zizania	$F + P\,P$
Lithachne	$F + P\,P$
Olyra	$F + P\,P$
Pariana	$F + P\,P$
Brachyelytrum	$F + F\,P$
Leersia	$F + F\,P$
Oryza	$F + F\,P$

According to the traditional system, these genera would be placed in about six tribes (table 1). Pilger (1954) also distributes them among as many tribes, but not in the same way. Page (1947) indicates that within the genera *Streptochaeta*, *Pharus*, *Olyra*, *Lithachne*, and *Pariana* the leaf anatomy is similar and also like that of the bamboos. Further affinities with the bamboos are suggested perhaps

scutellum bundle diverges directly below the coleoptile.—Fig. 36–40. Arundinoid or Danthonioid type. These embryos differ from the true panicoids only in the embryonic leaf which has few bundles and margins which merely meet rather than many bundles and overlapping margins. These drawings were made in the same manner as described for fig. 2–28. For the placement of these genera in the traditional system, see table 1.

[*]CORRECTION (January, 1962): Study of additional bamboo embryos has revealed an error in our former interpretation. In all Bambuseae examined, the vascular system is **festucoid**! These embryos, therefore, have the formula $F + PP$, and do not differ basically from those of the oryzoidolyroid group. *Zeugites* should be included here.

Centotheca, *Orthoclada*, and *Uniola*, along with several other genera, have an embryo formula of $P + PP$. They thus form a group, the **centothecoid**, distinct from the bamboos.

by a basic chromosome number of 12 which has been reported for the genera *Ehrharta, Phaenosperma, Leersia,* and *Oryza.* Walter Brown[15] indicates that he found $2n = 22$ for *Streptochaeta,* and this is also the number reported for *Brachyelytrum.* I am not aware of published reports of the chromosome numbers for the other genera, except for *Zizania* which appears to be 15. In spite of the differences in chromosome number between *Zizania* and *Oryza* there seems little doubt that these two genera are closely related.

Most agrostologists have treated *Brachyelytrum* as a member of the Agrostideae, and the type species was described originally as a *Muhlenbergia.* Pilger (1954), however, treated *Brachyelytrum* as a member of the Festuceae, while moving *Muhlenbergia* to the Eragrosteae. The separation of these two genera is certainly indicated, and *Muhlenbergia,* as was pointed out previously, has strong affinities with members of the Eragrosteae. There is some question, however, as to whether *Brachyelytrum* belongs with the Festuceae. Walter Brown[15] indicates that the leaf anatomy is festucoid, but the basic chromosome number of 11 and $F + F P$ embryo suggest rather a relationship with *Oryza* or perhaps *Stipa.*

Although investigations of the embryo, along with some other evidence, suggest that the genera of this group may be rather closely related, much more study is needed before their true relationships can be determined. It is of interest to note that Kennedy (1899) also was impressed by the similarities between the embryos of *Oryza* and *Olyra* and suggested that probably the two should be placed together.

Arundinoid-Danthonioid type.—Those genera having embryos of the formula $P - P F$ comprise a sixth and final group. Such embryos are, of course, basically panicoid and differ only in that the embryonic leaf has few vascular bundles and margins which merely meet rather than numerous bundles and overlapping margins (fig. 36–40). Since they are members of three different tribes when classified traditionally (table 1), a list of them is given below:

> *Aristida*
> *Cortaderia*
> *Phragmites*
> *Danthonia*
> *Lamprothyrsus*
> *Sieglingia*

Although included here on the basis of embryo type, *Aristida* does not appear to be closely related to others of the group. Holm (1901), who studied the leaf anatomy, reported that each bundle is surrounded by two parenchyma sheaths, a condition which seems to be unique among grasses. Hubbard

[15] Personal communication.

and Vaughan (1940) have created a new tribe, "the Aristideae" for this genus, and this disposition is followed by Pilger (1954). The present study of the embryo adds little except to show that the genus is basically panicoid and hence is not at all closely related to *Stipa,* even though these two genera resemble each other cytologically and to some extent morphologically.

Of the remaining five genera studied, *Cortaderia* and *Phragmites* are traditionally included in the Festuceae and *Danthonia, Sieglingia,* and *Lamprothyrsus* in the Aveneae. Such a placement is apparently quite unnatural, since the embryos are basically panicoid. De Wet (1956), who has studied the epidermis and internal anatomy of the leaves of *Danthonia* and its allies, reports a mixture of panicoid and festucoid characteristics. In *Cortaderia (Gynerium)* and *Phragmites,* Prat (1936) indicates a panicoid or intermediate internal anatomy.

It is generally recognized now that these genera are rather closely related. Hubbard (1948) includes *Phragmites* and its allies in the Arundineae and *Danthonia* and its kin in the Danthonieae. These tribes follow one another in his classification. De Wet (1954) indicates that the Danthonieae and Arundineae are very closely allied and points out that both are members of the Phragmitiformes of Avdulov (1931). The embryo studies reported here substantiate the views of both de Wet and Hubbard that the Arundineae and Danthonieae are closely related.

SUMMARY

Histological investigations were made of embryos of some 300 species of grasses representing over 150 genera and all tribes usually recognized. Previous reports that grass embryos are of two basic types (panicoid and festucoid) were confirmed. It is pointed out also that the embryo is small in proportion to the size of the caryopsis in festucoids, while usually relatively much larger in panicoids. Four important embryo characters are discussed, three of these evident in longitudinal section and one in transverse section. On the basis of these four characters, six distinctive embryo types may be recognized: true festucoids, true panicoids, chloridoid-eragrostoid, bambusoid, oryzoid-olyroid, and arundinoid-danthonioid. The embryo appears to offer unusual promise in suggesting relationships of anomalous genera, especially when employed in connection with other histological and cytological studies. In the majority of cases a striking correlation is found between the results of these embryo studies and those of the epidermis and anatomy of the leaves, as well as with size and number of chromosomes. All lines of evidence, including embryo studies, point to the fact that the Panicoideae, for the most part, is a natural and homogeneous group. The Festucoideae, on the other hand, appears to be extremely heterogeneous, many of its genera having much closer affinities with those of the Panicoideae. A tentative grouping of the genera

studied, based on the embryo type, is suggested.

OSBORN BOTANICAL LABORATORY,
YALE UNIVERSITY,
NEW HAVEN, CONNECTICUT

LITERATURE CITED

AVDULOV, N. P. 1931. Karyo-systematische Untersuchungen der Familie Gramineen. Bull. Appl. Bot. Suppl. 44. 428 pp. [Russian with German summary.]

BROWN, W. V. 1950. A cytological study of some Texas Gramineae. Bull. Torrey Bot. Club 77: 63–76.

BRUNS, E. 1892. Der Grasembryo. Flora 76: 1–33.

CÁCERES, M. R. 1950. Los carácteres anatómicos foliares de *Munroa mendocina* y *Blepharidachne Benthaniana*. Rev. Argentina Agron. 17 (4): 233–240.

DARLINGTON, C. D. AND A. P. WYLIE. 1956. Chromosome atlas of flowering plants. 519 pp. (Gramineae, pp. 417–458.) Macmillan Co. New York.

DE WET, J. M. J. 1954. The genus *Danthonia* in grass phylogeny. Amer. Jour. Bot. 41: 204–211.

———. 1956. Leaf anatomy and phylogeny in the tribe Danthonieae. Amer. Jour. Bot. 43: 175–182.

DUVAL-JOUVE, J. 1875. Histotaxie des feuilles de Graminées. Ann. Sci. Nat. Bot. VI. 1: 294–371.

GROB, A. 1896. Beiträge zur Anatomie der Epidermis der Gramineenblätter. Bibliotheca Bot. 7: 1–122.

HITCHCOCK, A. S. 1950. Manual of the Grasses of the United States. Ed. 2. (revised by AGNES CHASE) U. S. Dept. Agric. Misc. Publ. 200. 1051 pp.

HOLM, T. 1901. Some new anatomical characters for certain *Gramineae*. Beih. Bot. Centralbl. 11: 101–133.

HUBBARD, C. E. 1934. Gramineae. pp. 199–229. In J. HUTCHINSON, The families of flowering plants. Part II. Monocotyledons.

———. 1948. Gramineae. pp. 284–348. In J. HUTCHINSON, British flowering plants.

———, AND R. E. VAUGHAN. 1940. The Grasses of Mauritius and Rodriguez. 128 pp.

HUNTER, A. W. S. 1934. A karyosystematic investigation in the Gramineae. Canadian Jour. Res. 11: 213–241.

KENNEDY, P. B. 1899. The structure of the caryopsis of

grasses with reference to their morphology and classification. U. S. Dept. Agric. Div. Agrost. Bull. 19: 1–44.

LOHAUSS, K. 1905. Der anatomische Bau der Laubblätter der Festucaceen und dessen Bedeutung für die Systematik. Bibliotheca Bot. 13 (63): 1–114.

MARTIN, A. C. 1946. The comparative internal morphology of seeds. Amer. Midl. Nat. 36: 513–660. (Gramineae, pp. 536–542.)

PAGE, VIRGINIA M. 1947. Leaf anatomy of *Streptochaeta* and the relation of this genus to the bamboos. Bull. Torrey Bot. Club 74: 232–239.

PÉE-LABY, E. 1938. Étude anatomique de la feuille des Graminées de la France. Ann. Sci. Nat. Bot. VIII. 8: 227–346.

PILGER, R. 1940. Gramineae III. Unterfamilie Panicoideae. In A. ENGLER UND K. PRANTL, Die natürlichen Pflanzenfamilien. Ed. 2. 14e: 1–208.

———. 1954. Das System der Gramineae. Bot. Jahrb. 76: 281–384.

PRAT, H. 1931; 1932. L'épiderme des Graminées, Étude anatomique et systématique. Thésis, Paris, 1931; Ann. Sci. Nat. Bot. X. 14: 117–324. 1932.

———. 1936. La Systématique des Graminées. Ann. Sci. Nat. Bot. X. 18: 165–258.

REEDER, J. R. 1953. Affinities of the grass genus *Beckmannia* Host. Bull. Torrey Bot. Club 80: 187–196.

STEBBINS, G. L. 1956. Cytogenetics and evolution of the grass family. Amer. Jour. Bot. 43: 890–905.

TATEOKA, T. 1957. Miscellaneous papers on the phylogeny of Poaceas (9) (Micrairoideae, Anomochloideae, Oryzoideae, Olyroideae, Bambusoideae). Jour. Japanese Bot. 32: 42–49. [In Japanese]

TIEGHEM, P. VAN. 1897. Morphologie de l'embryon et de la plantule chez les Graminées et les Cypéracées. Ann. Sci. Nat. Bot. VIII. 3: 259–309.

THE BAMBUSOID EMBRYO: A REAPPRAISAL[1]

John R. Reeder

Osborn Botanical Laboratory, Yale University, New Haven, Connecticut

ABSTRACT

REEDER, JOHN R. (Yale U., New Haven, Conn.) The bambusoid embryo: a reappraisal. Amer. Jour. Bot. 49(6): 639–641. Illus. 1962.—The embryo in members of the Bambuseae is shown to have a vascular system of the festucoid type. This is contrary to a previous report in which this character was considered to be panicoid. Embryos of representatives of 9 different genera are discussed and figured. The corrected formula for the bamboo embryo is given as $F + P\,P$, and it is pointed out that on the basis of embryo structure, bamboos cannot be distinguished from those grasses designated as oryzoid-olyroid. It is suggested that these might all be included within a single subfamily, the Bambusoideae. Six genera (*Bromuniola*, *Centotheca*, *Lophatherum*, *Megastachya*, *Orthoclada*, and *Uniola*) with embryos of the formula $P + P\,P$ are also discussed. This group is designated the centothecoid, and it is pointed out that they appear to be transitional between bambusoid and chloridoid-eragrostoid grasses.

THE SYSTEMATIC value of caryopses and embryos of grasses has been recognized by a number of workers. More than 60 years ago, the eminent French anatomist Van Tieghem (1897) pointed out basic differences between embryos of panicoid and festucoid grasses and also suggested certain realignments among the genera. Although this work was generally overlooked until rather recently, the importance of the embryo in grass systematics is now firmly established. The observations of Van Tieghem were based primarily upon longitudinal sections of the embryo, the greatest importance being placed upon the course of the vascular system. Recently it has been shown that when 3 characters evident in longitudinal section are combined with one seen in transverse section, a number of embryo types may be recognized (Reeder, 1957). Further, groupings based upon embryo data show a close correspondence with those of other fundamental studies such as cytology (Avdulov, 1931), leaf epidermis (Prat, 1931, 1932), and leaf cross-section (Brown, 1958).

In the paper cited above (Reeder, 1957), 6 major embryo groups were recognized: *festucoid*, *panicoid*, *chloridoid-eragrostoid*, *bambusoid*, *oryzoid-olyroid*, and *arundinoid-danthonioid*. Investigations carried out since 1957 have tended to confirm the validity of these basic groupings, with the exception of the *bambusoid* which needs further clarification.

The bambusoid embryo was considered to have a formula $P + P\,P$. This means that when it is examined in median sagittal section, the vascular system appeared to show a more or less distinct internode between the point of divergence of the scutellum bundle and the coleoptile, an epiblast is present, and the lower part of the scutellum is free from the coleorhiza, the 2 being separated by a distinct cleft. Moreover, in a transverse section through the coleoptile region, the embryonic leaf is seen to have a relatively large number of vascular bundles and the margins overlap more or less strongly. Such an embryo is basically panicoid, differing from that found in *Panicum* or *Andropogon* only in the presence of an epiblast. Three members of the Bambuseae, *Arundinaria*, *Guadua*, and *Dendrocalamus*, were listed as having $P + P\,P$ embryos. In addition, *Orthoclada* and *Uniola* were reported as having embryos with this same basic formula.

Since the publication of the paper cited above, "seeds" of representatives of 6 additional bamboo genera have become available. Careful study of longitudinal sections of embryos of these bamboos, along with a reexamination of those sectioned previously, has revealed a basic error in our former interpretation of the course of the vascular system. It is with considerable chagrin that I must now report that in all of these embryos the vascularization is of the festucoid type—there is actually no internode between the point of divergence of the scutellar trace and the coleoptile! The corrected embryo formula for all Bambuseae studied is, therefore, $F + P\,P$ (Fig. 1–9).

As mentioned previously, at the time the 1957 paper was published, embryos of only 3 bamboos had been examined. As is more or less well known, these grasses bloom only infrequently and as a result we have had great difficulty in securing "seeds" of representatives of this group. In most bamboos the growing point is large and the plumule consists of several embryonic leaves. Since each leaf has a large number of bundles, tracing the vascular supply is somewhat more difficult than with most other embryos. In this case we were very uncertain as to whether the vascular system should be classified as panicoid or festucoid. Our decision to consider it panicoid

[1] Received for publication January 3, 1962.

This research was supported in part by Grant G–9070 from the National Science Foundation.

The author is indebted to F. A. McClure for the gift of several bamboo fruits, and to H. F. Decker for information on the embryos of *Bromuniola*, *Lophatherum*, and *Megastachya*.

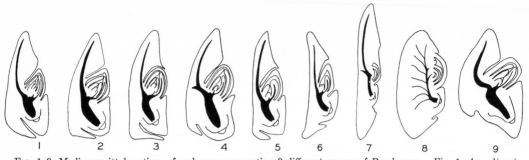

FIG. 1–9. Median sagittal sections of embryos representing 9 different genera of Bambuseae.—Fig. 1. *Arundinaria tecta* (Walt.) Muhl.—Fig. 2. *Guadua aculeata* Rupr. ex Fourn.—Fig. 3. *Dendrocalamus strictus* (Roxb.) Nees.—Fig. 4. *Pseudosasa japonica* (Sieb. & Zucc. ex Steud.) Makino.—Fig. 5. *Phyllostachys pubescens* Mazel ex H. de Leh.—Fig. 6 *Sasa nipponica* (Makino) Makino & Shibata.—Fig. 7. *Cephalostachyum fuchsianum* Gamble.—Fig. 8. *Melocanna baccifera* (Roxb.) Kurz.—Fig. 9. *Pleioblastus simonii* (Carr.) Nakai. Note that although these embryos exhibit a considerable amount of difference in form, they are all of the same basic type. The vascular system is festucoid, i.e., the coleoptile is not raised above the point of divergence of the scutellar bundle, an epiblast is always present, and the scutellum extends to the base of the embryo and is separated from the coleorhiza by a distinct cleft. Although not shown in the figures, the margins of the first embryonic leaf overlap distinctly. All of these embryos fit the formula $F + P\,P$. These drawings were made with a microprojector. They are not all to the same scale.

was influenced, it must be confessed, by reports that the leaf anatomy and epidermis show certain panicoid characteristics.

As one looks back on the published figures (Reeder 1957, Fig. 29–31), the "neck" (or so-called internode) between the scutellar trace and coleoptile appears suspiciously short. Further, it will be noted that in all cases the cleft between the scutellum and the coleoptile does not extend below the point at which the embryonic leaves arise within the latter organ. This is similar to all embryos having unquestioned festucoid vascularization (Reeder 1957, Fig. 2–10; 32–35). In all cases, in embryos with definite panicoid vascularization, the cleft between the scutellum and coleoptile extends some distance below the base of the coleoptile opening. Interpretation of the vascular system in the Bambuseae as festucoid is, moreover, in agreement with the conclusion of Yakovlev (1950), who studied the structure and development of the embryos of numerous grasses.

The relative size of the embryo in relation to the seed as a whole has been shown to be of some systematic value. In festucoid grasses, the embryos are rather small and the major part of the seed consists of endosperm. True panicoids, on the other hand, have relatively large embryos and the amount of endosperm is correspondingly reduced. In some cases the embryo may be as long as the seed and occupy fully half the space inside the seed coat. In a previous paper (Reeder 1957, Fig. 1) diagrams of caryopses of a number of festucoid and panicoid grasses are presented to show the relative size of embryo to endosperm. On the basis of these criteria, "seeds" of Bambuseae are of the festucoid type (Fig. 10). This may be considered as further evidence of the correctness of the interpretation of the vascular system as festucoid.

When the bamboo embryo is interpreted cor-

rectly as having a formula $F + P\,P$, it will be noted that it is not fundamentally different from those designated as oryzoid-olyroid. Grasses of the latter group are also similar to bamboos in their anatomy, cytology, and even gross morphology. Most oryzoid-olyroid grasses have a basic chromosome number of 12, and this is also the number reported for all bamboos thus far studied cytologically. The leaf cross-section is likewise similar, and the epidermis in both groups is characterized by having bicellular microhairs of a similar form, as well as dumbbell-shaped siliceous cells. Rather broad leaves with a short petiole are also characteristic of both groups, and cross veins in the leaves are common. Although oryzoid-olyroid grasses are predominantly herbaceous, this is by no means universal. The culms of species of *Olyra* and *Lithachne* are lignified and similar to those of typical bamboos. It appears, therefore, that bamboos and grasses designated as oryzoid-olyroid share so many fundamental characteristics that it would not be illogical to include them all within a single subfamily, the Bambusoideae.

Since the bamboo embryo appears to differ in no important respect from those of the group designated oryzoid-olyroid, 2 questions immediately arise. Firstly, are there no embryos known with the formula $P + P\,P$? Secondly, are there only 5 major groups of grasses, with respect to embryo type, rather than 6 as formerly supposed? These 2 questions may be answered together. Actually, several grasses are known to have the embryo formula $P + P\,P$, and these have a number of features in common, in addition to embryo structure, thus forming a rather distinctive group. Two of these genera, *Uniola* and *Orthoclada*, were reported previously (Reeder 1957, p. 766) and, on the basis of supposedly similar embryos, were grouped with the bamboos. Four additional genera have been found

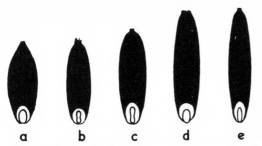

Fig. 10. Outline drawings of caryopses representing 5 different genera of Bambuseae.—a. *Dendrocalamus strictus.* —b. *Guadua aculeata.*—c. *Arundinaria tecta.*—d. *Phyllostachys pubescens.*—e. *Pleioblastus simonii.* Note the relatively small embryo and large amount of endosperm. All figures × 3.

recently to have embryos of this same type. These are *Bromuniola, Centotheca, Lophatherum,* and *Megastachya* (Fig. 11–17). In longitudinal section, these embryos are identical with those of typical chloridoid-eragrostoids. The only embryo character which separates these 2 groups is to be seen in a transverse section of the first embryonic leaf. In chloridoid-eragrostoid embryos, this character is festucoid—the margins of the leaf meet but do not overlap. In the group under discussion, which may be termed the *centothecoid,* the leaf is panicoid—the margins overlap more or less strongly.

The centothecoid grasses appear to be somewhat transitional between bambusoids and chloridoid-eragrostoids. Cytologically they are like the former group in having a basic chromosome number of 12 inasfar as they have been examined. Chloridoid-eragrostoid grasses typically have a basic chromosome number of 9 or 10. The cross-section of the leaf is more nearly bambusoid than chloridoid, and this is also true for features of the epidermis. The lodicules of centothecoids, although vascularized, are truncate and thus very similar to those of the chloridoid-eragrostoid group, while the bamboo lodicule is typically lanceolate or elliptical. In gross morphological features, the centothecoids show certain affinities with bamboos in that the leaf blades are often broad and frequently show cross-veins and a short petiole.

In summary, contrary to the author's previous report, the bamboo embryo is shown to have a vascular system of the festucoid type. This means that the branch to the scutellum and those to the coleoptile and embryonic leaves arise at approximately the same point. The corrected embryo formula for the Bambuseae is, therefore, $F + PP$.

A group of 6 genera having embryos of the formula $P + PP$ is also discussed. On the basis of a number of features, in addition to embryo structure, they appear to be somewhat transitional between bamboos and chloridoids. This group, which includes the genus *Centotheca,* is designated as centothecoid.

Using the embryo type as the principal criterion, one may recognize 6 basic groups of grasses. These are: *festucoid, bambusoid* (including *oryzoid-olyroid*), *centothecoid, arundinoid-danthonioid, chloridoid-eragrostoid,* and *panicoid.* The centothecoid group is here recognized for the first time. The author's previous interpretation of the bamboo embryo as distinct from the oryzoid-olyroid type is shown to be erroneous.

LITERATURE CITED

AVDULOV, N. P. 1931. Karyo-systematische Untersuchungen der Familie Gramineen. [Russian with German summary]. Bull. Appl. Bot. Suppl. 44. 428 p.

BROWN, W. V. 1958. Leaf anatomy in grass systematics. Bot. Gaz. 119: 170–178.

PRAT, H. 1931; 1932. L'épiderme des Graminées. Étude anatomique et systématique. Thésis, Paris, 1931; Ann. Sci. Nat. Bot., X, 14: 117–324. 1932.

REEDER, J. R. 1957. The embryo in grass systematics. Amer. Jour. Bot. 44: 756–768.

VAN TIEGHEM, P. 1897. Morphologie de l'embryon et de la plantule chez les Graminées et les Cypéracées. Ann. Sci. Nat. Bot., VIII, 3: 259–309.

YAKOVLEV, M. S. 1950. Structure of endosperm and embryo in cereals as a systematic feature. [In Russian]. *In* Morf. i Anat. Rast. Trudy Bot. Inst. Akad. Sci. S.S.S.R. ser. 7, p. 121–218.

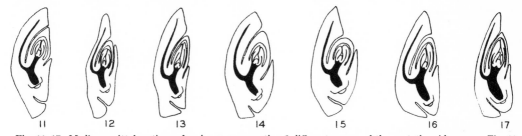

Fig. 11–17. Median sagittal sections of embryos representing 6 different genera of the centothecoid group.—Fig. 11. *Centotheca latifolia* (Osbeck) Trin.— Fig. 12. *Orthoclada laxa* (L. Rich.) Beauv.—Fig. 13. *Lophatherum gracile* Brongn.— Fig. 14. *Megastachya mucronata* (Poir.) Beauv.—Fig. 15. *Bromuniola gossweileri* Stapf & C. E. Hubb.—Fig. 16. *Uniola laxa* (L.) B.S.P.—Fig. 17. *U. latifolia* Michx. Note the great uniformity of these embryos. The vascular system is of the panicoid type, i.e., there is a distinct elongation between the point of divergence of the scutellar bundle and the coleoptile, all have a well-developed epiblast, and there is a distinct cleft between the lower part of the scutellum and the coleorhiza. Although not shown in the figures, the margins of the embryonic leaf overlap as in the bamboos. These embryos all fit the formula $P + PP$. The drawings were made in the same manner as described for Fig. 1–9.

THE COMPARATIVE MORPHOLOGY OF THE ICACINACEAE. V. THE PUBESCENCE AND THE CRYSTALS [1]

Charles E. Heintzelman, Jr.[2] and Richard A. Howard

PREVIOUS STUDIES in this series on the Icacinaceae have shown that it is possible to differentiate levels of increasing structural specialization within the family. It also was shown that such levels of specialization are of taxonomic as well as of phylogenetic interest in the grouping of genera. Evidence derived from these studies of the structure of the plant has been used to support and direct further taxonomic investigations.

The present paper concerns the types of pubescence and crystals found within the family.

THE PUBESCENCE.—A comparative study of the pubescence was undertaken when groups of closely related genera in the Icacinaceae were found to possess similar types of pubescence. A survey revealed that the hair-types forming the indument were constant throughout all the species of a genus and therefore might be used to characterize certain genera. Herbarium material of forty-nine of the fifty-eight genera now recognized in the family was available for sudy.

An indument is found on some part of the plant in all genera of the Icacinaceae. The hairs constituting this indument may be persistent or deciduous and can be found on the young stems, the petioles, the lamina of the leaf, the rachises of the inflorescence, the calyces, the petals, the filaments of the stamens but never the anthers, the ovarian appendages, the ovary and the style but never the stigma, the inner surface of the locule or the mature fruit, or the outer surface of the mature fruit.

Each hair is considered to have two general regions, called the body and the base. These may or may not be morphologically distinguishable. The base is the lower portion of the hair and is usually

[1] Received for publication July 24, 1947.

[2] Charles Edward Heintzelman, Jr. (1917–1943) received his A.B. degree from Miami University in 1940 with a major in botany. To pursue his interest in botany he came to Cambridge, Massachusetts, and worked as personal technician to Prof. I. W. Bailey in the Biological Laboratories at Harvard University. Heintzelman entered the Graduate School at Harvard in the fall of 1941 as an Ames Memorial Scholar and completed one full semester of work leading to a Ph.D. degree before he left school in February of 1942 to join the U. S. Naval Reserve. After flight training at Squantum, Massachusetts, and Jacksonville, Florida, he was commissioned an ensign in the Naval Reserve in the fall of 1942. As a member of the 101st Bombardment Squadron, Heintzelman saw action at Midway, off the New Hebrides, from Henderson Field on Guadalcanal, and from Kahili Field on Bougainville. He was reported missing during an engagement centering around Kahili Field on March 8, 1943, and was declared presumptively dead on December 10, 1945. A posthumous award of the Order of the Purple Heart was made by the Navy Department.

This paper was a cooperative work and was ready for publication in 1942, but when both authors entered the service its publication was delayed. The paper was revised and additional material was added in 1947.

below the surface of the epidermis. The body of the hair is the free portion above the surface of the epidermis. In some hairs the wall of the body and the wall of the base are of equal thickness (fig. 27, 55). Other hairs have a thickened ring or collar extending into the lumen which separates the body and the base (fig. 17, 25, 47). The collar protrudes varying distances into the lumen and may completely subdivide the lumen, forming a small basal cell (fig. 17). In some genera the hair base may have a thicker wall than does the body of the hair. This basal wall frequently possesses thin areas or pits on either the sides or the bottom (fig. 27) which often give the appearance of sieve areas. In other hairs only the sides of the base are thickened, forming a heavy ring at the base of the hair (fig. 36). These variations are relatively consistent on one plant specimen and usually through the species.

The hairs are all unicellular and usually occur singly, although clusters are found in five genera and peltate-stellate clusters in two other genera. The hairs are formed from single epidermal cells. Their bases are commonly the same size as the adjacent epidermal cells. Variations do occur, as occasionally the hair base will be sunken in the leaf tissue (fig. 9), but more often there is an intimate association of the surrounding cells with the hair (fig. 25, 50). The surrounding cells may have extra thick walls (fig. 27, 44, 56) or they may, as in *Alsodeiopsis* and several other genera, protrude somewhat above the leaf surface and support the hair (fig. 25). These supporting cells frequently have only their radial walls thickened but they are definitely oriented, forming distinct stellate or radiate patterns. The number of surrounding cells is not constant.

The cell walls of individual hairs show considerable variation in thickness, sculpturing, and lamination. The walls may be very thin, as is usually the case in hairs found on staminal filaments (fig. 33), or they may be uniformly thickened, often nearly to the exclusion of the lumen of the hair (fig. 40). Some hairs, such as those found in *Medusanthera*, characteristically have a very thick wall in the body of the hair and taper to a very thin wall in the base (fig. 21, 40). In others the lumen may be extensive (fig. 1, 27. 55) or may be greatly restricted in the body by regular (fig. 18, 56) or irregular (fig. 13, 37) thickenings of the wall. Rugose inner surfaces of the walls form one or more septations of the lumen in hairs of *Apodytes* (fig. 13) while in *Natsiatum* the walls are irregularly thickened but without septations. The outer surface of the hair is smooth or only slightly striated in most genera (fig. 1, 24, 40), but in several the wall surface is pitted (fig. 30, 56) and in others the outer surface is irregularly covered with small protuberances (fig. 31,

Reprinted by permission of R. A. Howard and the publisher from the AMERICAN JOURNAL OF BOTANY, **35**, 42–52 (1948).

31a). These protuberances are apparently of a composition different from that of the bulk of the wall since they stain differently with Sudan III. Hairs with pitted walls and hairs with walls possessing protuberances are usually found together on the same organ of the plant. It is possible that these are developmental stages in which the pitted hair is younger.

The hairs of the Icacinaceae can be classified into ten general types.

1. The *normal* type (fig. 1) of hairs includes those forming an elongate conical or tapering body. These are usually erect or arching, although they may be sharply reflexed against the surface (fig. 31). Normal hairs are found in twenty-seven of the forty-nine genera examined. They are found on all parts of the plant, and all of the wall variations previously mentioned occur in them. The hairs found in the domatia on the leaves of *Citronella* may be of this type or of the *cylindrical* type (Howard, 1942b). Those found in the locule of the ovary and on the fruit are of this type.

2. The *cylindrical* hair (fig. 33) has been found only on the inner surfaces of the petals and on the filaments of the stamens. Its presence or absence on these parts is of considerable diagnostic value (Howard, 1940, 1942, 1942a). The cylindrical hair is thin-walled, possesses a large lumen, and is many times as long as broad. It is commonly club-shaped with a round or obtuse apex. A group of genera related to *Mappia* characteristically possess, on the fleshy midrib of the petals, a dense pubescence of these club-shaped hairs which collapse readily on drying. In *Emmotum* each cylindrical hair of the midrib collapses readily and in a regular pattern. When re-expanded with caustic soda these hairs are moniliform. We can not be sure from herbarium specimens if this is the condition in living material. The hairs of *Emmotum* are usually deeply colored. This is the only example of pigmentation in the pubescence found in the family. *Poraqueiba* differs from *Emmotum* in having hairs on the lateral margins of the petals as well as on the fleshy midrib. All of these hairs are shorter and lack the definite wall pattern just described for those of *Emmotum*.

The fleshy inflexed apex of the valvate petals is typical of the Icacinaceae. These apices are commonly short-papillate, but when the papillae do elongate, the hairs formed resemble those found on the fleshy midrib rather than those on the exterior surface of the petal. Occasionally hair-like papillae will be found on the apices of petals which lack a pubescence on the midrib.

Eight genera of the Icacinaceae, *i.e.*, *Stemonurus* and related genera, have a pubescence on the stamens. In most of these, the pubescence is on the adaxial surface of a fleshy, flattened filament. These hairs are of the cylindrical type possessing a large lumen and thin walls, and they usually have a rounded apex. The hairs are generally club-shaped and taper from the apex to the base. They collapse irregularly when dry but re-expand to a smooth-walled, club-shaped hair. Staminal hairs are clustered immediately below the anther and folded over them when the stamens are immature. It is claimed by many observers that this protects the developing anthers. Elongation of the filament at anthesis usually occurs between the pubescence and the anthers. *Lasianthera* and *Discophora* differ from the other genera of this group in that each stamen has an adaxial fleshy appendage at the midpoint of the filament. The pubescence of the filament is limited to this appendage in *Discophora* and is on the appendage and the apical abaxial portion of the filaments in *Lasianthera*. Filament hairs collapse readily in all genera. The walls of each hair are usually smooth but definite striae are often evident. *Urandra* has small, spirally arranged protuberances developed on the walls of the staminal hairs. No moniliform hairs have been found on the stamens.

3. One type of hairs is so characteristic of the many genera of the family that we suggest they be called the *icacinaceous* hairs (fig. 36). It is found in thirty-two of the forty-nine genera examined, and since it is characteristic of the genus *Icacina*, has been named for it. The *icacinaceous* hair has a short stalk arising from the base, and a body at right angles to this stalk (fig. 51). It differs from a strictly normal hair in the possession of a stub of a second arm (fig. 36) or an indication of the same in the lumen of the hair (fig. 51). These hairs may have thin or thick walls, uniform or irregular walls. They usually taper to the end. This hair might be considered a one-armed malpighiaceous hair. All stages of transition (fig. 55) may be found between the icacinaceous and malpighiaceous hair-types; however, unless the second arm is developed equal to the length of the stalk, the hair has been considered in the present group.

4. The true *malpighiaceous* hair (fig. 2, 3), which has two well-developed arms attached by a stalk in the middle of the body, is found in six genera of the family. The stalk is usually slightly flattened and widens from the base to the body of the hair (fig. 53). The hairs are usually thin-walled and possess large lumina. Many examples were found in which the hairs were definitely inflated (fig. 2), often forming bizarre shapes. The longest malpighiaceous hairs were found on the pistils of *Leretia* and *Oecopetalum*. These hairs were oriented parallel to the style and were, in some cases, 100 times longer than wide.

5. A simple *globular* type of hair (fig. 29, 46, 48) is relatively common in the lianoid genera of the family. These hairs are thin-walled with large lumina and with rounded apices larger than the bases so that they taper either gradually or abruptly to the base. They are never found as the sole type of pubescence but are always associated with other types of hairs. Some authors have considered them to be glandular, but in all our work no true glandular hairs were found in the family. All globular hairs are essentially short hairs, varying from

TABLE 1. *Pubescence and crystals in the Icacinaceae.*

Tribes and genera of the Icacinaceae	Pubescence																Crystals									
	Special position of hairs				Type of hairs											Supporting cells present	Location of druses				Location of rhombics					Crystal sand present
	On pistil	Inside corolla	On filaments	Locule of fruit	Normal	Cylindrical	Icacinaceous	Malpighiaceous	Globular	Thin-base	Uncinate	Articulate	Peltate-stellate	Clustered	Pitted or rugose		In leaves	In flowers	In cortex	In pith	In leaves	In flowers	In cortex	In wood rays	In pith	

Icacineae

Acrocoelium (ex char.) ...																										
Alsodeiopsis	*			*		*										*	*	*	*			*		*	*	
Anisomallon																		*	*					*	*	*
Apodytes	*					*										*							*	*	*	*
Calatola	*					*	*										*	*	*	*	*	*		*		
Cantleya			*			*	*		*								*									*
Casimirella (ex char.) ...	*	*		*												*										
Cassinopsis	*			*													*	*	*	*						
Citronella	*				*		*										*	*	*	*	*	*	*	*		*
Codiocarpus				*		*											*	*	*	*						
Dendrobangia	*					*								*			*						*			
Desmostachys	*	*		*		*								*			*				*	*	*	*		
Discophora			*	*	*												*		*		*			*		*
Emmotum	*	*		*		*						*					*		*		*	*	*	*		
Gastrolepis			*		*	*											*		*		*		*			
Gonocaryum				*					*								*				*	*	*	*	*	*
Grisollea	*					*											*		*	*						
Humirianthera	*	*	*			*	*								*	*	*	*					*			
Icacina	*	*				*	*										*	*			*				*	
Irvingbaileya			*		*												*		*							
Jobalboa (ex char.)	*																*	*								
Lavigeria	*			*		*								*			*	*					*		*	*
Leptaulus	*			*		*											*	*								*
Leretia		*				*								*			*	*			*				*	
Leucocorema (ex char.) ...	*	*			*												*							*		*
Lasianthera			*			*	*										*							*		*
Mappia	*	*				*	*	*									*	*	*							
Medusanthera			*		*	*			*								*	*	*		*	*		*		
Merrilliodendron	*			*		*											*	*	*							
Nothapodytes	*	*		*		*	*										*	*	*							*
Oecopetalum	*					*	*										*	*	*	*						
Ottoschulzia				*		*	*										*	*	*			*				
Pennantia				*								*									*			*		
Pentastira (ex char.)	*																									
Pittosporopsis				*		*		*									*	*	*					*		
Platea	*											*					*	*					*	*		*
Pleurisanthes	*					*		*						*	*	*	*	*								
Poraqueiba		*			*						*						*	*						*		*
Pseudobotrys	*			*													*	*								
Rhaphiostylis	*					*											*	*			*			*	*	
Rhyticaryum	*					*					*			*		*	*	*	*							*
Stemonurus	*	*			*																*	*				*
Tridianisia (ex char.)....	*																									
Urandra			*			*											*	*	*	*				*		

Iodeae

Hosiea	*			*		*									*	*	*	*	*	*						
Iodes	*			*		*		*		*							*	*	*							
Mappianthus	*	*		*		*										*	*	*			*		*	*	
Natsiatum	*	*		*		*										*	*	*								
Natsiatopsis (ex char.)...	*																									
Polyporandra	*			*				*								*	*	*	*	*						

TABLE 1. *Continued.*

Tribes and genera of the Icacinaceae	Pubescence — Special position of hairs: On pistil	Inside corolla	On filaments	Locule of fruit	Type of hairs: Normal	Cylindrical	Icacinaceous	Malpighiaceous	Globular	Thin-base	Uncinate	Articulate	Peltate-stellate	Clustered	Pitted or rugose	Supporting cells present	Crystals — Location of druses: In leaves	In flowers	In cortex	In pith	Location of rhombics: In leaves	In flowers	In cortex	In wood rays	In pith	Crystal sand present
Sarcostigmateae																										
Sarcostigma	*		*														*	*	*	*			*	*		
Phytocreneae																										
Chlamydocarya	*		*	*	*		*				*						*	*	*							
Miquelia	*		*	*	*		*		*		*						*	*	*							
Phytocrene	*		*	*	*		*		*		*			*	*		*	*	*							
Polycephalium			*								*						*	*	*							
Pyrenacantha	*		*		*						*						*	*	*							
Stachyanthus (ex char.)	*																									
Trematosperma (ex char.)	*																									

scarcely as long as broad to four–five times as long as broad.

6. The *thin-base* type of hair (fig. 21, 40) is characteristic of *Citronella* and *Medusanthera* and is found in a few other genera. It is a long, tapering hair with a thick wall and restricted lumen in the body and a very thin-walled base which is difficult to see in most preparations. These hairs are found on all parts of the plant.

7. The *uncinate* hair (fig. 23, 24, 26) is found in all the lianoid genera of the Iodeae and the Phytocreneae and the genus *Pennantia* of the Icacineae. The hooks are well formed although the body is usually thin-walled. In *Pennantia* the uncinate hairs predominate in the pubescence of the pedicels and are infrequent on the leaves. In the lianoid genera of the Iodeae and the Phytocreneae, however, uncinate hairs are abundant on the leaves. In two species of *Iodes* and in all species of *Pyrenacantha* examined, the pubescence of the rudimentary pistil in the male flowers may be composed entirely of uncinate hairs.

8. The *articulated* hairs (fig. 8, 10, 20) found in *Poraqueiba* and *Emmotum* constitute the most unusual type of hair found in the family. They occur on all parts of the plant except the inner surface of the petals. These hairs have a very thick-walled body with a much restricted lumen. The body breaks off readily, leaving an elongate thin-walled papilla-like base in the epidermis (fig. 7). The hair bases are usually lighter in color than the surrounding epidermal tissues or are unpigmented and appear as small dots under low magnification. We believe it is these papilla-like hair bases that Miers calls glands (Miers, 1851–61). This mistake is an easy one to make, for sections of the leaf are required to understand the structure of these hairs. The papilla-like base has a well-developed lumen

and is slightly inflated. It is short and rarely developed to one-third the length of the body. Thickening in the wall of the body of the hair proceeds from the apex to the base and the nature of the articulation is not evident until the wall is quite thick. Then the body of the hair breaks off from the base. Superficial examination, therefore, shows long young hairs with thin walls and short papillae, which have been misinterpreted in the past as two types of hairs on the leaves.

9. *Peltate-stellate* hairs (fig. 9, 11, 18) are found in *Platea* and *Dendrobangia*. It seems advisable to use these terms hyphenated, since neither term used alone is strictly applicable to the hair groups found in these genera. The hair groupings consist of 5–15 hairs. They arise from cells slightly sunken below the epidermal layer and the group is free from the surrounding epidermal cells (fig. 9). The hairs composing the group are erect and fused or closely associated for part of their length before they bend sharply to lie parallel to the surface. This type of hair grouping differs from the next since the hairs are sharply bent parallel to the surface and the group lacks a middle central hair. The individual hairs of this group are usually thick-walled and the lumen is restricted to the base or usually below the bend of the hair.

10. The *clustered* type (fig. 4, 39, 41) is a group of 5–20 hairs associated only at their bases. All hairs of the cluster may be alike (fig. 39) or the central hair may be quite different from the others (fig. 4, 41). Normally all the hairs arch, but occasionally the central hair alone may be erect. In *Humirianthera* and *Pleurisanthes* the central hair is erect and of equal length with the others but differs in having the thickened wall pitted on the outer surface. In *Phytocrene* (fig. 4) the central hair may be either smooth or pitted, but it is several times as

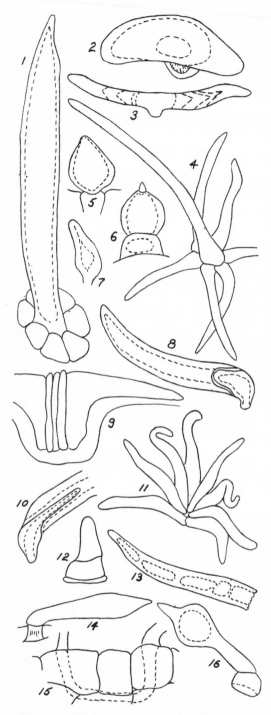

long as the other hairs of the cluster. The bases of all the hairs are thick-walled and a collar or thickened ring near the base is quite common.

DISCUSSION.—In many genera of the Icacinaceae only one type of hair is found on all parts of the plant. For example, in plants with a malpighiaceous type of pubescence these two-armed hairs may be found on the stem, leaf, petiole, inflorescence rachises, calyx, corolla, and pistil. In other genera the normal type of hair will prevail throughout the plant. In the lianoid Icacinoideae such genera as *Pleurisanthes, Rhyticaryum, Desmostachys,* and *Lavigeria* may have several types of hairs composing the indument. The Iodeae, Phytocreneae, and Sarcostigmateae may be characterized by the complexity and variability in hair-types.

Comparison of the pubescence in the various genera allows one to establish certain natural generic groupings. These relationships are supported by characters in other parts of the plant. For example, the possession of large cylindrical thin-walled hairs on the filaments might indicate a relationship of *Discophora, Lasianthèra, Cantleya, Gastrolepis, Medusanthera, Stemonurus* and *Urandra.* Bailey and Howard (1941, 1941a, 1941b) have indicated that there are similarities in the wood structure of these same genera, and the similarities and relationships in the flowers and in the fruits have been pointed out by Howard (1940, 1943a). Cylindrical hairs are found on the inside of the corolla of *Mappia, Nothapodytes, Humirianthera, Leretia, Leucocorema, Icacina,* and *Desmostachys.* This group of genera has been referred to as the *Mappia*-complex or the Mappiae by previous authors because of similarities of flowers and fruits (Howard, 1942). Bailey and Howard (1941) have placed all these

mexicana Robins. & Greenm. (Pringle 509); malpighiaceous hair from a leaf. ×270 —Fig. 4. *Phytocrene Blancoi* Merr. (Herb. Phil. Bur. Sci. 42817); cluster of hairs from a leaf. ×270 —Fig. 5. *Phytocrene anomala* Merr. (Ramos 1508); abnormal hair from a leaf. ×270 —Fig. 6. *Miquelia Cumingii* Baill. (Herb. Phil. Bur. Sci. 24572); abnormal hair from a leaf. ×550 —Fig. 7. *Emmotum nitens* Miers (Burchell 9233); papilla-like hair base from leaf. ×550 —Fig. 8. *Emmotum acuminatum* Miers (Ducke 376); articulated hair from a petal showing the body and the papilla-like base. ×550 —Fig. 9. *Platea apoensis* Elm. (Elmer 11412); section of hair from the petiole showing the sunken place of attachment. ×550 —Fig. 10. *Emmotum acuminatum* Miers (Ducke 376); basal portion of an articulated hair from a petal showing the elongated papilla-like base. ×550 —Fig. 11. *Platea philippinensis* Merr. (Elmer 9777); peltate-stellate hair from the calyx. ×270 —Fig. 12. *Iodes philippinensis* Merr. (Wenzel 1433); modified globular type of hair from a leaf. ×550 —Fig. 13. *Apodytes dimidiata* E. Mey. (Imp. For. Inst. 42); hair from the pistil showing septations in the lumen. ×550 —Fig. 14. *Pleurisanthes simpliciflora* Sleumer (Krukoff 8773); normal type of hair from a leaf. ×550 —Fig. 15. *Hosiea sinensis* Oliv. (Henry 5598); the detail of the depth of the base of a hair from a leaf. ×550 —Fig. 16. *Iodes liberica* Stapf (Linder 1102); abnormal hair from a leaf showing the inflated tip. ×550

Fig. 1–16. All drawings were made with a camera lucida.—Fig. 1. *Desmostachys Preusii* Engl. (AA 172–3); normal hair from a leaf. ×550 —Fig. 2. *Mappia mexicana* Robins. & Greenm. (Pringle 6645); inflated malpighiaceous hair from the calyx. ×550 —Fig. 3. *Mappia*

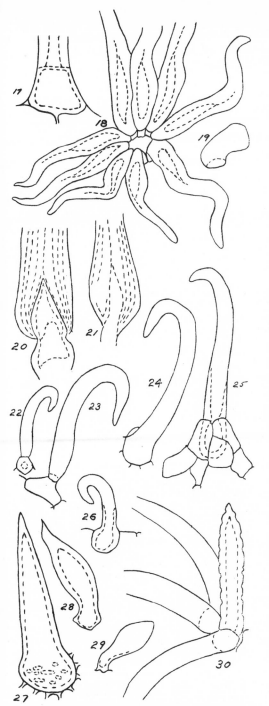

genera in the Group III A Icacinoideae because of similarities of wood structure. *Emmotum* and *Poraqueiba* likewise have petals which bear hairs on the adaxial surface, although these two genera do not fit into the previous group. The articulated hairs of *Emmotum* and *Poraqueiba* indicate a close relationship which is supported by similarities in wood structure. Hairs are found on the inner surface of the locule in fruits of *Leretia, Humirianthera* and *Casimirella*, which are very closely related genera, as well as in *Ottoschulzia*. However the last genus is not closely related to the other three.

Thus the characters used for establishing relationships between genera may find support in the hair-types, and the hair-types may therefore be used to check previously established relationships. The species of *Ottoschulzia* were formerly placed in the genus *Poraqueiba* until established as a distinct genus by Urban. In addition to the floral characters previously used, *Ottoschulzia* differs from *Poraqueiba* in having glabrous adaxial petal surfaces, a pubescence on the inner surface of the locules, and an icacinaceous type of hair. *Poraqueiba* has a pubescence on the inner surface of the petals, lacks the pubescence of the locule, and has an articulated type of hair on the rest of the plant. The genus *Discophora* is unlike any other New World genus but in the floral structure, the wood structure, and the type of fruit it is very closely related to *Lasianthera, Gastrolepis, Medusanthera* and *Stemonurus* of the Old World. This same relationship is indicated in the type of pubescence, since all these genera possess cylindrical hairs on the filaments. Baehni (1936) suggested that *Oecopetalum* was identical with *Poraqueiba*, but the great differences in the hair-types in these two groups, *i.e.*, icacinaceous in *Oecopetalum*, articulated in *Poraqueiba*, support the floral differences and differences in wood structure to maintain them as distinct.

Well. (Zenker 1418); globular hair from a leaf. ×550 —Fig. 20. *Poraqueiba guianensis* Aubl. (Huber 1288); base of an articulated hair from the petiole. ×550 —Fig. 21. *Citronella Smythii* (F. von Muell.) Howard (White 1408); base of the thin-base type of hair from a leaf. ×550 —Fig. 22. *Pyrenacantha Vogeliana* Baill. (Linder 261); uncinate hair from a leaf. ×270 —Fig. 23. *Miquelia Cumingii* Baill. (Herb. Phil. Bur. Sci. 24572); uncinate hair from a petiole. ×550 —Fig. 24. *Pennantia corymbosa* Forst. (Petrie 141); uncinate hair from the pedicel. ×270 —Fig. 25. *Phytocrene anomala* Merr. (Ramos 1508); uncinate hair from the leaf showing the supporting epidermal cells at the base. ×270 —Fig. 26. *Pennantia corymbosa* Forst. (Cockayne 6188); uncinate hair from the pedicel showing varying thickness of cell wall. ×270 —Fig. 27. *Pyrenacantha repanda* Merr. (Wenzel 2607); normal hair from a leaf showing the thin or pitted areas in the basal wall. ×270 —Fig. 28. *Iodes Hookeriana* Baill. (Ruse 420); globular hair from the leaf. ×550 —Fig. 29. *Iodes floribunda* Merr. (Toroes 77); globular hair from a leaf. ×550 —Fig. 30. *Humirianthera rupestris* Ducke (Ducke 25228); portion of a hair cluster from a leaf showing the rugose-walled central hair. ×110

Fig. 17–30.—Fig. 17. *Humirianthera rupestris* Ducke (Ducke 25228); base of a single hair from a cluster showing the collar at hair base. ×1100 —Fig. 18. *Dendrobangia boliviana* Rusby (Persaud 113); peltate-stellate hair cluster from a leaf. ×550 —Fig. 19. *Iodes africana*

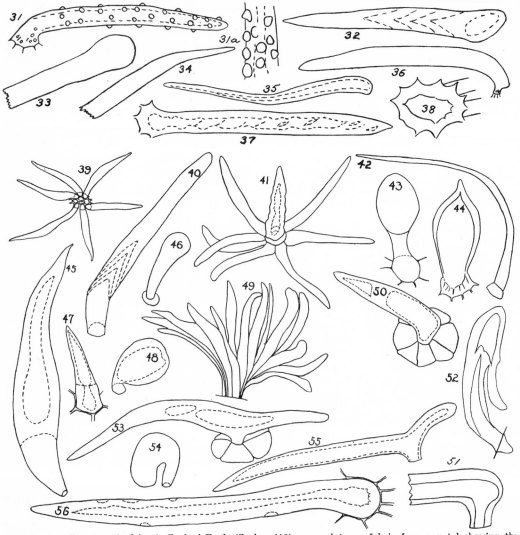

Fig. 31–56.—Fig. 31. *Alsodeiopsis Zenkeri* Engl. (Zenker 152); normal type of hair from a petal showing the protuberances. ×220 —Fig. 31 a. *Alsodeiopsis Zenkeri* Engl. (Zenker 152); section of the hair surface showing the spiral arrangement of the protuberances. ×550 —Fig. 32. *Medusanthera carolinensis* (Kaneh.) Howard (Kanehira 4578); thin-base type of hair from a leaf showing the lamination of wall from apex to the base. ×550 —Fig. 33. *Stemonurus affinis* Miers (Beccari 8028); cylindrical hair from a stamen. ×110 —Fig. 34. *Lavigeria macrocarpa* (Oliv.) Pierre (Mildbraed 10536); tip of a normal hair from the leaf. ×110 —Fig. 35. *Cassinopsis tinifolia* Harv. (Wilson without no. AA); normal hair from a leaf. ×110 —Fig. 36. *Nothapodytes foetida* (Wight) Sleumer (Wight 492); icacinaceous hair from a petal. ×220 —Fig. 37. *Iodes curtiflora* Elm. (Elmer 12498); normal hair from a leaf showing the irregular thickening of the inner wall. ×220 —Fig. 38. *Alsodeiopsis Zenkeri* Engl. (Zenker 152); thick-walled base of hair from a leaf. ×550 —Fig. 39. *Lavigeria macrocarpa* (Oliv.) Pierre (Mildbraed 10536); cluster of hairs from a leaf showing the uniformity of the cluster. ×220 —Fig. 40. *Medusanthera carolinensis* (Kanehira) Howard (Kanehira 2473); thin-base type of hair from a leaf. ×550 —Fig. 41. *Phytocrene Blancoi* Merr. (Herb. Phil. Bur. Sci. 42817); hair cluster from a leaf showing the thick-walled and rugose-walled central hair. ×270 — Fig. 42. *Iodes curtiflora* Elm. (Elmer 12498); normal hair from a leaf. ×110 —Fig. 43. *Phytocrene macrophylla* Blume (Elmer 11724); abnormally inflated globular hair from a leaf. ×550 —Fig. 44. *Miquelia Cumingii* Baill. (Herb. Phil. Bur. Sci. 49997); modified globular hair from a petal. ×550 —Fig. 45. *Cassinopsis ilicifolia* (Hochst.) Sleumer (AA specimen without no.); thick-walled normal hair from a petal. ×550 —Fig. 46. *Pleurisanthes parviflora* (Ducke) Howard (Krukoff 6954); globular hair from a leaf. ×550 —Fig. 47. *Polyporandra scandens* Becc. (Brass 829); normal hair from a leaf showing the collar-type thickening at the base. ×550 —Fig. 48. *Iodes liberica* Stapf (Linder 1102); globular hair from a leaf. ×550 —Fig. 49. *Dendrobangia boliviana* Rusby (Persaud 113); peltate-stellate cluster from a petiole. ×270 —Fig. 50. *Medusanthera glabra* (Merr.) Howard (Herb. Phil. Bur.

Some species of a genus which differ from the others in characters of wood and pollen grains may also possess distinct hair-types. *Nothapodytes pittosporoides* (Oliv.)· Sleumer, which Bailey and Howard (1941a) have indicated as being divergent from the other species of *Nothapodytes* in its wood structure, is distinct also in possessing an elongated normal type of hair in its indument, while other species of *Nothapodytes* have only the icacinaceous type of hair. *Stemonurus Merrittii* Merr. was recently placed in *Tylecarpus* (*Medusanthera*) by Sleumer (1940). It is distinct from the other species of *Stemonurus* with respect to its floral structure and in addition has the thin-base type of hair characteristic of *Medusanthera*. Its true relationships are with *Medusanthera* rather than with *Stemonurus*, but fruit, floral and anatomical characters justify its separation in a distinct genus, *Codiocarpus*, as Howard has done (1943). *Leretia parviflora* Sleumer, which Howard has transferred to *Pleurisanthes* (1942a), differs from the genus *Leretia* in lacking the thin-walled malpighiaceous hairs on the pistil and leaves and the cylindrical type of hair on the inner surface of the petals. Instead, this species possesses rugose-walled icacinaceous hairs on the petals and leaves and also clusters of hairs with the central hair larger than the others and with a thick pitted wall. This is in agreement with types of hairs found in *Pleurisanthes*.

The terms taxonomists use to describe the indument fall into two general categories. Those describing the individual hairs and concerning such characters as length, position, texture, stiffness, and shape are malpighiaceous, uncinate, club-shaped, erect, strict, or glandular. The other general group of terms describes the nature of the pubescent surface or its appearance to the eye. Included here are such terms as sericeous, ciliate, and lanate. This terminology is not satisfactory since the terms are general or relative and vary with the individual worker. In the Icacinaceae a combination of terms can be used to make definitions of pubescence explicit. Thus, instead of describing the calyx as ciliate, the calyx lobes of *Mappia* or *Calatola* can be described as ciliate with malpighiaceous hairs, those of *Citronella* as ciliate with icacinaceous hairs, and those of *Pseudobotrys* as ciliate with normal hairs. Likewise, the pubescence on the outside of the corolla or on the pistil may be hirsute or sericeous, but the hairs comprising this pubescence might well be of different types and could be described more explicitly. The characteristic and distinct forms of pubescence in the Icacinaceae are of considerable value in recognition of genera and in taxonomic descriptions.

Abnormalities among hair-types were expected and are of frequent occurrence. The most common type is the inflated hair (fig. 5, 6, 16, 43, 54). This is very common in some of the New World species of *Citronella* and in the Old World genus *Iodes*. The entire hair may be inflated or only a portion of it. In some of the icacinaceous hairs there may be a globular swelling at the tip or near the base of the hair. Branching occurs occasionally in some hairs. This is not always a dichotomy of the hair, for some retrorse branching occurs (fig. 52). Many abnormalities of form such as abrupt bends or contortions were found.

THE CRYSTALS.—Our observations on the crystals were made to determine the types of crystals present, their distribution throughout the plant, and the relative abundance in the tissues. We studied permanent slides of mature wood, stems, leaves and flowers. We also made water mounts of stems, leaves, and flowers to check our findings, since we soon discovered that the occurrence and the type of crystal were affected not only by the hydrofluoric acid used to soften the mature wood but also by the warm 1 per cent caustic soda used to clear the leaves and flowers. By the use of either of these chemicals the crystals may be completely removed or their form changed from rhombics to druse-like masses or to crystal sand. All material was checked with a polarizing microscope for accurate determination of crystalline form and structure and for the nature of the cellulose sheaths surrounding the crystals.

In the forty-eight genera for which we had adequate material, we found three types of crystals in the tissues of the plant. These we call druses, rhombic crystals, and crystal sand, using the terminology established by Solereder (1899), who made preliminary examinations of the crystals in this family. Druses are massive aggregate crystals. Rhombic crystals are large single crystals. Crystal sand includes those amorphous masses of crystalline materials of minute size as well as scattered and very minute crystalline particles revealed only by the aid of polarized light.

Druses are of general occurrence in the Icacinaceae and are found in tissues of the leaves, petioles, flowers, phloem, cortex and pith of the stems of all but three genera examined. No druses were found in the mature wood. The druses varied in size, with the larger druses in the softer tissues such as the phloem or the cortex. The small druses were present in thick coriaceous leaves with dense mesophyll or in the epidermal cells of membranaceous leaves. Some of the druses had cellulose sheaths but most of them were free in large thin-walled cells. Druses were found in the flowers of all genera examined

Sci. 1628) ; icacinaceous hair from a leaf. ✕550 —Fig. 51. *Calatola laevigata* Standley (Reko 3440) ; base of an icacinaceous hair showing an indication of a second arm in the lumen. ✕550 —Fig. 52. *Stemonurus Cumingianus* Miers (Wenzel 2840) ; abnormal branching of a thin-base hair from a leaf. ✕550 —Fig. 53. *Leretia cordata* Vell. (Blanchet 2347) ; malpighiaceous hair from the calyx. ✕270 —Fig. 54. *Iodes Seguini* Rehd. (Handel-Mazzetti 10374) ; abnormal globular hair from a leaf. ✕550 —Fig. 55. *Ottoschulzia cubensis* (Wright) Urban (Wright 2639) ; malpighiaceous hair from a petal. ✕270 —Fig. 56. *Polyporandra scandens* Becc. (AA 17839) ; normal hair from a leaf showing the pits in the thick walls. ✕550

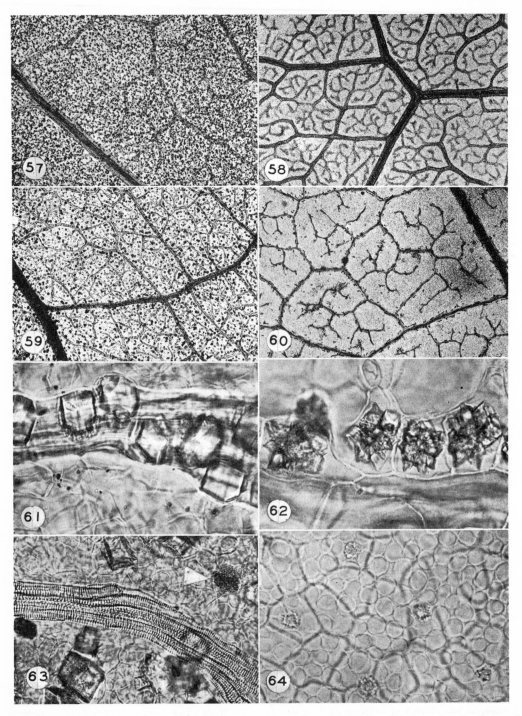

Fig. 57–64.—Fig. 57. *Citronella sarmentosa* (Baill.) Howard (Prony 1576-A); view of leaf showing abundance of crystalline material. ×35.—Fig. 58. *Citronella sarmentosa* (Baill.) Howard (Prony 1576-A); view of another section of the same leaf after the crystals have been removed. ×35.—Fig. 59. *Stemonurus javanicus* Blume (Vidal 151); view of leaf showing large rhombic crystals along the midrib and veins and scattered through the tissue. ×35.—Fig. 60. *Nothapodytes pittosporoides* (Oliv.) Sleumer (ex Herb. Kew without no. AA); view of the leaf showing abun-

except *Discophora,* which had large amounts of crystal sand. The druses could be found in either the cortex alone or in the cortex and the pith, but never in the pith alone.

Single rhombic crystals are of less frequent occurrence than are the druses. They are found in nearly all parts of the plant, in the leaves of twelve genera, in the flowers of four genera, in the cortical cells of thirteen genera, in the pith cells of eleven genera, and in the ray cells of the mature wood of twenty-three genera. Small rhombic crystals were found in the petals of *Calatola, Medusanthera,* and a few species of *Gonocaryum* and *Stemonurus.* Rhombic crystals were much more abundant in the tissues of the cortex than in the pith. The rhombic crystals in the ray cells were either solitary or infrequently paired in the cells. Many of the crystals had cellulose sheaths which were thin in some and thick in others. The sclerotic ray cells of *Emmotum* (Bailey and Howard, 1941b) frequently contained well-imbedded rhombic crystals. Most of the genera with a lianoid habit lacked rhombic crystals in the ray cells. Woody genera forming trees usually had rhombic crystals in the ray cells and frequently in strands of wood parenchyma.

Minute crystalline particles, called crystal sand, were found in tissues of the leaf, the cortex, and rarely in the flowers. Usually these particles were diffuse in the tissue, although in several genera there were characteristic large clusters of these minute crystalline particles. Such clusters are typical of the genus *Discophora.* When crystal sand was found in the leaf it was commonly associated with the midrib or the principal lateral veins. When crystal sand was found in the flowers it appeared only in the perianth and the pistil. No true cystoliths were found in the Icacinaceae.

The abundance and position of crystalline materials in the tissues of the plants examined were correlated. In all tissues the crystals were formed first near the vascular strands, becoming progressively diffuse away from the primary vascular strands in the inter-vascular spaces. Thus, in the leaves, the crystals were most common along the veins and midrib and less common in the mesophyll tissues of the lamina. The occurrence of crystals in the epidermal layers was infrequent. Crystals were found in the petiole only when they occurred in both the leaf and the cortex. If only a few crystals were present in the flowers they occurred in the perianth. As the amount of crystalline material increased it could be found successively in the ovary, the style, and finally in the filaments. No crystalline material was observed in the anthers.

The tribe Icacineae, with druses, rhombic crystals, and crystal sand, had more types of crystals than the other tribes. Druses and rhombic crystals were present in the Iodeae but no crystal sand was observed. The genera of the Phytocreneae had only druses, while the Sarcostigmateae had both druses and · rhombic crystals but no crystal sand. Thus crystal sand was lacking in the three tribes containing lianas and in the lianoid genera of the Icacineae as well. Rhombic crystals were found in the wood ray cells of only two lianoid genera. Druses and rhombic crystals occur together in the cortex only in *Citronella.* The cortical tissues of the other genera examined had either druses or rhombic crystals but not both. Druses and rhombic crystals together in the leaves were more common but were limited to the genera which are more primitive anatomically.

The occurrence of each of the three types of crystals appears to be a relatively stable character. While the type of crystal and the presence or absence of crystals can not be used alone as diagnostic characters, their occurrence is of value when used in combination with characters of structure and form.

SUMMARY

Earlier studies of the Icacinaceae have shown that the genera of the family are distinct on numerous characters and that the species are less clearly defined. The present comparative study concerned the pubescence of the plants, its occurrence and distribution, the types of hairs composing the indument, and the types and distribution of crystals throughout the plant. Ten distinct and characteristic forms of hairs were recognized and described. Many of these are typical of definite genera of the family and could be used to characterize those genera.

The value of pubescence characters in supporting generic relationships or differences established on the basis of other characters is clearly shown in this family. However, no broad phylogenetic lines of specialization can be drawn from the study of pubescence as was possible in wood structure. Obvious specializations in the pubescence occur among genera considered primitive as well as in the more advanced genera.

Three types of crystals were found in the Icacinaceae. The type of crystal or its presence or absence appears to be a relatively stable character but not a diagnostic character to be used alone.

SOCIETY OF FELLOWS,
  HARVARD UNIVERSITY,
    CAMBRIDGE, MASSACHUSETTS

dant druses along the midrib and veins. ×35.—Fig. 61. *Gonocaryum obovatum* Hochr. (Buitenzorg specimen 88 ex AA); rhombic crystals along the veins of a leaf. × 510.—Fig. 62. *Nothapodytes pittosporoides* (Oliv.) Sleumer (ex Herb. Kew without no. AA); section of a leaf showing series of druses along a vein. ×510.—Fig. 63. *Stemonurus javanicus* Blume (Vidal 151); section of leaf showing scattered rhombic crystals, and, at the arrow, a cluster of small crystals called crystal sand. Some particles of crystal sand are visible around the rhombic crystals. ×510.—Fig. 64. *Rhaphiostylis beninensis* (Hook. f. ex Benth.) Planch. (ex Kew Herb. 4712); section of leaf tissue showing scattered druses. ×510.

LITERATURE CITED

BAEHNI, C. 1936. Revision des Genres *Neoleretia, Mappia* et *Humirianthera.* Candollea 7: 167–189.

BAILEY, I. W., AND R. A. HOWARD. 1941. The comparative morphology of the Icacinaceae. II. Vessels. Jour. Arnold Arboretum 22: 171–187.

——, AND ——. 1941a. The comparative morphology of the Icacinaceae. III. Imperforate tracheary elements and wood parenchyma. Jour. Arnold Arboretum 22: 432–442.

——, AND ——. 1941b. The comparative morphology of the Icacinaceae. IV. Rays of the secondary xylem. Jour. Arnold Arboretum 22: 556–568.

HOWARD, R. A. 1940. Studies of the Icacinaceae. I. Preliminary taxonomic notes. Jour. Arnold Arboretum 21: 461–489.

——. 1942. Studies of the Icacinaceae. II. *Humirianthera, Leretia, Mappia* and *Nothapodytes*, valid genera of the Icacineae. Jour. Arnold Arboretum 23: 55–78.

——. 1942a. Studies of the Icacinaceae. IV. Considerations of the New World genera. Contrib. Gray Herb. 142: 1–60.

——. 1942b. Studies of the Icacinaceae. V. Revision of the genus *Citronella* D. Don. Contrib. Gray Herb. 142: 60–89.

——. 1943. Studies of the Icacinaceae. VI. *Irvingbaileya* and *Codiocarpus*, two new genera of the Icacineae. Brittonia 5: 47–57.

——. 1943a. Studies of the Icacinaceae. VII. Revision of the genus *Medusanthera* Seeman. Lloydia 6: 133–143.

——. 1943b. Studies of tne Icacinaceae. VIII. Brief notes of some Old World genera. Lloydia 6: 144–154.

MIERS, J. 1851–61. Contrib. Bot. 1: 107–111.

SLEUMER, H. 1940. Notizbl. 15: 247.

SOLEREDER, H. 1899. System. Anatom. der Dicotys. 227.

POLLEN MORPHOLOGY AND EVOLUTION IN HEDYOTIS SUBGENUS EDRISIA (RUBIACEAE)[1,2]

WALTER H. LEWIS

Missouri Botanical Garden and Department of Botany, Washington University, St. Louis, Missouri

ABSTRACT

Primarily on the basis of aperture structure, 31 species of *Hedyotis* subg. *Edrisia* (*Houstonia*) are separable into 5 palynological groups. Group 1 is characterized by a simple os circumscribed by varying nexinous thickenings, groups 2–4 combine this os with a crassimarginate one to form a compound os, while group 5 is known only with the crassimarginate os. The first type is considered primitive, the compound os specialized and more advanced, and the third type reduced and highly advanced. Other characteristics of the pollen, including size and shape, aperture number, thickness of sexine and nexine, and reticulum, are discussed in relation to the apertures, and their probable primitive and advanced expressions are outlined. The data agree with the phyletic trends found in the sporophyte on the basis of results from morphology, chromosome number and size, and distribution, and they support and add to an earlier phylogenetic scheme proposed for the subgenus. The evidence from palynology also supports the treatment of *Hedyotis* and *Houstonia* as congeneric.

ALTHOUGH excellent examples are known of the morphology of pollen aiding in systematic studies, particularly in delimiting boundaries of generic complexes such as *Polygonum* (Hedberg, 1947) and *Centauria* (Wagenitz, 1955), its value in systematics is nevertheless only slowly being appreciated. I know of only one study, for instance, which compares the pollen variability of a group of species with a proposed phylogeny in an attempt not only to verify the phylogenetic scheme, but also to find directional trends in the pollen morphology from primitive to more advanced expressions. This palynological research by Stern (1962a,b) suggested 2 main phyletic trends in *Dicentra*: a shift from a reticulate or foveolate exine to one which is verrucate; and a shift from distinct and numerically constant apertures to obscure and numerically inconsistent apertures. In addition, a less evident trend was apparent by an increase in aperture number from the basic 3 or 6 to 12 or more. These exine and aperture modifications accompanied gross morphological and anatomical specializations.

The equally variable pollen of *Hedyotis* subg. *Edrisia* (*Houstonia*) and the existence of a phylogenetic scheme based on different evidences (Lewis, 1962) presents an opportunity to test the validity of this phylogeny, to add new evidence

to the problem of generic limits between *Hedyotis* and its allies, and to suggest phyletic trends in rubiaceous pollen.

MATERIALS AND METHODS—Whole flowers, mature buds, or anthers only were removed from herbarium specimens and acetolyzed by the procedure outlined by Erdtman (1952, 1960). The material containing pollen was not, however, ground on a brass screen and filtered before acetolysis; rather, the filtering was completed after acetolysis and during washing. This procedure gave a superior concentration of pollen which was, by and large, free from debris. Most collections were also chlorinated before being mounted in glycerin jelly and sealed with paraffin.

Pollen from herbarium specimens, either acetolyzed or untreated, was ultra-thin sectioned following the fixing, embedding, and polymerizing procedures given by Praglowski (1957). Sections were cut using a glass knife at ca. 0.25μ in thickness and stained overnight in basic fuchsin.

Palynological terminology in general follows that of Erdtman (1952). All quantitative data for the pollen descriptions are given as means based on 10 random measurements usually presented as mean ranges in describing each group of species. For no character is the mean range of a species as great as the range for its species group and only rarely is there a significant structural difference between the pollen of species grouped together. In these few instances the details for the individual taxa are noted.

Pollen grains for 31 species of the subg. *Edrisia* have been studied. These species with their collectors and numbers, herbaria where specimens are filed, and localities by state (U. S.) or country are given under each species group. The few species not examined are rare with several represented only by a type collection which is in general not available for pollen extraction.

[1] Received for publication June 9, 1964.

[2] This study was initiated at the Palynological Laboratory, Stockholm-Solna, Sweden, during the tenure of a John S. Guggenheim Memorial Foundation Fellowship (1963–64). To the Foundation for this award and to Professor G. Erdtman for his invitation to the Laboratory and assistance during my visit there, I am deeply grateful. To all his staff, particularly Messrs. S. Nilsson and J. Praglowski, and Mrs. A. Hagland, I am pleased to acknowledge their aid.

This study was supported in part by contract AT(30–1)–3119 from the AEC issued to Professor Erdtman and in part by grant G–21818 from the NSF.

Herbarium vouchers of my collections are deposited at the Missouri Botanical Garden (MO) with duplicates at Southern Methodist University (SMU); collections of others are with these institutions or at the Riksmuseum, Stockholm (S), the Royal Botanic Gardens, Kew (K), or the U. S. National Museum (US). To the directors and staffs of these herbaria, I extend my sincere thanks for their cooperation in extracting pollen material for study.

RESULTS—Pollen of *Hedyotis* subg. *Edrisia* is: isopolar, radially symmetrical, suboblate to prolate, longest axis 17.5–41.4 μ; 3-(4-)aperturate; apertures equatorial, composite, with long, smooth-membraned colpi and simple or compound ora, often sunken below surrounding exine; amb angular and goniotreme, less commonly circular and peritreme; sexine usually 2–3 times as thick as nexine, reticulate, OL-pattern at high adjustment, simplibaculate; nexine varying in thickness, less frequently ± even; intine about $\frac{1}{2}$ as thick as exine, somewhat thicker near apertures.

The morphology of the aperture, in association with variations in the thickness of equatorial nexine, proved to be the most important diagnostic feature of the pollen. Its complexity and diversity require explanation. All apertures are composite, i.e., composed of an outer colpus and an inner os. The colpus is invariably a long, narrow furrow, but the os may be a margined pore, an internal structure of varying shape, or the aperture may consist of both kinds of ora. Ora are, therefore, either simple or compound. One kind of os, designated A, is delimited by a very thin layer of nexine in the equatorial zone (nexine 1) surrounded by a much thickened layer (nexine 2) as illustrated by the longitudinal section in Fig. 17. Os A may form a part of a continuous thin nexinous belt in the equatorial zone (synclinorate) (A$_1$) or it may be discontinuous from adjacent ora. In the latter form, the thin nexinous area ends some distance from the colpus in a diffuse, indistinct manner, probably as a result of a gradual alteration in the thickness of nexine (A$_2$), or an os may have definite limits, usually in the shape of an elongate diamond, probably due to abrupt rather than gradual changes in nexine thickness (A$_3$). The second type of os, designated B, consists of a distinct pore lacking nexine. In *Hedyotis* subg. *Edrisia* this os is always surrounded by a thick nexinous margin or is crassimarginate (B$_1$) as shown by the transverse section through an os in Fig. 18. Elsewhere in the Rubiaceae, such ora are found with very thin margins or are tenuimarginate (B$_2$). They, in fact, appear emarginate under the light microscope. Apertures with a colpus and a simple os are called colporate while those with a compound os are colpororate (e.g., Fig. 18 in transverse section, A$_3$, B$_1$; Fig. 4: A$_3$, B$_1$; Fig. 13: A$_1$, B$_1$).

Group 1—Hedyotis arenaria (Rose) Lewis, *Lewis 5341*, Mexico. *H. asperuloides* Benth., *Lewis 5337* (Fig. 1–2), Mexico; *Lewis 5341*,

Mexico. *H. brevipes* (Rose) Lewis, *Palmer 202* (S), Mexico. *H. mucronata* Benth., *Johnston 3755* (S), Mexico. *H. peninsularis* (T. S. Brandg.) Lewis, *Purpus 427* (US), Mexico. *H. saxatalis* Lewis, *Moran 7300* (MO), Mexico.

Pollen grains small (19 × 20 μ–22.7 × 23.5 μ), usually oblate spheroidal, somewhat extended equatorially; 3-(4-)aperturate; colpi long (13.1–17.3 μ), narrow (1.2–1.5 μ), occasionally constricted at the equator, colpus length/polar axis 0.6–0.8; ora simple, 2.0–3.3 μ high, extended horizontally and fading ca. 2–3 μ on each side of colpus (A$_2$); apocolpium diameter 6.7–10.7 μ, diameter/colpus length 0.5–0.63; sexine 1.0–1.3 μ thick, ratio of sexine to widest radius 1:9–1:11, about twice as thick as nexine midway between equator and poles; reticulum fine, infrequently medium-fine.

A simple, type A, os is characteristic of the pollen for all species of this group. Although this os type is found elsewhere in the subgenus, it always occurs with the type B os. The pollen of this group is always small with a thin sexine having fine or medium-fine reticulations.

Group 2—Hedyotis acerosa Gray, *Wynd & Mueller 99* (S), Mexico. *H. croftiae* (Britt. & Rusby) Shinners, *Lewis & Morris 5046*, Texas. *H. drymarioides* (Standl.) Lewis, *Runyan & Sharp 4039* (US), Mexico. *H. greenmanii* Fosb., *Lewis & Morris 5042*, Texas. *H. humifusa* Gray, *Lewis & Jones 5576*, Texas. *H. intricata* Fosb., *Palmer 292* (S), Mexico. *H. longipes* (S. Wats.) Lewis, *Lewis 5751*, Mexico. *H. microtheca* (Schl. & Cham.) Steud., *Fröderström & Hultén 1185* (S), Mexico. *H. palmeri* Gray, *Wynd & Mueller 400* (S), Mexico. *H. polypremoides* (Gray) Shinners, *Lewis 5538*, Texas; *Lewis 5541* (Fig. 3–6), Texas. *H. rubra* (Cav.) Gray, *Lewis 5524* (Fig. 7), New Mexico. *H. subviscosa* (Wright ex Gray) Shinners, *Lewis & Oliver 5429*, Texas.

Pollen grains medium, infrequently small (21.8 × 20.9 μ to 41.4 × 40.7 μ), suboblate to subprolate, commonly oblate- or prolate-spheroidal, somewhat extended equatorially; 3-aperturate; colpi long (16–34 μ), ± narrow (1.3–4.2 μ), widest at equator, rarely at apices, colpus length/polar axis 0.69–0.95; ora compound combining types A$_3$ and B$_1$; type A$_1$, 4.7–9.3 μ high at colpus, type B$_1$, 2.7 μ high × 2 μ wide to 5.3 μ high × 4 μ wide, usually somewhat lolongate, margin 1.3–2.0 μ thick; apocolpium diameter 6.7–10.7 μ, diameter/colpus length 0.28–0.5; sexine 1.0–1.7 μ thick, usually 1.3 μ, ratio sexine width to widest radius 1:9–1:13, usually 1:11, 2–3 times as thick as nexine midway between equator and poles; reticulum fine, in *H. rubra* medium where lumina 2 μ wide and muri thickened; nexine 0.4–0.7 μ thick midway between equator and poles, decreasing toward poles.

An os combining types A$_3$ and B$_1$ is found for all species of this group, an oral morphology peculiar to these species. The A os is usually diamond-shaped and the B os is invariably

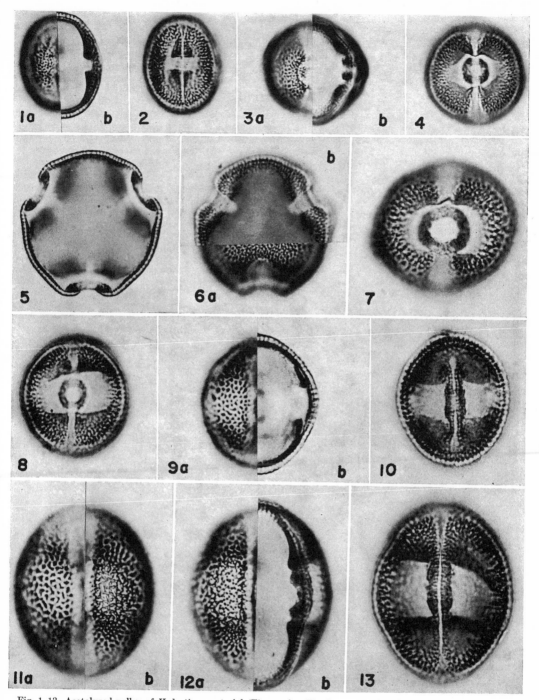

Fig. 1–13. Acetolyzed pollen of *Hedyotis*, equatorial (E) or polar (P) views, ×1500. Fig. 1–2. *H. asperuloides* (E), 1 cell.—Fig. 1a. Uppermost focus of sexine, OL-pattern, fine reticulum. 1b. Mid-longitudinal focus.—Fig. 2. Aperture, colporate, os A₂.—Fig. 3–6. *H. polypremoides* (E Fig. 3–4, 1 cell; P Fig. 5–6, 1 cell).—Fig. 3a. Uppermost focus of sexine, OL-pattern, fine reticulum. 3b. Mid-longitudinal focus.—Fig. 4. Aperture, colpororate, os A₃, B₁.—Fig. 5. Equatorial transverse focus showing 3 apertures, thin sexine.—Fig. 6a. Uppermost focus of sexine, OL-pattern, fine reticulum. 6b. Lower focus showing colpi ends and apocolpium.—Fig. 7. *H. rubra* (E), aperture, colpororate, os A₃, B₁.—Fig. 8. *H. wrightii* (E), aperture, colpororate, os A₁, B₁.—Fig. 9–10. *H. nigricans* var. *filifolia* (E), 1 cell.—Fig. 9a. Uppermost focus of sexine, OL-pattern, medium reticulum. 9b. Mid-longitudinal focus.—Fig. 10. Aperture, colpororate, A₁, B₁.—Fig. 11–13. *H. canadensis* (E), 1 cell.—Fig. 11a. Uppermost focus of sexine, OL-pattern, medium reticulum. 11b. Lower focus, LO-pattern.—Fig. 12a. Next lower focus of sexine showing broken muri, simplibaculate. 12b. Mid-longitudinal focus.—Fig. 13. Aperture, colpororate, os A₁, B₁.

crassimarginate. Apart from the aperture, pollen of these species differs from that of the foregoing group by its larger size and usually longer colpi. The pollen of the 2 groups have in common a relatively thin sexine which is, except for *H. rubra*, by and large finely reticulate.

Group 3—*Hedyotis nigricans* (Lam.) Fosb. var. *nigricans, Lewis 4992,* Texas; *Lewis 5536,* New Mexico. *H. nigricans* var. *filifolia* (Chapm.) Shinners, *Lewis 5677* (Fig. 8–9), Florida. *H. wrightii* (Gray) Fosb., *Oliver 190* (MO) (Fig. 10), Mexico; *Meyer & Rogers 2513* (MO), Mexico.

In general, the pollen of these 2 species resembles the description given for the pollen of group 2. A major variation is that the type A os is synclinorate (A_1) rather than being discontinuous (A_3). Of the species studied, only the 4 species composing group 4 also have compound ora with a type A_1 os. The type B_1 os of *H. wrightii* pollen is usually lalongate and similar in shape to that found for most species of group 2, but for *H. nigricans,* the os tends to be lolongate, thus more closely resembling the oral shape for those species of group 4. The pollen of *H. nigricans* and *H. wrightii* differs from the pollen of species in group 4 since their grains are always smaller (to $26.7 \times 24.3 \mu$) and spheroidal to prolate spheroidal with shorter colpi and more finely reticulated sexines. Although the pollen of these species is distinguishable from the pollen in groups 2 and 4,

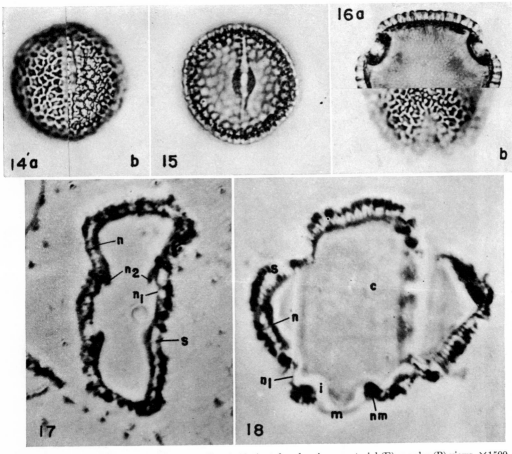

Fig. 14–18. Pollen of *Hedyotis* and *Pentas.*—Fig. 14–16. Acetolyzed grains, equatorial (E) or polar (P) views, ×1500.—Fig. 17–18. Ultra-thin sections using phase contrast, ×2000.—Fig. 14–15. *H. caerulea* (E), 1 cell.—Fig. 14a. Uppermost focus of sexine, OL-pattern, coarse reticulum. 14b. Lower focus of sexine, LO-pattern.—Fig. 15. Aperture, colporate, os B_1.—Fig. 16. *H. crassifolia* (P). a. Equatorial transverse focus showing 2 of 3 ora and thick sexine. b. Uppermost focus of sexine, coarse reticulum.—Fig. 17. *Pentas lanceolata* (Forsk.) Deflers subsp. *lanceolata* (*Lewis 5928,* Kenya) from acetolyzed herbarium material in longitudinal section illustrating nexine (n), thick nexine 2 defining the limits of the synclinorate os (n_2), very thin nexine of equatorial zone (n_1), sexine (s).—Fig. 18. *H. purpurea* (*Schallert 132,* North Carolina) from non-acetolyzed herbarium material in slightly oblique section at equator illustrating 1 aperture in cross section and cytoplasm (c), intine (i), nexine (n), crassimargin of os B_1 (nm), very thin nexine 1 defining limits of os A_3 (n_1), sexine (s), colpus membrane (m).

many basic characteristics are common to all groups and on this basis there is little doubt of their close palynological relationship.

Group 4—Hedyotis canadensis (Willd. ex R. & S.) Fosb., *Heimburger & Price* s.n. (MO) (Fig. 11–13), Canada. *H. longifolia* (Gaertn.) Hook. var. *longifolia, C & M Heimburger* s.n. (MO), Canada. *H. nuttalliana* Fosb., *Moldenke 19187* (S), Virginia. *H. purpurea* (L.) T. & G. var. *purpurea, Lewis 5620,* Texas. *H. purpurea* var. *calycosa* (Gray) Fosb., *Lewis 5634,* Mississippi.

Pollen grains medium (33.3 × 26.0μ–39.9 × 27.0μ), prolate or subprolate; 3-aperturate; colpi long (26.7–34.7μ), narrow (1.5–2.0μ), constricted at equator, colpus length/polar axis 0.7–0.88; ora compound combining types A$_1$ and B$_1$; A$_1$ os 8.0–10.7μ high at colpus, occasionally narrowing between colpi, B$_1$ os lolongate, 8.0 × 1.5μ to 3.0 × 2.0μ, crassimarginate (1.2μ [usually 2.0] thick); apocolpium diameter 7–12μ, diameter/colpus length 0.2–0.4; sexine 1.2–1.4μ thick, ratio of sexine width to widest radius 1:14–1:16, twice thickness of nexine midway between equator and poles; reticulum medium-fine or usually medium, lumina to 2μ wide; nexine averaging 0.7–0.8μ in thickness, decreasing toward poles.

A compound os with types A$_1$ and B$_1$ is common to the pollen of the 4 species included in this group. The synclinorate ora are very broad adjacent to the colpi and the crassimarginate ora are lolongate. As I have already noted, this aperture is found for the pollen of the preceding 2 species. The similarity of the aperture is further strengthened by the lolongate os of *H. nigricans* (Fig. 10) and *H. canadensis* (Fig. 13), a shape not found elsewhere. The pollen of group 4 can, however, be separated from the pollen of *H. nigricans* and *H. wrightii* by its larger size, prolate and subprolate shape, and by having long colpi constricted equatorially and medium reticulated sexines.

Group 5—Hedyotis australis Lewis & Moore, *Lewis 5552,* Texas. *H. caerulea* (L.) Hook. var. *caerulea, Lewis 5613,* Arkansas (Fig. 14–15); *Terrell 3663* (US), Connecticut; *Terrell & Barclay 3396* (US), Alabama. *H. crassifolia* Raf., *Lewis 5553* (Fig. 16), Texas. *H. michauxii* Fosb., *Schallert* s.n. (S), North Carolina. *H. procumbens* (Gmel.) Fosb., *Lewis 5136,* Mississippi; Biltmore Herbarium 3973d (US), Florida. *H. rosea* Raf., *Lewis 5555,* Texas.

Pollen grains medium, occasionally small (20 × 21.4μ), oblate spheroidal, extended equatorially; 3-aperturate, 4-aperturate in *H. rosea*; colpi long (16–25μ), ± narrow (3–4μ), widest at equator, length/polar axis 0.76–0.87; ora simple, type B$_1$, commonly lolongate, occasionally circular to lalongate, 2.0 × 1.7μ–4.0 × 2.7μ, crassimarginate (1–1.5μ thick); apocolpium diameter 6.7–13.3μ, diameter/colpus length 0.42–0.67; sexine thick (1.4–2.4μ), ratio of sexine width to widest radius 1:5–1:7 excepting *H. procumbens* (1:10.5), slightly

thicker at equator, 3–4 times as thick as nexine, excepting *H. procumbens* in which 2 layers are about equally thick; reticulum coarse, lumina to 4μ wide; nexine ± evenly thickened, rather thin (0.6–0.8μ) excepting *H. procumbens.*

A simple, type B$_1$, os is unique to the pollen of all species in group 5. In association with the absence of a type A os, the nexine is more or less evenly thickened throughout the equatorial region of the cell. Other distinguishing features of the pollen include a thick, coarsely reticulate sexine even when the pollen size is markedly decreased (as in *H. rosea,* which has the smallest grains in the subgenus). The pollen of *H. procumbens* is somewhat isolated from that of the other species by having in particular a thick nexine about equal in thickness to the sexine.

In this survey I have ignored pollen differences encountered among species having heterostyly, chromosomal races, or both. These are largely confined to minor variations in pollen size and in the sexine, which will be discussed in a future paper.

DISCUSSION—Based primarily on the morphology of the aperture, the species of *Hedyotis* subg. *Edrisia* can be placed in 5 groups with each group having a similar pollen morphology. The results can be compared with a phylogenetic scheme proposed largely on chromosomal, geographical, and gross morphological data (Lewis, 1962), a summary of which will introduce the discussion for each pollen group.

Group 1—Basic chromosome number $x = 13$ (known for 5 species); Baja California; ranked morphologically as most primitive. The species "are the least differentiated of those studied" and they "have remained closest to the primitive condition in the subgenus."

Among several aperture types found for the pollen of subg. *Edrisia,* the colporate pollen with a type A os of group 1 is structurally the most simple and unspecialized. Although this simple aperture is limited to these 6 species, *Hedyotis* s.l. and the Hedyotideae, in general, are known to have precisely the same oral type. Moreover in the subg. *Edrisia,* this aperture forms the basis in 3 of the 4 remaining groups of more complex apertures involving os B. It would appear, therefore, that the undifferentiated type A os exists as an anomaly in the subg. *Edrisia,* a remnant clearly associating it palynologically with more tropical allies while at the same time forming a basis for more specialized aperture conditions in the subgenus.

This conclusion is in complete agreement with the cytomorphological characteristics of this group of species. It further supports the conclusions of Fosberg (1941, 1954), Shinners (1949), and Lewis (1961) that the lack of discontinuity between the characters defining *Houstonia* (*Hedyotis* subg. *Edrisia*) and *Hedyotis* s.l. necessitates their merger.

The species of group 1 also have small to nearly medium-sized pollen grains with thin, finely reticulated sexines. These characteristics may be indicative of primitiveness.

Group 2—Basic chromosome number $x = 11$ (known for 9 species); upland Mexico and adjacent areas; ranked morphologically as intermediate. The species of this group "illustrate a more advanced morphology than do those of Baja California [group 1] . . . evolving into a highly endemic group of species."

Apertures for all 13 species included in group 2 are 3-colpororate combining a clearly defined, usually diamond-shaped lalongate os (A_1) with a $\pm$ circular, crassimarginate os (B_1). The type A os is similar to that found for species of group 1 except that the limits are more clearly defined, but the type B os is an additional aperture structure. This combination of oral types is obviously more specialized than is 1 alone, yet the compound os is the most common form in the subgenus. Its occurrence elsewhere in *Hedyotis* is infrequent; in fact, more species are known with this aperture form in the subg. *Edrisia* than in all other species of the tribe Hedyotideae combined (Lewis, 1965, and unpublished). It is probably no coincidence that most genera in the tribe are tropical in distribution and that most species of the subg. *Edrisia* are indigenous to subtropical or largely temperate regions. Under these circumstances I find it understandable that among a temperately successful group of species would be found a number of unique macro- and micro-morphological characters as a result of quite different selective forces at work during their evolution. The specialized aperture is probably an example of this.

Pollen of these species is otherwise similar to the pollen of group 1 except that for *H. rubra* the grains are larger and the sexine reticulations are more coarse.

Group 3—Basic chromosome numbers $x = 9(10)$, 11; widespread in southern U. S. and Mexico; ranked morphologically as intermediate. "Plants of *H. nigricans* with $n = 10$ are not easily distinguished from *H. wrightii* ($n = 11$) and it is not too speculative to suggest an origin from a taxon similar to *H. wrightii* by the loss of a chromosome pair. By additional loss the $n = 9$ individuals of *H. nigricans* . . . must have formed."

In that paper (Lewis, 1962), I placed *H. wrightii* with the species of group 2, while noting its similarity to *H. nigricans*. The pollen of the 2 species is alike and varies from that of group 2 by having synclinorate rather than dissected ora (A). Otherwise the pollen is very close and this supports the earlier conclusion of an affinity between the species of groups 2 and 3.

Group 4—Basic chromosome number $x = 6$; eastern North America; ranked morphologically as intermediate. "The relationship of those species in the $x = 6$ line with other groups in North America is not clear. It is difficult to suggest an origin from species with $x = 7$ [part of group 5] . . . " because, as I noted, the gross morphology of the latter is advanced in comparison with those species of group 4.

Palynologically there is a remarkable affinity between species of group 4 and those of groups 2 and 3, particularly with *H. nigricans*. This similarity is even more striking when it is realized that the colpororate aperture combining oral types A and B is almost unique to these 3 groups within the tribe. In addition to this specialized aperture, the groups share a gross morphology "intermediate" rank within the subgenus.

I hesitated suggesting such an association earlier chiefly because of the disparity in chromosome numbers between species of this group (based on 6) and of *H. nigricans* in group 3 (based on 9 and 10). This must be considered an example of chromosomal data leading to indecision. Following the study of pollen, however, I suggest that the *H. purpurea* group descended from a taxon not unlike *H. nigricans* following chromosomal loss from a complement of $x = 9$. It is quite conceivable that aneuploids with fewer chromosomes than $n = 9$ may yet be found for *H. nigricans*; the chromosomal survey for species in group 4 has been more thorough (Lewis and Terrell, 1962), and I doubt that a numerical bridge now exists among taxa of this group. On the other hand, hypoaneuploidy from an $n = 9$ stock might have given rise to unsuccessful lines which were eliminated, but which eventually gave rise to a taxon with $n = 6$ having a stable and advantageous genotype.

The distinguishing palynological features of this group are their consistently large, prolate or subprolate grains with medium reticulated sexines.

Group 5—Basic chromosome numbers $x = 7$ and 8; eastern North America; ranked morphologically as advanced. Species of this group are the most advanced in the subgenus with those in the 2 chromosomal lines closely related (Lewis, 1962).

The aperture structure for species grouped in these lines is identical, viz., colporate with only type B_1 os. The apertures are, therefore, structurally simpler than those of the preceding 3 groups, not a simplification based on the undifferentiated os (A) of species in group 1 and *Hedyotis* in general, but rather of an os (B) which is found in the specialized apertures of groups 2, 3, and 4, and rarely in *Hedyotis*. It would appear that the os A has been lost in the evolution of these species to give rise to a reduced aperture condition which, in this subgenus, is the terminilization of advancement. Accompanying this, the equatorial, irregularly thickened nexine has become $\pm$ even in thickness. A second aperture character is also noteworthy. A 3-aperture grain is almost universal in the subgenus; only *H. rosea* of group 5 is consistently 4-aperturate.

This suggests that a 3-aperturate condition is basic for the taxon while 4 apertures are a more specialized and thus a more advanced expression. Stern (1962a, b) also noted a similar but more striking trend of increased aperture number among the more specialized subgenera of *Dicentra*.

Apart from the aperture, pollen of these species is uniquely thick-walled and coarsely reticulate. These apparently specialized pollen characteristics are not known for the other groups, although the trend to medium reticulated sexines is found in species of groups 2 and 4. Finally, the smallest pollen grains in the subgenus are found in this group and this feature may also represent an advanced trend paralleling the reductional modifications known for the aperture.

These data are in complete agreement with those from cytomorphology in which I suggested an origin of this group from a reduction in chromosome number from $x = 9$. The species were found to have a high index of advancement of which the loss of long-styled flowers, the predominantly annual habit, and the reduced stems (to less than 1 dm) were among the more important diagnostic criteria. A parallel reduction involving some of the same playnological and gross morphological characteristics has also been described for the related African genus *Kohautia* (Lewis, 1965).

The several phyletic trends noted for the pollen in the subg. *Edrisia* may be summarized as follows. (1) Apertures with simple ora having horizontal extensions due to nexinous thinnings (type A, group 1) are primitive to the more specialized apertures combining type A with the crassimarginate os type B (groups 2, 3, 4). (2) The most advanced aperture lacks type A os and is represented solely by type B os without nexinous

thinnings (group 5). (3) A 3-aperturate condition is primitive to the more specialized 4-aperturate form (1 species, group 5). (4) A rather thin sexine is primitive to a very thick sexine (group 5). (5) A fine though distinctly reticulated sexine having small lumina and narrow muri is primitive to a coarsely reticulated sexine having wide lumina and muri (group 5). (6) Medium-small grains are primitive to rather large grains (group 4) or to very small grains (*H. rosea*, group 5). This 2-directional modification in cell size parallels a change in chromosome size, viz., to large chromosomes (group 4) and to very small chromosomes (*H. rosea*, group 5). (7) Grains ± spheroidal in shape are primitive to those with extremes in shape, i.e., to prolate (group 4) and possibly to oblate (not known).

For all species or groups of species these modifications and trends in pollen structure parallel definite alterations in the gross morphology of the sporophyte and in chromosome number and size. It has been possible in several instances to more clearly illustrate relationships between major groups of species by using the characteristics of the pollen—relationships which otherwise remained obscure. By synthesizing the results from palynology with those from other disciplines (Lewis, 1962), a hypothetical phylogeny for *Hedyotis* subg. *Edrisia*, including all groups, is proposed and summarized in Fig. 19.

Conclusions regarding the probable evolution of pollen characteristics apply only to the pollen of subg. *Edrisia*. Similar trends equally correlating gross morphological specialization and reduction and chromosomal change with pollen modifications have, however, been found for several related genera in Africa (Lewis, 1965). How significant, even in the Rubiaceae, these supposed phyletic trends in pollen are as indicators of the degree or level of advancement attained by any taxon is not yet known beyond *Hedyotis* and its allies.

LITERATURE CITED

ERDTMAN, G. 1952. Pollen morphology and plant taxonomy. Angiosperms. Almqvist and Wiksell, Stockholm.

——. 1960. The acetolysis method. A revised description. Svensk. Bot. Tidskr. 54: 561–564.

FOSBERG, F. R. 1941. Observations on Virginia plants, part I. Va. Jour. Sci. 2: 106–111.

——. 1954. Notes on plants of the eastern United States. Castanea 19: 25–37.

HEDBERG, O. 1947. Pollen morphology in the genus *Polygonum* L. s. lat. and its taxonomic significance. Svensk. Bot. Tidskr. 40: 371–404.

LEWIS, W. H. 1961. Merger of the North American *Houstonia* and *Oldenlandia* under *Hedyotis* (Rubiaceae). Rhodora 63: 216–223.

——. 1962. Phylogenetic study of *Hedyotis* (Rubiaceae) in North America. Amer. Jour. Bot. 49: 855–865.

——. 1965. Cytopalynological study of African

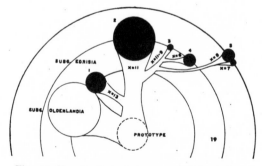

Fig. 19. Hypothetical phylogeny of *Hedyotis* in the Americas from a prototype giving rise to the largely tropical subg. *Oldenlandia* and to 5, chiefly temperate, groups of subg. *Edrisia* at 3 "levels of advancement." Group 1 is palynologically closely allied to subg. *Oldenlandia*, groups 2–4 are more specialized palynologically and similar, and group 5 is considered the most advanced, often with reduced pollen features. The smallest circles represent 2 extant species, others to scale; overlapping circles indicate groups with very similar pollen.

Hedyotideae (Rubiaceae). Ann. Mo. Bot. Gard. (in press).

———, AND E. E. TERRELL. 1962. Chromosomal races in eastern North American species of *Hedyotis* (*Houstonia*). Rhodora 64: 313–323.

PRAGLOWSKI, J. R. 1957. On the cutting of ultra-thin sections, p. 135–147. *In* G. Erdtman, [ed.], Pollen and spore morphology/plant taxonomy: Gymnospermae, Pteridophyta, Bryophyta. Almqvist and Wiksell, Stockholm.

SHINNERS, L. H. 1949. Transfer of Texas species of *Houstonia* to *Hedyotis* (Rubiaceae). Field and Lab. 17: 166–169.

STERN, K. R. 1962a. The use of pollen morphology in the taxonomy of *Dicentra*. Amer. Jour. Bot. 49: 362–368.

———. 1962b. Phylogenetic trends in the pollen morphology of *Dicentra*. (Abstr.) Amer. Jour. Bot. 49 (pt. 2): 679.

WAGENITZ, G. 1955. Pollen Morphologie und Systematik in der Gattung *Centauria* L. s.l. Flora 142: 15–279.

POLLEN WALL ULTRASTRUCTURE AND ITS BEARING ON THE SYSTEMATIC POSITION OF BLENNOSPERMA AND CROCIDIUM (COMPOSITAE)[1]

JOHN J. SKVARLA[2] AND B. L. TURNER

Cell Research Institute and Department of Botany, The University of Texas, Austin

ABSTRACT

Electron microscopy is used to help resolve the question of the taxonomic relationships of the genera *Blennosperma* and *Crocidium*. Ultrastructural features of their pollen walls indicate that these taxa, long placed in the tribes Helenieae and Senecioneae, respectively, are closely related and that their tribal affinities are with the Senecioneae. Additional ultrastructural observations are made for 40 or more species in the Helenieae and Senecioneae. Three major pollen wall types can be recognized: Anthemoid, Helianthoid and Senecioid. The distribution and significance of these pollen types among the Astereae, Heliantheae, Helenieae, Anthemideae and Senecioneae are discussed.

IN A RECENT electron-microscopic survey of pollen wall morphology in the tribes Heliantheae and Anthemideae (Skvarla, 1965), each tribe was characterized as having distinctive internal pollen wall features. This work has now been expanded to include genera of the tribes Inuleae, Cichorieae, Mutisieae, Astereae, Senecioneae and Helenieae. The present report, representing a portion of the study of the Helenieae and Senecioneae, consists of a comparison of the pollen of *Blennosperma* and *Crocidium*, particularly as this might relate to their phyletic position.

While the similarities of the pollen morphology of species from different tribes in the Compositae have been previously demonstrated (Stix, 1960; Skvarla, 1965), the present study emphasizes the utility of the electron microscope for the detection of structural characters which cannot be resolved readily, if at all, by conventional light microscopy.

MATERIAL AND METHODS—Pollen samples of *Blennosperma nanum, B. bakeri, B. chilense*, and *Crocidium multicaule* were obtained from herbarium sheets at the University of Texas and from the University of California (Table 2). The electron-microscopic techniques used in this study have been described in detail elsewhere (Skvarla, 1965) and are only briefly outlined here. The steps in the procedure consisted of: (1) soaking of mature inflorescences in 70% alcohol, (2) acetolyzing (3), staining with sodium cacodylate-buffered OsO_4, (4) incorporating in

[1] Received for publication July 22, 1965.
Supported in part from grant funds NIH–GMO7289 to the senior author and NSF GB–1216 to the junior author. They thank Dr. Robert Ornduff for providing some of the plant materials and for valuable assistance with the manuscript.
[2] Present address: Department of Botany and Microbiology, University of Oklahoma, Norman 73069.

Reprinted by permission of the authors and the publisher from the AMERICAN JOURNAL OF BOTANY, 53, 555–563 (1966).

agar pellets, (5) dehydrating in a graded ethyl alcohol series and embedding in Araldite-Epon resins, (6) sectioning at $1/40\,\mu$ with diamond knives, and (7) examining with RCA electron microscope models EMU 3–F and 3–D.

Additionally, some samples were prepared by a modified dehydration and embedding technique which considerably shortened preparation time (Skvarla, in preparation).

For light-microscopic observations of whole pollen grains, a portion of the acetolyzed pollen (step 2 above) was mounted directly on glass microscope slides containing glycerin jelly; coverslips were affixed and sealed with ZUT slide ringing compound.[3] Measurements and observations were made with an AO Spencer Phasestar microscope. Photomicrographs were made using a Leitz Ortholux microscope and Kodak High Contrast Copy Film.

Light-microscopic observations were also made on "thick sections" $(1\,\mu)$ adjacent to the $1/40\,\mu$ cuts used for electron-microscopic study. Photomicrographs were made using a Zeiss Phase Contrast microscope and Kodak M Plates.

BLENNOSPERMA AND CROCIDIUM COMPARED— Under the light microscope whole pollen grains of *Blennosperma* (Fig. 1, 2) and *Crocidium* (Fig. 6, 7) have the following characteristics: triangular in polar view, tricolporate with numerous spines (average length $2.1\,\mu$ for *B. nanum* and $3.4\,\mu$ for *C. multicaule*), and barely perceptible cavea (bladders). Maximum diameters (in median optical sections) of *B. nanum* and *C. multicaule* range from $20–21\,\mu$ and $22–25\,\mu$ respectively.

In addition to whole mounts of pollen, $1\,\mu$ sections were examined with phase-contrast microscopy. Comparison of Fig. 3 with 8 indicates the morphological similarities between the two species. One μ sections permit increased resolution of structural details, as well as stain differentiation of exine units at the germ pore margins.

Exines of *Blennosperma* and *Crocidium* viewed with the electron microscope demonstrate the presence of two distinct wall layers which, as described previously for the Compositae (Skvarla, 1965), can be recognized as endexine (inner, one-unit layer) and ektexine (outer, three-unit layer: Faegri, 1956). The endexine in the areas between the germ pores (i.e., interapertural areas) is

[3] Bennett's Paint Products, Salt Lake City, Utah.

sporadically lamellate and commonly highly disrupted on the inner surface (Fig. 4, 5, 9, 10A). At the germ pore margins the endexine is increased in thickness and is conspicuously lamellate. The foot layer of the ektexine (which lies directly above the endexine) is quite variable in thickness. Generally, portions of the foot layer directly under the spines are dome-shaped and almost equal in thickness to the immediately appressed endexine (Fig. 4, 5, 9, 10). Away from the spine areas the foot layer decreases in thickness, becoming appreciably thinner than the juxtaposed endexine. As a rule, the foot layer in *Blennosperma* is slightly thicker than that in *Crocidium*.

The disrupted inner surface of the endexine creates difficulties in estimating endexine–foot layer thicknesses. In both *Blennosperma* and *Crocidium* the foot layer is approximately ⅓ the thickness of the endexine (except under the spines, where they are nearly equal). The foot layer in interspinal regions may occasionally appear to equal or exceed the thickness of the endexine (Fig. 4, 9); however, from a large number of different sectional views, the inner surface of the endexine is nearly always seen to be disrupted, and a reconstructed projection would show an endexine considerably thicker than the foot layer (see Fig. 10A).

Cavea (areas of separation between columellae and foot layer units of the ektexine, as described by Skvarla, 1965) are well developed and of equal proportions in both taxa. Columellae are solid, single units, usually conjunctate-digitate in form. *Crocidium* possesses somewhat more completely fused basal regions than those found in *Blennosperma*. In both taxa the thin tectum, which is formed from the outer extremities of the columellae, is highly perforate. The spines, which are also part of the tectum, are short and bluntly rounded protuberances characterized by a single channel located near the base of each.

In summary, it is apparent from the electron-microscopic observations that the pollen of *Blennosperma* and *Crocidium* are nearly identical. It can be seen from Fig. 1–10 that the resolution afforded by optical microscopy is inadequate for critical comparison of the pollen characters within these genera. On the other hand, the electron micrographs (Fig. 4, 5, 9, 10) permit not only a detailed comparison of structure, but quantification as well (e.g., endexine–foot layer relationships

---

Fig. 1–5. *Blennosperma nanum.*—Fig. 1. Photomicrograph of median-optical view. Note that cavea and columellae are barely recognizable, × 3,000.—Fig. 2. Photomicrograph of pollen grain surface showing germinal aperture, × 2,000.—Fig. 3. Phase-contrast photomicrograph of 1 μ sectioned exine. Note improvement over Fig. 1 in that cavea, columellae, and spines are readily distinguishable, × 3,000.—Fig. 4. Low-magnification electron micrograph of oblique-median section. The foot layer is domed and thickened under spine areas; the endexine is conspicuously disrupted (unlabeled arrows), × 6,150.—Fig. 4A. Electron micrograph of tangential view illustrating complexity of columellae and highly variable thickness of the foot layer (arrows denote interspinal areas), × 6,150.—Fig. 5. Enlarged view of area enclosed by brackets in lower left corner of Fig. 4. Note conjunctate columellae and domed foot layers (extreme right and left margins), × 54,000. (See key to labeling, p. 557.)

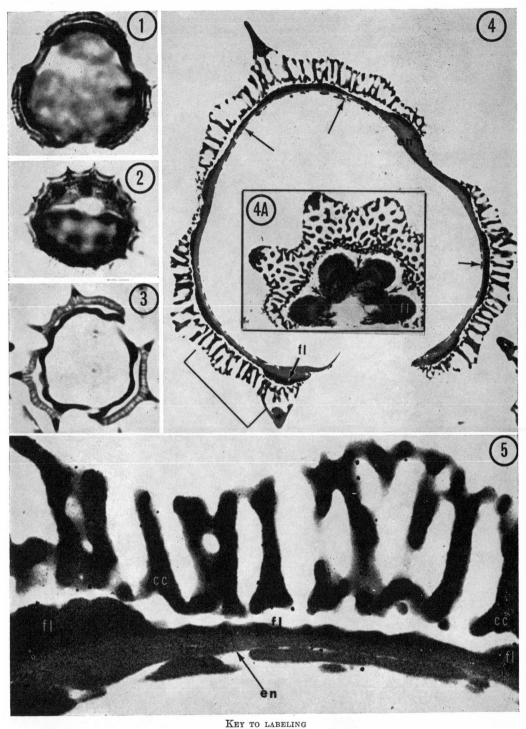

KEY TO LABELING

fl —foot layer
en —endexine
cav—cavea

f —internal foramina
la—lamellations
cc—conjunctate columellae

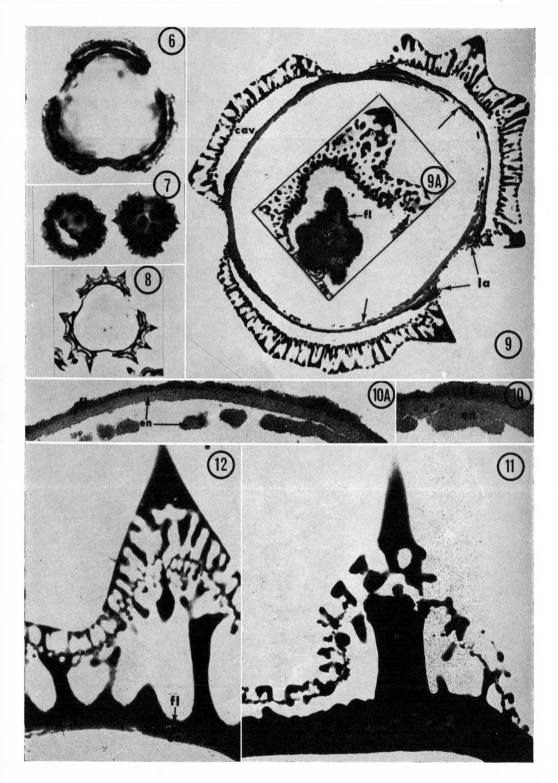

as discussed above). The advantage of electron-microscopy over light microscopy in interpreting pollen wall structure in these genera concurs with observations made in studies in the Heliantheae and Anthemideae (Skvarla, 1965).

TRIBAL COMPARISONS—In order to obtain a better insight into the tribal relationships in the Compositae, Skvarla (1965) examined the ultrastructure of pollen walls of representative species of the Anthemideae, Astereae, and Heliantheae. The present study extends these ultrastructural comparisons to the tribes Helenieae and Senecioneae (Table 1, 2). Together, these studies have revealed pollen wall morphologies representing three major types: Helianthoid, Anthemoid and Senecioid (unfortunately the authors have been unable to equate these pollen types with those proposed by Stix, 1960). This terminology is adopted for convenience only. However, it does reflect the characteristic pollen types found in the majority of taxa in the tribes concerned.

The Helianthoid type (Fig. 13), characteristic of the Astereae and Heliantheae, is distinguished mainly by the presence of numerous internal foramina and a thin, uniform endexine; the Anthemoid type (Fig. 12), confined to the Anthemideae except for the species noted in Table 1 and 2, is distinguished by a complex ektexine, lack of internal foramina and cavea, and possession of a thickened endexine; the Senecioid type (Fig. 15), characteristic of the Senecioneae and subtribe Ambrosiinae of the Heliantheae, is distinguished by its lack of an internal foramina, possession of a thickened foot layer and usually disrupted inner endexine. (The Helenieae are excluded from the comparisons indicated since nearly all workers agree that it is a polyphyletic group; in addition, no new pollen types have emerged from our survey of this tribe.)

As indicated, the variability of pollen morphology in the Senecioneae is evidenced by the occurrence of Senecioid (Fig. 9, 15), Helianthoid (Fig. 14), and Anthemoid (Fig. 11) pollen types (see Table 2). There may even be more than one pollen type within a genus; for example, in *Senecio* both Helianthoid and Senecioid pollen types can be found (Fig. 14, 15). It should be

noted that a major character used to distinguish between the Senecioid and Helianthoid types is the presence or absence of internal foramina. This morphological feature also has proved to be useful in the recognition of the Ambrosiinae (Skvarla, 1965).

In summary of the tribes examined, three major pollen types can be recognized at the ultrastructural level: Helianthoid, Anthemoid, and Senecioid. *Blennosperma* and *Crocidium* possess Senecioid-type pollen and, as will be indicated below, are perhaps best treated together as members of the tribe Senecioneae.

DISCUSSION[4]—*Blennosperma*, with three annual species, and the monotypic genus *Crocidium* are taxonomically isolated genera with dubious affinities (Ornduff, 1963; 1964). *Blennosperma*, in particular, has been shifted from tribe to tribe while *Crocidium*, since first described by Hooker in 1834, has had an unaltered, if not respectable, position in the Senecioneae.

Blennosperma was first described as a member of the tribe Anthemideae by Lessing in 1832; it was subsequently placed by DeCandolle (1838) in the Heliantheae (which he treated as but a subdivision of the much larger tribe Senecioneae); Gray (1884) assigned the genus to the Helenieae with considerable hesitation, for he "keyed" *Blennosperma* with genera of the Heliantheae (subtribe Millerinae) and commented (p. 60) that *Blennosperma* "perhaps belongs here rather than to the Heleniodeae where it has no near relatives; perhaps it should stand next to *Crocidium* . . . ."

In spite of Gray's apt suggestion, subsequent highly competent synantherologists such as Bentham (1876) and Hoffman (1884) followed the tribal dispositions accorded these genera by Gray, and recent, mostly floristic, workers such as Rydberg (1914; 1927), Keck (1959) and Ferris

[4] It is desirable to report that *Blennosperma* and *Crocidium* were not singled out for intensive investigation; rather, the senior author, while making a routine survey of genera belonging to the tribes Helenieae and Senecioneae, was struck with the strong resemblance of the ultrastructure of their pollen walls. He became aware of the systematic implications of his findings only after consultation with the junior author.

Fig. 6–12. *Crocidium multicaule.*—Fig. 6. Photomicrograph of median-optical view, × 3,000.—Fig. 7. Photomicrograph showing triangular outline in near polar view (at right) and oblique view of furrow (at left), × 1,000.—Fig. 8. Phase-contrast photomicrograph of 1 μ sectioned exine, × 1,300.—Fig. 9. Low-magnification electron micrograph of oblique-median section. Note disrupted endexine (unlabeled arrows); note also that foot layer–endexine ratio is slightly less than in *Blennosperma*, × 6,500.—Fig. 9A. Tangential view. Note similarities to Fig. 4A, × 6,100.—Fig. 10 and 10A. Electron micrographs showing foot layer–endexine relationships. In Fig. 10, an area beneath a spine, the foot layer is domed and approximately ½ the endexine thickness. In 10A, an interspinal area, the disruptions of the inner portions of the endexine (vertical arrow) give an initial impression of an endexine–foot layer ratio of 1:1; however, when the disrupted endexine segments are taken into account (horizontal arrow), it becomes apparent that the true ratio of foot layer to endexine is approximately 1:3. Fig. 10, 10A, × 30,000.—Fig. 11. *Sinclairia hypoleuca.* Electron micrograph demonstrating Anthemideae-like pollen wall morphology of some species in the Senecioneae. Note extremely thick endexine and columella, ×8,200.—Fig. 12. *Aaronsohnia factorovskyi.* Electron micrograph of typical exine of tribe Anthemideae. The endexine–foot layer ratios are equal and the columellae of the ektexine are complexly ramified, × 14,000. (See key to labeling, p.557.)

TABLE 1. *Species of Helenieae examined by electron microscopy*

Species	Voucher	Pollen type
Amblyopappus pusillus H. and A.	TEX 156749	Senecioid[a]
Bahia nudicaulis Gray	TEX 208730	Helianthoid
Cacosmia rugosa H. B. K.	TEX 198115	Anthemoid-like[b]
Espejoa mexicana DC.	TEX 187896	Helianthoid
Hulsea carnosa Rydb.	TEX 158534	Helianthoid
Hymenopappus newberryii (Gray) Johnston	TEX 158685	Helianthoid
Jaumea peduncularis (H. and A.) Oliv. & Hier.	TEX 228726	Helianthoid
Lasthenia chrysostoma (F. and M.) Greene	TEX 216165	Helianthoid
L. coronaria (Nutt.) Ornduff	TEX 216168	Helianthoid
L. glabrata Lindl.	TEX 216167	Helianthoid
L. minor (DC) Ornduff subsp. *minor*	TEX 156759	Helianthoid
Monolopia lanceolata Nutt.	TEX 182080	Helianthoid
Palafoxia hookeriana T. and G.	TEX 158910	Helianthoid
Pericome caudata Gray	TEX 223243	Helianthoid
Psilostrophe villosa Rydb.	TEX 107574	Helianthoid
Sartwellia mexicana Gray	TEX 189328	Helianthoid
Venegasia carpesioides DC.	TEX 182717	Helianthoid

[a] Perhaps best placed in Senecioneae (Skvarla and Turner, unpubl.).
[b] Perhaps best placed in the subtribe Liabinae of Senecioneae (Turner, unpubl.).

TABLE 2. *Species of Senecioneae examined by electron microscopy*

Species	Voucher	Pollen type
Bartlettia scaposa Gray	TEX 193198	Helianthoid
Blennosperma bakeri Roderick	UC —	Senecioid
B. chilense Less.	UC 169808	Senecioid
B. nanum (Hook.) Blake	TEX 199783	Senecioid
Crocidium multicaule Hook.	TEX 160646	Senecioid
Emilia coccinea (Sims) Sweet	TEX 211081	Senecioid
Euryops tenuissimus Less.	TEX 109166	Senecioid
Gynoxys parvifolia Cuatr.	TEX 231020	Helianthoid
Gynura pseudochina (L.) DC.	TEX 227124	Senecioid
Haploesthes greggii Gray	TEX 172745	Helianthoid
Liabum klattii Rob. and Greenm.	TEX 177296	Anthemoid-like
L. caducifolium Rob. and Bartl.	TEX 228763	Anthemoid-like
Petasites hyperboreus Rydb.	TEX 160578	Senecioid
Peucephyllum schottii Gray	TEX 160591	Senecioid
Psathyrotes annua (Nutt.) Gray	TEX 160594	Helianthoid
Schistocarpha bicolor Less.	TEX 189585	Helianthoid
S. platyphylla Greenm.	TEX 185546	Helianthoid
S. sinforosi Cuat.	TEX 231030	Helianthoid
Senecio ampullaceus Hook.	TEX 233053	Senecioid
S. coymolachensis Cabrera	TEX 231037	Senecioid
S. glabellus Poir.	TEX 160901	Helianthoid
S. loeseneri Hieron.	TEX 231038	Senecioid
S. riddellii T. and G.	TEX 195408	Senecioid
S. verticillatus Klatt	TEX 231005	Senecioid
Sinclairia hypoleuca (Greenm.) Rydb.	TEX 207164	Anthemoid-like
Werneria stuebelii Hieron.	TEX 231011	Senecioid

(1960) have been content to maintain the status quo, although Rydberg did erect the monotypic subtribe Blennospermatanae to accommodate *Blennosperma*, presumably in recognition of what was thought to be its isolated position in the Helenieae. Ornduff (1964) commented that "many characters of the genus are somewhat anomalous in Helenieae," but concluded that "its correct tribal placement awaits further study." In-terestingly enough, Ornduff commented on the peculiar superficial papillae of the achenes of *Blennosperma* which "break open and omit pairs of tenuous filaments which imbibe water . . ." much in the manner of *Crocidium*, a feature which Gray (1884; p. 80) also noted in *Crocidium*, which has ". . . hyaline oblong papillae which detaching when wetted, throw out a pair of spiral threads in the manner of *Senecio*."

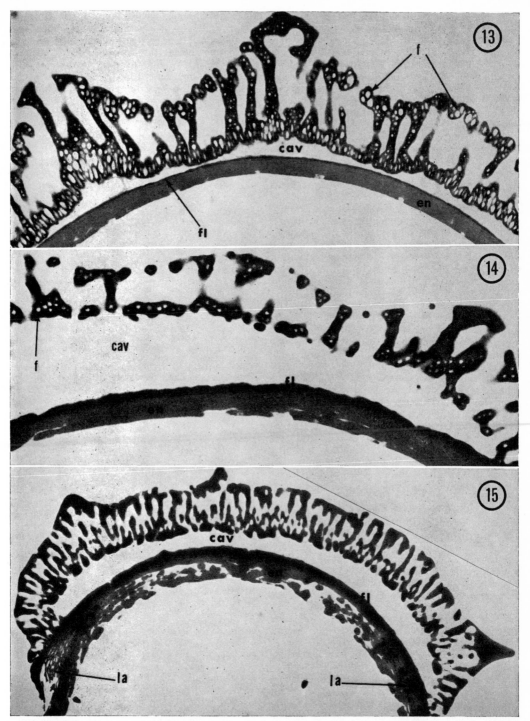

Fig. 13–15. *Hemizonia corymbosa*. Electron micrograph of exine typical of Heliantheae. Internal foramina are common in columellae and the foot layer is thin in relation to the endexine, × 14,400.—Fig. 14. Electron micrograph of *Senecio glabellus* exine. In comparison to Fig. 13 note that columellae are shorter and foot layer is thicker, × 19,200.—Fig. 15. *Senecio loeseneri*. Compare with Fig. 14. Note lack of internal foramina in columellae and highly disrupted endexine comparable to endexines of *Blennosperma* and *Crocidium*, × 8,500. (See key to labeling, p. 557.)

As noted above, *Crocidium* has never been removed from the Senecioneae, but Bentham (1876) in the *Genera Plantarum* reflected uncertainty over its phyletic position by placing a question mark after the generic name, and by his comments to the effect that *Crocidium* is a distinctive genus with doubtful affinities, possessing the habit of Baeriae (Helenieae), style of Astereae, and involucre and pappus of the Senecioneae Oddly enough, he positioned *Blennosperma* in the Helenieae between *Closia* (= *Perityle*) and *Villanova* without question or comment.[5] Ornduff et al. (1963) would also exclude *Crocidium* from Senecioneae for, while not assigning an extratribal position, they concluded that it "surely belongs elsewhere . . . ."

The above encapsulated account largely summarizes the differing taxonomic treatments accorded *Blennosperma* and *Crocidium*. The junior author became interested in the problem through his attempt to make tribal redispositions of several generic groups which reside in the obviously polyphyletic Helenieae. Most of the 14 subtribes recognized for the Helenieae by Rydberg (1914) can be assigned to either the tribes Heliantheae or Senecioneae (Turner, unpubl.), the subtribe Blennospermatanae, as obvious from the above account, being one of the most questionable groups. Because *Blennosperma* has the superficial habit of a number of annual taxa belonging ·to the Anthemideae (e.g., *Anthemis*) of the Mediterranean regions of Europe, and because of its somewhat similar ecological niche in the western U.S., the relationship of the genus was initially sought in that tribe. (It might be added th 1t *B. nanum* was originally described as a questionable species of *Chrysanthemum*.) In fact, without the pollen data presented here, the junior author would perhaps have been content to relegate Blennospermatanae to the Anthemideae without further ado.

Quite apart from the evidence presented above, it seems likely that *Blennosperma* and *Crocidium* are sufficiently similar in other ways to be treated as members of the same tribe, if not subtribe. We have made detailed morphological comparisons and note a striking similarity in their floral structures; e.g., similar vascularization in their involucral bracts and hemispheric receptacles, similar ray flowers, styles and achenes, to say nothing of the remarkable papillae of their achenes, noted by both Gray (1884) and Ornduff (1964) (see above account). Perhaps one reason that most taxonomists have failed to note these similarities is that in *Blennosperma* the disk flowers are staminate and do not form achenes,

[5] Bentham treated a number of obviously closely related composite genera in this fashion; e.g., placing *Hymenopappus* and the congeneric *Leucampyx* in the Helenieae and Anthemideae, respectively (Turner, 1956); and *Galinsoga* and the congeneric *Stemmatella* in the subtribes Galinsoginae and Verbesininae, respectively (Turner, unpubl.).

their style branches being quite fused. However, the ray florets of the two genera, both style branches and achenes, are similar, the principal distinction being that *Blennosperma* possesses sessile ligules while those of *Crocidium* arise from a well-developed tube.

Both genera possess base chromosome numbers of nine: *Blennosperma* with $n = 9$, 7, and 16 (Ornduff, 1964)[6]; and *Crocidium* with $n = 9$ (Ornduff et al., 1963). Finally we have also examined their flavonoid patterns by two-dimensional paper chromatography and can report that, while they differ in several spots, they appear to contain the same general class of compounds (probably isoflavones).

[6] Ornduff (1963) has suggested that the only South American species of the genus, *B. chilense* with $n = 16$, had an amphiploid origin from the two North American species, *B. bakeri* ($n = 7$) and *B. nanum* ($n = 9$). While such an hypothesis is attractive on numerical grounds, it appears equally likely that *B. chilense* is a tetraploid on a base of $x = 8$, having been derived from an extinct or as yet undetected race or races of *B. chilense* with $n = 8$. Unfortunately the flavonoid chromatography of the several taxa is essentially alike so that the hypothetical amphiploid origin of the species could not be tested by this approach. However, in our opinion, the floral morphology of *B. chilense*, which is hardly an intermediate *B. bakeri* $\times$ *B. nanum*, as well as its extra-continental distribution, makes the likelihood of the production, from at least recent hybridization, between these taxa remote indeed. After all, if *B. bakeri* possesses seven chromosome pairs then most likely there was, at one time or another, a taxon with $n = 8$.

LITERATURE CITED

BENTHAM, G. 1876. Compositae. *In* G. Bentham and J. D. Hooker, Genera plantarum . . .2: 163–533.

DECANDOLLE, A. P. 1838. Compositae (part). *In* Prodromus systematis naturalis . . . 7: 1–801.

FAEGRI, K. 1956. Recent trends in palynology. Bot. Rev. 22: 639–664.

FERRIS, R. S. 1960. Compositae, Vol. 4, p. 98–613. *In* L. Abrams and R. S. Ferris [ed.], Illus. Flora Pacific States. Stanford Univ. Press.

GRAY, A. 1884. Compositae. *In* Synop. Flora N. Amer. 1, pt. 2: 1–474.

HOFFMAN, O. 1884. Compositae, p. 87–391. *In* A. Engler and K. Prantl [ed.], Die natürlichen Pflanzenfamilien IV (5).

HOOKER, W. J. 1834. Flora Bor. Amer. 1: 335.

KECK, D. D. 1959. *Blennosperma*, p. 1158–1159. *In* P. A. Munz [ed.], A California flora. Univ. California Press, Berkeley.

LESSING. C. F. 1832. Synopsis generum Compositarum . . . Dumker and Humblot, Berlin.

ORNDUFF, R. 1963. Experimental studies in two genera of Helenieae (Compositae): *Blennosperma* and *Lasthenia*. Quart. Rev. Biol. 38: 141–150.

———. 1964. Biosystematics of *Blennosperma* (Compositae). Brittonia 16: 289–295.

———, P. H. RAVEN, D. W. KYHOS, AND A. R. KRUCKEBERG. 1963. Chromosome numbers in Compositae. III. Senecioneae. Amer. J. Bot. 50: 131–139.

RYDBERG, P. A. 1914. Helenieae (part). N. Amer. Flora 34: 1–75.

———. 1927. Senecioneae (part). N. Amer. Flora 34: 309–360.

SKVARLA, J. 1965. An electron microscopic study of pollen morphology in the Compositae with special reference to Ambrosiinae. Ph. D. dissertation, the University of Texas.

STIX, E. 1960. Pollenmorphologische untersuchungen an Compositen. Grana Palynol. 2: 41–114.

TURNER, B. L. 1956. A cytotaxonomic study of the genus *Hymenopappus* (Compositae). Rhodora 58: 163–186.

SECTION II

Cytology, Embryology, and Genetics

McKelvey, S. D., and K. Sax. 1933. Taxonomic and cytological relationships of *Yucca* and *Agave*. J. Arnold Arboretum **14**: 76–81.

Di Fulvio, T. E., and M. S. Cave. 1965. Embryology of *Blandfordia nobilis* Smith (Liliaceae), with special reference to its taxonomic position. Phytomoph. **14**: 487–499.

Ownbey, M. 1950. Natural hybridization and amphiploidy in the genus *Tragopogon*. Amer. J. Bot. **37**: 487–499.

Wagner, W. H., Jr. 1954. Reticulate evolution in the Appalachian Aspleniums. Evolution **8**: 103–118.

Thompson, H. J. 1960. A genetic approach to the taxonomy of *Mentzelia lindleyi* and *M. crocea* (Loasaceae). Brittonia **12**: 81–93.

Kyhos, D. W. 1965. The independent aneuploid origin of two species of *Chaenactis* (Compositae) from a common ancestor. Evolution **19**: 26–43.

Ball, P. W., and V. H. Heywood. 1962. The taxonomic separation of the cytological races of *Kohlrauschia prolifera* (L.) Kunth sensu lato. Watsonia **5**: 113–116.

Rollins, R. C. 1958. The genetic evaluation of a taxonomic character in *Dithyrea* (Cruciferae). Rhodora **60**: 145–152.

The papers in this section deal with problems of interpreting variation patterns or with obtaining information for use in making taxonomic or phylogenetic judgments. The tools used are those offered by chromosome cytology, embryology, and genetics. The problems investigated are generally rather simple ones of the kind frequently encountered by systematists. The methods of solution range in complexity from very simple approaches to highly sophisticated, detailed studies.

The use (and abuse) of chromosome numbers as an aid to establishing plant relationships is well known to plant systematists, and today nearly every practicing taxonomist can make a tolerable squash preparation for counting chromosomes. There are features of chromosomes other than their number which are also of great value in taxonomic work. These include chromosome size, chromosome morphology, and meiotic behavior, particularly in hybrids. The papers included in this section illustrate the use of each of these chromosomal characteristics in taxonomy, although they do not represent the range of opinions concerning how such data should be applied taxonomically. In addition, I have added a paper each on the taxonomic use of embryological characters, on the use of genetic analysis, and one on a primarily morphological study of diploid and polyploid races. Papers in other sections related to the topics covered in this section are Lewis and Epling's paper on *Delphinium* (Section IV) and Reeder's papers on grass embryos (Section I).

The short paper by McKelvey and Sax on relationships between *Yucca* and *Agave* is a classic. In many early taxonomic works these genera were placed in the Liliaceae and Amaryllidaceae respectively, but the striking similarities in chromosome-size patterns discovered by these workers led them to suggest a closer affinity between these (and some other) genera than is indicated by their placement in separate families. Subsequent investigators who used other lines of approach have confirmed this early suggestion that *Yucca* and *Agave* are closely related, and the two are now generally included in one family.

Plant embryology considers all events and structures related to the production of pollen, embryo sac, and the embryo, as well as to fertilization events and subsequent embryogenesis. Another method of examining generic affinities is illustrated by the publication of Di Fulvio and Cave on the embryology of *Blandfordia nobilis* and its relatives. Table 1 in their paper shows the kinds of embryological characters that can be used for taxonomic purposes. Although the genus *Blandfordia* will not be familiar to most readers, its relatives *Hemerocallis, Hosta, Kniphofia,* and *Phormium* are all well-known ornamental plants.

The paper by Ownbey on amphiploidy in *Tragopogon* is also a classic of relatively recent vintage. It illustrates an extremely important evolutionary phenomenon in angiosperms — speciation by polyploidy. *Tragopogon* provides a rare example of the formation of such polyploids in historic times. The morphological and cytological comparisons between the diploid parents, their sterile diploid hybrids, and the derivative, relatively fertile tetraploids are especially interesting.

Wagner's study of Appalachian Aspleniums is not strictly a cytological paper, but it provides an interesting comparison with Ownbey's study since polyploidy is also involved in *Asplenium* evolution. The resultant morphological and geographical patterns are considerably more complex than in *Tragopogon*. This is probably due to the greater length of time over which hybridization has occurred in *Asplenium* and this, in turn, has allowed for extensive genetic segregation and backcrossing. The resultant polyploid complex presents numerous problems of taxonomic interpretation as well as an interesting evolutionary story. The lack of clear morphological distinctions among the taxa is a familiar characteristic of polyploid complexes. The papers by Ownbey and Wagner present studies of interspecific relationships in genera where species have hybridized naturally under field conditions.

The next two papers in this section examine relationships among species in which controlled artificial hybridizations have been used to work out details of the relationships among the species. The first of these is a study by Thompson of two taxa in the loasaceous genus *Mentzelia*. These taxa are very closely related but occupy distinct geographical ranges. This spatial isolation is an effective barrier to interbreeding, but the two taxa can be artificially hybridized with relative ease. Study of the artificial hybrids indicates that there is also a sterility barrier separating the two taxa. These observations led Thompson to conclude that taxonomically the two taxa should be considered distinct species. Kyhos' study is also a cytogenetic investigation, but it is more directly concerned with evolutionary relationships than with obtaining data to support a taxonomic judgment. In this instance, the taxa studied are three very closely related species of *Chaenactis*. In contrast to the *Mentzelia* example, the ranges of these species overlap, and where they come together, natural interspecific hybridization is frequent. There is also a difference in chromosome number in the trio. Kyhos presents a detailed analysis of chromosomal relationships among these three species and concludes that two of them have been independently derived from the third by aneuploid reduction in chromosome numbers.

The last two papers in this series deal with taxonomic problems at the intraspecific level. Ball and Heywood deal with a situation in the Old World caryophyllaceous genus *Kohlrauschia* (now *Petrorhagia*) where diploid and tetraploid races exist in what was generally considered to be a single species. Close study of the plants revealed consistent and obvious seedcoat differences between the diploids and tetraploids in addition to the differences in geographical distribution of the two races. These authors do not make an *a priori* assumption that in general polyploid races showing slight morphological distinctions should be given taxonomic status, but they believe that in this case it is useful to make a taxonomic separation.

The last paper in the series deals with the cruciferous genus *Dithyrea* in which plants with glabrous and pubescent fruits but with no other apparent differences have been accorded taxonomic recognition by some authors. The results of Rollins' hybridization program involving the two variants indicate that this striking character difference is under the control of a single gene. Therefore, the pubescence character is considered to be of no taxonomic significance.

TAXONOMIC AND CYTOLOGICAL RELATIONSHIPS
OF YUCCA AND AGAVE

Susan Delano McKelvey and Karl Sax

With plate 55

The senior author, during the past two years, has made an extensive study of *Yucca* and related genera. These genera have been collected from western Texas, New Mexico, Arizona, and the southern areas in California, Nevada, Utah and Colorado. The distance covered in this area has approximated 25,000 miles, and no day of travel passed without encountering numerous species of these plants.

Identification of *Yucca* species in the field has been difficult because of the extreme variability of all species, and the overlapping range of two or more similar species. For example, in the group of filiferous-leaved Yuccas with dehiscent fruit, the leaf characters have at times been used as a basis for species differentiation, but as a practical guide in the field these characters are often unreliable and confusing. On a single inflorescence the flowers vary little in size and form, but two inflorescences from adjoining plants, apparently of the same species, may differ in habit; the flowers may differ in shape and size of corolla-segments, ovary and style; and vary in length, form and pubescence of filaments. Among the fleshy-fruited Yuccas, one species seems to have two distinct forms; one with a vigorous fleshy inflorescence and large flowers, and the other with a compact, more ligneous inflorescence and more numerous small flowers.

In regions where closely allied species occur, their separation in the field is extremely difficult. Within the range attributed to *Y. angustissima* are plants of vigorous growth quite different than the expected type. In some respects, they resemble *Y. glauca* whose range is supposed to begin hundreds of miles further east. At the point of worst confusion has one encountered intermediate segregates from species hybrids, or are different types variants of a single species?

In most respects the allied genera *Clistoyucca, Hesperoyucca* and *Samuela,* separated by Trelease (1902), are similar to *Yucca. Yucca* and *Agave* are also similar in various striking details although these genera are placed in different families by most taxonomists.

The occurrence of transitional forms of *Yucca* species and the similarity of closely, and even distantly related genera, has led to a cytological study of these plants in order to compare their chromosome number and morphology. Material was collected in the field by the senior

Reprinted by permission of K. Sax and the publisher from the
JOURNAL OF THE ARNOLD ARBORETUM, **14,** 76–81 (1933).

author. Flower buds at different stages of development were fixed in a mixture of acetic acid and alcohol, and later transferred to 70 percent alcohol. Chromosome counts were obtained from aceto-carmine smears by the junior author.

Permanent smears were also made from pollen mother cells of *Agave americana* collected at the Bermuda Biological Station, from *Agave virginica* from the Missouri Botanical Garden, and from *Yucca flaccida* and *Y. filamentosa* grown in the Arnold Arboretum.

The chromosomes of *Yucca flaccida* have been described in detail by O'Mara (1931). At the first meiotic division there are 5 pairs of long chromosomes and 25 pairs of very small chromosomes. The long chromosomes have an average chiasma frequency of 3 per bivalent at metaphase, while each small bivalent has only a single terminal chiasma. The pairing is very regular and lagging univalents or other abnormalities were not observed. The extreme differences in chromosome size and the large number of chromosomes is rather unusual in the plant kingdom.

All of the species of *Yucca* examined have the same chromosome constitution. These include *Y. flaccida*, *Y. filamentosa*, *Y. elata*, *Y. constricta*, *Y. rupicola*, *Y. macrocarpa*, and *Y. angustissima*. The chromosomes of *Y. flaccida* and *Y. filamentosa* are shown at different stages of meiosis (figures 1, 2, and 3). The five pairs of large chromosomes are conspicuous at all stages. There is considerable variation in the size of the 25 small chromosomes, but all are relatively small.

The closely related genera examined also have exactly the same chromosome constitution as *Yucca*. These include *Hesperoyucca Whipplei*, *Hesperaloe parviflora*, and *Samuela Faxoniana*. Unfortunately, favorable material was not obtained from the related genera *Nolina* and *Dasylirion*. Counts from somatic cells of *Nolina* show that there are about 38 chromosomes which differ considerably in size, and most, if not all, of those chromosomes have median or sub-median spindle fiber constrictions. The more distantly related genus *Dracaena* (*D. arborea*) also has about 38 somatic chromosomes.

The species of *Agave* studied have 5 pairs of large chromosomes and 25 pairs of small chromosomes. The chromosomes of *A. virginica* and of *A. americana* are shown at different stages of the first meiotic division (figures 4, 5, and 6). Aceto-carmine smears of *Agave consociata* also show the same chromosome number and morphology. According to Mr. S. Horovitz of the University of Buenos Aires, *Agave filifera* also has 5 large and 25 small pairs of chromosomes.

The Agavoideae include according to Engler and Prantl the genera

Agave, Polianthes, Bravoa, Furcraea (Fourcroya) and *Beschorneria,*
all natives of central America, and the Australian genus *Doryanthes.*
According to Heitz (1926) *Furcraea altissima* has 10 large somatic
chromosomes and about 40 small ones while *F. Lindeni* has 10 large
chromosomes but only 30 small ones. We have found 10 large chromosomes and 50 small ones in aceto-carmine preparations of root tips
from *Furcraea Bedinghousii,* but in order to get satisfactory preparations it was necessary to isolate single dividing cells and flatten the
metaphase chromosomes by heat and slight pressure. According to
Heitz, Müller's work on *Beschorneria* shows chromosome numbers similar to those of *Furcraea.*

As a rule pollen grain size is generally correlated with chromosome
number in closely related species. The size and morphology of the
pollen grains appear to be very similar in the following species;—
*Yucca macrocarpa, Y. Treculeana, Y. baccata, Y. elata, Y. Reverchoni,
Y. Thompsoniana, Y. mohavensis, Clistoyucca brevifolia, Hesperaloe
parviflora, Hesperoyucca Whipplei, Agave Havardiana* and several unidentified species or varieties of *Yucca* and *Agave.* Each species and
variety examined had almost 100 percent of morphologically perfect
pollen grains.

DISCUSSION

The confusing variation within species and the intermediate forms of
Yucca might be interpreted as the result of extensive hybridization
between species and varieties. All of the species examined show regular chromosome behavior at meiosis and practically all of the pollen
is morphologically perfect. If the questionable forms are hybrids the
parental varieties or species must be closely related and possess very
similar genoms. In respect to chromosome number and chromosome
morphology all of the species studied seem to be very similar. If the
chromosomes of different species are compatible with each other, a
considerable amount of crossing might be expected and would be limited only by geographic isolation and differences in time of flowering.
The cytological analysis alone offers little help in solving the cause of
variations within and between species of *Yucca.*

The striking similarity of the chromosomes of *Yucca* and *Agave* and
their allied genera indicates a close relationship between these two
groups, even though they are referred to different families. The chromosome constitution, 5 pairs of large chromosomes and 25 pairs of
small chromosomes, is so unusual that it cannot be due to chance.
The two genera are also similar in many taxonomic characters. A
brief comparison of the two genera, and of the families to which they

belong, has been prepared by Dr. Ivan M. Johnston of the Arnold Arboretum, and is quoted below.

"*Yucca* belongs to the Liliaceae and *Agave* to the Amaryllidaceae. The Amaryllidaceae, having an inferior rather than a superior ovary, are evidently more specialized in basic floral structure. Taken as a whole the two families differ only in this character of the ovary. There is every evidence that the Amaryllidaceae have been derived from the Liliaceae and there are some very good reasons to suspect that the former are a polyphyletic group with the several points of origin in the Liliaceae.

Yucca and *Agave* are similar in many striking details. Both are coarse fibrous perennials with usually firm, long-enduring, monocarpic leaf-rosettes that are not common in their families. The large panicles are similar in basic structure and pattern.

Yucca has a superior ovary; the filaments are attached at the base of the corolla, bearing small firmly affixed anthers which do not surpass the corolla-lobes.

Agave has an inferior ovary; the stamens are attached in the corolla throat, the linear filaments bear large linear versatile anthers usually protruding beyond the corolla-lobes.

While *Yucca* is more simple than *Agave* in structure of ovary, and presumably belongs to a generally more primitive family, its staminal structures and the complex symbiotic relation required in its pollination are distinctly far in advance over conditions found in *Agave*. It is evident, therefore, that *Agave* could scarcely have been evolved from *Yucca* (including *Samuela*, *Hesperoyucca*, *Cleistoyucca* and *Hesperaloe*) as now constituted.

Yucca is generally accepted as having relations in *Nolina*, *Dasylirion* and *Dracaena* of the Liliaceae. *Furcraea*, in the Amaryllidaceae, is a relative of *Agave* although it possesses many important details of habit and floral structure very similar to those found in the relatives of *Yucca*. If *Yucca* is a reasonably close relative of *Agave*, as I believe it is, then it is probable that the affinity is to be traced through the related genera mentioned."

In the Dracaenoideae only the Yucceae have 5 large and 25 small pairs of chromosomes. All of these chromosomes have terminal spindle fiber attachments. In the two species examined (*Nolina* sp. and *Dracaena arborea*) in the Nolineae and Dracaeneae the somatic chromosome number seems to be about 38. These chromosomes do show considerable size differences but not as extreme as in *Yucca*, and the spindle fiber attachment constrictions seem to be median.

In the Agavoideae the two genera studied, *Agave* and *Furcraea*, have chromosomes very similar to those of *Yucca*. The cytological comparison shows a very close relationship between the Yucceae and certain genera of the Agavoideae, but *Nolina* and *Dracaena* do not seem to be the connecting link between these groups.

According to Engler and Prantl, all genera of the Yucceae, and with the exception of the Australian genus *Doryanthes*, all genera of the Agavoideae, are natives of Central America. These genera are closely related as indicated by both taxonomic and cytological characteristics. It is of interest to note that the African Aloinae, including the genera *Aloe, Gasteria, Apicra* and *Haworthia*, are in some respects similar to the Yucca-Agave group. All of these African genera have the same chromosome number, and the chromosome complex includes both large and small chromosomes. There are 4 pairs of large chromosomes and 3 small ones in each of these genera (Gaiser, 1930). The morphological characters and the similarity in size differentiation of the chromosomes seems to indicate a remote affinity between the Aloinae of the Old World and the Yucca-Agave group of the New World.

SUMMARY

Yucca and *Agave* are similar in many taxonomic characters although one genus is placed in the Liliaceae and the other in the Amaryllidaceae. *Yucca* and the closely allied genera *Hesperoyucca, Hesperaloe,* and *Samuela*, have 5 pairs of large chromosomes and 25 pairs of small chromosomes at the meiotic divisions. Exactly the same chromosomes constitution is found in *Agave* and in at least one species of the closely related genus *Furcraea*. The similarity in taxonomic characters and chromosome constitution indicates that these genera have had a common origin and are closely related.

The variability within and between species of *Yucca* is not correlated with any variation in chromosome number or irregularity in chromosome behavior.

HERBARIUM AND CYTOLOGICAL LABORATORY
ARNOLD ARBORETUM, HARVARD UNIVERSITY

LITERATURE CITED

GAISER, L. O. (1930). Chromosome numbers in Angiosperms. (Bibl. Genetica, **6**:171–466.)

HEITZ, E. (1926). Der Nachweis der Chromosomen. (Zeit. f. Bot. **18**:625–681.)

O'MARA, J. (1931.) Chromosome pairing in Yucca flaccida. (Cytologia, **3**:66–76.)

TRELEASE, W. (1902). The Yucceae. (Missouri Bot. Garden Ann. Rep. **13**:27–133.)

Taxonomic and Cytological Relationships of Yucca and Agave.

DESCRIPTION OF PLATE 55

The drawings were made from permanent smears of pollen mother cells. Magnification about 2500.

1. *Yucca flaccida.* Diakinesis.
2. *Yucca filamentosa.* Metaphase.
3. *Yucca flaccida.* Telophase.
4. *Agave virginica.* Diakinesis.
5. *Agave virginica.* Metaphase.
6. *Agave americana.* Telophase.

EMBRYOLOGY OF *BLANDFORDIA NOBILIS* SMITH (LILIACEAE), WITH SPECIAL REFERENCE TO ITS TAXONOMIC POSITION[1]

T. E. DI FULVIO

Museo Botánico, Universidad de Córdoba, Córdoba, Argentina

M. S. CAVE

Department of Botany, University of California, Berkeley, U.S.A.

Introduction

Blandfordia is a liliaceous genus of five species native to Australia and Tasmania. Krause (1930) placed it in the tribe Hemerocallideae together with *Phormium, Hosta, Leucocrinum, Hesperocallis*, and *Hemerocallis*, but Hutchinson (1934) removed it to the tribe Kniphofieae which includes *Kniphofia* and *Notosceptrum*. In their work on the Asphodeloideae Schnarf & Wunderlich (1939) presented embryological data on *Hosta, Hemerocallis*, and *Kniphofia*; Cave (1948, 1955) has given them for *Leucocrinum, Hesperocallis*, and *Phormium*. But up till now, nothing has been known embryologically of *Blandfordia*.

Recently some material of *Blandfordia nobilis* Smith (1804-5) was received, thus giving an opportunity to study the remaining genus of the Hemerocallideae and to compare it embryologically with the genera already investigated.

Materials and Methods

Inflorescences of *Blandfordia nobilis* were fixed in 3 parts absolute alcohol to 1 part glacial acetic acid. Dehydration was carried out in a butyl alcohol series (Sass, 1958), and the material was

1. This investigation was carried out at the Department of Botany, the University of California, Berkeley, during the senior author's tenure of a fellowship from the Consejo Nacional de Investigaciones Científicas y Técnicas de la República Argentina. The results were presented at the Segundo Congreso Mexicano de Botánica in San Luis Potosí, Mexico, in September 1963.

embedded in Tissuemat. Sections were cut 10 to 15 microns thick, stained with Heidenhain's iron alum haematoxylon, counterstained with fast green, and mounted in piccolyte. Material for the other genera was prepared in the same way, with the exception of fixation, CRAF being used in some instances. The following list gives the origin of the material:

Blandfordia nobilis Smith. New South Wales (Cave 6304); (N.S.W. 66106; UC 1,220,340).

Hemerocallis flava L. Cultivated at the University of California Botanical Garden, Berkeley (Cave 3811).

Hemerocallis flava L. (?). Cultivated in the campus of the University of California, Berkeley (Cave 6362).

Hemerocallis fulva L. Cultivated in the campus of the University of California, Berkeley (Di Fulvio 6322).

Hesperocallis undulata Gray. San Bernardino County, California (Cave 4113).

Hosta caerulea Tratt. Yun Nan Sen, China. (Maire 2230, UC 222720).

Kniphofia sp. Cultivated in a private garden, Berkeley (Cave 5705).

Kniphofia (Burbank hybrids). Cultivated at the University of California Botanical Garden, Berkeley (Cave 6360).

Leucocrinum montanum Nutt. Bould-r County, Colorado (Cave 4721 and 6256); (Weber 3684. UC 766423).

Leucocrinum montanum Nutt. Modoc County, California (Cave 6243).

Phormium tenax Forst. Cultivated at the University of California Botanical Garden, Berkeley (Cave 4838 and 4839).

Phormium tenax Forst. var. *variegatum* Hort. Cultivated at the University of California Botanical Garden, Berkeley (Cave 6358).

Observations

MICROSPORANGIUM — In *Blandfordia nobilis* the anthers are dorsifixed, although externally they appear basifixed because the connective, which is massive in the upper half of the theca, is hollowed out in the lower half and surrounds the filament as a sheath, reaching almost to the base of the anther (Fig. 1 A-D).

Near maturity a cross section of the anther (Fig. 1 E) shows the following cell layers:

(a) Epidermis, formed in great part by cells more or less flattened, becoming noticeably elongated or even 2-layered in lateral zones of the theca distal to the connective, but very small towards the zone of dehiscence. The external surface of the cells appears striated due to undulations of the cuticle. Stomata, surrounded by 4 or 5 epidermal cells occur in the region of the connective. In the sheath formed around the filament by the connective, the cells of the internal epidermis and those of 1 or 2 subjacent layers show helicoidal thickenings on the walls which resemble those of the fibrous layer.

(b) Endothecium or fibrous layer, formed by elongated cells which also reach their maximum size on the distal sides of the theca, where they may be replaced frequently by 2 or 3 superimposed smaller cells. The walls show thickened bands which extend and approach or unite on the internal tangential face, while they are thin or disappear on the one which is in contact with the epidermis. The fibrous layer, somewhat less developed, continues in part of the connective.

(c) Middle layer of at least 2 rows of flattened cells between the fibrous layer and the tapetum.

(d) Tapetum of the glandular type. Numerous Ubisch bodies (Ubisch, 1927; Rowley, 1962) or spheroids (Rowley et al., 1959) are found in contact with the internal tangential walls of its cells. These structures also exist between the radial walls, but are fewer.

Dehiscence of the anther is longitudinal. The pollen is subspheroidal, suboblate, with major axis of 28-31 microns and minor axis of 21-25 microns. One-sulcate pollen grains with granular sexine are 2-nucleate at shedding (Fig. 1 E).

MEGASPORANGIUM—In *Blandfordia* from 20 to 25 seeds in 6 longitudinal rows are contained in the 3-locular, 3-carpellate ovary with lateral septa (cf. 10 of Summary and Fig. 6 E). Ovules are anatropous without an aril (Fig. 1 F), and their placentation is axile. At fertilization the outer integument consists of 4 layers of cells and the inner integument

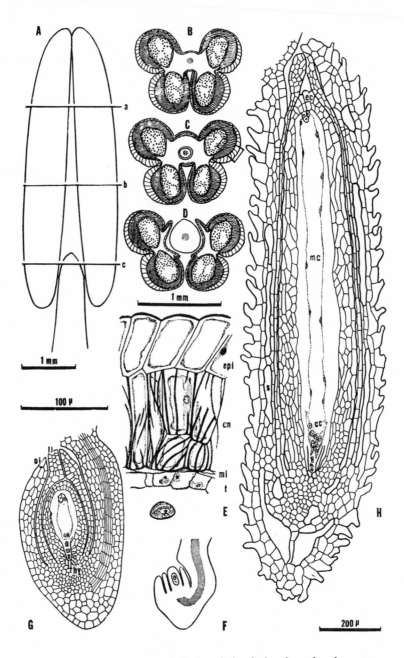

FIG 1 — Sporangia of *Blandfordia nobilis* (*cc*, chalazal chamber of endosperm; *ec*, epidermal calyptra developed from nucellar epidermis; *en*, endothecium; *epi*, epidermis; *hy*, hypostase; *ii*, inner integument; *mc*, micropylar chamber of endosperm; *ml*, middle layer; *oi*, outer integument; *s*, space; *t*, tapetum).   A. Anther, dorsal view.   B-D. Transections through the anther at levels a-c respectively.   E. Detail of the zone marked in C.   F. Ovule with megaspore mother cell.   G. Ovule with mature embryo sac.   H. Developing seed with 2-celled embryo in helobial endosperm. Scale between D and E applies to B, C, D; that below A, that of 100 microns to E; and that of 200 microns to F-H.

of 2. The micropyle is formed by the latter only, which possesses in this region a large number of cell layers and surpasses the former (Fig. 1 G). In later stages the outer integument grows over the micropyle and the cells of its outer epidermis become papillate, while its middle cell layers degenerate, giving a spongy appearance (Fig. 1 H).

Two instances were found in which a single outer integument, surrounded 2 embryo sacs, each with an inner integument, and one instance in which both inner and outer integuments were common to 2 embryo sacs.

In the young ovule the nucellus is formed by about 3 layers of cells in the micropylar region (Fig. 2 A, B), the innermost of which is derived from the parietal cell and disappears early (Fig. 2 C). The outer layers are formed by periclinal divisions of the nucellar· epidermis and persist as a nucellar cap (Figs. 1 H; 2 C). The hypostase is differentiated around the chalazal constriction where the antipodals lie (Fig. 1 G), and the vascular trace from the raphe ends near it.

MEGASPOROGENESIS AND MEGAGAMETO-PHYTE — The megaspore mother cell undergoes meiosis to produce a linear tetrad of megaspores (Fig. 2 D-G). Generally the dyad produced after the first meiotic division consists of a large chalazal cell and a small micropylar cell (Fig. 2 F) which often does not divide again (Fig. 2 H, I), so that usually only triads are seen (Fig. 2 H). In the second meiotic division the chalazal cell produces the functioning megaspore and, towards the micropyle, a cell which degenerates immediately. After 3 mitotic divisions the functioning megaspore develops into an 8-nucleate gametophyte which becomes organized in the usual way (Figs. 2 J-N; 3 A). The synergids are somewhat dentate and possess a weak filiform apparatus. The antipodals are persistent and are situated in the chalazal constriction surrounded by the hypostase. The polar nuclei occupy various positions, as if they undergo a displacement through the central cell (Fig. 3 A-E), but their fusion takes place near the antipodals before fertilization (Fig. 3 F).

FERTILIZATION — This is porogamous and in some cases 2 pollen tubes were seen reaching the sac, one exhibiting 2X-bodies, the other 4. In these cases no synergids have been seen.

ENDOSPERM — This is helobial (Fig. 1 H). The first division of the primary endosperm nucleus takes place in the chalazal zone (Fig. 4 A), resulting in a large micropylar cell and a smaller chalazal cell (Fig. 4 B, D). The second division can be simultaneous in both cells (Fig. 4 C), but later the process becomes slower in the smaller cell. This type of development conforms to the type considered normal by Swamy & Parameswaran (1963) for the Liliaceae in that 32 nuclei have been seen in the chalazal chamber and approximately 128 in the micropylar when the embryo is at the 4-celled stage.

EMBRYO — The first division of the zygote is transverse (Fig. 3 G, H). The basal cell then divides again (Fig. 3 I) in the same plane while the apical cell divides longitudinally (Fig. 3 J). In the material available there were no embryos of more advanced development.

Discussion

Six genera compose the tribe Hemerocallideae according to Krause (1930): *Hosta, Hemerocallis, Phormium, Blandfordia, Leucocrinum,* and *Hesperocallis.* A comparative study of the embryological characters (Figs. 5 A-F; 6 A-E; Table 1) indicates that each presents similarities and differences with respect to the others, so that it is difficult to see relationships. The fact that different authors, e.g. Bentham & Hooker (1883), Krause .(1930), and Hutchinson (1934) associated them in different groups may indicate that the relationship between them is not close. ·*Blandfordia* was kept in the Hemerocallideae by the first two authorities, while Hutchinson placed it in the Kniphofieae, a position not supported by the embryological characters. In *Blandfordia* the ovule is anatropous, lacks an aril, and has a nucellar cap of several layers (Fig. 5 F), while in *Kniphofia* the ovule is hemitropous, with a well developed aril and a single layer of epidermal cells over the mature sac (Fig. 5 G). In *Kniphofia* the

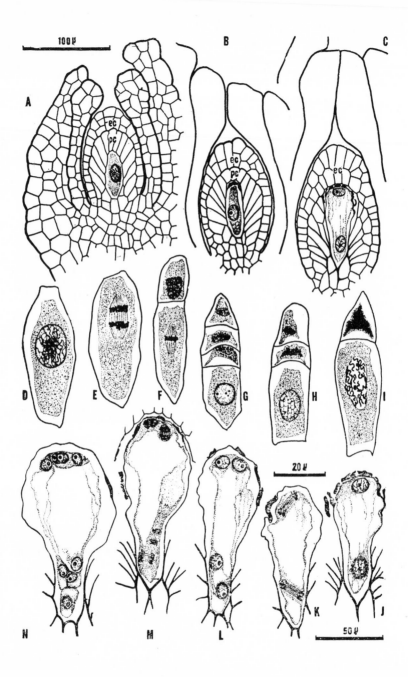

Fɪɢ. 2 — Megasporogenesis and megagametophyte of *Blandfordia nobilis* (*ec,* epidermal cap; *pc,* parietal cells). A-C. Longisections of ovules showing successive developmental stages of the nucellus. D. Megaspore mother cell. E-I. Different stages in the formation of megaspores; G. Tetrad. H. Triad. I. Dyad (in F, H, I, the micropylar nucleus does not divide again). J-N. Successive stages in the maturation of the embryo sac. Scale of 100 microns applies to A-C; that of 20 microns to D-I; and that of 50 microns to J-N.

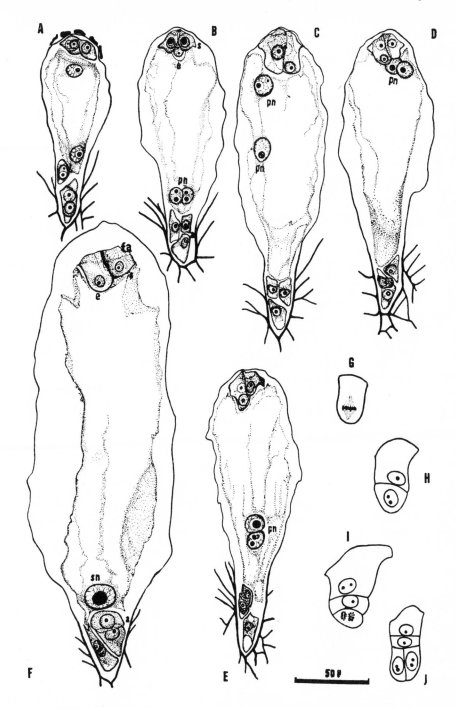

FIG 3 — Mature megagametophyte and young embryo of *Blandfordia nobilis* (*a*, antipodals; *e*, egg cell; *fa*, filiform apparatus; *pn*, polar nuclei; *s*, synergids; *sn*, secondary embryo sac nucleus). A–E. 8-nucleate embryo sac showing the polar nuclei in different positions. F. Mature embryo sac with fused polar nuclei. G. First division of the zygote. H–J. Developing proembryos.

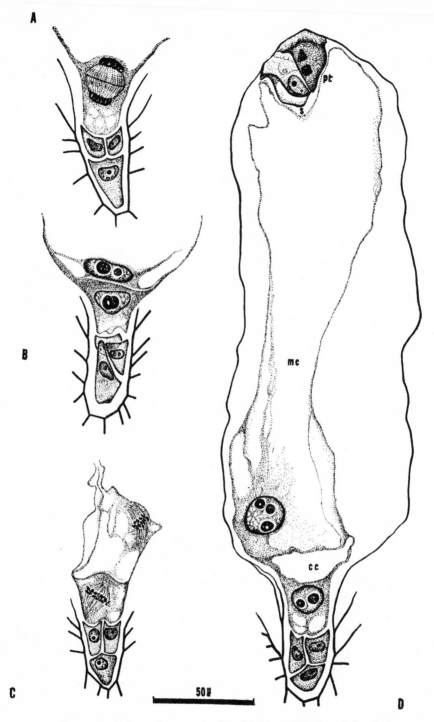

FIG. 4 — Development of the endosperm in *Blandfordia nobilis* (*cc*, chalazal chamber; *mc*, micropylar chamber; *pt*, pollen tube with 2 x-bodies; *s*, synergid). A. Chalazal end of embryo sac showing division of primary endosperm nucleus. B. 2-nucleate endosperm. C. Division in both micropylar and chalazal chambers. D. Embryo sac with 2-celled endosperm.

TABLE 1 — EMBRYOLOGICAL CHARACTERS IN SIX GENERA IN THE HEMEROCALLIDEAE AND *KNIPHOFIA*

GENUS	BASIC CHROMOSOME NUMBER	MICROSPORE DELIMITATION	POLLEN[2]	CAPSULE[4]	SEPTA OF OVARY AT ANTHESIS	OVULE	NUMBER OF CELL LAYERS IN INTEGUMENTS	
							Outer	Inner
Hemerocallis	11	Successive	1-sulcate single 88μ×65μ	Loculicidal	Lateral	Anatropous without aril	6-7	4[5]
Phormium	16	Simultaneous	3-chotomosulcate single 38μ×37μ	do	do	do	6	2
Leucocrinum	14	Successive	1-sulcate single or in tetrads 75μ×72μ[3]	do	do	do	4	2
Hosta	6+24[1]	do	1-sulcate single 103μ×91μ	do	?	do	?	?
Hesperocallis	6+18[1]	do	1-sulcate single 66μ×61μ	do	Lateral	do	4	2
Blandfordia	17	?	1-sulcate single 31μ×24μ	Septicidal	do	do	4	2
Kniphofia	6	Simultaneous	1-sulcate single 43μ×42μ	Loculicidal	Angular	Hemitropous with aril	3-4	2

1. Large + small chromosomes.

2. Measurements of pollen grains were taken from the following: *Hemerocallis fulva* (Di Fulvio 6322); *Phormium tenax* var. *variegatum* (Cave 6358); *Leucocrinum montanum* (Cave 6256, 6243); *Hosta caerulea* (Maire 2230); *Hesperocallis undulata* (Cave 4113); *Blandfordia nobilis* (Cave 6304); *Kniphofia* (Burbank hybrids) (Cave 6360).

3. Pollen grains remain in tetrads in California material, but are single in Colorado material.

4. According to data from Bentham & Hooker (1883).

5. External epidermis much differentiated.

117

TABLE 1 — EMBRYOLOGICAL CHARACTERS IN SIX GENERA IN THE HEMEROCALLIDEAE AND *KNIPHOFIA* — *Contd.*

GENUS	PARIETAL CELL	PERICLINAL DIVISIONS IN NUCELLAR EPIDERMIS	NUCELLAR COVERING OF MATURE FEMALE GAMETOPHYTE	CHALAZAL CONSTRICTION IN EMBRYO SAC	HYPOSTASE	RATIO OF MATURE FEMALE GAMETOPHYTE TO NUCELLUS	ENDOSPERM	GEOGRAPHIC DISTRIBUTION
Hemerocallis	−	−	None	−	−	$\frac{1}{2}$	Nuclear	Europe, Central Asia
Phormium	−	+	Multi-layered	+	+[7]	$\frac{1}{2}$	Helobial[8], multinucleate chalazal cell	New Zealand
Leucocrinum	+	+	do	−	+	$\frac{1}{2}$	Helobial?	North America
Hosta	+	+	Multi-layered[9]	+	+	$\frac{3}{4}$	Helobial, multinucleate chalazal cell	China, Japan
Hesperocallis	+	−	1-layered	+	+	$\frac{1}{2}$	Helobial?	North America
Blandfordia	+	+	Multi-layered	+	+	$\frac{7}{8}$	Helobial, multinucleate chalazal cell	Australia, Tasmania
Kniphofia	+	−	1-layered	+	+	$\frac{1}{2}$	Helobial, binucleate chalazaal cell	Africa, Madagascar

6. At least in seeds with adventitious embryos (Hu 1963).

7. Cell walls only slightly thickened.

8. In material of *Phormium tenax* var. *variegatum* (Cave 6358).

118

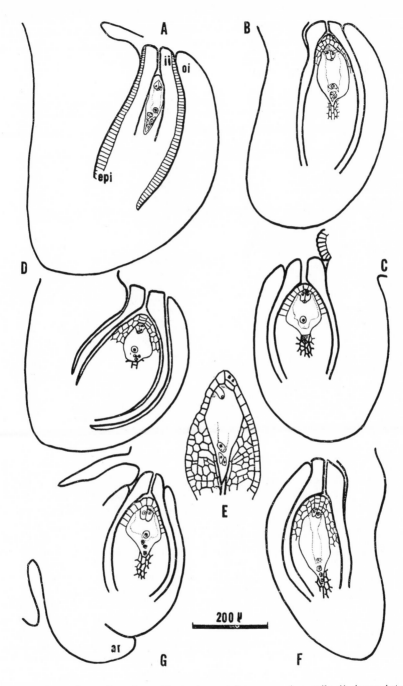

FIG. 5 — Longisections of ovules with mature embryo sacs (*ar*, aril; *ii*, inner integument with *epi* outer epidermis differentiated; *oi*, outer integument). A. *Hemerocallis flava* (Cave 3811). B. *Phormium tenax* (Cave 4838). C. *Hesperocallis undulata* (Cave 4113). D. *Leucocrinum montanum* (Cave 4721). E. *Hosta plantaginea* (redrawn from Schnarf & Wunderlich, 1939). F. *Blandfordia nobilis* (Cave 6304). G. *Kniphofia* sp. (Cave 5705).

119

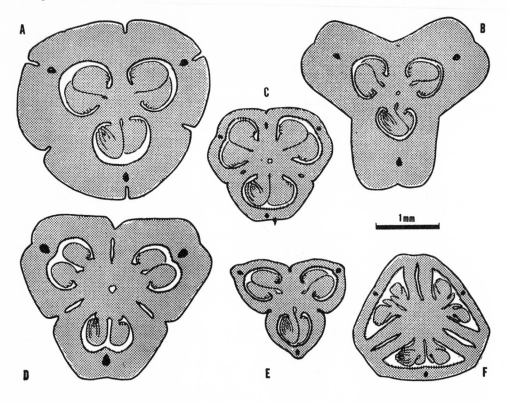

FIG. 6 — Cross-sectional diagrams of ovaries showing position of septa. A. *Hemerocallis flava* (Cave 6362). B. *Phormium tenax* (Cave 4838). C. *Leucocrinum montanum* (Cave 4721). D. *Hesperocallis undulata* (Cave 4113). E. *Blandfordia nobilis* (Cave 6304). F. *Kniphofia* sp. (Cave 5705).

septa are angular, i. e. they extend from the corners of the triangular ovary to the centre (Fig. 6 F, Table 1), whereas in *Blandfordia* they are lateral. The endosperm in both genera is helobial, but in *Blandfordia* the chalazal chamber contains numerous nuclei while in *Kniphofia* it is only 2-nucleate — at least in seeds of 2 to 8-celled embryos (Schnarf & Wunderlich, 1939 and personal observations).

Unfortunately in *Blandfordia* it was impossible to get chromosome counts or study delimitation of microspores due to scarcity of material. Smith-White (1959) stated that *Blandfordia nobilis* and two other Australian species were diploid (2n = 34), while one Tasmanian genus was tetraploid. Dr Barbara Briggs (personal communication) has counted 34 chromosomes in root tip cells of *B. nobilis*

and 54 in *B. cunninghamii*, the chromosomes not showing extreme size differences such as are seen in *Hosta* and *Hesperocallis*. In one embryo sac mother cell at diakinesis in the present investigation of *Blandfordia nobilis* it was obvious that there was a fairly high number of chromosome pairs — at least several times the number characteristic of *Kniphofia* (n = 6). A much more comprehensive study of chromosome number in *Blandfordia* is needed before any taxonomic relationships can be made out.

Comparisons of *Blandfordia* with other genera of the Hemerocallideae do not indicate close affinities. It differs from *Hemerocallis* (Figs. 5 A; 6 A) in all characters enumerated in Table 1, except for the anatropous ovule without aril and the lateral septa. In fact, *Hemerocallis* shows many differences when compared with all the other genera of the Hemerocallideae. Cave (1948) suggested its separation from the other genera of the tribe, and the present study shows that *Blandfordia* is also not closely related, and should also be separated from it.

Phormium presents some similarities with *Blandfordia* (Figs. 5 B; 6 B). Both show the nucellar epidermis with periclinal divisions forming a nucellar cap of several layers, and in both the hypostase surrounds a chalazal constriction, (although not a very noticeable one in *Phormium*). In both, the septa are lateral (Fig. 6 B), and the chalazal chamber of the endosperm is multinucleate. But there are also marked differences between the two genera in the pollen grains, the absence or presence of the parietal cell, the number of cell layers in the outer integument, length of the mature embryo sac to the nucellus, and the mode of dehiscence of the capsule. The position of *Phormium* in the Hemerocallideae or Agavaceae has already been discussed by Cave (1955).

In the characteristics of the ovule and of the female gametophyte *Leucocrinum* and *Hosta* are the genera that present the greatest number of similarities with *Blandfordia* (Figs. 5 D, E; 6 C). Nevertheless, differences in geographic distribution, characteristics of the microspores, as well as the karyotypes and capsule dehiscence, make a close relationship questionable.

The embryological and cytological characteristics of *Hesperocallis* (Fig. 5 C; Table 1) show close relationships with *Hosta* (Cave 1948). The lack of periclinal divisions in the nucellar epidermis and the nucellar cap of 1 cell layer differentiate it from *Hosta* and *Blandfordia*, while the position of the septa is the same as in the latter genus (Fig. 6 D, E). The mature female gametophyte in form and structure is similar to that of *Kniphofia* at a comparable stage of development, but *Hesperocallis* lacks an aril. Cytologically as well as in microsporogenesis and geographic distribution the latter two genera are very different. The dehiscence of the capsule is loculicidal like that in *Hosta* and *Kniphofia*, and different from that in *Blandfordia*.

With the present investigation there are now available embryological data for all the six genera of the Hemerocallideae. The data suggest that *Hemerocallis* should be separated from the other members of the tribe, and that *Blandfordia* should not be placed with *Kniphofia*. But much more study, both embryological and in other fields, is needed on these genera and in the whole liliaceous complex before phylogenetic and taxonomic relationships can be determined.

Summary and Conclusions

The embryology of *Blandfordia nobilis* Smith is described and considered in reference to the comparative morphology of the Hemerocallideae and Kniphofieae.

1. Anthers are dorsifixed, tetralocular, with longitudinal dehiscence. The wall is constituted by epidermis, endothecium, at least 2 middle layers, and a glandular tapetum. The pollen is subspheroidal, suboblate, 1-sulcate, and 2-nucleate at shedding. The sexine is granular.

2. The ovary is 3-carpellate and 3-locular with 20-25 ovules per locule. Septa are lateral (cf. 10).

3. Ovules are anatropous with axile placentation, crassinucellate, bitegmic, and without aril. The inner integument has 2 layers of cells, the outer 4. The middle cell layers of the latter degenerate partly after fertilization, and the cells of the outer epidermis become papillate. The micropyle is formed by the inner integument. A hypostase surrounds a chalazal constriction. The parietal cell forms an ephemeral wall layer, while a nucellar cap, persisting into the seed, is produced by peri- and anticlinal divisions of the nucellar epidermis.

4. The embryo sac is of the *Polygonum*-type and is developed from the chalazal megaspore of a linear tetrad. Synergids are dentate with a faint filiform apparatus. Polar nuclei occupy various positions, but they fuse near the antipodals before fertilization. The antipodals are persistent and are located in the chalazal constriction formed by the hypostase.

5. Fertilization is porogamous. Occasionally 2 pollen tubes enter the same sac.

6. Endosperm is helobial with multinucleate chalazal chamber.

7. The zygote divides transversely, as does the basal cell. The apical cell divides longitudinally.

8. *Phormium* has helobial endosperm, with a multinucleate chalazal chamber.

9. Nuclear endosperm is confirmed for *Hemerocallis*.

10. In *Hemerocallis*, *Phormium*, *Leucocrinum*, *Hesperocallis*, and *Blandfordia*, cross sections of ovaries at anthesis show the septa as lateral, i.e. extending from the middle of the side walls of the triangular ovary to the centre.

11. In *Kniphofia*, at this stage, the septa are angular, i.e. extending from the corners of the triangular ovary to the centre.

12. The chalazal cell of the helobial endosperm of *Kniphofia* has only 2 large nuclei.

13. Pollen grains in *Leucocrinum* material from Colorado are single, while those in material from California remain together in tetrads.

14. *Blandfordia*, as well as *Hosta*, *Hesperocallis*, *Phormium*, and *Leucocrinum* should be separated from *Hemerocallis* in the Hemerocallideae.

15. *Blandfordia* should not be placed in the Kniphofieae.

The authors wish to express their gratitude to the Director and personnel of the National Herbarium of New South Wales and to Dr Barbara Briggs, especially, for making the material available.

Literature Cited

BENTHAM, G. & HOOKER, J. D. 1883. Genera Plantarum Vol. III, Part 2. London.

CAVE, M. S. 1948. Sporogenesis and embryo sac development of *Hesperocallis* and *Leucocrinum* in relation to their systematic position. Amer. J. Bot. **35**: 343-349.

— 1953. Cytology and embryology in the delimitation of genera. Chronica Bot. **14**:140-153.

— 1955. Sporogenesis and the female gametophyte of *Phormium tenax*. Phytomorphology **5**: 247-253.

EAMES, A. J. 1961. Morphology of the Angiosperms. New York.

HU, S. Y. 1963. Studies in the polyembryony of *Hosta caerulea* Tratt. II. Observations on the development of adventive embryo under hormone-treatments. Acta Bot. Sin. **11**: 21-25.

HUTCHINSON, J. 1934. The Families of Flowering Plants. Vol. II. Monocotyledons. London.

KRAUSE, K. 1930. Liliaceae. *In* Engler, A., & Prantl, K., Die natürlichen Pflanzenfamilien **2 (15a)**: 227-386. Leipzig.

MAHESHWARI, P. 1950. An Introduction to the Embryology of Angiosperms. New York.

ROWLEY, J. R. 1962. Nonhomogeneous sporopollenin in microspores of *Poa annua*. L. Grana Palyno. **3**:(3) 3-20.

ROWLEY, J. R., MUHLETHALER, K. & FREY-WYSSLING, A. 1959. A route for the transfer of materials through the pollen grain wall. J. Biophys. Biochem. Cytol. **6**: 537-538.

SASS, J. E. 1958. Botanical Microtechnique. Iowa.

SCHNARF, K. & WUNDERLICH, R. 1939. Zur vergleichenden Embryologie der Liliaceae-Asphodeloideae. Flora **133**: 297-327.

SMITH, J. E. 1804-5. Exotic Botany. London.

SMITH-WHITE, S. 1959. Cytological evolution in the Australian flora. Cold Spring Harbor Symp. Quant. Biol. **24**: 273-289.

SWAMY, B. G. L. & PARAMESWARAN, N. 1963. The helobial endosperm. Biol. Rev. **38**: 1-50.

UBISCH, G. V. 1927. Zur Entwicklungsgeschichte der Antheren. Planta **3**: 490-495.

NATURAL HYBRIDIZATION AND AMPHIPLOIDY IN THE GENUS TRAGOPOGON[1]

Marion Ownbey

THE OLD-WORLD GENUS *TRAGOPOGON* (Compositae) is represented in North America by three introduced weedy species, *T. dubius* Scop. (*T. major* Jacq.), *T. porrifolius* L., and *T. pratensis* L. These are coarse herbs from thick biennial taproots which in *T. porrifolius* furnish the familiar salsify or vegetable oyster. The three species are widespread on this continent. In southeastern Washington and adjacent Idaho, all are found. *T. dubius* is the most common here, having successfully invaded waste places, roadsides, fields, and pastures, until its occurrence is practically continuous throughout the region. *T. porrifolius* and *T. pratensis* are more restricted in distribution, being almost wholly confined to towns, and the latter is absent from some towns. It grows abundantly, for instance, in Moscow, Idaho, but has not been found in Pullman, Washington, 10 mi. away. Like *T. dubius*, both *T. porrifolius* and *T. pratensis* can withstand considerable competition, and although their ecological amplitude is not so great, it is strange that they have not become more generally established. According to herbarium records, *T. porrifolius* was established in Pullman prior to 1916 (*Pickett* 314) and *T. dubius* in Pullman prior to 1928 (*Jones* 2066). Local botanists remember the sudden appearance of the latter in great abundance about 1930. *T. pratensis* was collected in Spokane County, Washington, as early as 1916 (*Suksdorf* 8729, 8911).

THE PARENTAL SPECIES.—Each of the three species as it occurs in our area is sharply defined by a combination of qualitative and quantitative characters (table 1) and, with the exceptions to be discussed below, there is never the slightest difficulty in recognizing a given individual as a member of one of the three discrete populations. The genetic hiati are broad, sharp, and absolute, and there simply is no biological intergradation between the entities. The species differ in habit; in the color, shape, crisping, curling, and indument of the leaves; in the color, number, and shape of involucral bracts; in the number of flowers per head; in the relative lengths of involucral bracts and ligules; in the color of ligules; in the shape and relative length of the beak and body of the fruit; in the color of fruit and pappus; and in other ways.

Tragopogon dubius.—This species (fig. 1) is easily recognized by its pale lemon-yellow ligules, all shorter than the involucral bracts. The habit is low

and bushy, the branches originating from near the base of the stem. The leaves taper uniformly from base to apex, and are neither crisped on the margins nor curled backward at the tip. They are usually conspicuously floccose when young, becoming glabrate and somewhat glaucous with age. The peduncles of well developed heads are strongly inflated and fistulose toward the apex. The flowers of the head are many, ranging in number from 104–180 in the heads counted, with an average of well over 100 flowers per head. The bracts of the involucre are usually thirteen per head—exactly this number in 75 per cent of the first heads of a random sample of forty plants of a pure colony growing under favorable conditions. Occasionally a particularly robust plant may have as many as seventeen bracts in the first head, and frequently the number may be as few as eight on depauperate plants or in late heads. The bracts are long and narrow—always longer than the longest ligules—and are not margined with purple. The expanded mature heads range from 8–12 (av. 10.5) cm. in diameter. The achenes are slender, ranging from 25–36 (av. 33) mm. long, including the beak. The body is gradually narrowed to and not strongly differentiated from the beak. The outer achenes are pale brown, the inner ones straw colored, and the pappus is whitish.

Meiosis was studied in pollen mother cells from two plants, using the aceto-carmine smear technique (employed throughout this study). In both plants, six bivalents regularly were formed at metaphase I (fig. 14). Mature pollen grains, stained with iodine throughout this study, appeared to be 99 per cent good. The mean diameter of mature pollen protoplasts was 29.3 μ. The calculated diameter of mature pollen protoplasts of mean volume was 29.2 μ. These values are identical with those for *T. pratensis*. The species is highly fertile (fig. 5), not more than 2 or 3 per cent of the flowers failing to produce fruits under normal conditions, and even the poorly developed achenes toward the center of the head uniformly contain apparently viable embryos.

Tragopogon porrifolius.—This species is distinguished at once by its pale to dark violet ligules. Lengths of the longest ligules in the wild species are grouped around two means. In the form with long outer ligules, these are nearly as long as the involucral bracts. In the other form, the outer ligules are short, like the inner ones, averaging about half the length of the involucral bracts or less. Both forms are frequent in our populations, the former being more abundant than the latter. The habit is stout but strict, with the branches fewer in number

[1] Received for publication November 12, 1949.

This investigation was supported in part by funds provided for biological and medical research by the State of Washington Initiative No. 171.

Reprinted by permission of the author and publisher from the
AMERICAN JOURNAL OF BOTANY, 37, 487–499 (1950).

TABLE 1. *A morphological comparison of the three introduced diploid species of Tragopogon.*

Dubius	Porrifolius	Pratensis
Leaves tapering uniformly from base to apex, neither crisped on margins nor curled backward at tip, usually conspicuously floccose when young, glabrate and somewhat glaucous with age.	*Leaves* tapering uniformly from base to apex, neither crisped on margins nor curled backward at tip, glabrous and glaucous, somewhat broader than in *T. dubius.*	*Leaves* narrowed more abruptly below, the margins concave and crisped, the tips recurved, obscurely floccose when young, later glabrate, pale green, not glaucous.
Peduncles strongly inflated toward apex.	*Peduncles* strongly inflated toward apex.	*Peduncles* scarcely at all inflated, even in fruit.
Heads averaging well over 100 flowers (up to 180 counted), in fruit 8–12 cm. in diameter (av. 10.5).	*Heads* averaging about 90 flowers (up to 117 counted), in fruit 9–11 cm. in diameter (av. 10.0).	*Heads* averaging about 75 flowers (up to 96 counted), in fruit 5–6 cm. in diameter.
Bracts usually 13 (sometimes as many as 17 on the first head of vigorous plants or as few as 8 on the latest heads or on depauperate plants), long and narrow, not margined with purple, longer than the outer ligules.	*Bracts* usually 8 or commonly 9 on the first head, rarely as many as 12, broader than in *T. dubius,* not margined with purple, longer than the outer ligules.	*Bracts* usually 8 or commonly 9 on the first head, rarely as many as 13, broad and short, margined with purple, about equaling the outer ligules in length.
Ligules pale lemon yellow, all shorter than the bracts.	*Ligules* pale to deep violet-purple, all shorter than the bracts, the longest sometimes less than half as long.	*Ligules* chrome yellow, the outer ones about equaling the bracts in length.
Achenes slender, 25–36 mm. long (av. 33), gradually narrowed to the not strongly differentiated beak, outer pale brown, inner straw colored; pappus whitish.	*Achenes* thicker, 29–35 mm. long (av. 32), abruptly tapering to a slender beak longer than the body, outer usually dark brown, inner paler; pappus brownish.	*Achenes* thicker, 20–25 mm. long, abruptly tapering to a slender beak which is often shorter than the body, outer usually dark brown, passing to straw colored inwardly; pappus whitish.

and usually originating higher on the stem than in *T. dubius.* The leaves taper uniformly from base to apex, and are neither crisped on the margins nor curled backward at the tips. They are somewhat broader than in *T. dubius* and glabrous and glaucous from the beginning. The peduncles of well developed heads are strongly inflated and fistulose toward the apex. The number of flowers per head ranged from 84 to 117 (av. 93) in the heads counted. The bracts of the involucre are usually eight per head—exactly this number in 62 per cent of the first heads on a random sample of twenty-nine plants growing under favorable conditions, and in 90 per cent of the second heads of the same plants. Heads with nine bracts are common, this number accounting for 34 per cent more of the first heads and the remaining 10 per cent of the second heads in the population sampled. Heads with as many as twelve bracts, however, are occasionally found. No head with fewer than eight bracts has been noted. The bracts are relatively broader and shorter than in *T. dubius.* They are usually longer than the longest ligules—often twice as long—and are not margined with purple. The expanded mature heads range from 9–11 (av. 10) cm. in diameter. The achenes are stout, ranging from 28–36 (av. 31.7) mm. long including the beak. The thick body is abruptly narrowed to and clearly differentiated from the somewhat longer beak, which is stouter than in *T. dubius.* The outer achenes are dark brown or rarely paler, the inner ones paler, and the pappus is brownish.

Pollen mother cells of three plants were examined. In all three plants, six bivalents regularly were formed at metaphase I of meiosis (fig. 15). Mature pollen grains appeared 97.5 per cent good. The mean diameter of mature pollen protoplasts was 30.8 μ. The calculated diameter of mean volume was 31.0 μ. In comparison with those for the other diploid species, and the tetraploid involving *T. porrifolius* and *T. dubius,* these values appear a little high. This species is highly fertile (fig. 6), not more than 2 or 3 per cent of the flowers failing to produce fruits under normal conditions, and even the poorly developed achenes toward the center of the head uniformly contain apparently viable embryos.

Tragopogon pratensis.—This species (fig. 2) is marked by chrome-yellow ligules, the longest about equaling the involucral bracts in length. The *forma minor* with all ligules much shorter than the involucral bracts has not been found in our area. The habit is slender and much branched. The leaves are abruptly narrowed below, resulting in concave margins which are conspicuously crisped. The long acuminate tips are curled backward. The herbage is obscurely floccose when young, later glabrate, and pale green, not glaucous. The slender peduncles are scarcely at all inflated, even in fruit. The number of flowers per head ranged from fifty-one to ninety-six (av. seventy-five) in the heads counted. The number of involucral bracts per head is usually eight (70 ± per cent) or nine (30 ± per cent), rarely as many as thirteen (two observed). The bracts, which about equal the outer ligules in length, are short, broad, and margined with purple. The expanded mature heads average between 5 and 6 cm. in diameter. The achenes are stout, ranging from 20–25 mm. in length, including the beak. The thick body is abruptly narrowed to and clearly differentiated from the usually somewhat shorter beak. The outer achenes are usually dark brown, passing to straw colored inwardly, and the pappus is whitish.

Pollen mother cells of four plants were examined. In three plants, meiosis was regular with six bivalents at metaphase I (fig. 16). In one, a chromatin bridge (but no fragment) was observed in some anaphase I configurations. Since no fragment was found, this may have been a delayed separation of one of the longer chromosome pairs. It was not found in any of the other plants. Mature pollen grains, appeared 98.5 per cent good. The mean diameter of mature pollen protoplasts was 29.3 μ. The calculated diameter of mature pollen protoplasts of mean volume was 29.2 μ. These values are identical with those of *T. dubius*. The species is highly fertile (fig. 7), not more than 2 or 3 per cent of the flowers failing to produce fruits under normal conditions, and even the poorly developed achenes toward the center of the head uniformly contain apparently viable embryos.

INTERSPECIFIC DIPLOID HYBRIDS.—Wherever any two of the three introduced diploid species grow together, natural hybrids can be expected. These hybrids are not found except in patches including both of their parents. All three possible hybrids have been found. They combine certain dominant characteristics derived from the parents involved, and on this basis form three additional classes. In most features, they are not intermediate, but display a re-combination of the characteristics which mark their parents. In two cases, those involving *T. porrifolius* and the two yellow-flowered species, a striking "new" character, bicolored ligules, appears through the interaction of genes for anthocyanin coloration derived from *T. porrifolius* and for yellow plastids derived from the yellow-flowered parent. There is also a gene involved which restricts the anthocyanin to the distal portion of the ligule. As a result, the ligules in these two hybrids are reddish brown to violet brown distally and yellow proximally.

The frequency of the hybrids varies from place to place, presumably depending on the relative opportunities for cross pollination between the parents 2 or more years previously. They usually can be found wherever the two parental species are growing together, and sometimes form a very considerable percentage of the individuals in a patch. The only actual frequency count was made by Dr. Gerald B. Ownbey at Pullman in 1946. He found in one patch, extending for 750 ft. along a roadside, 782 individuals of *T. dubius*, 123 of *T. porrifolius*, and 20 *T. dubius* × *porrifolius* hybrids. His results

by 50-ft. intervals are presented as table 2. This appears to be a relatively typical situation. The total number of individuals of each hybrid combination flowering annually in the Pullman-Moscow area runs into the thousands.

The hybrid individuals as a whole are strikingly uniform for each parental combination. There is some variation in color intensity of the ligules in the hybrids involving *T. porrifolius*, but this is no greater than in this parental species. The factor governing ligule length, also, is passed from *T. porrifolius* to its hybrid offspring, producing long- and short-liguled individuals in about the same proportions as in the parental species.

All three hybrid combinations are extremely sterile. This sterility is usually obvious at a glance (fig. 8, 9, 10). The heads, after flowering, do not continue to develop normally, even though a few fruits with embryos are produced. The bracts of the involucre do not grow as in the species, and the peduncle does not enlarge appreciably. Almost all of the ovaries abort at the flowering stage or shortly thereafter. In all three hybrid combinations, however, individual plants have been observed which appear to develop normal heads of achenes, and at maturity these heads of achenes expand normally. Three such plants were observed in *T. dubius* × *porrifolius*, five in *T. dubius* × *pratensis*, and eleven in *T. porrifolius* × *pratensis*. Each set of these plants was found in only one very limited area, suggesting close genetic relationship between the mem-

TABLE 2. *Frequency of Tragopogon dubius, T. porrifolius, and F₁ hybrids by 50-ft. intervals along roadside, Pullman, Washington, 1946.*

Interval	dubius	porrifolius	hybrids
1	11	18	0
2	56	20	0
3	129	6	0
4	114	1	0
5	44	4	1
6	11	0	0
7	8	2	0
8	19	3	1
9	31	7	0
10	65	14	1
11	99	11	0
12	43	8	8
13	26	5	4
14	51	6	4
15	75	18	1
Totals	782	123	20
Per cent	84.5	13.3	2.2

bers of the set. Paradoxically, these quasi-fertile hybrid individuals were the most sterile of any examined. Although from 15–28 per cent of the flowers produced mature fruits that superficially appeared to be fully developed, direct observation showed that at most only 0.4 per cent produced fruits with embryos.

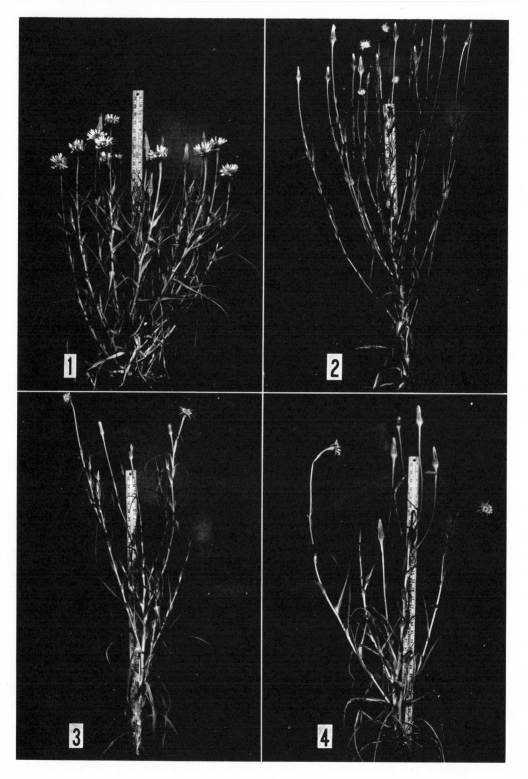

The sterile hybrids are often taller, more branched, and more floriferous than the diploid species, particularly with age. They do not, however, possess the marked "gigas" characteristics of the amphiploids to be discussed later.

From the uniformity of the hybrids within each of the three classes, and their sterility, it is inferred that most, of not all, of those observed are F_1 individuals. Evidence for back-cross or F_2 generations is presented in a later section. The characteristics of hybrid individuals of each of the parental combinations follow:

Tragopogon dubius $\times$ *porrifolius* F_1.—Hybrids of this parentage are marked by bicolored ligules, violet brown (or infrequently reddish brown) distally and yellow at the base. They are distinguished from *T. porrifolius* $\times$ *pratensis* hybrids by their uniformly tapering leaves with neither crisped margins nor recurved tips, the number and shape of the involucral bracts which are not margined with purple, and the generally more violet cast of the ligules. The leaves are obscurely floccose when young, but soon become glabrate and glaucous. The habit is generally more strict that in *T. dubius*. The few mature fully developed achenes show a close resemblance to those of *T. porrifolius* in size, shape and color.

The number of bracts per head was determined on the first heads of forty-six plants growing under favorable conditions. Of these, thirty-six (78 per cent) had thirteen bracts, six (13 per cent) had twelve bracts, and the remaining four (9 per cent) had eleven bracts. As in *T. dubius*, late heads and those of depauperate plants were noted commonly to have as few as eight involucral bracts. The bracts resemble those of *T. dubius* in shape as well as number.

These F_1 hybrids are highly sterile (fig. 8). One hundred eighty-seven heads collected at maturity yielded only 161 fruits with embryos. The number of flowers per head was found to average 130 in ten heads. This figure is likely high, since these heads were from particularly robust plants. These same ten heads also produced an average of 1.7 fruits with embryos per head *vs.* the general average of 0.87 for the entire lot. On the basis of 130 flowers per head, the fertility of the hybrid is 0.67 per cent.

Pollen mother cells of two plants were examined. Metaphase I of meiosis was irregular in both plants. In the first, two bivalents and eight univalents were found; in the second a ring of four, two bivalents, and four univalents were observed (fig. 17). Notwithstanding these irregularities, spore-tetrad formation was not conspicuously abnormal. Mature pollen grains, however, were found to be 92 per cent visibly abortive. No mature pollen grains exceeding the diploid size range were observed.

Three quasi-fertile plants, otherwise indistinguishable from the usual F_1 type, were found. Nineteen heads from these plants yielded only seven fruits with embryos. The average number of flowers for 13 heads was 105, and fertility, calculated on this basis, 0.35 per cent. Pollen mother cells were not examined.

Tragopogon dubius $\times$ *pratensis* F_1.—Hybrids of this parentage (fig. 3) are yellow-flowered, the shade being intermediate between those of the parents. They are easily recognized by their recombination of characteristics marking the parents, together with their usually obvious sterility (fig. 9). The relative lengths of involucral bracts and ligules are those of *T. dubius,* as are the number of bracts per head and their shape. The bracts, however, are margined with purple as in *T. pratensis,* and the leaves resemble this parent in their shape, color, crisped margins, and recurved tips. The influence of *T. pratensis* is also evident in the size and shape of the few fully developed achenes matured, although in color these approach those of *T. dubius.*

The number of bracts per head was determined in sixty heads collected for seed. Of these, twenty-three (38 per cent) had thirteen bracts, thirteen (21 per cent) had twelve bracts, eleven (18 per cent) had eleven bracts, five (8 per cent) had ten bracts, five (8 per cent) had nine bracts, and three (5 per cent) had eight bracts. These same 60 heads yielded 101 fully developed fruits, some of which, it was subsequently discovered, lacked embryos. On a basis of an assumed average of 100 flowers per head —no more reliable figure is available—this is a maximum fertility of less than 1.7 per cent. Taking the achenes without embryos into consideration, and the possibility that the assumed number of flowers per head is low, the actual fertility may be as low as 1 per cent.

Five quasi-fertile plants, otherwise indistinguishable from the usual F_1 type, were observed. One of these was studied in considerable detail. As usual in this hybrid (fig. 9), only one or two fruits per head developed beyond anthesis in the earlier heads, but later heads appeared fertile. Twelve later heads from this plant yielded only three fruits with embryos, although many fruits appeared fully developed until they were broken in two. Four heads averaged 114 flowers per head, and on this basis, fertility was 0.22 per cent. It is likely that this plant furnished some of the pollen mother cells studied.

Pollen mother cells of three plants were examined. All three plants were nearly regular with the usual six bivalents at metaphase I of meiosis (fig. 18), occasionally with a pair of univalents, or possibly a ring of four. Evidence of pairing between heteromorphic chromosomes was observed in four cells. A few microspore groups at the tetrad stage contained five and six cells, sometimes of uniform

Fig. 1–4. *Tragopogon.*—Fig. 1. *T. dubius.*—Fig. 2. *T. pratensis.*—Fig. 3. Diploid *T. dubius* $\times$ *pratensis.*—Fig. 4. Amphiploid *T. dubius* $\times$ *pratensis* (*T. miscellus*).

Fig. 5–13. Fruiting heads of *Tragopogon* (×⅓).—Fig. 5. *T. dubius.*—Fig. 6. *T. porrifolius.*—Fig. 7. *T. pratensis.*—Fig. 8. Diploid *T. dubius × porrifolius.*—Fig. 9. Diploid *T. dubius × pratensis.*—Fig. 10. Diploid *T. porrifolius × pratensis.*—Fig. 11. Amphiploid *T. dubius × porrifolius* (*T. mirus*).—Fig. 12. Amphiploid *T. dubius × pratensis* (*T. miscellus*).—Fig. 13. Quasi-fertile diploid *T. porrifolius × pratensis.*

size and sometimes of varying sizes. Mature pollen grains were found to be 93 per cent visibly abortive. No mature pollen grains exceeding the diploid size range were observed.

T. porrifolius × pratensis F₁.—Hybrids of this parentage exhibit bicolored ligules which are red-dish brown (or infrequently violet brown) distally and yellow at the base. They are distinguished from *T. dubius × porrifolius* hybrids by their abruptly tapering leaves with crisped margins and recurved tips, the number and shape of the involucral bracts, which are margined with purple, and the generally more reddish cast to the ligules. The leaves are glabrous or nearly so from the beginning, and are not very glaucous. The habit is generally strict. Mature, fully developed achenes show a close similarity to those of *T. porrifolius* in size, shape, and color.

The number of involucral bracts per head was counted in sixty-two heads collected for seed. Of these, fifty-two (84 per cent) had eight bracts, eight (13 per cent) had nine bracts, one (1.6 per cent) had ten, and one (1.6 per cent) had seven. Occasionally, a head is found with as many as eleven bracts. These same 62 heads yielded 120 fully developed achenes, a few of which, it was subsequently discovered, lacked embryos. On the basis of an assumed average of ninety flowers per head—no more reliable figure is available—this is a maximum fertility of about 2 per cent.

Eleven quasi-fertile plants (fig. 13), otherwise indistinguishable from the usual F_1 type (fig. 10), were observed. Eight heads from eight of these plants, averaging ninety-five flowers per head, yielded only three fruits with embryos, although 28 per cent of the potential fruits in them appeared fully developed otherwise. This is a fertility of 0.4 per cent.

Pollen mother cells or four plants, including one of the quasi-fertile ones, were examined. Chromosome pairing at metaphase I of meiosis varied greatly. Although six bivalents were found in a number of cells (fig. 19), there were often from two to ten univalents—this last number in the quasi-fertile plant. Microspore groups of three (one much larger than the other two) and six, as well as the usual four were observed. Mature pollen grains from one of the normal hybrids, were found to be only 60 per cent visibly abortive; from one of the quasi-fertile plants, 96 per cent were abortive. No mature pollen grains exceeding the diploid size range were observed in either.

Two AMPHIPLOID SPECIES.—In the season of 1949 four small colonies were detected in which the members differed from the corresponding diploid hybrids in their very evident fertility and in the possession of conspicuous "gigas" features. These four colonies were immediately suspected to represent two newly originated allotetraploid species ($n =$ 12), and this chromosomal constitution has since been confirmed. These allotetraploids differ in none of their characters from the corresponding diploid hybrids, but they are much larger in every way. The stems and leaves are thicker, coarser, more massive and succulent. The heads are larger both in flower and in fruit, and the fruits larger and thicker. The mean volume of the spherical pollen grains is almost precisely the sum of the mean volumes of those of the parental species. The fertility averages between 52 and 66 per cent, although there is wide variation in individual plants beyond these limits. In all four colonies, the amphiploids occurred with both the parental species, and the diploid F_1 hybrid. In one patch, three species, three F_1 hybrids and one amphiploid species grew together.

Tragopogon dubius $\times$ *porrifolius Amphiploid* (*T. mirus*).—Two colonies of this amphiploid (fig. 11) were studied, one in Pullman, Washington, and one in Palouse, Washington, 15 mi. away. Extensive search revealed no other individuals. Only *T. dubius* and *T. porrifolius*, with frequent diploid F_1 hybrids between them, are found in either of these two towns. The Pullman colony was studied more intensively. It consisted of fifty-six flowering individuals growing close together in fertile bottom land along a railroad track. The Palouse colony consisted of twenty-five or more individuals growing on a dry hillside. Both these and the associated parental species and diploid F_1 hybrids were considerably smaller than at the Pullman site, which is attributable to the less favorable habitat.

In the Pullman colony, the bract number was thirteen in ten of the twelve heads—one per plant —examined, eleven and nine, respectively, in the remaining two heads. Of five heads (from five plants) from the Palouse population, one had twelve bracts, one had ten, two had nine, and one had eight. The number of flowers was found to average 147 per head in the 12 heads from Pullman, 89 per head in 4 heads from Palouse. The twelve heads from Pullman averaged seventy-six fruits with embryos per head, a fertility of 52 per cent; those from Palouse, fifty-nine fruits with embryos per head, a fertility of 66 per cent.

Pollen mother cells of three plants from the Pullman colony were examined. In all three plants, twelve bivalents were observed at meiotic metaphase I of some cells (fig. 20). Multivalent formation was frequent, however, and many cells could not be analyzed completely. Among the multivalents studied, the maximum number of associated chromosomes discerned was six (fig. 21). It will be recalled that the F_1 hybrid showed a ring of four. Where multivalents were not formed, a strong secondary association between similar bivalents was frequently noted. Spore-tetrad formation appeared normal, with the four microspores notably larger than in the diploid species and hybrids. Mature pollen grains appeared to be 92 per cent good. The mean diameter of mature pollen protoplasts was 37.0 μ. The calculated diameter of protoplasts of mean volume was 36.8 μ. The mean volume of the pollen protoplasts was 8 per cent less than the sum of the mean volumes of those of the parental species. This difference is probably not significant.

Tragopogon dubius $\times$ *pratensis Amphiploid* (*T. miscellus*).—Two colonies of this amphiploid (fig. 4, 12) were studied, both in Moscow, Idaho. Extensive search in Moscow and other towns where the parental species and F_1 hybrids between them occur, revealed no other individuals. All three diploid species and the three diploid hybrids are frequent in Moscow, but only this amphiploid occurs here. Each colony included between thirty and thirty-five individuals, scattered over a few hundred square yards. They were separated by about a mile. At one

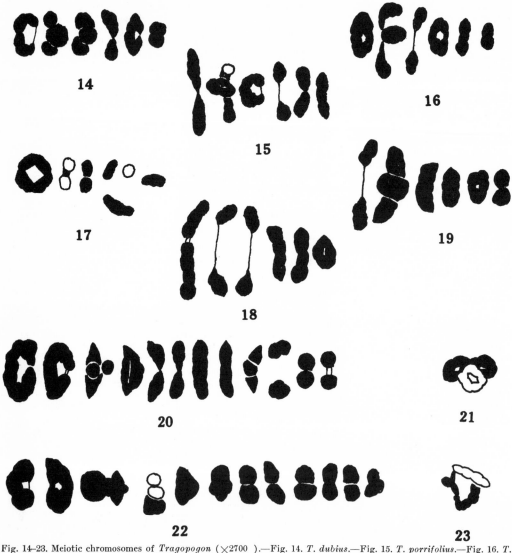

Fig. 14–23. Meiotic chromosomes of *Tragopogon* (×2700).—Fig. 14. *T. dubius.*—Fig. 15. *T. porrifolius.*—Fig. 16. *T. pratensis.*—Fig. 17. *T. dubius* × *porrifolius.*—Fig. 18. *T. dubius* × *pratensis.*—Fig. 19. *T. porrifolius* × *pratensis.*—Fig. 20. Amphiploid *T. dubius* × *porrifolius* (*T. mirus*).—Fig. 21. Multivalent from same interpreted as VI.—Fig. 22. Amphiploid *T. dubius* × *pratensis* (*T. miscellus*).—Fig. 23. Multivalent from same interpreted as heteromorphic IV.

site, in bottom land along a railroad track, conditions were favorable for full development. At the other, along a roadside away from the creek, conditions were not so favorable, and the plants were smaller and less vigorous, as were also those of the parental species and diploid hybrids which occurred there.

In the first colony, the bract number was thirteen

in nine of twenty-six heads, twelve in seven heads, eleven in four heads, nine in one head, and eight in one head. Twenty-three heads averaged 115 flowers and 64 fruits with embryos per head, a fertility of 56 per cent.

In the second colony, the bract number was thirteen in two of eighteen heads, twelve in one, eleven in two, ten in seven, nine in five, and eight in one.

Plate 1. Flowering heads of *Tragopogon*. (See frontispiece.) Arranged as in fig. 5–13. *T. dubius* (lower left), *T. porrifolius* (top center), and *T. pratensis* (lower right) form a triangle, along the sides of which are arranged the diploid hybrids, *T. dubius* × *porrifolius* (left center), *T. dubius* × *pratensis* (below center), and *T. porrifolius* × *pratensis* (right center). Adjacent to the diploid hybrids are the corresponding amphiploids, *T. mirus* (upper left), and *T. miscellus* (bottom center). At upper right is the head of the quasi-fertile diploid *T. porrifolius* × *pratensis* hybrid.

Sixteen heads averaged ninety-one flowers and fifty-three fruits with embryos per head, a fertility of 58 per cent.

Pollen mother cells of two plants from the first population were examined. In both, regular or nearly regular plates of twelve bivalents were observed at metaphase I of meiosis (fig. 22). Quadrivalents and some univalents, however, were frequent, and some cells could not be analyzed completely. One configuration interpreted as a quadrivalent involving two heteromorphic chromosome pairs (fig. 23) is of probable significance. It will be recalled that there was evidence also of heteromorphic pairing in the corresponding diploid hybrid. Spore-tetrad formation appeared normal, with the microspores notably larger than in the diploid species and hybrids. Mature pollen grains appeared 91.5 per cent good. The mean diameter of mature pollen protoplasts was 36.3 μ. The calculated diameter of protoplasts of mean volume was 36.4 μ. The mean volume of the pollen protoplasts was only 3 per cent less than the sum of the mean volumes of those of the parental species. This difference is not significant.

F_2 AND BACKCROSS GENERATIONS.—Although the high degree of sterility, both of the pollen and ovules, of the three diploid interspecific hybrids would impose a limitation of major importance on the occurrence of F_2 and backcross individuals, these should nevertheless be expected to appear in small numbers wherever interspecific hybridization is extensive. Furthermore, the well marked dominant characters evident in the F_1 generation should provide "markers" for the study of introgression into the parental species. The absence of such evidence of gene flow across the interspecific barriers, together with the sterility of the individuals showing recombination of characters, was the basis for the earlier statement that most, if not all, of these individuals represent the F_1 generation. Among the thousands of plants examined, however, three individuals appeared to represent a later hybrid generation. Two of these resembled *T. pratensis* very closely, except for the color of the ligules, which in one were pale orange, and in the other, deep red. That these individuals were of hybrid origin was confirmed by their sterility, which approximated 70 per cent. The other species involved must have been *T. porrifolius*. The third individual involved *T. dubius* and *T. porrifolius*. It was characterized by very pale ligules, and may have represented either a backcross to *T. dubius* or an F_2 segregate. It was about 99 per cent sterile. In the absence of positive evidence to the contrary, it seems improbable that introgression into any of the three species is taking place.

DISCUSSION.—The genus *Tragopogon* has furnished a classic example of interspecific hybridization since Linnaeus in the summer of 1759 obtained what is usually considered to be the first interspecific hybrid produced for a scientific purpose, that between *T. pratensis* and *T. porrifolius* (Linnaeus, 1760; Focke, 1881, 1890; Lotsy, 1927; Winge, 1938).[2] This genus now likewise supplies the second and third well documented examples of the origin of a species through amphiploidy in natural populations in historic time. The other example is that of *Spartina Townsendii* (Huskins, 1931), but both parents of this species are themselves undoubtedly also polyploid.

Linnaeus, after rubbing the pollen from the flowers of *Tragopogon pratensis* early in the morning, sprinkled the stigmas with pollen *T. porrifolius* at about eight o'clock. The heads were marked, and the seeds harvested and planted in a separate place. The F_1 hybrids flowered in 1759, producing purple flowers, yellow at the base. Seeds of these F_1 hybrids, along with an essay describing this and other experiments and observations bearing on sex in plants, were submitted in a competition sponsored by the Imperial Academy of Sciences at St. Petersburg. The essay was awarded the prize on September 6, 1760, and the seeds planted in the botanical garden at St. Petersburg, where the F_2 flowered in 1761. These were observed by Kölreuter who recorded (1761) his conclusion that "the hybrid goat's-beard . . . is not a hybrid plant in the real sense, but at most only a half hybrid, *and indeed in different degrees*" (italics added). This record of segregation in the F_2 of an experimental hybrid, a century before Mendel, has escaped recent notice, even of Roberts (1929), who brought together the pertinent facts. I am indebted to Dr. Jens Clausen for calling it to my attention.

This cross was repeated by Focke (1890), Lotsy (1927), and Winge (1938). Focke's detailed, point by point comparison of the parental species and F_1 hybrids has been overlooked by later workers. Lotsy's contribution is in the form of a color plate illustrating the flowering heads of the parental species, F_1, and F_2 segregates. No attempt at analysis of the spectacular segregation in the F_2 is attempted in the paper. Winge's investigations covered a period of 15 years, and carried the hybrids through the F_7 generation. He was particularly concerned with the genetic bases of specific differences, and gives a detailed account of five independent segregating pairs of genes affecting flower color. It was possible by selection to recover both parental species in apparently pure form from the segregating hybrids. Full fertility was regained in the F_2 and subsequent generations. The chromosomes of the two parental species and hybrids of different generations were thoroughly investigated. Both species and hybrids were diploid, $2n = 12$, with the regular formation of six bivalents at metaphase I of meiosis. No meiotic irregularities were noted which

[2] Zirkle (1935) maintains that the first artificial hybrid was produced by Thomas Fairchild, a London horticulturist, prior to 1717, between the carnation (*Dianthus Caryophyllus*) and the sweet william (*D. barbatus*). The evidence that this hybrid resulted from a deliberate experimental cross pollination is conflicting and inconclusive.

would explain the low fertility of the F_1 hybrids. Root-tip mitoses revealed differences in morphology of the somatic chromosomes of the two species, and these differences were found in the reconstituted parental types of hybrid parentage. No tetraploids were found among the 113 plants of Winge's F_2 cultures, although root-tips of 82 were examined. The observation of limited sectors of tetraploid tissue in root-tips of two of these plants, however, is perhaps of significance.

Aside from the work of Winge, chromosome numbers of five species of *Tragopogon* have been reported casually by Poddubnaja-Arnoldi *et al.* (1935) as follows: *T. brevirostris*, $2n = 12$; *T. Cupani*, $2n = 24$; *T. major (dubius)*, $2n = 12$; *T. marginatus* $2n = 12$; and *T. porrifolius*, $2n = 12$. As the only previously known tetraploid species, *T. Cupani* is of considerable interest. Examination of a single specimen so named, preserved in the Herbarium of the Missouri Botanical Garden, suggests the possibility that this may be the amphiploid involving *T. porrifolius* and *T. pratensis* which has not been found in either Winge's cultures or our wild populations.

In later papers, Focke (1897, 1907) reports additional hybrids including *T. orientalis* × *porrifolius*, *T. dubius* × *porrifolius*, and the triple hybrid (*T. pratensis* × *porrifolius*) × *orientalis*. The first and last of these were sterile, but the second always matured about a quarter of the usual number of fruits. From it was obtained a fertile, constant line of plants with brownish-purple flowers, which was grown for about eight generations. Focke considered this line to represent a newly originated species, *T. phaeus*, but it does not seem to be our amphiploid of the same parentage. A second constant, fertile form, *T. hortensis*, of uncertain origin, also appeared in his cultures. The first plant of this line was unusually robust, but this characteristic was lost in later generations. It is neither of our amphiploids.

There are numerous brief references to natural hybridization in *Tragopogon*. Linnaeus (1760) records the spontaneous appearance in 1757 of *T. porrifolius* × *pratensis* in a part of his garden where he had planted its parental species. Schultz-Bipontii (1846) noted this hybrid and also *T. major* × *pratensis* in his garden. The occurrence of *T. porrifolius* × *pratensis* in wild populations has been reported in Denmark (Lange, 1864), Germany (Focke, 1887), France (Rouy, 1890), and Sweden (Rouy, 1890). In the United States, it has been found in Illinois (Sherff, 1911) and Michigan (Farwell, 1930). That the hybrid occurred with its parents is definitely stated in most instances. In central Germany, Haussknecht (1884, 1888) found all three possible hybrid combinations of the species occurring there, *T. major* × *orientalis*, *T. major* × *pratensis*, and *T. orientalis* × *pratensis*. The sterility of the first and last was noted. *T. major* × *orientalis* is also recorded for Austria by Dichtl (1883) and Waisbecker (1897). Chenevard (1899) reports *T. crocifolius* × *major?* growing with its presumed

parents in France [?] and Cockerell (1912) found sterile *T. dubius* × *porrifolius* growing with its parents at Boulder, Colorado. Further search of the literature would probably reveal many additional records, but these are sufficient to show that natural hybridization in *Tragopogon* is extensive and involves several species.

The chromosome studies reported in the present paper were directed primarily toward the determination of the ploidy levels of the entities involved and the detection of gross meiotic irregularities which might explain the high degree of sterility in the F_1 together with the success of the amphiploids. The material is suitable for much more detailed analysis, which modify considerably these preliminary observations.

The chromosome complement of all three diploid species consists of three longer and three shorter pairs. The three longer pairs are further generally distinguishable at meiosis by the number and position of chiasmata. At first metaphase, one long pair usually forms a ring with two terminal chiasmata, or through absence of one chiasma, a chain. The second pair is characterized by a submedian localized chiasma, and sometimes by one or two others. The chiasma number in the third long pair is more variable. There are often probably three, but these chromosomes may form a ring with only two, or a chain with only one. The three short pairs are less easily distinguished at metaphase, although one may be a little larger than the other two. Generally in these there is a single terminal chiasma.

The bivalents formed in the F_1 hybrids usually correspond closely to those of the diploid species, indicating a rather high degree of homology between the chromosomes of the different species, at least as far as pairing is concerned. Univalents, when formed, come mostly from the three short pairs. Conclusive evidence as to which two of the long pairs form the ring of four in the *T. dubius* × *porrifolius* F_1 has not been obtained.

The bivalents of the amphiploids also correspond closely to those of the diploid species, except that there are twice as many. Often this correspondence is obscured by some multivalent formation. Where multivalents are not formed, a strong secondary association between similar bivalents was sometimes noted. Although the chromosomes, at least in *T. dubius* × *pratensis* F_1 and *T. porrifolius* × *pratensis* F_1, are able to form normal-appearing allosynaptic bivalents, pairing in the amphiploids, on the whole, seems to be strongly autosynaptic. It should be observed that residual allosynapsis might be expected again to occur in the progeny of such amphiploids as *T. miscellus* when crossed with a third species, and that meotic pairing in this hypothetical hybrid might not indicate the third species to be an ancestor of the amphiploid.

The high degree of sterility in the F_1 could be caused by evolutionary differentiation of the chromosomes of each species brought about by translocation or interchange of segments between the non-homologous chromosomes of the genome. Ring formation in T. dubius × porrifolius and evidence of heteromorphic pairing in T. dubius × pratensis indicate that differences in homology do exist. Around these structural differences, with the resultant interference with random chromosome recombination (because of non-viability of deficient gametes), could be built the association of distinctive genes which mark each species. If all six chromosomes of each parental genome were non-homologous for deficiencies caused by translocation or interchange of essential segments, as compared with the corresponding member of the other parental genome, only those gametes containing a reconstituted parental genome with respect to these structural differences would be viable. Disregarding crossing-over, and given random distribution of the chromosomes of each of the six pairs, one genome of each of the parental species should be reconstituted in each $2^6 =$ sixty-four gametes. In other words, approximately 3.1 per cent of the gametes should contain a parental set of chromosomes. The maximum fertility, if only reconstituted gametes were viable, would be 3.1 per cent, and the F_2 would fall into three classes, reconstituted parental species, 25 per cent for each, and reconstituted F_1 hybrids, 50 per cent. Since any deficient chromosome segments of one parental species might be compensated for by the addition through crossing-over of non-deficient segments of the other parent, the net effect of crossing-over would be an increase in the variability of the F_2, and the genes on the crossover segments would behave in the manner which Winge has described. Some such mechanism might explain the restored fertility in the F_2 and subsequent generations of Winge's hybrids, and the infrequency of detectable later generations in our wild populations.

The mechanism of origin of the amphiploid species, whether by somatic or gametic doubling in the F_1 is obscure. Winge's observation of tetraploid sectors in root-tip tissues would favor the former explanation, as would the absence of pollen grains exceeding the diploid size range in all of the diploid hybrids examined in the present study. Supporting the latter explanation would be the presence of spore triads in some of our hybrids, which suggests that diploid pollen grains might be produced, and the lack of extended vegetative growth. It should be noted that positive evidence favoring either of these mechanisms was observed only in the one of the three hybrid combinations for which no amphiploid is known, that between T. porrifolius and T. pratensis.

Whatever the mechanism of origin, it is apparent that the amphiploids do not originate with great frequency. The four known colonies probably represent four independent instances of chromosome doubling, and the subsequent establishment of the resultant tetraploid. Considering the frequency of all three F_1 hybrid combinations, however, chromosome doubling must be an exceedingly rare event.

For theoretical reasons, its frequent occurrence in species hybrids with essentially regular meiotic pairing is not to be expected, and amphiploids derived from such should be unsuccessful.

In spite of these theoretical handicaps, the amphiploids of Tragopogon have appeared, and have attained a degree of success. Although the populations are still small and precarious, fertility is good, and these species are competing successfully with their parents. Crossing-over has not led to deterioration, presumably because each chromosome usually pairs with its exact homologue, and the consequences of crossing-over, therefore, are not deleterious. Fertility ought to improve with succeeding generations, since any genetic factor which will increase fertility—and there is wide variation in this respect—will enjoy a real selective advantage.

The ecological characteristics of the new amphiploids are not yet apparent. In all instances, they occur within the ecological amplitude of the most restricted parental species. The ecological requirements of natural amphiploids are often such that they have achieved an ecological and geographical distribution somewhat different from the species from which they are presumed to have been derived (Clausen et al., 1945). Since, in both instances, the present amphiploids combine genomes from species with significantly different ecological requirements, it will be interesting to follow their ecological development. At the present time, it is apparent that they have not spread far from their point of origin.

TAXONOMIC CONSIDERATIONS.—The two newly originated amphiploids are to be considered taxonomic species for the following reasons: (1) They are natural groups characterized by a combination of distinctive morphological features. (2) They are reproducing themselves under natural conditions. (3) Gene interchange between the amphiploids and the parental species is prevented by a genetic barrier (ploidy level), and presumably residual sterility factors—evident in the F_1 hybrids—would prevent free interbreeding between the two.

Search of the systematic literature has not revealed the existence of these amphiploid species in Europe, although it would be surprising if they do not occur there. The identification of many obscure species which have been proposed in Tragopogon must await a comprehensive taxonomic and cytogenetic study of the genus. Accordingly, these two amphiploids are here described as new species.

Tragopogon mirus Ownbey, sp. nov.—Herbae biennes primum obscure floccosae deinde glabrae glaucaeque. Folia lineari-lanceolata semi-amplexicauliusque ad 5 cm. lata paulatim attenuata, marginibus non crispis, apicibus non cirrosis. Capitula multiflora, pedunculis inflatis fistulosis usque ad 15 mm. crassis. Bracteae involucri lineari-lanceolatae ubique virides, in plantis robustioribus plerumque 13. Ligulae bicoloratae ad apicem lilacinae ad basem flavae bracteis paulum breviores. Achenia rostraque conjuncta 25–35 mm. longa, exteriora fusca, interiora straminea, rostro corpore subaequilongo, pappo cervino.

Type: Washington. Whitman County: in fertile bottom land, Pullman, June 9, 1949, *Ownbey 3195,* in Herbarium of the State College of Washington, Pullman.

Tragopogon **miscellus** Ownbey, sp. nov.—Herbae biennes primum obscure floccosae deinde glabrae viridesque. Folia lineari-lanceolata semi-amplexicaulia usque ad 3 cm. lata abrupte attenuata, marginibus crispis, apicibus cirrosis. Capitula pluriflora, pedunculis inflatis fistulosis usque ad 10 mm. crassis. Bracteae involucri lineari-lanceolatae in plantis robustioribus plerumque 13, marginibus purpureis. Ligulae flavae bractea dimidia subaequilongae. Achenia rostraque conjuncta 25-35 mm. longa, exteriora fusca, interiora straminea, rostro corpore subaequilongo vel longiore, pappo cinereo.

Type: Idaho. Latah County: in fertile bottom land, Moscow, June 10, 1949, *Ownbey 3196,* in Herbarium of the State College of Washington, Pullman.

SUMMARY

Three diploid ($n = 6$) species of the Old World genus *Tragopogon* (Compositae), *T. dubius, T. porrifolius,* and *T. pratensis,* have become widely naturalized in North America. In southeastern Washington and adjacent Idaho, where all three occur, extensive natural hybridization is taking place. Each species crosses readily with both of the others, and wherever two or more grow together, easily detected F_1 hybrids are frequent. These diploid hybrids for all three species combinations are highly sterile, not more than 1–2 per cent of the flowers producing fruits with embryos. They are intermediate only in the sense that they recombine certain dominant characteristics of the parental species involved. F_2 and back-cross individuals are absent or nearly so. Meiosis in the hybrids is fairly regular, although some multivalents and univalents are formed, particularly in *T. dubius* $\times$ *T. porrifolius.* Four small amphiploid populations were discovered in 1949. These represent apparently four recent and independent instances of the doubling of the chromosome sets, two cases each for the *T. dubius* $\times$ *porrifolius* and *T. dubius* $\times$ *pratensis* hybrids. These two tetraploid entities ($n = 12$) are fairly regular meiotically, usually forming bivalents at metaphase I in pollen mother cells. They are moderately fertile, on the average from 52–66 per cent of the flowers producing fruits with embryos. They are established and true-breeding entities, although population size is still precariously small. Morphologically, they are like the corresponding diploid hybrids except for conspicuous "gigas" features and their very evident fertility. Their cell volume, as revealed by measurement of the spherical pollen grains, is almost precisely the summation of the cell volumes of the two parental genomes. They are accorded species rank, described and named *T. mirus* (amphiploid *T. dubius* $\times$ *porrifolius*) and *T. miscellus* (amphiploid *T. dubius* $\times$ *pratensis*).

DEPARTMENT OF BOTANY,
STATE COLLEGE OF WASHINGTON,
PULLMAN, WASHINGTON

LITERATURE CITED

CHENEVARD, P. 1899. Notes floristiques. Bull. Trav. Soc. Bot. Genève 9:130.

CLAUSEN, J., D. D. KECK, AND W. M. HIESEY. 1945. Experimental studies on the nature of species. II. Plant evolution through amphiploidy and autoploidy, with examples from the Madiinae. Carnegie Inst. of Washington. Publ. No. 564.

COCKERELL, T. D. A. 1912. *Tragopogon* in Colorado. Torreya 12: 244–247.

DICHTI, P. A. 1883. Ergänzungen zu den "Nachträgen zur Flora von Nieder-Österreich." (Fortsetzung). Deutsch. Bot. Monatschrift 1: 187–188.

FARWELL, O. A. 1930. Botanical gleanings in Michigan. VI. Amer. Midl. Nat. 12: 113–134.

FOCKE, W. O. 1881. Die Pflanzen-Mischlinge. Gebrüder Bornträger. Berlin.

———. 1887. *Tragopogon porrifolius* $\times$ *pratensis.* Abhandl. Naturwiss. Ver. Bremen 9: 287–288.

———. 1890. Versuche und Beobachtungen über Kreuzung und Fruchtansatz bei Blütenpflanzen. Abhandl. Naturwiss. Ver. Bremen 11: 413–421.

———. 1897. Neue Beobachtungen über Artenkreuzung und Selbststerilität. Abhandl. Naturwiss. Ver. Bremen 14: 297–304.

———. 1907. Betrachtungen und Erfahrungen über Variation und Artenbildung. Abhandl. Naturwiss. Ver. Bremen 19: 68–87.

HAUSSKNECHT, C. 1884. Botanischer Verein für Gesamtthüringen. I. Sitzungsberichte. Mitteil. Geogr. Ges. (für Thüringen) Jena 2: 211–217.

———. 1888. Kleinere botanische Mitteilungen. Mitteil. Geogr. Ges. (für Thüringen) Jena 6 (Bot. Ver. Gesamtthüringen): 21–32.

HUSKINS, C. L. 1931. The origin of *Spartina Townsendii.* Genetica 12: 531–538.

KÖLREUTER, J. G. 1761. Vorläufige Nachricht von einigen das Geschlecht der Pflanzen betreffenden Versuchen und Beobachtungen. Gleditsch. Leipzig. (Not seen). Reprinted by W. Pfeffer in Ostwald's Klassiker der exakten Wissenschaften 41: 3–37. 1893.

LANGE, J. 1864. Haandbog i den danske Flora. Ed. 3. C. A. Reitzel. Copenhagen.

LINNAEUS, C. 1760. Disquisitio de quaestione ab Academia imperiali scientiarum Petropolitana in annum MDCCLIX pro praemio proposita: "Sexum plantarum argumentis et experimentis novis. . . ." Academy of Sciences, St. Petersburg. (Not seen.) Reprinted as "Disquisitio de sexu plantarum. . . ." in Amoenitates Academicae 10: 100–131. 1790; in English translation as "A dissertation on the sexes of plants," by J. E. Smith. Nichol. London. 1786.

LOTSY, J. P. 1927. What do we know of the descent of man? Genetica 9: 289–328. Plate II.

PODDUBNAJA-ARNOLDI, W., N. STESCHINA, UND A. SOSNOVETZ. 1935. Der Charakter und die Ursachen der Sterilität bei *Scorzonera tausaghys* Lipsch. et Bosse. Beih. Bot. Centralblatt 53A: 309–339.

ROBERTS, H. F. 1929. Plant hybridization before Mendel. Princeton University Press. Princeton, N.J.

ROUY, M. G. 1890. Remarques sur la synonomie de quelques plantes occidentales. Bull. Soc. Bot. France 37: XIV–XX.

SHERFF, E. E. 1911. *Tragopogon pratensis* × *porrifolius*. Torreya 11: 14–15.

SHULTZ-BIPONTII, K. H. 1846. *Tragopogon*. In P. B. Webb and S. Berthelot's Historie Naturelle des Iles Canaries. 32(2): 469.

WAISBECKER, A. 1897. Beiträge zur Flora des Eisenburger Comitates. Österreich. Bot. Zeitschr. 47: 4–9.

WINGE, Ö. 1938. Inheritance of species characters in *Tragopogon*. A cytogenetic investigation. Compt. Rend. Trav. Lab. Carlsberg Série Physiol. 22: 155–193. Plates I and II.

ZIRKLE, C. 1935. The beginnings of plant hybridization. University of Pennsylvania Press. Philadelphia, Pa.

RETICULATE EVOLUTION IN THE APPALACHIAN ASPLENIUMS [1]

Warren H. Wagner, Jr.

Department of Botany, University of Michigan, Ann Arbor, Michigan

Received, October 20, 1953

Introduction

To be able to postulate the course of evolution in a group of organisms on the basis of indirect evidence is one of the goals of phylogenetic research, since in many groups direct evidence is difficult or impossible to obtain. Occasionally a worker may be fortunate enough to confirm his indirect and comparative techniques by direct evidence, such as the discovery of a postulated ancestral type, or the production of a postulated form by hybridization experiments. In the present study of the evolution of the Appalachian Aspleniums, a complex group of small ferns of the eastern United States, the methods used have been indirect ones, morphological, anatomical, and cytological. But in future years it is to be expected that experimental proof of the conclusions of this study will be forthcoming. The indirect steps used as evidence of reticulate evolution in the Appalachian Aspleniums are thus subject to validation by direct tests.

Wherry (1925, 1936) pointed out that the Appalachian Aspleniums "form a series showing intermediates between certain long-recognized species." His basic end-point species were five in number: *Asplenium pinnatifidum* (lobed spleenwort), *A. montanum* (mountain spleenwort), *A. bradleyi* (cliff spleenwort), *A. platyneuron* (ebony or brownstem spleenwort), and *A. rhizophyllum* (the walking-fern, usually treated as *Camptosorus rhizophyllus* but for sake of simplicity retained in *Asplenium* here). Detailed studies of the morphology of these five end-

point species and comparisons of them with their various intermediates suggest that within the complex totalling 11 described entities, the real extremes are only three in number. These three species are *A. montanum, A. platyneuron,* and *A. rhizophyllum.* All the remaining taxa, commonly treated as species or hybrids—including the familiar *A. pinnatifidum* and *A. bradleyi*—lie somewhere between these three extremes in their morphology.

Among students of the Filicineae it has been rather conventional to consider as hybrids only those intermediate forms which occur as single, sterile plants with obvious parents growing nearby. But with the increasing recognition of allopolyploidy as a factor in species formation in plants, sterility *per se* is no longer the sole signpost of hybrid origin. Indeed, the best-known fern hybrid, *Asplenium ebenoides* (*A. platyneuron* × *A rhizophyllum*), though usually sterile, occurs as a fertile form in one large population in Alabama. It has not, however, been examined cytologically until the present study (Wagner, 1953), nor have any others of the Appalachian Aspleniums been so investigated. The aim of the present work has been not only to clarify the cytological picture of the group, but also to use any other available indirect approaches to its evolutionary history. Thus certain morphological and anatomical features were found valuable in interpreting the intermediate forms. The evidence now indicates that a complex of eight described entities, *A. ebenoides, A. pinnatifidum, A. trudellii, A. kentuckiense, A. gravesii, A. bradleyi, A. bradleyi* × *A. platyneuron,* and *A. bradleyi* × *A. montanum,* has arisen as a result of hybridiza-

[1] This study was aided by a Faculty Research Grant from the Horace H. Rackham School of Graduate Studies.

Reprinted by permission of the author and publisher from
Evolution, **8,** 103–118 (1954).

136

tion between three ancient and original species.

The three basic species are entirely distinctive, whereas the remaining taxa constitute a difficult group, as shown by diverse herbarium identifications and taxonomic interpretations. *Asplenium montanum* (fig. 1, M) shows notably the following peculiarities: (1) triangular, long-petiolate, 2–3-times dissected leaf blades, (2) dark-brown color of the leaf axis present only at the base of the flattened petiole, (3) "glossy" upper leaf surface, resulting from the markedly elongate, practically straight-walled form of the epidermal cells, and (4) occurrence strictly in acid-rock crevices. The closest relative of *A. montanum* appears to be the wide-ranging *A. adiantum-nigrum* of the western United States, Africa, Eurasia,

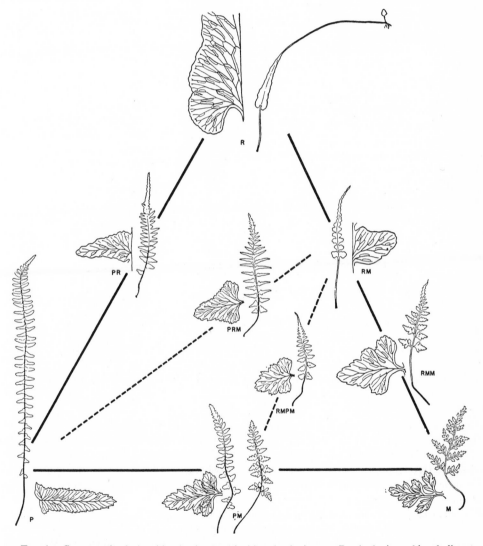

Fig. 1. Concept of relationships in the Appalachian Aspleniums. R. *Asplenium rhizophyllum;* P. *A. platyneuron;* M. *A. montanum;* PR. *A. ebenoides;* RM. *A. pinnatifidum;* PM. *A. bradleyi* (frond on left, Frederick Co., Va., *Gilbert 250;* frond on right, Madison Co., Mo., *Russell*); RMM. *A. trudellii;* RMPM. *A. gravesii;* PRM. *A. kentuckiense.*

TABLE I

Species	2n	n
Asplenium montanum		
Harford Co., Md.	72	36
Pike Co., Ohio	72	36
Asplenium platyneuron		
Montgomery Co., Md.	72	36
Harford Co., Md.	72	—
Hocking Co., Ohio	72	—
Licking Co., Ohio	—	36
Hardy Co., W. Va.	—	36
Asplenium rhizophyllum		
Ross Co., Ohio	—	36
Fairfield Co., Ohio	72	—
Shenandoah Co., Virginia	72	36
Monroe Co., Indiana	—	36
Asplenium ebenoides		
Montgomery Co., Md.	72	(72 univalents)
Hale Co., Alabama (Groff)	144	72
Hale Co., Alabama (Logue)	144	72
Asplenium pinnatifidum		
Shenandoah Co., Va.	144	72
Hardy Co. W. Va.	144	72
York Co., Pa.	—	72
Licking Co., Ohio	—	72
Monroe Co., Indiana	—	72
Asplenium bradleyi		
Harford Co., Md.	144	72
Pike Co., Ohio	144	—
Asplenium trudellii		
York Co., Pa.	108	(ca. 36 univalents, ca. 36 bivalents)
Hardy Co., W. Va.	108	(ca. 36 univalents, ca. 36 bivalents)
Pike Co., Ohio	108	(ca. 36 univalents, ca. 36 bivalents)

(Voucher specimens deposited in the Department of Botany University of Michigan)

and Hawaii, a species which also possesses the "glossy" upper epidermal cells. *A. montanum* is confined to the eastern United States, occurring from northern Georgia and Tennessee in the Appalachian Region to western Massachusetts. *A. platyneuron* (fig. 1, P), the second of the basic species, has the following distinctions: (1) linear- to oblanceolate-elliptic, once-pinnate, short-petiolate leaf blades, (2) leaf axis entirely dark-brown, including the rounded midrib, (3) upper epi-dermal cells oblong, undulate-walled, and (4) occurrence on rocks and soils of a variety of pH reactions. It appears to be most closely related to *A. trichomanes* and *A. resiliens,* and its hybrids with the former have been twice recorded (*A. virginicum* Maxon). *A. platyneuron* has a very wide range, extending from Texas and Florida in the south to Wisconsin and Kansas to southern Quebec in the north. *A. rhizophyllum* (*Camptosorus rhizophyllus*) possesses these characteristics: (1) triangular-attenuate, simple leaf-blades, with extremely long, rooting tips, (2) leaf axis green except for the base of the petiole, (3) upper epidermal cells as in *A. platyneuron,* but the venation pattern anastomosing, and (4) occurrence confined almost exclusively to well-shaded, moss-covered tops and sides of rocks and boulders, the pH reaction of the rock substratum predominantly circumneutral. Its closest relative is *A. sibiricum* of northeastern Asia. *A. rhizophyllum,* like *A. platyneuron,* is a rather common fern and has a broad range, extending from Alabama and Georgia north to Minnesota and Quebec. The morphological characteristics of these three basic species are intricately blended among the members of the Appalachian Asplenium complex. The chromosome numbers (table 1) of the basic species cannot be used to distinguish them since they all have the same —$2n = 72$, with 36 pairs at meiosis. The number 36 seems to be characteristic of the entire family Aspleniaceae, as was found in European species of *Asplenium, Ceterach,* and *Phyllitis* by Manton (1950) and Hawaiian species of *Diellia* by Wagner (1952).

METHODS

Observations upon the different described taxa were made in the field and in the herbarium. Some of the entities are, however, exceedingly rare, and field observation of these was impossible, although localities where they had been collected in the past were visited. Dried leaflets were cleared in sodium hydroxide solutions, stained with tannic-acid and iron chloride, and mounted on microscope slides in diaphane in order to examine venation patterns and other anatomical features. Leaf-outline drawings were made on a tracing table, and epidermal-cell drawings with a Bausch and Lomb microprojector. For the cytological study, living plants were grown under greenhouse conditions by Mr. Walter F. Kleinschmidt at the University of Michigan Botanical Gardens. Somatic chromosome counts were obtained from crosiers

and young leaflets placed in saturated aqueous solution of paradichlorobenzene for 3 hours to shrink the chromosomes, then placed in fixative. Meiotic studies were made from young sori, fixed directly. The fixative used was 4 parts chloroform; 3 parts ethyl alcohol; and 1 part glacial acetic acid. The specimens were squashed after 24 hours in the solution, and stained in aceto-orcein.

ASPLENIUM EBENOIDES

The first of the intermediates to be discussed is *Asplenium ebenoides*. Probably no other fern of the New World has attracted so much attention as this hybrid. Wherever its parents, *A. platyneuron* and *A. rhizophyllum,* grow in close proximity, this intermediate appears with gratifying regularity, but usually as a solitary plant, and with sufficient rarity to make its discovery a challenge to the plant collector. Although its hybrid origin was strongly suspected, the finding of the large and obviously self-reproducing population of this fern at Havana Glen, Hale Co., Alabama, some eighty years ago, cast doubt on its true nature. Nevertheless, the careful experiment of Slosson (1902) produced plants by hybridization of the putative parents which were morphologically like *A. ebenoides,* thus firmly establishing the hypothesis of its hybrid origin. Until the present, however, the cytological behavior of the hybrid remained unknown, and the capacity of the Alabama population to reproduce remained unexplained. Two possible hypotheses—hereditary obligate apogamy, and allopolyploidy—were considered as possible explanations of the fertility of this usually sterile plant. Obligate apogamy, it should be noted, is already known in two species of *Asplenium, A. monanthes* and *A. resiliens,* both of which, though chiefly subtropical, occur in the eastern United States.

The cytological studies of two living plants of the usual, sterile form of *A. ebenoides* from Montgomery Co., Maryland, reveal that there is complete non-

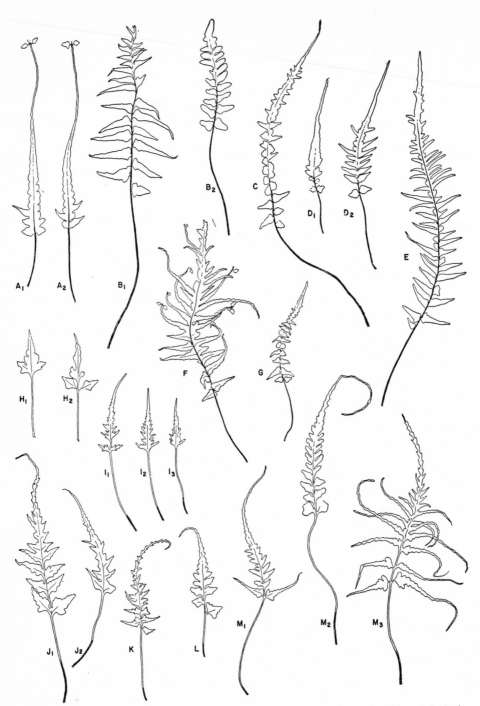

Fig. 2. Leaves showing extreme irregularity. A-G. *Asplenium ebenoides* (*Asplenium rhizophyllum* × *A. platyneuron*): A. Jefferson Co., W. Va., *Wagner & Rawlings 2016*; B. Montgomery Co., Md., *Palmer 1899;* C. Shenandoah Co., Va., *Wagner 241;* D. Hale Co., Ala., *Maxon & Pollard;* E. Hale Co., Ala. (cultivated, *Groff*); F. Loudoun Co., Va., *Gilbert 237;* G. Montgomery Co., Md., *Wagner.* H. *Asplenium inexpectatum* (*A. rhizophyllum* × *A. rutamuraria*), Adams Co., Ohio, *Braun.* I-M. *Asplenium pinnatifidum* (*A. rhizophyllum* × *A. montanum*): I. Patrick Co., Va., *Heller;* J. Jefferson Co., W. Va., *Palmer;* K. Jackson Co., Ill., *French;* L. Madison Co., Mo., *Pinkerton;* M. Warren Co., Ky., *Sadie Price.*

140

pairing of chromosomes in meiosis. At meiotic metaphase there are visible 72 univalents, 36 from each of the parents (fig. 7, C). By contrast, the investigations of fertile Alabama specimens of this taxon from two collections reveal that the allopolyploid hypothesis explains the situation: dividing somatic cells show 144 chromosomes (fig. 7, D_1), and during the first meiotic metaphase 72 normal-appearing chromosome pairs are evident (fig. 7, D_2). The spores produced are normal, but like the stomata, are larger than those of the diploid relatives.

The only certain record of the normal, sexual life cycle in *A. ebenoides* is this occurrence in Hale Co., Alabama. Whether vegetative reproduction explains the multiple plants sometimes found in other localities is not known. *A. ebenoides* may produce young plants not only at the tips of the leaf blades, but also at the tips of the pinnae; as many as 8 or 10 young plants may be produced on a single luxuriant frond. The large fronds of this plant are usually conspicuously irregular in the lobulation of the blade (fig. 2, A-G), giving them a characteristic bizarre appearance.

It is possible that the origin of the fertile form of *A. ebenoides* by allopolyploidy occurred in recent times and only in one locality, and that this explains why its distribution is so narrow compared to the broader distributions of the two following intermediate types.

ASPLENIUM BRADLEYI

"Bradley's spleenwort" or "cliff spleenwort," though wide-ranging from Okla-

homa and Georgia to New Jersey, is rather rare, becoming abundant only locally on steep rock cliffs. However, in recent times the possibility of hybrid origin of this fern has received no attention. As early as 1880, D. C. Eaton, who described it as a species, wrote the following:

"*A. bradleyi* varies a good deal in the shape of the fronds and in the degree of incision of the pinnae, the narrower and less divided forms having some resemblance to *A. platyneuron* and the larger forms looking more like *A. montanum*, or the European *A. lanceolatum*. If there could be a hybrid between *A. platyneuron* and *A. montanum*, it would be very much like our plant."

Figure 1, PM, shows two of the different leaf forms of this taxon to illustrate its variability. With present-day knowledge of hybridization in the ferns, and with the evidence now at hand, its describer would not have expressed as much doubt as to its possible hybrid nature. Morphologically it is indeed intermediate between the two parents suggested by him: The rachis of *A. platyneuron* is dark brown, and nearly round in cross-section (fig. 3, P), with two delicate ridges running along the top side, the ridges separated from each other by a distance of approximately one-half the diameter of the rachis. In contrast, *A. montanum* has a green rachis which is flattened-triangular in cross-section, the two adaxial ridges appearing as conspicuous, rounded flanges, separated by a wide, shallow groove containing a medial bulge. The midrib of *A. bradleyi* (fig. 3, PM) is intermediate, being brown only in the lower half, and but slightly flattened; the two ridges are separated from each other a distance approximately

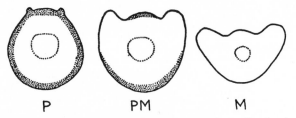

FIG. 3.   Diagrams from tracings of midrib cross-sections: P. *A. platyneuron;* PM. *A. bradleyi;* M. *A. montanum.*

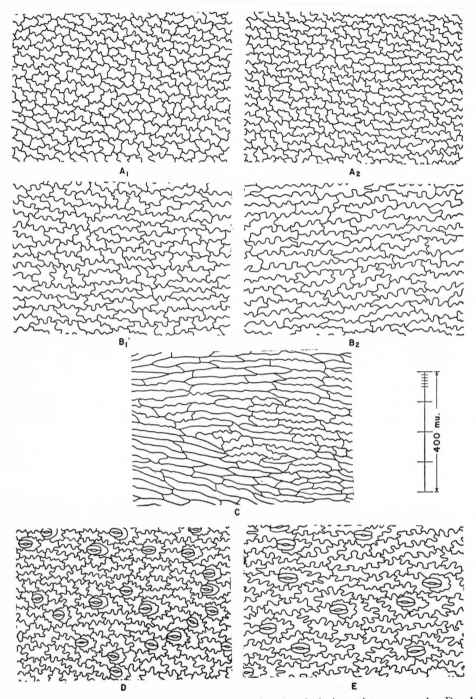

FIG. 4. Epidermal cells. A-C. Upper epidermis: A. *Asplenium platyneuron:* A₁. Duval Co., Fla., *Churchill;* A₂. Bullock Co., Ga., *Harper.* B. *A. bradleyi:* B₁. Dade Co., Mo., *Steyermark 40273;* B₂. Etowah Co., Alabama, *Eggert.* C. *A. montanum,* Alleghany Co., N. C., *Correll 10817.* D, E. Lower epidermis: D. *A. platyneuron,* Duval Co., Fla., *Churchill;* E. *A. bradleyi,* Dade Co., Mo., *Steyermark 40273.*

equal to the diameter of the rachis, and the upper groove formed between them shows only a slightly elevated, central bulge. Such other *A. platyneuron* features as more or less truncate basal margins of the leaflets and reduced lower pinnae are combined with the elongated tendency of the upper epidermal cells (fig. 4, cf. A, B, and C), the stalked and divided basal pinnae, and the restriction to acid-rock habitats characterizing *A. montanum.*[2]

No individuals of *A. bradleyi* have yet been recorded which are diploid and sterile, although they should be sought for in habitats where the supposed parents occur side-by-side in appropriate conditions. The chromosome number of *A. bradleyi* populations which have been studied is in accord with the allopolyploid hypothesis, being 144, with normal pairing at meiosis (fig. 7, F). Hybrids of *A. bradleyi* have been recorded with both *A. platyneuron* and *A. montanum.* Probably *A. bradleyi* originated by allopolyploidy in the past at least once, and perhaps several times, but it now has a rather broad range, extending in particular well to the west of the westernmost known limit of one of its putative parents, *A. montanum.*

ASPLENIUM PINNATIFIDUM

This intermediate is a familiar but rather uncommon fern which occurs from Alabama and Georgia northward to New Jersey, Indiana, and Oklahoma. Its resemblance to *A. ebenoides* is sufficiently close so that the two species are frequently confused. Eaton wrote (1879) that it "bears considerable resemblance to *A. ebenoides* but has a green, herbaceous midrib or rachis, a sinuous-margined prolongation, thicker texture, and is very rarely, if indeed ever, proliferous." Like *A. ebenoides, A. pinnatifidum* frequently attracts attention by the irregular appearance of its leaf-forms (e.g., Copeland

---

[2] Reports of *A. bradleyi* on "limestone" have proved to be erroneous. Cf. Wherry, Amer. Fern Jour., 21: 111, 1931.

1902), to be discussed below. The larger fronds in any population may be expected to have elongated pinnae at the base of the blade (forma *elongatum* Morton). *A. pinnatifidum* also resembles *A. ebenoides* in combining the peculiar features of *A. rhizophyllum* with those of the more typical Aspleniums. Concerning the genus *Camptosorus* as conventionally recognized and typified by *A. rhizophyllum,* Copeland (1947, p. 170) wrote: "*Camptosorus* is evidently derived from *Asplenium. A. pinnatifidum* Nutt. presents a more definite place of origin in the parent genus." Thus Copeland considers *A. pinnatifidum* (which has also been treated as *Camptosorus pinnatifidus* Wood) as an *Asplenium* prototype of *Camptosorus.* Perhaps the most suggestive resemblance of the two taxa is the attenuated, simple tip of the leaf which, though usually shorter in *A. pinnatifidum* is much like that of *A. rhizophyllum.* However, production of young plants on the leaf tip in *A. pinnatifidum* is decidedly rare and I have found only a few examples. The other major distinction of *A. rhizophyllum* from more typical Aspleniums, that of anastomosing veins, is much more common than budproduction in *A. pinnatifidum,* but the vein areoles form casually and infrequently.

The likelihood is far greater that the *A. rhizophyllum*-like features of *A. pinnatifidum,* rather than indicating community of origin, arose abruptly through hybridization of *A. montanum* with *A. rhizophyllum.* The first suggestion in the literature of this possibility seems to be that by the writer (1950). The chromosome numbers of the five populations thus far investigated accord with this hypothesis, having the $4n$ number, and four additional populations examined showed the corresponding large-sized stomata. Not only does *A. pinnatifidum* show tendencies toward the features of anastomosing veins, attenuate leaf-tip, and leaf-tip reproduction of *A. rhizophyllum,* but its lamina is thick-textured as in *A. montanum;* moreover there is a definite tendency toward elongation of the upper epidermal cells, and the basal pinnae or lobes, though simple, have the same outline as in *A. montanum.* The habitat of *A. pinnatifidum* is usually mediacid or subacid soil on rock cliffs as in *A. montanum,* although Craw (1932) found 3 occurrences in Indiana to have neutral soil-reaction, and the writer has seen it in close association with *Pellaea glabella,* a predominantly calcareous soil plant, at Black Hand, Ohio.[3]

One distinctive feature of *A. pinnatifidum* which points especially strongly to its hybrid origin is the irregularity of the blade outline, seen primarily in larger leaves. The two other hybrids between *A. rhizophyllum* and more typical Aspleniums (*A. platyneuron,* fig. 2, A-G; *A. ruta-muraria,* discovered by Braun, 1939, fig. 2, H) likewise display this condition. Rather than a symmetrical system of pinnae or lobes as is characteristic of most ferns, the blades of these hybrids show conspicuous irregularities in pattern, short lobes next to long ones on the same side of the blade, and different patterns of lobulation on opposite sides.[4]

Asplenium trudellii

Oddly enough, the widespread plant known as *A. trudellii,* which has been interpreted both as a variant of *A. pinnatifidum* and as its hybrid with *A. montanum,* lacks the peculiarity of irregular leaf-blades, a feature which is sometimes helpful in distinguishing it from *A. pinnatifidum. A. trudellii* has been investigated cytologically from three localities, respec-

[3] Dr. E. T. Wherry has since informed me that the same species-association occurs at Cumberland Falls, Kentucky.

[4] The phenomenon of irregularity of leaves of putative hybrids between ferns with widely different leaves is not confined to the Aspleniaceae; it appears, for example, in the Aspidiaceae, *Pleuroderris michleriana* (*Tectaria incisa* × *Dictyoxiphium panamense*), and in the Pteridaceae, *Pteris heteromorpha* (*P. cretica* × *P. vittata*) and *P. cadieri* (*P. cretica* × *P. quadriaurita*).

tively in Pennsylvania, West Virginia, and Ohio, and the findings not only bear on its own interpretation but on that of *A. pinnatifidum* as well. Although its describer considered it "possibly in part the result of hybridization between *A. pinnatifidum* and *A. montanum*" (Wherry, 1925), its most recent treatment (Morton, *in* Gleason, 1952) is as a variety of *A. pinnatifidum.* In 1932, however, Dr. Paul Kestner of Lausanne, Switzerland, found that spores of all specimens of *A. trudellii* he received from Georgia and Tennessee were sterile. In spite of the sterility of its spores—which may also be recognized under the microscope by their irregularity and abortion—this plant, remarkably, is often relatively common where it occurs. But apparently it is never found in the absence of the two presumed parents, *A. pinnatifidum* and *A. montanum.*

Present cytological evidence makes it probable that *A. trudellii* is a hybrid, but its morphology, though intermediate, usually seems somewhat closer to *A. pinnatifidum* than to *A. montanum.* The chromosome number in all the plants from the three populations studied is 108, i.e., $3n$. Also at meiosis there are approximately 36 pairs and 36 univalents, as would be expected in a backcross of an allopolyploid hybrid of *A. montanum* and *A. rhizophyllum* with one of its parents. In 18 well-spread sporocytes the total units of any kind estimated averaged 73.2 (70–75), with 36.3 bivalents (33–42) and 36.9 univalents (33–39). The genetic constitution of *A. trudellii* may thus be now considered to be two genomes of *A. montanum* and one genome of *A. rhizophyllum.*

In spite of its production in considerable numbers, it is dubious whether *A. trudellii* will ever become a reproductive species like *A. pinnatifidum,* because its triploid chromosome complement makes this unlikely. *A. pinnatifidum,* on the other hand, is reproductively a normal species in its present-day behavior, with a typical, sexual life cycle. Its rather

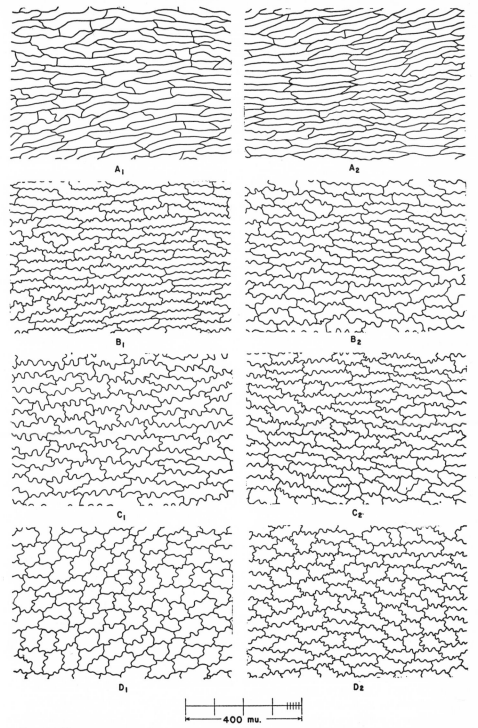

Fig. 5. Upper epidermal cells. A. *A. montanum:* A₁. Macon Co., N. C., *Correll 6679;* A₂ Sevier Co., Tenn., *Tryon 33.* B. *A. trudellii:* B₁ Etowah Co., Alabama, *Eggert;* B₂. Kentucky, *Rule.* C. *A. pinnatifidum:* C₁. Carter Co., Mo., *Steyermark 11875;* C₂. Union Co., Ill., *Hubricht B2287.* D. *A. rhizophyllum:* D₁ Smith Co., Va., *Small;* D₂. Shenandoah Co., Va., *Arts 900.*

wide range suggests ancient origin at least once by doubling of chromosomes in an original hybrid. Plant collectors should certainly seek in the field individuals of *A. pinnatifidum* which are diploid and sterile, to be expected where *A. rhizophyllum* and *A. montanum* occur in close proximity.

ASPLENIUM KENTUCKIENSE AND A. GRAVESII

Asplenium kentuckiense, discovered and described first by McCoy (1936), represents the theoretical central point morphologically in the entire Appalachian Asplenium complex. Although McCoy did not discuss its hybrid origin, Wherry (1936) first suggested that it represented an intermediate between *A. pinnatifidum* and *A. platyneuron.* (The other plant, *A. stotleri,* mentioned by Wherry in this connection, is now believed to involve an additional species outside the complex.) Besides the morphology of *A. kentuckiense,* which is intermediate between the two supposed parents, additional observations indicate that it is the cross of *A. platyneuron* and *A. pinnatifidum:* (1) three plants were collected by Mr. Floyd Bartley in Hay Hollow, Pike Co., Ohio, in the immediate vicinity of the two putative parents; (2) in southern Illinois, where *A. kentuckiense* was found by Earl (specimen in Chicago Museum), only *A. platyneuron* and *A. pinnatifidum* of possible parents are present, neither *A. bradleyi* nor *A. montanum* being known from that state. Specimens believed to represent *A. platyneuron* × *A. pinnatifidum* are now known from scattered points in Kentucky, Ohio, Illinois, and Arkansas, and they all possess abortive spores. Although no living plants have been available for study, the stomatal sizes of preserved material indicate the 3n condition.

Stomatal size seems especially useful in the determination of dried material of the rarer ferns in this complex, the material being relaxed in sodium hydroxide solutions, cleared, and treated as described above. The stomata of one pinna or fragment of all these plants under discussion may vary in length as much as 11 to 18 microns, and the averages of different collections of one species as much as 5 to 10 microns. Nevertheless it has usually proven possible by averaging 30 measurements of stomatal lengths of a pinna from a single collection to distinguish the polyploid levels. The fertile tetraploids have conspicuously large stomata. Individual collections of known or theoretical triploids may have values which overlap some of the diploids and some of the tetraploids, as shown in the chart below of averages of 30 stomatal lengths in microns of each of 31 collections:

Diploids

> (range of averages of 11 collections, 39–45).
> *A. rhizophyllum* (3 collections)..41 (40–41)
> *A. ebenoides* (2 collections).....40 (39–40)
> *A. platyneuron* (3 collections)...42 (40–43)
> *A. montanum* (3 collections).....42 (40–45)

Triploids

> (range of averages of 9 collections, 42–51).
> *A. bradleyi* × *montanum* (2 collections)
> 44 (42–45)
> *A. trudellii* (4 collections)......46 (42–51)
> *A. kentuckiense* (3 collections)..45 (43–48)

Tetraploids

> (range of averages of 11 collections, 46–58).
> *A. gravesii* (4 collections).......49 (46–53)
> *A. ebenoides* (1 collection)......54
> *A. pinnatifidum* (3 collections)...55 (50–58)
> *A. bradleyi* (3 collections)......56 (52–58)

Asplenium gravesii, described by Maxon (1918) as a hybrid of *A. pinnatifidum* and *A. bradleyi,* has been found in a limited number of localities in Georgia, Alabama, Ohio, and Pennsylvania. "Judging *A. gravesii* on both gross and minute characters, there can be little doubt of its hybrid nature, making all allowance for the unusually high variability of the supposed parents, of one or the other of which it might at first be thought an extreme state" (Maxon, loc. cit.). *A. gravesii* may be distinguished from *A. kentuckiense* by having less brown on the leaf-axis, pinna shape, thicker texture of the blade, somewhat more elongate upper

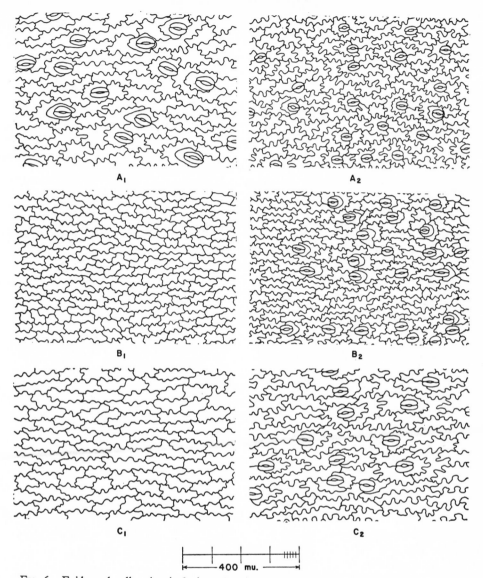

Fig. 6. Epidermal cells: A. *Asplenium ebenoides,* upper epidermis: A₁. Hale Co., Alabama, *Maxon & Pollard* (4n); A₂. Montgomery Co., Md., *Wagner.* B. *A. kentuckiense,* S. Illinois, *Earl;* B₁. Upper surface; B₂. Lower surface. C. *A. gravesii,* Trenton, Ga., *Graves:* C₁. Upper; C₂. Lower surface.

epidermal cells (cf. fig. 6, B and C), and the usually somewhat larger stomatal sizes suggesting the 4n state. However, the two ferns are similar morphologically, and young plants especially may prove to be difficult to identify on gross characteristics. Both are exceedingly rare, and no living material has been seen by the author or is expected in the near future.

These two intermediate ferns, *A. gravesii* and *A. kentuckiense,* combine morphologically distinctions of all three of the basic diploid species, in respect to such features as the extent of brown on the leaf-axis, the degree of attenuation of the leaf-tip, pinna shape, etc. But *A. kentuckiense* possesses unusual theoretical interest in this problem since it presumably repre-

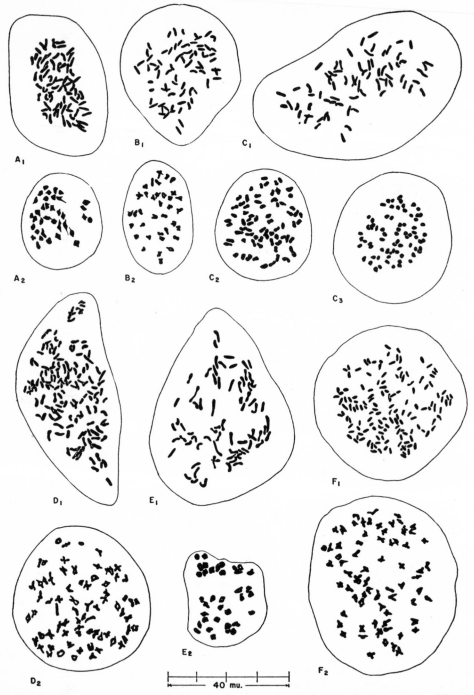

FIG. 7. Chromosomes of Appalachian Aspleniums. A. *Asplenium platyneuron:* A₁. Montgomery Co., Md., $2n = 72$; A₂. Hardy Co., W. Va., 36 pairs. B. *Asplenium rhizophyllum:* B₁. Shenandoah Co., Va., $2n = 72$; Monroe Co., Indiana, 36 pairs. C. *Asplenium ebenoides* (sterile form), Montgomery Co., Md.: C₁. $2n = 72$; C₂ and C₃. 72 univalents at meiotic metaphase. D. *Asplenium ebenoides* (fertile form), Hale Co., Alabama: D₁. $2n = 144$; D₂. 72 pairs. E. *Asplenium montanum,* Harford Co., Md.: E₁. $2n = 72$; E₂. 36 pairs. F. *Asplenium bradleyi:* F₁. Pike Co., Ohio, $2n = 144$; F₂. Harford Co., Md., 72 pairs.

sents the precise morphological central point between the "poles" of the triangle of basic, diploid species (fig. 1, PRM). Thus it should theoretically be possible to produce triploid *A. kentuckiense* in all of the following experimental crossings:

A. montanum (2*n*) × *A. ebenoides* (4*n*)
A. rhizophyllum (2*n*) × *A. bradleyi* (4*n*)
A. platyneuron (2*n*) × *A. pinnatifidum* (4*n*)

DISCUSSION

Stebbins (1950) has discussed the role of polyploidy in plant evolution, and cites a number of established or suspected allopolyploids among flowering-plants, including *Galeopsis tetrahit* (*G. pubescens-speciosa*) and *Iris versicolor* (*I. setosa-*

virginica) and others which occur as normal species. Only recently, however, has allopolyploidy in species of the Filicineae been subjected to investigation: Manton (1950) has shown that seven European ferns with normal life-cycles, including *Dryopteris filix-mas* and *Polystichum aculeatum*, are either suspected or demonstrated allopolyploids. More recently (Manton and Walker, 1953) it has been shown that the American *Dryopteris clintoniana* is a hexaploid and "is perhaps the amphidiploid hybrid between normal *D. cristata* [a tetraploid species] and *D. goldiana* [a diploid]."

Perhaps the most interesting aspect of the Appalachian Asplenium complex is that the polyploid taxa combine features

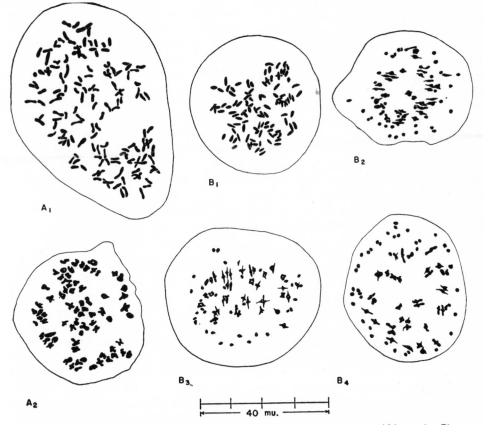

FIG. 8. Chromosomes of Appalachian Aspleniums. A. *Asplenium pinnatifidum:* A₁. Shenandoah Co., Va., 2*n* = 144; A₂. Monroe Co., Indiana, 72 pairs. B. *A. trudellii:* B₁. York Co., Pa., 2*n* = 108; B₂. York Co., Pa., approximately 36 pairs and 36 univalents at meiotic metaphase; B₃, B₄. Hardy Co., W. Va., approximately 36 pairs and 36 univalents.

of diploids of widely different morphology and relationship. The suspected allopolyploid, *"Scolopendrium hybridum,"* of Europe (Manton, 1950) likewise combines features of very unlike putative parents, *Asplenium (Scolopendrium) hemionitis* and *A. (Ceterach) ceterach.* The polyploids of the Appalachian Asplenium complex appear to be "typical or genomic allopolyploids" (Stebbins, op. cit., p. 226) resulting from hybridization of distantly related species in which the chromosomes are so different that normal pairing would be impossible in the diploid. The polyploid intermediates between the presumably basic diploid species in this complex are clear-cut intermediates, and there is evidently no tendency toward introgression between parent species since gene interchange through the diploid hybrids is extremely unlikely.

Two of the diploid species of this complex, *Asplenium rhizophyllum* and *A. platyneuron,* are much more abundant than their apparent allopolyploid derivatives, in contrast to many of the previously reported allopolyploids among plant species. One of the allopolyploids discussed here, namely *A. ebenoides,* is very limited in range, while the two others, *A. bradleyi* and *A. pinnatifidum*—although generally less common than *A. montanum* where their ranges overlap with it—have extended their ranges farther westward than this presumably parental, diploid species, but not farther northward.

Of the theoretically possible sterile hybrids in this complex, five still remain to be discovered, but their arising under natural field conditions seems extremely unlikely because of parental differences in ranges and habitat preferences. Even what is perhaps the most expected of the still unknown hybrids, *A. rhizophyllum* × *A. pinnatifidum,* may never be found under natural conditions because these species so rarely occur close together. Of the four theoretically possible fertile polyploid hybrids, only one—hexaploid *A. kentuckiense*—has not yet been found in the natural state, although the possibility

of the origin of such a form should be recognized by field-workers.

CONCLUSIONS

The Appalachian Aspleniums comprise 11 described taxa, of which 3 represent morphological extremes and the remainder intermediates. *A. ebenoides* is a usually sterile hybrid of *A. platyneuron* and *A. rhizophyllum* with 72 univalents at meiotic metaphase, although one population from Alabama is a fertile allopolyploid, forming 72 normal bivalents at meiosis. *A. bradleyi* is apparently the allopolyploid hybrid of *A. montanum* and *A. platyneuron;* it back-crosses with both parents. *A. pinnatifidum* likewise is evidently an allopolyploid hybrid, and its morphology, the irregularity of the leaves, and the pairing behavior of its putative backcross (*A. trudellii*) with one of the parents indicates that its parentage is *A. montanum* × *A. rhizophyllum.* *A. kentuckiense* and *A. gravesii* are both evidently trihybrids, the former 3*n*, the latter 4*n*, and *A. kentuckiense* morphologically represents the theoretical central point of the whole complex. A hypothesis of reticulate evolution is thus presented for the Appalachian Aspleniums which postulates that three original diploid species, *A. montanum, A. platyneuron,* and *A. rhizophyllum,* have given rise to 8 additional taxa through hybridization.

ACKNOWLEDGMENTS

I am indebted to Dr. G. Ledyard Stebbins and to Dr. Edgar T. Wherry for critical reading of the manuscript, and to Mr. Walter F. Kleinschmidt for growing the living plants. I wish also to thank those persons who so kindly supplied living materials for study, including Mr. Floyd Bartley, Mr. Donald F. M. Brown, Mr. Neal W. Gilbert, Miss Mary E. Groff, Dr. Charles B. Heiser, Dr. Everett G. Logue, Dr. Erich Steiner, Mr. Harry Trudell, and Dr. Wherry, and those herbaria which sent dried materials, including the University of Pennsylvania,

U. S. National Museum, Chicago Museum, University of Illinois, and Missouri Botanical Garden. Mr. Hubert M. Vogelman helped me with the drawings.

LITERATURE CITED

ALSTON, A. H. G. 1940. Notes on the supposed hybrids in the genus Asplenium found in Britain. Linn. Soc. London Proc., Session 152, 1939–40 (Part 2): 132–144.

BRAUN, E. LUCY. 1939. A new fern hybrid—Asplenium cryptolepsis × Camptosorus rhizophyllus. Amer. Fern Journ., 29: 133–135.

COPELAND, E. B. 1902. Two fern monstrosities. Bot. Gazette, 34: 143–144.

——. 1947. Genera Filicum. Waltham, Mass.

CRAW, JOE E. 1932. Hydrogen-ion reaction of native Indiana fern soils. Butler Univ. Bot. Studies, 2: 151–158.

EATON, D. C. 1879–80. Ferns of the United States. I and II. Salem, Mass.

GLEASON, H. A. 1952. The new Britton and Brown Illustrated Flora of the northeastern United States and adjacent Canada. Vol. I. Lancaster, Pa.

MANTON, I. 1950. Problems of cytology and evolution in the Pteridophyta. Cambridge.

MANTON, I., AND S. WALKER. 1953. Cytology of the Dryopteris spinulosa complex in Eastern North America. Nature, 171: 1116–1118.

MAXON, WILLIAM R. 1918. A new hybrid Asplenium. Amer. Fern Journ., 8: 1–3.

McCoy, THOMAS N. 1936. A new Asplenium from Kentucky. Amer. Fern Journ., 26: 104–106.

SLOSSON, MARGARET. 1902. The origin of Asplenium ebenoides. Torrey Bot. Club Bull., 29: 487–495.

STEBBINS, G. L., JR. 1950. Variation and evolution in plants. New York.

WAGNER, W. H., JR. 1950. Cytotaxonomic analysis of evolution in Pteridophyta (review). Evolution, 5: 177–181.

——. 1952. The fern genus Diellia. Univ. Calif. Publ. Bot., 26: (no. 1): 1–212.

——. 1953. A cytological study of the Appalachian spleenworts. Amer. Fern Journ., 43: 109–114.

WHERRY, E. T. 1925. The Appalachian Aspleniums. Amer. Fern Journ., 15: 47–54.

——. 1927. Notes on Asplenium trudellii. Amer. Fern Journ., 17: 135–138.

WHERRY, E. T., AND WILLIAM D. GRAY. 1936. Variants of some Appalachian Aspleniums. Amer. Fern Journ., 26: 77–86.

A GENETIC APPROACH TO THE TAXONOMY OF
MENTZELIA LINDLEYI AND M. CROCEA (LOASACEAE)

HENRY J. THOMPSON

Department of Botany, University of California

Los Angeles

While a morphological approach to taxonomy can suggest the genetic discontinuities in a genus, a genetic approach measures them more directly. A genetic approach need not involve the laborious task of artificial hybridization. Frequently the preliminary investigations of a monographer will indicate where two taxa are likely to be found growing together and in such areas adjacent, mixed, or intermediate populations of two taxa are natural genetic experiments more significant than the production of artificial hybrids. They are more significant because they indicate the degree of genetic integrity that prevails under natural conditions; such information is not obtained from artificial hybridizations. On the other hand, when taxa are allopatric and have the same chromosome number a genetic approach to taxonomy must be a direct one involving artificial hybridization. *Mentzelia lindleyi* T. & G. and *M. crocea* Kell., as discussed in this paper, present a problem of this kind.

Mentzelia lindleyi and *M. crocea* are spring flowering annuals with rounded, papillose seeds and linear filaments. These characters place them in Section *Trachyphytum,* whereas their large, mucronate petals with some orange pigment at the base distinguish them from other members of this section. The only Mentzelias likely to be confused with *M. lindleyi* and *M. crocea* are *M. gracilenta* T. & G. and *M. nitens* Greene. *Mentzelia gracilenta* grows in the inner Coast Ranges generally south of *M. lindleyi,* and can be distinguished from *M. lindleyi* and *M. crocea* by its smaller, blunt or retuse petals. *Mentzelia nitens* occurs on the Mojave Desert and is most readily distinguished from *M. lindleyi* and *M. crocea* by the lack of orange pigment in its petals. The relationship of *M. lindleyi* and *M. crocea* to other members of Section *Trachyphytum* has been briefly discussed in a previous paper (Thompson and Lewis, 1955).

Mentzelia lindleyi is characterized by broad yellow-orange petals with a prominent orange spot at the base and by its habit, many individuals branching at or just above the ground level. Plants of this sort occur in the inner Coast Ranges of Central California. *Mentzelia crocea* differs in having narrower, yellow petals with a faint orange spot at the base and by branching well above the ground level. Such plants occur in the foothills of the west slope of the Sierra Nevada. The differences in branching pattern between *lindleyi* and *crocea* is not a reliable field character but is most apparent in garden-grown material. The branching pattern is readily modified, so that when *lindleyi* grows in tall grass it tends to branch from above whereas *crocea* plants "pinched back" by browsing animals branch from below. Figure 1 summarizes pictorially the differences between *lindleyi* and *crocea* and the map in Figure 2 shows their distributions. The distribution data are based on the specimens in Dudley Herbarium, Stanford University; Pomona College Herbarium; Rancho Santa Ana Botanic Garden Herbarium; the Herbarium of the University of California, at Berkeley, and at Los Angeles.

Mentzelia lindleyi and *M. crocea* occupy very similar habitats. Both grow on slopes in loose soil or talus in sunny exposures and, although they occur on

Reprinted by permission of the author and publisher from

BRITTONIA, **12**, 81–93 (1960).

opposite sides of the central Valley of California, both are found in the Foothill
Woodland plant community (Munz and Keck, 1949) usually with *Pinus sabiniana*
and *Quercus douglasii*. When grown in the uniform conditions of the experimental garden at Los Angeles, *lindleyi* and *crocea* do not show any differential
response in rate of development or time of flowering. These observations of
habitat and growth under uniform conditions suggest that *lindleyi* and *crocea*
are not ecologically differentiated to a degree comparable to their morphological
differentiation.

Both species were observed in several natural populations, and plants from
three of these populations of *crocea* and one of *lindleyi* were grown in the experimental garden. The map in Figure 2 shows the location of these popula-

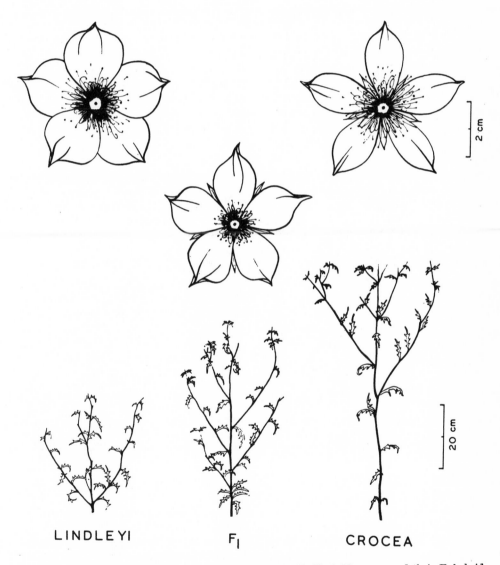

LINDLEYI   F₁   CROCEA

FIG. 1. Flowers and branching pattern in *Mentzelia lindleyi, M. crocea* and their F₁ hybrid.

tions. Another strain of *M. lindleyi* grown for several years in the UCLA
Botanical Garden has also been used in the hybridizations. Collection data for
all five strains used in the hybridization studies are listed in Table 1. Meiosis has
been studied in squash preparations of microsporocytes of individuals of *M.
lindleyi* and *M. crocea* representing all five of the populations referred to above.
All of these plants are tetraploid with 18 pairs of chromosomes at meiotic
metaphase I. In Section *Trachyphytum*, to which *M. lindleyi* and *M. crocea*
belong, the base chromosome number is $x = 9$ with polyploids extending to the
octoploid level (Thompson and Lewis, 1955.)

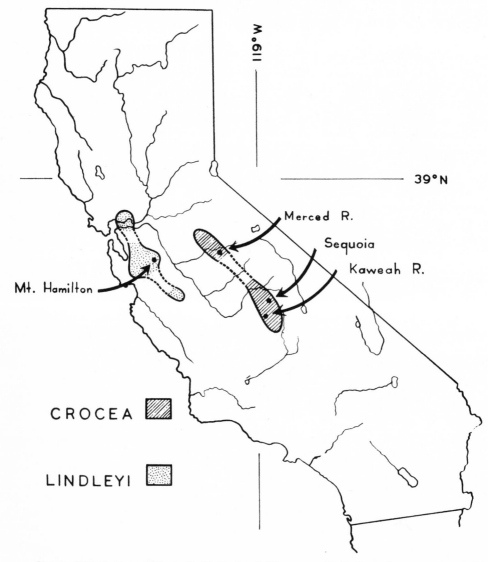

Fig. 2. Distribution of *Mentzelia lindleyi* and *M. crocea*. *M. lindleyi* also occurs in wild-
flower plantings in coastal California. The named populations have been used in the hybridization studies.

Thus *M. lindleyi* and *M. crocea* have the same chromosome number, are allopatric but occupy similar habitats, and are recognizably different, yet are more similar to each other than to any other taxon. There is some question as to the taxonomic implications of the differences between them. Are they different enough to be accorded specific rank, should they be considered subspecies, only or should they be given no formal taxonomic recognition? Each of these viewpoints has been expressed by one or more taxonomists. When Kellogg (1876) described *M. crocea* he offered it as a species distinct from *M. lindleyi*. Wolf (1938), after a careful morphological comparison that included growing representatives of both taxa in the experimental garden, indicated that they should be considered subspecies. Darlington (1934), in revising the genus *Mentzelia* relegated *crocea* to the synonymy of *M. lindleyi*. A reevaluation of the evidence from comparative morphology and distribution would serve merely as another vote on the problem of the oppropriate rank for these taxa. Further morphological study could lead only to the conclusion that although different enough from each other to be recognized, *lindleyi* and *crocea* are more closely related to each other than to any other taxon. The same conclusion might readily be reached by any taxonomist after a cursory study. Through a genetic approach, however, it is possible to obtain new information which can be reflected in the taxonomy.

TABLE 1. *Mentzelia* collections used for the cytological and hybridization studies.

M. lindleyi		
Cultivated	Cultivated in the UCLA Botanical Garden. The seeds originally from Rex Pierce Seed Company.	*Thompson 1569*
Mt. Hamilton	Adobe Creek Road at Del Puerto Road, eastern Mt. Hamilton Range, Santa Clara County.	*Thompson & Lewis 1616*
M. crocea		
Merced	Bear Creek near junction with Merced River, Mariposa County.	*Thompson & Lewis 1621*
Sequoia	Generals Highway, one mile above Amphitheater Point, Sequoia National Park, Tulare County.	*W. Ernst in 1953* Cultured as no. 1575
Kaweah	South Fork of Kaweah River near confluence with Kaweah River, Tulare County.	*Thompson & Lewis 1622*

All collections are from California. Voucher specimens are in the herbarium of the University of California, Los Angeles.

Both *M. lindleyi* and *M. crocea* are colonial, occurring in populations ranging from a few hundreds to several thousands of individuals. In the expanded flowers of *lindleyi* and *crocea* the petals are rotately spread and the flowers are more than four cm across. The tips of the numerous anthers outline a hemisphere, from the center of which extend the stigma and style. Although the plants are self-compatible, the stigma exceeds the anthers in length, thus preventing automatic self-pollination; plants isolated in an insect-free screen house do not set seeds. During one morning's observations in the Mt. Hamilton population of *M. lindleyi*, large carpenter bees (*Xylocopa sp.*) were the most frequent visitors. They can bring about some cross-pollination because in alighting on a flower they frequently touch its extended stigma before its

anthers. These pollinators, however, also cause considerable selfing by landing
in the flower so forcefully that they bend the style and stigma back into the
anthers. They also tend to work over all the flowers of one plant before moving
on to the next. At present it appears that in nature *lindleyi* and *crocea* exhibit
considerable selfing. Some outcrossing takes place, but no measurement of its
frequency is available.

HYBRIDIZATION

The five strains used in this study were crossed in the combinations indicated
in Figure 3. There is no barrier to initial crossability; all the F_1 hybrids produced were vigorous. As shown in Figure 1, the hybrid between *M. lindleyi*
and *M. crocea* is intermediate in the characters that distinguish the parent
strains. The fact that one can readily distinguish the F_1 from the two parents
suggests that the morphological difference between *lindleyi* and *crocea* is greater
than an initial comparison of the two indicates. Studying the plants growing
in natural populations, and then growing the parents and hybrid together in
the garden sheds some light on the degree of their morphological differences
by indicating that a third morphological type, the intermediate hybrid, is

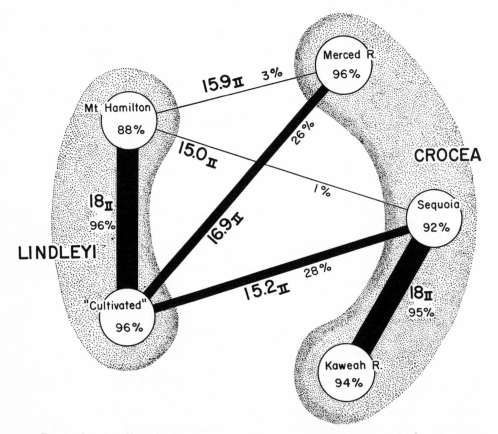

Fig. 3. Crossing diagram showing average chromosome pairing and percentage of normal
pollen in parental plants and F_1 hybrids of *Mentzelia lindleyi* and *M. crocea*. Figures in the
population circles refer to parental plants and those along the hybrid lines refer to F_1 progeny.
All parental plants had 18_{II}. Width of lines indicates relative percentages of normal pollen.

recognizably distinct.

A question of considerable evolutionary and taxonomic importance, however, concern the fertility of these hybrids. Fertility is not at all easy to measure; once measured, it is still difficult to interpret taxonomically. In attempting to measure it, studies have been made of five different stages in the reproductive cycle that determine effective fertility: 1) chromosome pairing, 2) pollen production, 3) seed production, 4) seed germination, and 5) seedling vigor.

Chromosome Pairing: Chromosome pairing, in all cases, was studied in metaphase and early anaphase stages in squash preparations of microsporocytes. Chromosomes were lightly stained with orcein and observed with a phase microscope. All the parent plants of *M. lindleyi* and *M. crocea* that have been examined cytologically form 18 pairs of chromosomes. Table 2 shows the amount of pairing found in each hybrid combination and also indicates the average

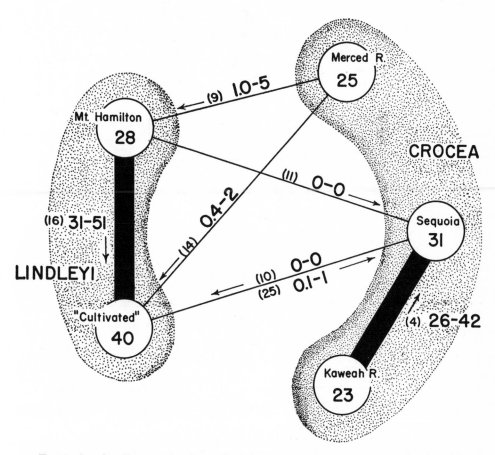

FIG. 4. Crossing diagram showing seed set in parental plants and F₁ hybrids of *Mentzelia lindleyi* and *M. crocea*. The figures in the population circles are the average numbers of seeds per capsule in the parental plants. Figures along the hybrid lines are data from F₁ plants. The arrows near these data point toward the seed parent of the F₁; the figure in parentheses is the number of flowers selfed and sibbed in each F₁ progeny; the next two figures are the average and maximum numbers of seeds per capsule. Width of hybrid lines indicates relative degree of seed set.

number of pairs per cell. In figuring the number of pairs per cell the trivalents, which occur with an average frequency of 0.08 per cell, were counted as pairs. This was appropriate since pairing is only being used as a measure of chromosome homology, and by inference, of genetic similarity. In most hybrid combinations two, or sometimes three of the many F_1 plants were studied cytologically. In all cases chromosome pairing in the two or three sibling F_1 plants seemed sufficiently alike to justify the summing of the data for the two or three individuals studied in any particular progeny.

As may be determined from Table 2, hybrid plants of Cultivated *lindleyi* and

TABLE 2. Chromosome configurations in hybrids between various populations of *Mentzelia lindleyi* and *M. crocea* as determined from squash preparations of microsporocytes at metaphase and early anaphase.

	lindleyi ♀ × *lindleyi* ♂ Cultivated × Mt. Hamilton (67 cells, 2 plants)	*crocea* ♀ × *crocea* ♂ Sequoia × Kaweah (78 cells, 2 plants)	*crocea* ♀ × *lindleyi* ♂ Sequoia × Mt. Hamilton (170 cells, 3 plants)	*lindleyi* ♀ × *crocea* ♂ Cultivated × Merced (120 cells, 2 plants)	*lindleyi* ♀ × *crocea* ♂ Cultivated × Sequoia (121 cells, 3 plants)	*lindleyi* ♀ × *crocea* ♂ Mt. Hamilton × Merced (30 cells, 2 plants)
18_{II}	67	77	9	34	6	2
$17_{II}, 2_I$			29	52	20	10
$16_{II}, 4_I$		1	28	14	21	6
$15_{II}, 6_I$			38	8	24	3
$14_{II}, 8_I$			25	2	20	4
$13_{II}, 10_I$			21		9	
$12_{II}, 12_I$			6		8	2
$11_{II}, 14_I$			2		1	1
$10_{II}, 16_I$			2			
$9_{II}, 18_I$			1			
$16_{II}, 1_I, 1_{III}$			2	1	7	
$15_{II}, 3_I, 1_{III}$			2	7	1	
$14_{II}, 5_I, 1_{III}$			4	1	2	1
$13_{II}, 7_I, 1_{III}$						1
$12_{II}, 9_I, 1_{III}$					1	
$11_{II}, 11_I, 1_{III}$			1		1	
$16_{II}, 1_{IV}$				1		
Average Number of pairs/cell	18.0	18.0	15.0	16.9	15.2	15.9

Mt. Hamilton *lindleyi* have 18 pairs of chromosomes as do hybrids between plants of Sequoia *crocea* and Kaweah *crocea*. Figure 5a shows the regular pairing in such a hybrid. The hybrids between *crocea* and *lindleyi*, however, regularly show some reduction and irregularity in pairing. In these hybrid combinations the average number of chromosome pairs per cell ranged from 15.0 to 16.9 and approximately 9% of all cells analyzed showed a trivalent. Figure 5b shows a microsporocyte with 13 pairs and 10 univalents in a hybrid from the cross Sequoia *crocea* × Mt. Hamilton *lindleyi*. At anaphase I the univalents

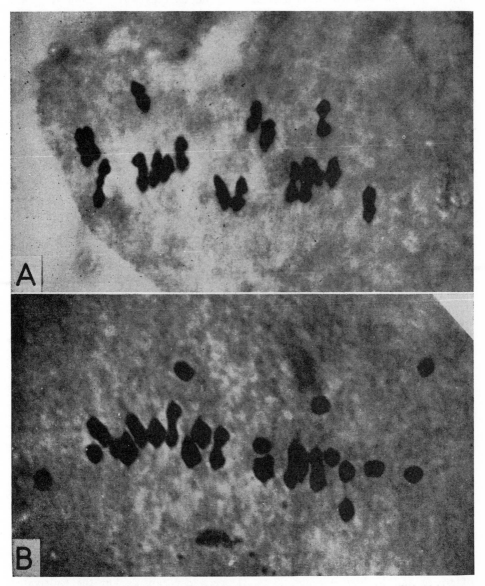

FIG. 5. Photomicrographs of squash preparations of microsporocytes. A. Hybrid between Cultivated *lindleyi* and Mt. Hamilton *lindleyi* showing 18_{II}. B. Hybrid between Sequoia *crocea* and Mt. Hamilton *lindleyi* showing $13_{II}10_{I}$. Both figures × 1000.

segregate at random producing spores deficient in whole chromosomes as well as corresponding cells with extra chromosomes. Only 20 anaphase cells were analyzed, however; this number is too small to indicate the frequency of gametes deviating from the normal number of 18 chromosomes. Chromosome pairing in the hybrids between the five populations is summarized in Figure 3 where the average number of chromosome pairs per cell for each hybrid is recorded along each hybrid line.

Pollen: Pollen was stained with cotton blue in lactophenol. Darkly stained, spherical pollen was scored as normal. Any pollen that was irregular in shape or had a shrunken or nonstaining protoplast was scored as abnormal. The abnormal pollen in surely inviable and some of the pollen scored as normal on the basis of shape and stainability may be nonfunctional. Only the first few flowers produced by a plant were used for pollen counts and two slides were prepared from two different flowers of each individual. Two counts, each of about 300 pollen grains, were made from each slide, to check on the accuracy of the counting method and indicate the flower to flower variation of normal pollen in a single individual. This check on the pollen scoring procedure indicated that differences of less than 10% could be due to the sampling and scoring method; hence, differences of less than 10% are not considered to indicate a reduction in fertility. To estimate the percentage of good pollen for the plants of a particular population or progeny, pollen counts were made from three individuals selected at random. Percentage of normal pollen of the three individuals were in general agreement so the three counts were averaged to arrive at the percentage for that population or progeny.

Pollen counts of garden plants grown from seed harvested in each of the parental populations are recorded in Figure 3. These counts establish the percentage of normal pollen production characteristic of the natural populations. Percentage of normal pollen from each hybrid is recorded along the line connecting the two parent populations in the crossing diagram. Hybrids between Mt. Hamilton *lindleyi* and Cultivated *lindleyi* and between Sequoia *crocea* and Kaweah *crocea* showed percentages of normal pollen equivalent to those of the parents. Hybrids between *crocea* and *lindleyi* showed considerable reduction in percentages of normal pollen. Hybrids between *lindleyi* and *crocea* have a higher percentage when Cultivated *lindleyi* is used and a lower percentage when Mt. Hamilton *lindleyi* is used.

Seed production: Seed production was measured by counting the number of apparently normal seeds per capsule. This was recorded only for capsules that were selfed or sibling crossed by hand pollination; hence, partial pollination such as might occur in open pollinated flowers could be ruled out as a cause of low seed set. Only vigorous plants were used. Pollinations were made only on the first few flowers to open on an individual plant because it was apparent that later flowers produced smaller capsules with fewer seeds. Seed counts were made in this manner on garden plants grown from seeds harvested in the parent populations. The average number of seeds per capsule is recorded in the circles representing each parental strain in Figure 4. Most populations of *crocea* and *lindleyi* average 23 to 31 seeds per capsule but the Cultivated strain of *lindleyi* averaged 40 seeds per capsule. The data for the hybrids are recorded along the appropriate hybrid line connecting the parental strains in

Figure 4. The first figure, in parentheses, indicates the number of flowers pollinated; the second figure is the average number of seeds per capsule; and the
third is the maximum number of seeds per capsule for that hybrid combination.
Hybrids between Cultivated *lindleyi* and Mt. Hamilton *lindleyi* and between
Sequoia *crocea* and Kaweah *crocea* have seed production essentially like their
parents. Hybrids between *crocea* and *lindleyi,* however, produce few seeds per
capsule when selfed or sibbed. Considering all the hybrids between *lindleyi* and
crocea, flowers sufficient to give a possible 2000 seeds, were selfed or sibbed;
actually only 11 seeds were obtained.

Germination, vigor and fertility of the F_2: When the 11 seeds obtained
from self and sibling crosses of F_1 plants were sown, only four germinated. Two
of these seedlings proved to be weak and died about two months after germination. The other two F_2 plants were as vigorous and tall as the F_1. Thus, only
two vigorous F_2 plants were produced out of a potential 2000, an effective fertility of 0.1%. One of the vigorous F_2 plants (6063) was the result of a self-
pollination of an F_1 derived from Cultivated *lindleyi* ♀ $\times$ Merced *crocea* ♂. This
F_2 individual had nearly clear yellow flowers with even less orange than *crocea*.
With respect to shape the flowers were like the F_1, whereas the leaves resembled
those of the *lindleyi* parent. This plant branched from below like *lindleyi* but
had a long central axis like *crocea*. Partly as a result of this distinctive branching pattern, the total aspect was conspicuously different from either *lindleyi,*
crocea, or the F_1. Chromosome pairing of this plant was not studied but its
pollen was only 1% normal. This plant did not set any seeds, although numerous
flowers were selfed and crossed to both *lindleyi* and *crocea*.

The other vigorous F_2 (6060) resulted from selfing an F_1 derived from
Sequoia *crocea* ♀ $\times$ Cultivated *lindleyi* ♂. This plant also lacked orange pigment in the petals but had the same amount of orange pigment in the
lower one-half of the filaments as does *lindleyi*. The shape of the flowers
and the leaves were like the *crocea* parent. The branching pattern was
like that of the F_1. In general appearance this plant resembled some of the
backcrosses to *crocea*. In this F_2 individual chromosome pairing was analyzed
in 42 cells. Of these only four cells showed 18_{II} and the average number of pairs
per cell was 16.2. This plant produced 30% normal pollen. Several flowers were
selfed or outcrossed but only three seeds were produced, these from one of the
selfed flowers.

Backcrosses: When the F_1 hybrids between *lindleyi* and *crocea* were used
as female parents in backcrosses they produced an average of four seeds per
capsule. Sufficient backcross pollinations were made to yield a potential 600
seeds but only 62 were obtained. Of these only ten germinated; only four plants
reached maturity. Three of these were backcrosses to *lindleyi* and one was a
backcross to *crocea*. Thus backcrossability is quite low, only about 0.7% of the
potential, but the backcross is somewhat easier to produce than the F_2. In
appearance the four backcross plants were in general intermediate between the
F_1 and the backcross parent. The fertility of the B_1 plants is only slightly
higher than the F_1. Chromosome pairing was studied in only one individual,
a backcross to *lindleyi*, and in this only 15 cells were analyzed. Eight of these
cells showed 18_{II} and the average number of pairs per cell was 17.3. This individual produced only 12% normal pollen and four selfed flowers set an average
of 5 seeds per capsule. Another plant, produced by backcrossing to *lindleyi*, had

21% normal pollen and four selfed flowers produced an average of nearly ten seeds per capsule. The third plant, also from a backcross to *lindleyi*, produced 16% good pollen and four selfed flowers formed an average of about five seeds per capsule. The one B_1 plant produced by backcrossing to *crocea* did not flower but formed buds that withered and dropped off before meiosis occurred. The average normal pollen of the B_1 plants was 16% and they averaged 6.6 seeds per capsule when selfed. Thus the B_1 plants are somewhat more fertile than the F_1 but one generation of backcrossing does not restore normal fertility.

DISCUSSION AND CONCLUSIONS

Mentzelia lindleyi and *M. crocea* are more similar to each other than to any other taxon. Although this similarity may indicate phylogenetic relationship, it tells little about the degree of evolutionary and genetic divergence between *lindleyi* and *crocea*. Their morphological differences could be due to a few genes, or they could be indicative of two widely divergent genetic systems. Because *lindleyi* and *crocea* are allopatric it is impossible to observe their genetic interaction in nature; only experimental hybridization gives information about their genetic relationship.

The high sterility of F_1 hybrids between *lindleyi* and *crocea* suggests a considerable genetic and evolutionary hiatus between them. Two factors, lack of chromosomal pairing and genetic recombination, contribute to this sterility. In the F_1 hybrid combinations only 5% to 28% of the microsporocytes have regular meiosis with 18_{II}. In the remaining cells (those with unpaired chromosomes), the unpaired chromosomes segregate randomly at anaphase, resulting in gametes deficient in whole chromosomes. Such gametes are in general nonfunctional and undoubtedly cause some of the observed sterility. The sterility of the F_1 plants, however, as measured by the number of vigorous F_2 plants resulting from self and sibling crosses of the F_1, is greater than can be accounted for by the lack of chromosomal pairing. For example, in the F_1 between Cultivated *lindleyi* and Merced *crocea*, 28% of the microsporocytes have normal meiosis with 18_{II} of chromosomes and 43% of the microsporocytes have $17_{II}2_I$. All of the pollen derived from the 18_{II} sporocytes should have 18 chromosomes. With random segregation of the univalents, one-half of the divisions of the $17_{II}2_I$ sporocytes should result in 19-17 chromosome segregations and one-half in 18-18 chromosome segregations. Thus, in spite of the fact that 43% of the microsporocytes have $17_{II}2_I$, one-half of the spores formed from these cells, or 21% of all spores, should have 18 chromosomes. Even ignoring the possibility of 18 chromosome spores coming from the microsporocytes with fewer than 17 pairs and more than 2 univalents, we can expect a minimum of 49% (i.e., 28% plus 21%) of all microspores to have 18 chromosomes. Plants of this F_1, however, have only 26% good pollen. This indicates that even some of the microspores with 18 chromosomes are not functional. Disruption of chromosomal pairing alone cannot account for the low pollen fertility; one must conclude that nonfunctional genotypes are produced by genetic recombination. Some of these nonfunctional genotypes segregated at meiosis are eliminated at the haploid phase as nonfunctional pollen. The low seed-set in the F_1 plants and the low seed-germination and low vigor of the F_2 generation indicate that other genotypes, not eliminated as haploids, are combined by fertilization in genotypes that are eliminated at these later stages in development.

Lack of chromosomal pairing and of genetic recombination both contribute to the sterility of the F_1. It is this sterility that is the basis for the genetic isolation of *lindleyi* and *crocea*. The fact that the fertility of the F_1 is blocked at several stages is of considerable importance. Each of the numerous points at which fertility is blocked may be recorded as an additional difference between *lindleyi* and *crocea*. These differences point out the evolutionary hiatus between *lindleyi* and *crocea* and indicate that *lindleyi* and *crocea* are genetically far more different than is indicated by chromosome pairing alone.

The difficulty of obtaining backcross plants from the F_1 between *lindleyi* and *crocea* and the low fertility of the few backcross plants is of interest. It suggests that the various factors that cause the sterility are segregating independently so that the probability of recovering the parental combination is very low. By selfing and sibbing the few backcross plants available it may be possible to derive a fertile strain relatively homozygous for a recombination genotype possessing some of the factors that would isolate it from *lindleyi* and some that would isolate it from *crocea*. Stebbins (1957) has done this in hybrid derivatives of *Elymus glaucus* $\times$ *Sitanion jubatum* to demonstrate the origin of the microspecies in *Elymus glaucus*.

The genetic nature of the sterility between *lindleyi* and *crocea* has taxonomic significance. A barrier of this sort indicates considerable evolutionary divergence and provides a basis for interpreting morphological differences. The morphological difference between *lindleyi* and *crocea* is such that most modern taxonomists have considered them to be only subspecifically distinct, but now we can view this morphological difference against the background of their genetic diversity. With this new perspective it appears that *M. lindleyi* and *M. crocea* should be considered two distinct species.

TAXONOMY

Descriptions of the genus *Mentzelia* and of Section *Trachyphytum* have been published by Darlington (1934). Descriptions, synonymy, citation of specimens, and comments on the types of *M. lindleyi* T. & G. and *M. crocea* Kell. have been presented by Wolf (1938). There is little need to repeat such information here, but the following key and partial synonomy summarize the taxonomic conclusions of this paper.

Plants mostly 2 to 4 dm tall, branching at the base; petals obovate, the width more than one-half the length, golden yellow with the basal one-eighth dark orange; Coast Ranges. *M. lindleyi.*
Plants mostly 4 to 7 dm tall, branching from above; petals ovate, the width less than one-half the length, yellow with the basal one-sixteenth orange; Sierra Nevada Foothills. *M. crocea.*

Mentzelia lindleyi T. & G. Fl. N. Am. **1**: 533. 1840.
  Bartonia aurea Lindley, Bot. Reg. **22**: *pl. 1831.* 1836. Not *Mentzelia aurea* Nutt. 1818.
  Acrolasia aurea (Lindl.) Rydb. Bull. Torrey Club **30**: 278. 1903.
  Mentzelia lindleyi T. & G. subsp. *typica* Wolf, Occ. Papers Rancho Santa Ana Bot. Gard. 1: 70. 1938.

Mentzelia crocea Kellogg, Proc. Calif. Acad. I, **7**: 110. 1876.
  Mentzelia lindleyi T. & G. subsp. *crocea* (Kell.) Wolf, Occ. Papers Rancho Santa Ana Bot. Gard. 1: 71. 1938.

I am grateful to Professor Harlan Lewis and Mr. Peter H. Raven for reading the manuscript and offering helpful suggestions. Miss Joyce Johnson assisted with growing the plants and preparing the manuscript. Mrs. Rosemary O'Connor prepared some of the illustrations. Funds for the support of this study were made available through the Faculty Research Committee of the University of California, Los Angeles.

LITERATURE CITED

Clausen, Jens. 1951. Stages in the evolution of plant species. viii+206 pp. Ithaca, Cornell University Press.

Darlington, Josephine. 1934. A monograph of the genus *Mentzelia*. Ann. Mo. Bot. Gard. 21: 103–226.

Kellogg, A. 1876. On some new species of California plants. Proc. Calif. Acad. Sci. I, 7: 110.

Munz, P. A., & Keck, D. 1949. California plant communities. Aliso 2: 87–105.

Stebbins, G. L. 1957. The hybrid origin of microspecies in the *Elymus glaucus* complex. Proc. Intern. Genetics Symposia 1956: 336–340. (Supplement volume of Cytologia).

Thompson, H. J. & Lewis, H. 1955. Chromosome numbers in *Mentzelia* (Loasaceae). Madroño 13: 102–107.

Wolf, C. B. 1938. A revision of *Mentzelia lindleyi*. Occ. Papers Rancho Santa Ana Bot. Gard. 1: 69-73.

THE INDEPENDENT ANEUPLOID ORIGIN OF TWO SPECIES OF CHAENACTIS (COMPOSITAE) FROM A COMMON ANCESTOR[1]

DONALD W. KYHOS

Stanford University, Stanford, California

Accepted September 10, 1964

Very similar species are of great interest to students of evolution because such species probably have evolved recently, making it likely that much of the evidence of their origin can be reconstructed. In very few instances of closely similar non-polyploid plant species is there evidence to suggest that one is the ancestor of another. A notable example is the cytological evidence for the origin of Crepis fuliginosa ($n = 3$) from C. neglecta ($n = 4$) or its near ancestor (Tobgy, 1943). Similarly, Sherman (1946) showed that Crepis kotschyana ($n = 4$) has been derived from an ancestor like C. foetida ($n = 5$). Another convincing example of an aneuploid species with a living diploid ancestor was described by Lewis and Roberts (1956) in their studies of Clarkia biloba ($n = 8$) and C. lingulata ($n = 9$). These two species are so similar that they can only be distinguished by petal shape and chromosome number. Cytogenetic analysis showed that C. lingulata has an additional chromosome composed of parts of two chromosomes of the C. biloba genome. The presence of duplicated chromosome material in C. lingulata clearly establishes it as a derivative of C. biloba. Recently, Jackson (1962) described a case in Haplopappus that also suggests the origin of one diploid species from another. What was considered Haplopappus gracilis was found to consist of two extremely similar species,

one with a chromosome number of $n = 4$, the other with $n = 2$. Cytological evidence indicates in this instance, as in Crepis, that aneuploid reduction is the most probable explanation for the difference in chromosome number, with the $n = 2$ species the derived one.

The purpose of this paper is to present a unique example in Chaenactis (Compositae) in which the cytogenetical evidence indicates beyond reasonable doubt that an extant species of relatively mesic habitats, C. glabriuscula DC., has given rise independently to two similar desert species, C. fremontii Gray, and C. stevioides H. & A., by aneuploid reduction in chromosome number.

Chaenactis comprises approximately 24 herbaceous species, all endemic to western North America. There are at least nine annual species, and four of these, C. glabriuscula, C. stevioides, C. fremontii, and C. xantiana form a closely related assemblage,[2] judging from their similarity and frequent natural hybridization. The first three will be considered in detail in this paper. The yellow-flowered C. glabriuscula is the most variable, and some of its intergrading variants have been treated as separate species.[3] Chaenactis stevioides and C. fremontii have white flowers, but are otherwise very similar morphologically to certain populations of C. glabriuscula. Despite their overall similarity, the gametic chromosome number of C. glabrius-

[1] Part of a dissertation submitted in partial fulfillment of the requirements for the Ph.D. degree in Botany at the University of California, Los Angeles. Sincere appreciation is expressed to Drs. F. H. Lewis and P. H. Raven for their valuable criticism of the manuscript. This work has been supported in part by Grant 2G-365-R1 from the U. S. Public Health Service, National Institutes of Health.

[2] I consider Chaenactis gillespiei to be C. stevioides, and C. mexicana and C. latifolia to be either C. stevioides or C. glabriuscula, whereas C. furcata may be distinct, although closely related to this group.

[3] For example, C. orcuttiana, C. heterocarpa, and C. tanacetifolia by Stockwell, 1940, and C. tanacetifolia and C. tenuifolia by Ferris, 1960.

Reprinted by permission of the author and publisher from EVOLUTION, 19, 26–43 (1965).

TABLE 1. *Pollen and seed fertilities. Pollen and seed fertilities of* Chaenactis glabriuscula, C. stevioides, *and* C. fremontii *generally range between 90 to 99 per cent.*

Collection number	Pollen fertility		Seed set fertility		Identity of the plant
	Sample size	Per cent good	Sample size	Per cent good	
62-53	500	41.1	300	36.0	Natural F₁ hybrid be-
62-57	Pollen sterile		300	48.6	tween *C. fremontii* and *C.*
62-58	300	36.3	300	44.3	*stevioides*
62-59	300	36.0	300	41.6	
62-87	300	8.0	300	42.3	Natural F₁ hybrid be-
62-88	300	5.3	300	51.6	tween *C. glabriuscula* and
62-89	300	35.6	300	43.6	*C. stevioides*
60-155	300	11.3	300	36.0	Artificial F₁ hybrid be-
60-156	300	14.0	300	37.6	tween *C. glabriuscula* and
63-7	300	37.6	300	45.6	*C. fremontii*
63-82	300	54.0	300	42.3	
64-23	300	41.6	—	—	Natural F₁ hybrid be-
64-24	300	50.0	—	—	tween *C. glabriuscula* and
					C. fremontii

cula is $n = 6$, and that of *C. stevioides* and *C. fremontii* is $n = 5$, with distinct karyotypic differences between the latter species.

These three species grow together in relatively limited areas. *Chaenactis glabriuscula* occurs in comparatively mesic areas toward the coast, coming into limited contact with the other two species only at the edge of the desert. Similarly, on the desert *C. fremontii* and *C. stevioides* seldom grow together, even though the distribution of *C. fremontii* is essentially included within that of *C. stevioides*. Within their few local areas of sympatry the distinctiveness of the species is still maintained even though hybridization between them is sometimes frequent. Autogamy can be eliminated as a factor maintaining these species, since all three are strongly self-incompatible. Moreover, there is no evidence that differential pollination plays any part in isolating these species. Their most frequent pollinators visit them indiscriminately in areas of sympatry. For example, at Cabazon, California, the most important pollinator is a small beetle,[4]

which rapidly visits the flowers of *C. glabriuscula* and *C. fremontii* at random.

Ecological factors apparently strongly limit these species and their hybrids. Microdistributional patterns are rigidly maintained in sympatric areas, despite the fact that the seeds are well equipped for dispersal. Moreover, the suitable habitats of *C. fremontii*, where it is sympatric with *C. glabriuscula* in the San Gorgonio Pass of California, are often no larger than a square foot, and yet for at least six years these patterns have not varied, even though the strong winds of this area scatter the seeds widely. Unquestionably a large proportion of the seeds of the two species falls onto unsuitable sites and fails to grow, resulting in these stable microdistributional patterns. Similar stable patterns have also been observed in sympatric areas of *C. glabriuscula* and *C. stevioides*, as well as *C. stevioides* and *C. fremontii*.

The behavior of these species in cultivation also suggests that they are very sensitive to edaphic factors. For example, in one soil mixture *C. fremontii* failed to

---

[4] *Byturosoma fusca* (Lec.) of the Melyridae; kindly determined for me by J. F. Lawrence.

Specimens are preserved at the California Insect Survey, Berkeley, California.

germinate at all, whereas *C. glabriuscula* and *C. stevioides* planted at the same time in the same soil germinated readily and grew to maturity. In another soil mixture *C. glabriuscula* failed to germinate, whereas *C. fremontii* and *C. stevioides* germinated easily. Subsequently, the *C. fremontii* plants grew to maturity, but the *C. stevioides* plants died before flowering.

Even when hybrids are produced in nature, they are strongly limited by edaphic conditions. This is indicated by the occurrence of the greatest number of hybrids in areas that are disturbed by man's activities. For example, at Cabazon, California, where *C. glabriuscula* and *C. fremontii* grow together, the frequency of hybrids and their derivatives increased from less than five to more than 10 per cent of the population the next growing season after a bulldozer cleared a firebreak in this area. This increase in hybrids was evident not only by a comparison with previous years, but by comparing the disturbed and undisturbed areas that were immediately adjacent in the firebreak area. The increase in hybrids in this instance cannot be the result of increased hybridization, but can only be explained by a greater proportion of hybrid seeds, already present in the soil, reaching maturity in the disturbed area than elsewhere. I have also observed similar occurrences in other sympatric areas, involving the other two species combinations.

In addition to these factors, which may be termed external, the chromosomal differences between these species presumably are of major importance in maintaining their distinctness. Chromosomal relationships will be discussed in detail in the cytogenetic section of this paper.

MATERIALS AND METHODS

Seeds from wild populations of *C. glabriuscula* and *C. fremontii* from Cabazon, California, were used to start cultures in the experimental garden of the University of California, Los Angeles, and interspecific pollinations were made by rubbing the flowering heads together. The resulting seeds were sown and numerous hybrids were obtained for cytogenetic studies. In addition to these artificial F_1 hybrids between *C. glabriuscula* and *C. fremontii*, two natural F_1 hybrids between these species were obtained at the extreme southwest margin of the Mohave Desert (see Table 4 for exact localities).

I found it difficult to grow *C. stevioides* in cultivation, as did Rancho Santa Botanic Garden on several occasions (Everett, 1957). For this reason naturally occurring F_1 hybrids were used for the cytogenetic studies of the hybrid combinations involving this species; three *C. stevioides* × *C. glabriuscula* F_1 hybrids were obtained in the hills bordering the southwest portion of the Mohave Desert, and four *C. stevioides* × *C. fremontii* F_1 hybrids were obtained in the Anza-Borrego State Park (see Table 4). Single branches were removed from these natural hybrids to be used as voucher specimens. These plants were left *in situ*, and seed set was determined at maturity.

Anthers for cytological study were fixed in a Carnoy's mixture of six parts absolute ethanol, three parts chloroform, and one part glacial acetic acid, and were squashed in acetocarmine. Pollen fertility was estimated by the percentage of grains that stained with cotton blue in lactophenol.

Voucher specimens are deposited in the herbarium of the University of California, Los Angeles.

CYTOGENETICS

Some of the chromosomes of *Chaenactis glabriuscula*, *fremontii*, and *stevioides* have distinctive characteristics. It is possible to recognize these chromosomes in interspecific hybrids, permitting a detailed analysis of the chromosome arrangements of the three species (see Figs. 1 and 2).

Chromosome Identification and Notation

Meiosis in the species.—Two of the six chromosome pairs of *C. glabriuscula* are readily identified at meiosis. In Fig. 3, these two pairs are labeled *Ag* and *Bg*.

These letters are arbitrarily assigned to the chromosomes; the uppercase letters denote different chromosomes, the lowercase letters the species to which the chromosome belongs. The Ag pair, in addition to being the largest, is subacrocentric and in some individuals frequently shows an attenuated region at or near the centromere, giving the short arm the appearance of a satellite. The Bg pair includes the nucleolar organizer and can be identified because of its attachment to the nucleolus. The four remaining pairs cannot be recognized consistently. The mean chiasma frequency in the six pairs is 8.93, with chiasmata notably infrequent in the nucleolar-organizing arms. These descriptions are based on examination of 214 plants from 24 populations.

Three of the five pairs of *C. fremontii* are easily identified (Fig. 4). One of them $(E' + F'f)$ is the largest pair and is metacentric; another (Af) is the largest subacrocentric and appears to be identical with the Ag pair of *C. glabriuscula*; a third pair $(C'f)$ is attached to the nucleolus. The mean chiasma frequency in the five pairs is 6.16 with chiasmata rarely occurring in the nucleolar-bearing arms. These descriptions are based on examination of 139 plants from 18 populations.

Two pairs of *C. stevioides* can be recognized consistently (Fig. 5). One (As) consists of the largest subacrocentrics of the complement, but it lacks the attenuation at the centric region that occurs in the largest subacrocentrics of *C. glabriuscula* and *C. fremontii*. Another pair $(D's)$ is easily identified by its attachment to the nucleolus. The mean chiasma frequency in the five pairs is 5.91, and chiasmata rarely occur in the nucleolar-bearing chromosome arms. The three remaining pairs cannot be consistently identified. These chromosome descriptions are based on examination of 135 plants from 17 populations.

Meiosis in the interspecific hybrids.— The modal and maximum meiotic configurations of the three hybrid combinations of *C. glabriuscula*, *C. fremontii*, and *C. stevioides* are diagrammed below.

A more detailed description of meiosis in the three hybrids is as follows: The modal and maximum meiotic association in *Chaenactis glabriuscula* × *C. fremontii* is a chain of three and four pairs (Figs. 2, 6, and 7). The four pairs at diakinesis form chiasmata in essentially a normal frequency and position, but two pairs cannot be entirely homologous, because only one member of each pair organizes the nucleolus. One of the two remaining pairs (A) is the largest of the diploid set. One or both homologues

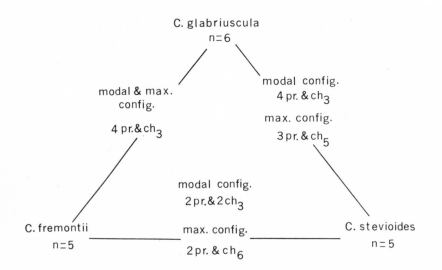

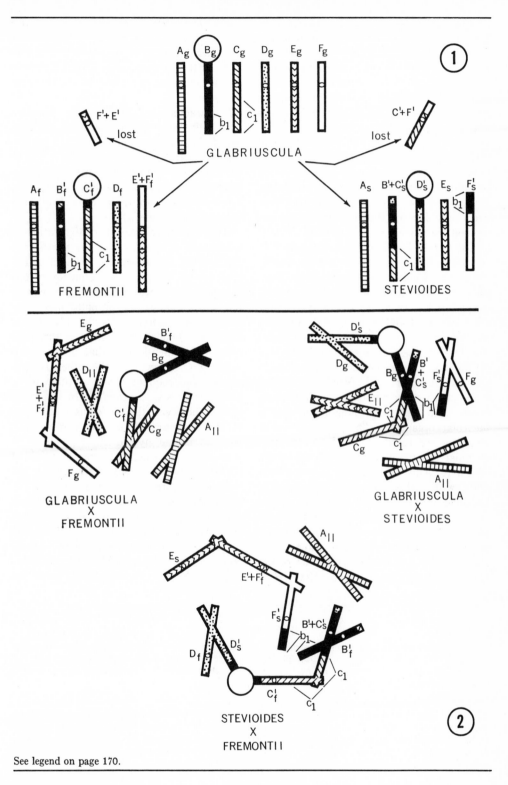

See legend on page 170.

of this pair may have an attenuated centromeric region. The remaining pair has no distinguishing characteristics, but can be identified by the process of elimination. The chain of three consists of a large metacentric with two smaller chromosomes attached to its ends by chiasmata. Bridges and accompanying fragments also occur in a low frequency (Table 2). The description of the chromosomes in this hybrid is based on a sample of over 1,000 meiotic prophase cells from 22 different garden and two natural F_1 hybrids; however, only four of these hybrids were examined extensively (see Table 2).

The hybrid *Chaenactis glabriuscula* × *C. stevioides* has a maximum meiotic configuration of a chain of five and three pairs (Fig. 8). The chain of five occurs with a frequency less than one per cent. Almost all remaining PMCs have a chain of three plus four pairs (Figs. 9 and 10, and Table 2). One of these four pairs is composed of the largest chromosomes (A) of each species. Another pair ($DgD's$) appears to be structurally homozygous throughout except that only one homologue has a nucleolar organizer. The other nucleolar organizer is located in the short arm of a terminal chromosome (Bg) of the chain of three. This chromosome forms chiasmata with either the short arm or the proximal portion of the long arm of the central chromosome ($B' + C's$) of the chain of three (Fig. 9). The remaining chromosome (Cg) of the chain of three forms chiasmata only with the distal part of the long arm of the central chromosome ($B' +$

$C's$). The very uncommon chain of five results when a short arm of one of the two remaining pairs (FF') forms a chiasma with the distal part of the long arm of the nucleolar chromosome of the chain of three. The last pair has no distinguishing characteristics, but can be identified by elimination. Bridges and accompanying fragments also occur in a low frequency in this hybrid (see Table 2). The description of the chromosomes in this hybrid is based on a collective sample of 1,162 PMCs from three F_1 hybrid individuals (see Table 2).

The maximum meiotic configuration in *Chaenactis stevioides* × *C. fremontii* is a chain of six and two pairs (Fig. 11). The chain of six occurs in a frequency of less than two per cent; in most of the remaining PMCs these six chromosomes form two chains of three (Figs. 12, 13, 14, and Table 2). One of the chains of three appears to be identical to that in *C. glabriuscula* × *C. fremontii*; the other is similar to the frequent chain of three in *C. glabriuscula* × *C. stevioides*. In the latter hybrid, however, the nucleolus is attached to the short arm of the Bg chromosome, whereas in the hybrid *C. stevioides* × *C. fremontii* it is attached to the short arm of $C'f$ at the opposite end of the chain. The chain of six results from a chiasma between the short arm of one of the terminal chromosomes ($F's$) of the first chain of three and the distal part of the long arm of the terminal chromosome ($B'f$) of the second chain of three. The two remaining pairs are readily distinguished, since one

---

Fig. 1. A diagram of the probable structural arrangement of the chromosomes of *Chaenactis glabriuscula, C. stevioides,* and *C. fremontii.* The approximate positions of the centromeres are indicated by ovals in the chromosomes. The nucleoli are indicated by larger circles attached to the ends of the chromosomes.

Fig. 2. A diagram of the modal pairing configurations of the chromosomes in the hybrids between *Chaenactis glabriuscula, C. stevioides,* and *C. fremontii.* The maximum configurations occur in the hybrid *C. glabriuscula* × *C. stevioides,* and *C. stevioides* × *C. fremontii* when chiasmata are also formed between the areas designated as B_1. The approximate positions of the centromeres are indicated by ovals in the chromosomes. The nucleoli are indicated by larger circles attached to the ends of the chromosomes.

TABLE 2. *Frequencies of chromosome configurations in hybrids.*

C. fremontii × C. stevioides

Collection number	$2_{11} + 2$ ch₃	$2_{11} +$ ch₃ + linear ch₃ dissociation	$2_{11} +$ ch₃ + forked ch₃ dissociation	$2_{11} +$ ch₈	Nucleolar pair dissociation	Bridge and fragment frequency
62-53	186	10	1	3	–	$3/700 = 0.004$
62-57	193	5	1	1	1	$4/600 = 0.007$
62-58	357	8	9	14	–	$3/600 = 0.005$
62-59	192	18	13	2	5	$3/600 = 0.005$
Totals	928 (91.07%)	41 (4.02%)	24 (2.36%)	20 (1.96%)	6 (0.59%)	

C. glabriuscula × C. stevioides

Collection number	$4_{11} +$ ch₃	$4_{11} +$ partially dissociated ch₃	Nucleolar pair dissociation	Other univalents	$3_{11} +$ ch₅	Bridge and fragment frequency
62-87	90	7	2	1	–	$9/600 = 0.02$
62-88	624	51	19	3	4	$42/739 = 0.06$
62-89	328	23	8	1	1	$11/1,162 = 0.01$
Totals	1,042 (89.68%)	81 (6.97%)	29 (2.49%)	5 (0.43%)	5 (0.43%)	

C. glabriuscula × C. fremontii

Collection number	$4_{11} +$ ch₃	$4_{11} +$ partially dissociated ch₃	Nucleolar chromosome univalents	Nucleolar chromosome and ch₃ dissociation	Bridge and fragment frequency
60-155	102	8	1	–	$2/412 = 0.005$
60-156	92	7	1	–	$9/816 = 0.01$
63-7	403	89	6	1	$2/526 = 0.004$
63-82	83	17	–	–	$2/473 = 0.004$
Totals	680 (83.95%)	121 (14.93%)	8 (0.99%)	1 (0.12%)	

of them ($DfD's$) is heterozygous for a nucleolar-organizer, and the other (A) is the largest of the chromosome set. One homologue of this largest pair has a centric region that tends to stretch, giving it a satellited appearance (Figs. 12 and 13). Bridges and accompanying fragments also occur in a low frequency in this hybrid (see Table 2). The description of the chromosomes in this hybrid is based on a collective sample of 1,019 PMCs from four F₁ hybrid individuals (see Table 2).

Genome Analysis of Chaenactis glabriuscula, stevioides *and* fremontii

It is possible to determine the general chromosome arrangement of each species (Fig. 1) by correlating the chromosome configurations in the three possible F₁ hybrids involving *Chaenactis glabriuscula, stevioides,* and *fremontii* (Fig. 2). This was done by assigning letters to the six chromosomes of *C. glabriuscula* and utilizing them as a standard. The largest chromosome, which in some plants had a satellited appearance, was given the letter A (Fig. 3), the nucleolar organizer chromosome B, and the remaining four chromosomes, which could not be distinguished from each other consistently, were assigned letters without attempting to match letters with particular chromosomes.

The chromosomes of *C. fremontii* were designated in this system by studying meiosis in its F_1 hybrid with *C. glabriuscula.* In this hybrid the largest pair is easily recognized because of the satellited appearance of one or both homologues (Fig. 6). Since this pair appeared normal, the largest chromosome of *C. fremontii* was considered homologous with the *A* chromosome of *C. glabriuscula.* There are two pairs in this hybrid that are heterozygous for the nucleolar organizing region (Fig. 6). This clearly indicates that the nucleolar organizers are on different chromosomes in *C. glabriuscula* and *C. fremontii.* The nucleolar chromosome in *C. fremontii* was assigned the letter *C* to indicate that it is different from the nucleolar chromosome (*B*) in *C. glabriuscula.* Also, in the hybrid *C. glabriuscula* × *C. fremontii* there is a chain of three which consists of a relatively large central metacentric, with two smaller chromosomes attached to its ends (Figs. 6 and 7). This configuration indicates that chromosomes *D* and *E*, *E* and *F*, or *D* and *F* are joined to form the large metacentric of *C. fremontii.* The *E* and *F* chromosomes were arbitrarily designated as the two involved. The remaining pair in this hybrid was assigned the letter *D*.

The above assignment of letter designations to the chromosomes of *C. glabriuscula* and *C. fremontii* has predetermined the letters to be assigned to the chromosomes of *C. stevioides.* The actual identification of the chromosomes of *C. stevioides* can be accomplished by the homologies indicated by the chromosome pairing in the hybrids *C. glabriuscula* × *C. stevioides* and *C. stevioides* × *C. fremontii.* On the basis of the diakinesis studies in these two hybrid combinations, the largest chromosome of *C. stevioides* appears to be completely homologous with the *A* chromosome of *C. glabriuscula* and *C. fremontii,* since a normal pair is always formed (Figs. 9, 12, and 13).

Hybrids of *C. glabriuscula* with either *C. fremontii* or *C. stevioides* usually show a chain of three indicating that each of the five chromosome species has a compound chromosome with respect to *C. glabriuscula.* Since the hybrid between *C. fremontii* and *C. stevioides* usually shows two chains of three (Figs. 12, 13, and 14), the compound chromosomes of these species must involve basically different combinations. This immediately eliminates chromosomes *E* and *F* as major components of the *C. stevioides* compound chromosome, since these are the chromosomes that are joined in *C. fremontii.* This leaves chromosomes *B*, *C*, and *D* as possible components of the *C. stevioides* compound chromosome. From *C. glabriuscula* × *C. stevioides* it can be established that chromosome *B* is one component of the *C. stevioides* compound chromosome, since a nucleolar chromosome, which must be the *B* chromosome of *C. glabriuscula,* pairs with the short arm and the proximal portion of the long arm of the compound chromosome (Fig. 9). In order to decide whether *C* or *D* is the other member of the *C. stevioides* compound chromosome, it is essential to be able to distinguish between the chain of three containing the *C. fremontii* $E' + F'$ compound chromosome and the chain of three containing the *C. stevioides* compound chromosome in *C. fremontii* × *C. stevioides.* This can be done with certainty, because the $E' + F'$ compound chromosome of *C. fremontii* is metacentric, whereas the compound chromosome of *C. stevioides* is subacrocentric. These structural differences lead to different patterns of chiasma formation, which further aid in distinguishing the two chains of three. The two chromosomes that are homologous with $E' + F'$ of *C. fremontii* form chiasmata mostly near the distal ends of their long arms, resulting in a linear chain of three (Figs. 6, 7, 12, 13, and 14). Both of the chromosomes that are homologous with the *C. stevioides* compound chromosome commonly form chiasmata between their long arms and the long arm of the *C. stevioides* chromosome. This results in a chain of three having a "Y" or forked shape configuration (Figs. 9, 12, 13, and 14). Because of the characteristics of the

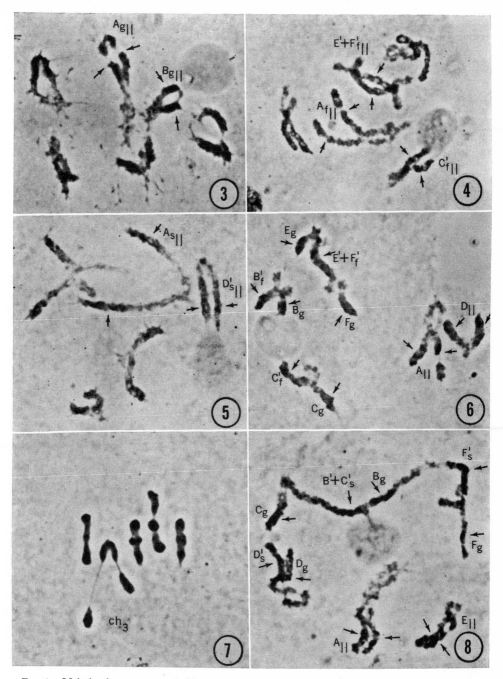

FIG. 3. Meiotic chromosomes of *Chaenactis glabriuscula* at diakinesis. The recognizable chromosomes are labeled with capital letters. The lowercase letters denote the species to which the chromosomes belong. The symbol II stands for pair. Arrows indicate the approximate positions of the centromeres. Magnification 970.

FIG. 4. Meiotic chromosomes of *Chaenactis fremontii* at diakinesis. See Fig. 3 for an explanation of the symbols. Magnification 970.

Legend continued on page 174.

173

chain containing the *C. stevioides* compound chromosome it is possible to distinguish one end of the chain from the other, permitting the identification of the components of the *C. stevioides* compound chromosome. For example, in *C. stevioides* × *C. fremontii*, it is apparent that a nucleolar chromosome, which must come from *C. fremontii*, pairs only with the distal portion of the long arm of the *C. stevioides* compound chromosome (Figs. 11, 12, and 13). By previous designation this is the *C* chromosome of *C. fremontii*; hence, the compound chromosome of *C. stevioides* must represent a union of *B* and *C*. The observation that the nucleolus is attached to different ends of the chain of three containing the *C. stevioides* compound chromosome in the hybrids *C. stevioides* × *C. glabriuscula* and *C. stevioides* × *C. fremontii* is consistent with the determination that the nucleolar region is on different chromosomes in *C. glabriuscula* and *C. fremontii*. The only remaining undesignated *C. stevioides* chromosome, which contains the nucleolar organizer, must be *D*, since all other components have been accounted for.

The very uncommon chain of six in *C. fremontii* × *C. stevioides* provides additional information about the relative chromosome structure of the species. This chain of six results from a chiasma between the two chains of three (Fig. 11). This union consistently occurs between the most distal portion of the long arm of the *C. fremontii B* chromosome and the short arm of either the *E* or *F* chromosome of *C. stevioides* (the *F* chromosome was arbitrarily chosen in this case) and indicates a homology between these regions. If this homology is due to the *F* chromosome of *C. stevioides* including part of the *B* chromosome, then in *C. stevioides* × *C. glabriuscula* a chain of five should occur. Moreover, it can be predicted that this chain of five should result from a union of the short arm of one member of a nonnucleolar chromosome pair with the distal part of the long arm of the nucleolar chromosome of the chain of three. Examination of a large number of cells in *C. stevioides* × *C. glabriuscula* revealed that this predicted configuration does occur in a low frequency of approximately 0.5 per cent (Fig. 8).

Thus the meiotic chromosome pairing of the three hybrid combinations integrates perfectly, providing a consistent picture of the genome arrangements of the three species.

Interpretation of Chromosomal Rearrangements Between Species

Chaenactis glabriuscula × *C. fremontii*. —A reciprocal translocation is the most

---

Fig. 5. Meiotic chromosomes of *Chaenactis stevioides* at diakinesis. See Fig. 3 for an explanation of the symbols. Magnification 970.

Fig. 6. Maximum (and modal) pairing configuration at diakinesis in the hybrid *Chaenactis glabriuscula* × *Chaenactis fremontii*, which consists of four pairs and a chain of three. Note that two of the pairs are heterozygously involved in nucleolar organization. See Fig. 3 for an explanation of the symbols. Magnification 970.

Fig. 7. Maximum (and modal) pairing configuration at metaphase in the hybrid *Chaenactis glabriuscula* × *Chaenactis fremontii*, which consists of four pairs and a chain of three. The chain of three is indicated by the symbol ch₃. Magnification 970.

Fig. 8. Maximum pairing configuration at diakinesis in the hybrid *Chaenactis glabriuscula* × *Chaenactis stevioides*, which consists of a chain of five and three pairs. Note the firm attachment of the chain of five to the major nucleolus. The chain of five is linear in this PMC, instead of having its usual forked appearance because a chiasma has occurred in the short nucleolar bearing arms of chromosomes *Bg* and *B' + C'*. One homologue of pair *D'D* has organized a small nucleolus, which by chance lies close to the *Cg* chromosome. See Fig. 3 for an explanation of the symbols. Magnification 970.

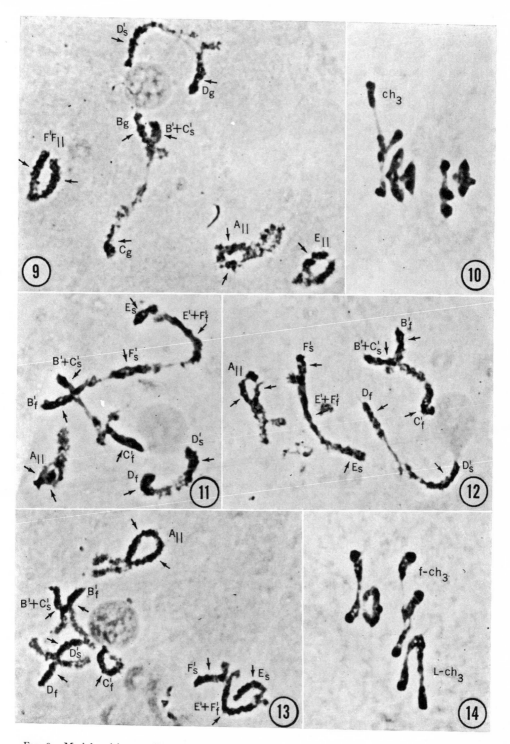

Fig. 9. Modal pairing configuration at diakinesis in the hybrid *Chaenactis glabriuscula* × *Chaenactis stevioides*, which consists of a chain of three and four pairs. Note the "Y" or forked shaped

probable explanation for the transposition of the nucleolar locus from *B* to *C*. During meiosis this translocation might be expected to produce a maximum configuration of a ring of four chromosomes with the nucleolus attached. Instead, the configuration that consistently occurs is two pairs, each heterozygous for the capacity to organize the nucleolus. The lack of a ring of four in this instance is probably due to three factors: 1) since it is likely that the translocation exists in the short chromosome arms, only chiasmata in these arms distal to the translocation would lead to ring or chain formation, and chiasmata in short arms are generally infrequent; 2) the translocation itself should further reduce the frequency of chiasmata; 3) these short arms bear nucleoli distally, and observations of such chromosome arms in other widely different organisms have shown chiasmata to be uncommon or rare in them (McClintock, 1941; Tobgy, 1943).

The large metacentric of *C. fremontii* is a combination of the *E* and *F* chromosomes of *C. glabriuscula*. The most probable explanation for this combination is a very unequal translocation followed by the loss of a small centric region and terminal segment of one of the chromosomes. Pachynema studies, however, suggest that an inversion and perhaps a duplication may also have been involved in the origin of the $E' + F'f$ chromosome.

Chaenactis glabriuscula × *C. stevioides*. —The nucleolar organizers are on different chromosomes, *B* and *D*, in *C. glabriuscula* and *C. stevioides*, presumably as a result of a reciprocal translocation. This translocation might be expected to form a ring of four as a maximum meiotic configuration; however, only pairs were observed, probably for reasons similar to those discussed for *C. fremontii* × *C. glabriuscula*. A second rearrangement involving chromosomes *B* and *F* apparently has given rise to the *F's* chromosome of *C. stevioides*, as indicated in *C. glabriuscula*

---

arrangement assumed by the chain of three, which is its typical appearance. A single member *Bg* of the chain of three is attached to the nucleolus. The *D'D* pair also heterozygously organizes the nucleolus. See Fig. 3 for an explanation of the symbols. Magnification 970.

FIG. 10. Modal pairing configuration at metaphase in the hybrid *Chaenactis glabriuscula* × *Chaenactis stevioides*, which consists of a chain of three and four pairs. The chain of three is indicated by the symbol ch₃. Magnification 970.

FIG. 11. Maximum pairing configuration at diakinesis in the hybrid *Chaenactis stevioides* × *Chaenactis fremontii*, which consists of a chain of six and two pairs. Note the attachment of one member, *C'f*, of the chain of six to the nucleolus, and one member of the *D'D* pair. Only pair *A* appears to be structurally homozygous. See Fig. 3 for an explanation of the symbols. Magnification 970.

FIG. 12. Modal pairing configuration at diakinesis in the hybrid *Chaenactis stevioides* × *Chaenactis fremontii*, which consists of two chains of three and two pairs. One of the chains of three has a "Y" or forked shaped appearance and is attached to the nucleolus at its non-forked end. The other chain of three is linear. Note the attachment of one member of pair *D'D* to the nucleolus also. One member of pair *A* displays an attenuated centromeric region. See Fig. 3 for an explanation of the symbols. Magnification 970.

FIG. 13. Modal pairing configuration at diakinesis in the hybrid *Chaenactis stevioides* × *Chaenactis fremontii*, which consists of two chains of three and two pairs. This configuration is the same as Fig. 12, but is included because it affords a better view of the linear chain of three. See Fig. 3 for an explanation of the symbols. Magnification 970.

FIG. 14. Modal pairing configuration at metaphase in the hybrid *Chaenactis stevioides* × *Chaenactis fremontii*, which consists of two chains of three and two pairs. One chain of three is forked (f-ch₃) and the other (l-ch₃) assumes a linear "V" shaped arrangement. Magnification 970.

TABLE 3. *Chiasma frequencies in the species.*

Collection number	Chiasma number at meiotic metaphase							
	5	6	7	8	9	10	11	12
Chaenactis fremontii								
57-83	14	46	29	10	1			
57-84	5	48	36	10	1			
60-127	15	68	15	2				
60-128	14	58	25	3				
62-71	17	50	27	6				
62-72	16	47	36	1				
63-49	30	63	6	1				
63-49a	22	66	11	1				
Totals	133	446	185	34	2			
Chaenactis stevioides								
61-3	34	54	12					
62-20	35	44	18	3				
62-21	46	50	4					
62-54	22	58	19	1				
62-135	75	24	1					
62-135a	24	49	23	4				
63-2	9	50	36	4	1			
63-5	6	56	35	3				
Totals	251	385	148	15	1			
Chaenactis glabriuscula								
60-202			4	12	49	31	4	
62-136			1	14	47	29	9	
63-27			6	21	56	14	3	
63-81				9	43	36	10	2
63-83		1	19	52	25	3		
63-84			3	23	42	28	4	
17033*		2	17	39	33	9		
17088*			5	22	42	25	6	
Totals		3	55	192	337	175	36	2

* Collection numbers of Peter H. Raven.

× *C. stevioides* by the occasional joining of chromosome pair $F'sFg$ to Bg as part of a chain of five (see Fig. 8).

The *glabriuscula* C chromosome appears to be homologous with only the distal portion of the long arm of the $B' + C'$ chromosome of *C. stevioides*, inasmuch as it pairs only in this region. The remainder of the *glabriuscula* C chromosome, i.e., its short arm, the centromere, and the proximal portion of its long arm, appears to have no equivalent in the *C. stevioides* genome. The remainder of chromosome $B' + C'$ of *C. stevioides*, i.e., the proximal portion of its long arm, its centromere, and most of its short arm, is homologous with the corresponding parts of the B chromosome of *C. glabriuscula*. The tip of the short arm of the *stevioides* $B' + C'$ chromosome probably has part of the D component as a result of the translocation discussed above that transferred the nucleolar organizer from B to D. The most distal part of the long arm of the *glabriuscula* B chromosome apparently is not homologous with the *stevioides* $B' + C'$ chromosome, because this distal portion occasionally forms a chiasma with the short arm of the *stevioides* F' chromosome, thereby producing a chain of five.

The $B' + C'$ compound chromosome of *C. stevioides* could have originated from the chromosomes of *C. glabriuscula* by a sequence of reciprocal translocations or from rejoining following three simultaneous breaks. In the first instance approximately one-half of the distal portion of the long arm of chromosome B of *glabriuscula* could have undergone an interchange with the short arm of F, followed by a second interchange in B at or very near the same point, but this time with the long arm of C. The centric portion and short arm of C and the short arm of F, which would have been united by this last interchange, subsequently were lost. In addition, the short arm of B could also have undergone an interchange with the short arm of D, thereby transferring the nucleolar locus from chromosome B to D. The sequence of the interchanges is irrelevant.

A simpler explanation for the origin of the compound chromosome of *C. stevioides* would be to assume three simultaneous breaks—one break in the proximal portion of the short arm of F, a second break in the proximal portion of the long arm of C, and a third break at about the middle of the long arm of B. The distal part of the long arm of C could then have attached directly onto the broken long arm of B and the distal part of the long arm of B could have permanently replaced the distal

177

part of the short arm of *F*. The distal part of the short arm of *F* and the large centric portion of *C* would have been lost. An interchange between the short arms of *B* and *D* could have occurred at any time before, during, or after the non-reciprocal breaks and rejoining.

The bridges with accompanying fragments that appear in meiotic anaphases in all three hybrid combinations suggest that these species differ by paracentric inversions. Pachynema studies, necessary to demonstrate inversions and their position, are difficult in this material. Only a single inversion loop has been identified at pachynema in *C. glabriuscula* × *C. fremontii*.

The chromosomal repatterning that has taken place in these three species has produced blocks of chromatin which appear to form few, if any, chiasmata. For example, in *C. glabriuscula* × *C. fremontii* the short arms of the nucleolar chromosomes, which presumably have a translocation, rarely form chiasmata. Any genes in these arms would be essentially free of genetic recombination. Also, the *D* pair in this hybrid forms chiasmata only in its long arm, and thus the short arms, which may differ by a duplication, appear to have no genetic recombination. Lastly, in this same hybrid, the chain of three usually forms chiasmata distally in the chromosome arms, so that any proximally located genes would be relatively free of genetic recombination. In *C. glabriuscula* × *C. stevioides* chiasmata formed in the chain of three are usually well removed from the presumed point of union of the two chromosomes that make up the compound chromosome, so that genes near the point of union should experience little recombination. Likewise, the nucleolar bearing chromosome arms in this hybrid, which probably have undergone a translocation, form relatively few chiasmata. Lastly, the short arm of the *C. stevioides* F chromosome, which is homologous with the distal portion of the long arm of the *C. fremontii* and *C. glabriuscula* B chromosome, in hy-

brids forms chiasmata in only 2.0 and 0.5 per cent of the PMCs, respectively. This means that in such hybrids only 1.0 and 0.25 per cent of the gametes, respectively, would contain chromosomes recombinant for these blocks of chromatin. Therefore, even though chromosomal pairing between these species is generally good, there are areas within their chromosomes that form few, if any, chiasmata in hybrids. These areas therefore could be important in limiting genetic recombination that might destroy the integrity of the species.

DISCUSSION

Chaenactis glabriuscula, C. stevioides, and *C. fremontii* are obviously closely related, since they are very similar in appearance and hybridize naturally. *Chaenactis stevioides* is essentially identical to some populations of the polytypic *C. glabriuscula,* except for flower color, chromosome number, and habitat preference. *Chaenactis glabriuscula* has yellow flowers, a chromosome number of $n = 6$, and occupies relatively mesic habitats, whereas *C. stevioides* and *C. fremontii* as well, have white flowers, a chromosome number of $n = 5$, and occur in the deserts and semiarid areas. The fact that *C. stevioides* appears to combine characteristics of both *C. glabriuscula* and *C. fremontii* suggested that it might have originated by hybridization, or that it is intermediate in a stepwise evolutionary series involving these three species. However, the cytogenetic evidence presented in this paper shows that even though *C. stevioides* and *C. fremontii* have several characteristics in common, including the same chromosome number of $n = 5$, they are, nevertheless, chromosomally more similar to the six paired *C. glabriuscula* than they are to each other (see Figs. 1 and 2). Moreover, the cytogenetic data provide compelling evidence that the chromosomes of *C. fremontii* and *C. stevioides* were derived by independent aneuploid reductions from the *C. glabriuscula* genome. The three species have approximately the same amount of

178

TABLE 4. *Collection localities (all collections by the author unless otherwise indicated).*

Collection number	Localities
	Chaenactis glabriuscula
60-202	Cabazon, Riverside Co., California
62-136	0.9 miles north of U. S. Highway 6, and 7.2 miles east of The Oaks, Los Angeles Co., California
63-27	Cabazon, Riverside Co., California
63-81	7.8 miles west of Coalinga near State Highway 198, Fresno Co., California
63-83	Placerita Canyon Rd., 3.9 miles east of U. S. Highway 6, Los Angeles Co., California
63-84	At the entrance to the marina, Venice, Los Angeles Co., California
17033*	19.4 miles south of Colonia Guererro, Baja California
17088*	1 mile southeast of the junction of Herring Rd. and Tejon Highway, south of Arvin, Kern Co., California
	Chaenactis stevioides
61-3	Wildrose Canyon at Wildrose Camp, Inyo Co., California
62-20	U. S. Highway 99, 6 miles south of Oasis, Imperial Co., California
62-21	Same as above
62-54	State Highway 78, 15 miles east of Banner in the Anza Desert State Park, San Diego Co., California
62-135	0.9 miles north of U. S. Highway 6, and 7.2 miles east of The Oaks, Los Angeles Co., California
62-135a	Same as above
63-2	Silver Bell Rd., 1.6 miles north of Speedway Blvd., Tucson, Pima Co., Arizona
63-5	Near State Highway 93-87 at summit in the Sacaton Mts., Pinal Co., Arizona
	Chaenactis fremontii
57-83	State Highway 138, 3 miles east of Pearblossom, Los Angeles Co., California
57-84	Same as above
60-127	Southwest Cabazon, Riverside Co., California
60-128	Same as above
62-71	U. S. Highway 80, 3.1 miles east of the Imperial Co. line, Imperial Co., California
62-72	Same as above
63-49	4.6 miles inside the northwest entrance to Joshua Tree National Monument, San Bernardino Co., California
63-49a	Same as above
	Chaenactis glabriuscula × *Chaenactis stevioides*
62-87	0.9 miles north of U. S. Highway 6, and 7.2 miles east of The Oaks, Los Angeles Co., California
62-88	Same as above
62-89	Same as above
	Chaenactis glabriuscula × *Chaenactis fremontii*
60-155	U.C.L.A. garden, parent species from Cabazon, Riverside Co., California
60-156	Same as above
63-7	Same as above
63-82	Same as above
64-23	1.4 miles south of Quartz Hill, California
64-24	Same as above
	Chaenactis stevioides × *Chaenactis fremontii*
62-53	Roadside, State Highway 78, 15 miles east of Banner in the Anza Desert State Park, San Diego Co., California
62-57	Same as above
62-58	Same as above
62-59	Same as above

* Collection number of Peter H. Raven.

euchromatin, but it is distributed in fewer chromosomes in the two desert species. In outcrossing annuals such as these *Chaenactis* species, it is particularly likely that the taxa with the lower chromosome number are the derived ones (Stebbins, 1950, p. 447). The lower chromosome number affords increased genetic linkage, providing a means of specialization. On this basis, it is to be expected that *C. fremontii* and *C. stevioides* would have a lower recombination index than their ancestor, *C. glabriuscula*. This lower recombination index should result not only from their lower chromosome number, but also from a lower chiasma frequency per PMC. This is in fact the case, since *Chaenactis glabriuscula* has a distinctly higher mean chiasma frequency per PMC, 8.93, than either *C. fremontii*, 6.16, or *C. stevioides*, 5.91 (Table 3). In *Chaenactis* additional evidence from cytology, ecology, and morphology, supports the proposed origin of *C. fremontii* and *C. stevioides*.

1) *Cytology*.—A comparison of the largest subacrocentric chromosome (A) in the three species suggests that *C. glabriuscula* is ancestral to both *C. stevioides* and *C. fremontii*. In *C. glabriuscula*, chromosome A is variable. In some individuals the centric area of one or both homologues is slow to condense during early diakinesis, making the short arm of this chromosome appear as a satellite. In other individuals, the A chromosomes do not evidence delayed condensation. In both *C. fremontii* and *C. stevioides* chromosome A is morphologically uniform. In *C. fremontii* it is always attenuated in the centromeric area at early diakinesis, whereas in *C. stevioides* it never shows this characteristic. This suggests that with respect to chromosome A, *C. fremontii* and *C. stevioides* may well be uniform segregates from the variable *C. glabriuscula*.

The chromosome numbers of *C. fremontii* and *C. stevioides* are undoubtedly derived rather than ancestral. This is indicated not only by their probable derivation, as described in this paper, but also by the pattern of chromosome numbers in the genus in relation to growth form. *Chaenactis fremontii* and *C. stevioides* are the only species with $n = 5$; all but three others have $n = 6$.[5] All of the species with chromosome numbers other than $n = 6$ are annuals, and annuals have long been known to be especially labile with respect to chromosome number and structural arrangement. All but two of the dozen or so perennial species have been counted and all have $n = 6$ (or a multiple of $n = 6$), as do the four remaining annuals (Raven and Kyhos, 1961, and unpublished). Since $n = 6$ is the only number known in the relatively primitive perennial members, and since within the $n = 6$ category is included the greatest array of distinctive species, it is highly probable that $X = 6$ is the basic haploid chromosome number of the genus, and that *C. fremontii* and *C. stevioides*, but not *C. glabriuscula* have derivative numbers.

2) *Ecology*.—The ecological characteristics of these species suggest that *C. stevioides* and *C. fremontii* are recent derivatives of *C. glabriuscula*. Both of the former are endemic to the deserts of western North America, which are of relatively recent formation (Axelrod, 1958). These deserts reached their full development as a concomitant of the extensive orogeny in western North America following the late Pliocene. On the other hand, the relatively mesic habitats of *C. glabriuscula* have been in existence much longer.

The ecological diversity of *C. glabriuscula* also suggests that it is older than either *C. fremontii* or *C. stevioides*. *Chaenactis glabriuscula* occurs in a wide variety of ecological situations from the coastal strand to the margins of the deserts, and at elevations up to 1,500 meters (Hall, 1907), whereas *C. stevioides* and *C. fremontii* are limited to relatively uniform habitats.

---

[5] *Chaenactis xantiana* with $n = 7$, and *C. carphoclinia* and *C. artemisiifolia* (including *C. lacera*) with $n = 8$.

The occurrence of vigorous populations of *C. glabriuscula* at the margins of the desert suggests that very little modification of this species would have been necessary to produce new taxa that could successfully occupy the deserts. Perhaps the most important change necessary to adapt *C. glabriuscula* to a desert environment would be the isolation of the proper gene combinations already present in this species. This may well be the selective basis of the chromosome alterations that differentiate *C. fremontii* and *C. stevioides* from *C. glabriuscula*.

3) *Morphology.*—The extensive morphological diversity of *C. glabriuscula* also suggests that it has had a longer history than either *C. fremontii* or *C. stevioides*. These latter species are by no means morphologically uniform, but are clearly much less variable than *C. glabriuscula*. Moreover, nearly all of the morphological characteristics of *C. fremontii* and *C. stevioides* can be duplicated within the various races of *C. glabriuscula*. Indeed, the two desert species might easily be considered segregates of the variable *C. glabriuscula*, were it not for the chromosomal differences and associated barriers to gene exchange.

The pappus characteristics of *C. glabriuscula* also suggest a more primitive status for this species than for either *C. stevioides* or *C. fremontii*. All of the perennials in the genus have 10 to 16 or more pappus scales. Of the three annuals considered here, only *C. glabriuscula* also has populations consisting of plants with up to 10 pappus scales. Such populations occur in the most mesic portions of the range of this species. Those in the driest areas consistently have four pappus scales, as do *C. fremontii* and *C. stevioides*.[6] This series strongly suggests a phylogenetic trend culminating in the most specialized desert annuals.

Although no single portion of the ecological or morphological evidence could be considered conclusive in itself, when con-

sidered as a body and in conjunction with the strong cytogenetic evidence, it seems a virtual certainty that *C. glabriuscula* is the living ancestor of *C. stevioides* and *C. fremontii*.

SUMMARY

In the Compositae, the annual species *Chaenactis glabriuscula* ($n = 6$), *C. fremontii* ($n = 5$), and *C. stevioides* ($n = 5$) are morphologically very similar. The two latter species are essentially confined to the deserts of California and other western states, whereas *C. glabriuscula* is common throughout much of California in more mesic areas, from the coast to the borders of the deserts. Cytogenetic studies revealed that even though the two desert species have the same haploid chromosome number of five, their chromosome arrangements are more similar to the six paired species, than they are to each other. The cytogenetic data establish beyond reasonable doubt that the genomes of five in the two desert species have been derived independently by aneuploid reduction from a genome of six. This and other evidence indicates that *C. glabriuscula* is the living ancestor of *C. fremontii* and *C. stevioides*.

LITERATURE CITED

AXELROD, D. I. 1958. Evolution of the Madro-Tertiary geoflora. Bot. Review, **24**: 433–509.

EVERETT, P. C. 1957. A summary of the culture of California plants at the Rancho Santa Ana Botanic Garden, 1927–1950. Rancho Santa Ana Botanic Garden, 223 pp.

FERRIS, R. S. 1960. Illustrated flora of the Pacific states. Vol. IV, Stanford University Press, Stanford, California, 732 pp.

HALL, H. M. 1907. Compositae of southern California. Univ. California Publ. Bot., **3**: 1–302.

JACKSON, R. C. 1962. Interspecific hybridization in *Haplopappus* and its bearing on chromosome evolution in the Blepharodon section. Amer. J. Bot., **49**: 119–132.

LEWIS, H., AND M. R. ROBERTS. 1956. The origin of *Clarkia lingulata*. Evolution, **10**: 126–138.

McCLINTOCK, B. 1941. Spontaneous alterations

---

[6] A few populations of *C. stevioides* in the most mesic sites have five to six scales.

in chromosome size and form in *Zea mays*. Cold Spring Harbor Symp. Quant. Biol., **9**: 72–81.

RAVEN, P. H., AND D. W. KYHOS. 1961. Chromosome numbers in Compositae. II. Helenieae. Amer. J. Bot., **48**: 842–850.

SHERMAN, M. 1946. Karyotype evolution: a cytogenetic study of seven species and six interspecific hybrids of *Crepis*. Univ. California Publ. Bot., **18**: 369–408.

STEBBINS, G. L. 1950. Variation and evolution in plants. Columbia Univ. Press, New York, 643 pp.

STOCKWELL, P. 1940. A revision of the genus *Chaenactis*. Contr. Dudley Herb., **3**: 89–168.

TOBGY, H. A. 1943. A cytological study of *Crepis fuliginosa, C. neglecta*, and their F_1 hybrid, and its bearing on the mechanism of phylogenetic reduction in chromosome number. J. Genet., **45**: 67–111.

THE TAXONOMIC SEPARATION OF THE CYTOLOGICAL RACES OF
KOHLRAUSCHIA PROLIFERA (L.) KUNTH *SENSU LATO*

By P. W. BALL and V. H. HEYWOOD

University of Liverpool

INTRODUCTION

It has been realised for some considerable time that *Kohlrauschia prolifera* (L.) Kunth contains both diploid and tetraploid plants (Blackburn, 1933, Böcher *et al.*, 1953, 1955). The cytotypes appear to have different distributions, the more widespread diploid being replaced in W.S.W. Europe by the tetraploid. Because of the close morphological similarity between the cytotypes, and the difficulty of separating them, *K. prolifera* has come to be widely referred to in the literature as an example of the phenomenon of semi-cryptic polyploidy (cf. Heywood, 1958, Larsen, 1960). In the course of a revision of the whole genus, we have had occasion to make a detailed study of the *K. prolifera* group, as a result of which it has become apparent that not only can the diploid and tetraploid races be separated fairly satisfactorily on the basis of their seed-coat morphology, but the differences had been recognised precisely many years previously.

Although it has usually been assumed that the tetraploids have arisen from the diploids by autoploidy, the morphological evidence suggests that another diploid species, *K. velutina* (Guss.) Reichb., is involved and that the tetraploid has been formed as a result of allopolyploidy between it and diploid *K. prolifera*.

TYPIFICATION OF K. PROLIFERA

This species was based on *Dianthus prolifer* L., *Sp. Pl.*, 410 (1753). Typification has proved difficult since there is no positive evidence that the specimen of *Dianthus prolifer* in the Linnean Herbarium has a claim to being selected as a lectotype. The sheet does not bear the *Species Plantarum* number normally found on those of species described in the first edition. If, however, the specimen is accepted as authentic there is no reason to suppose that it is other than diploid *Kohlrauschia prolifera*, although in the absence of seeds it cannot be identified with certainty. The synonyms and distribution given by Linnaeus could apply to either the diploid or tetraploid species. This kind of situation arises occasionally with the typification of species in polyploid groups where the various species may be separated from one another by micro-characters which are not available for examination in the type material. In such cases the wisest course is to accept a typification which does not upset the traditional interpretation of the species, unless there is strong evidence to the contrary. Accordingly the name *K. prolifera* (L.) Kunth is accepted here for the diploid species which occurs in most countries of Europe and to a small extent in N.W. Africa and Anatolia.

THE IDENTITY OF DIANTHUS NANTEUILII BURNAT

During the investigation of the genus it was necessary to account for *Dianthus nanteuilii* Burnat which was published in *Flore des Alpes Maritimes*, 1: 221-222 (1892) with a full description based on 38 specimens from various localities at Cannes and Agay. The leaf sheaths are described by Burnat as ' aussi larges que longues ' and the seeds are described in considerable detail : ' absolutely intermediate between the two preceding species [*D. prolifer* and *D. velutinus*] in dimensions and shape : more convex dorsally than in

Reprinted by permission of the authors and publisher from
WATSONIA, **5**, 113–116 (1962).

D. velutinus, and less hollow-concave than in the latter, the outer surface striate-tuberculous, with tubercles similar to those of *D. velutinus*, but much closer together and less projecting.'

Burnat considered the species (apart from the rare presence of glandular hairs) intermediate between *D. prolifer* and *D. velutinus*, but Nanteuil thought that a hybrid origin was unlikely in view of the commonness of the new form in the vicinity of Cannes while only one specimen of *D. velutinus* was seen. *D. prolifer* did not on the other hand appear to be less abundant although it flowered later. He gave the following times of maturity of the first seeds :

velutinus	20th May
intermediate	1st June
prolifer	25th June

Time of flowering needs further investigation both in the field and in cultivation, but *D. velutinus* does appear in the light of later observations to be the earliest of the three to flower (cf. Böcher *et al.*, 1953).

Further examination of large numbers of individuals by Nanteuil failed to reveal any transitional forms. This is confirmed by our own comparative studies on a wide range of material from diverse provenances.

It is interesting to note that, although Burnat appears to have been the first to publish a description of this species, there are two older sheets in the Kew Herbarium from the Pyrenees which have manuscript names and extensive and accurate descriptions appended.

KOHLRAUSCHIA VELUTINA (GUSS.) REICHB.

The third taxon involved in this complex, *K. velutina*, is characterized by its long leaf sheaths (at least twice as long as broad) and by its strongly tuberculate seeds. The epithet *velutina* refers to the dense glandular-tomentose indumentum which is usually found on some of the internodes in the middle part of the stem. This character is not, however, constant and forms with glabrous stems occur which have in the past been confused with *K. prolifera*, especially in Italy, Sicily and Sardinia.

K. velutina is diploid (Böcher *et al.* 1953, 1955) and is regarded by some writers, such as Briquet (1910), as only subspecifically distinct from *K. prolifera*. It is widely distributed in the Mediterranean region from Portugal and Spain to Turkey and Palestine. The karyotype has, however, been shown to be quite distinctive (Böcher *et al.*, *loc. cit.*) as discussed below.

TAXONOMIC COMPARISONS

The accompanying table sets out the differences between the three units. From this it will be seen that several characters can be employed to separate them, with *K. nanteuilii* occupying an intermediate position. Of these characters, however, the only constant and reliable ones are those of the seed testa.

TABLE 1

	K. prolifera	*K. nanteuilii*	*K. velutina*
Internodes (*middle part of stem*)	Glabrous	Glabrous to tomentose	Densely glandular-tomentose, rarely glabrous
Leaf sheaths	Broader than long to about as long as broad	1–2 times as long as broad	At least twice as long as broad
Width of Petal limb	2–3·5 mm	2–3 mm	1·2–2·5 (− 3) mm
Inner bracts	Obtuse	Obtuse or mucronate	Mucronate
Seed size	1·3–1·9 mm	1·2–1·9 mm	1–1·3 (− 1·4) mm
Testa pattern	Reticulate (Plate 6a)	Tuberculate (Plate 6b)	Tuberculate to papillose (Plate 6c)

PLATE 6

a. (top) *K. prolifera* (København 3325), b. (middle) *K. nanteuilii* (København 3248) c. (bottom) *K. velutina* (København 3303)

185

The details of the seed testa are shown in Plate 5. The characteristic pattern of each species is easily appreciated by using a low-power dissecting microscope, although with a little practice an ordinary × 10 hand-lens is adequate. Through the courtesy of Professor T. W. Böcher and Dr. Kai Larsen we have been able to examine specimens and seeds from spontaneous plants grown in Copenhagen whose chromosomes have been counted by them. This material is listed below :

Origin	Culture No. (København)	Origin	Culture No. (København)
nanteuilii 2n = 60		POLAND	
		Tomice, distr. Poznan	3324
CHANNEL ISLANDS		Poznan	3365
Jersey, St. Ouens Bay	3248	SWEDEN	
Jersey, Quenvais	3249	Öland	2963
FRANCE		Gotland	2878
Béziers	1733	DENMARK	
Port Vendres	1715	Kregme	2282
MADEIRA	3111	FRANCE	
SPAIN		Mt. Louis above La Cassagne	1696
Soria	3321	Luchon	1627
PORTUGAL		Bouleternère	1700
Coimbra	2483	SWITZERLAND	
CANARY ISLANDS		Hort. Bot. Lausaniensis	663
Gran Canaria	37, 38		
Tenerife	36		

Origin	Culture No. (København)	Origin	Culture No. (København)
prolifera 2n = 30		*velutina* 2n = 30	
HUNGARY		PORTUGAL	
Budapest	3325	Sacavem	3303
SPAIN		BELGIUM	
Lloret de Mar, Barcelona	3323	Hort. Bot. Antverpen	913

In all cases the correlation between chromosome number and seed testa type has been confirmed in the *prolifera-nanteuilii* pair. Similarly, the cultivated material of *K. velutina* has its characteristic testa configuration and the expected chromosome number of 2n = 30.

In view of the fallibility of the other characters used to separate the units, the seed testa pattern alone appears to be constantly correlated with level of polyploidy in the diploid-tetraploid *prolifera* pair. In cases such as these it is important that the constancy of the polyploid markers be checked over a wide range of material (Heywood, 1960, Heywood and Walker, 1961). We feel that the correlation is now well established in this group; moreover, examination of testas has been made of seed from extensive collections of herbarium material which on other characters and distributional grounds agree with determinations as *K. prolifera*, *K. nanteuilii* and *K. velutina*. Again the correlation has been satisfactory and no breakdown between the testa pattern differences has been noted. It is proposed therefore that the tetraploid form of *K. prolifera* be recognised as a separate species and the appropriate combination is made below :

Kohlrauschia nanteuilii (Burnat) P. W. Ball & Heywood, *comb. nov. Dianthus nanteuilii* Burnat, Fl. Alpes Marit., **1** : 221 (1892); *Tunica prolifera* proles *T. nanteuilii* Rouy & Fouc., Fl. Fr. **3** : 160 (1896); *Tunica nanteuilii* Gürke, Pl. Eur. **2** : 338 (1903); *Tunica prolifera* var. *nanteuilii* Briquet, Prodr. Fl. Corse **1** : 569 (1910).

Distribution : *British Isles.* V.c. 10, Isle of Wight; 11, S. Hants; 13, W. Sussex; 15, E. Kent (introduced); 28, W. Norfolk (introduced); Channel Islands, France, Corsica, Sardinia, Spain, Portugal, Morocco, Madeira, Canary Islands.

KOHLRAUSCHIA PROLIFERA (L.) Kunth occurs as a rare alien in the British Isles. Specimens have been seen from v.c. 14, E. Sussex, and v.c. 28, W. Norfolk, and it may also be found elsewhere.

THE ORIGIN OF K. NANTEUILII

It is suggested by Böcher *et al.* (1953) that the tetraploid race probably arose by autoploidy from diploid *K. prolifera*. As pointed out above, the morphological evidence does not lend support to this view since *K. nanteuilii* is intermediate in most characters between diploid *K. prolifera* and *K. velutina*. It seems possible therefore that *K. nanteuilii* may be an allotetraploid derived from the other two species. The strains of *K. velutina* examined cytologically by Böcher *et al.* were distinct from diploid *K. prolifera* in possessing a pair of very short chromosomes. If our theory is correct, an examination of the karyotype of *K. nanteuilii* may provide confirmation, since it should possess the short chromosome pair. Plants are being cultivated for this purpose.

DISCUSSION

The taxonomic recognition of polyploid races showing slight morphological divergence is a subject which has provoked considerable controversy (*cf.* Heywood, 1960; Löve, 1960). When no single morphological character can be detected which allows a constant separation to be made between polyploid races, it is doubtful if nomenclatural recognition serves any useful purpose. Similarly, when the characters proposed to distinguish the polyplotypes can be appreciated only by a specialist, it is of little value to recognise them as separate species knowing that the possibilities of correct identification by a non-specialist are slender (*cf.* Heywood, 1960, p. 183).

In this case, however, one morphological character, seed testa-pattern, which can be easily appreciated, appears to be constantly correlated with level of ploidy; other characters (as noted in Table 1) are satisfactory in a fair percentage of cases; and the geographical distribution of the diploid and tetraploid races is clearly distinct. There are, in addition, a number of physiological differences, although these need further investigation. These factors, as well as the probable alloploid origin of the tetraploid, seem to us to favour specific recognition. The close taxonomic similarity of the three species *K. prolifera*, *K. nanteuilii* and *K. velutina* could then be indicated in practice by grouping them in a species aggregate.

REFERENCES

BLACKBURN, K. (1933). On the relation between geographic races and polyploidy in *Silene ciliata*. *Genetica* **15**, 49–65.

BÖCHER, T. W., LARSEN, K. & RAHN, K. (1953). Experimental and cytological studies on plant species. I. *Kohlrauschia prolifera* and *Plantago coronopus*. *Hereditas* **39**, 289–304.

BÖCHER, T. W., LARSEN, K. & RAHN, K. (1955). Experimental and cytological studies on plant species. II. *Trifolium arvense* and some other pauciennial herbs. *Dan. Biol. Skr.* **8**, No. 3.

BRIQUET, J. (1910). *Prodrome de la Flore Corse*, 1. Genève & Bâle, Lyon.

HEYWOOD, V. H. (1958). *The presentation of taxonomic information. A short guide for contributors to Flora Europaea*. Leicester.

HEYWOOD, V. H. (1960). The taxonomy of polyploids in Flora Europaea. *Feddes Repert.* **63**, 179–192.

HEYWOOD, V. H. & WALKER, S. (1961). Morphological separation of cytological races in *Ranunculus ficaria* L. *Nature* **189**, 604.

LARSEN, K. (1960). Infraspecific cytological variation. *Planta Medica*, 8 Jahr. Heft 3.

LÖVE. A. (1960). Taxonomy and chromosomes – a reiteration. *Feddes Repert.* **63**, 192–202.

THE GENETIC EVALUATION OF A TAXONOMIC
CHARACTER IN DITHYREA (CRUCIFERAE)

Reed C. Rollins

Developing accuracy in the evaluation of plant characters and characteristics for taxonomic purposes is a long-standing problem. When differences are found between groups of plants which otherwise appear to be related, the immediate question arises as to what these differences mean. Specifically, what do the differences mean in terms of the genetic make-up of the natural group to which such plants be'ong and how valuable are they as taxonomic criteria? In our efforts to interpret speciation in relation to a given species or a group of species, we wish to rely upon those characters as indicators of relationship (or lack of it) that are so deeply seated in the genetic constitution of the species that they cannot be easily obliterated or greatly modified by the direct effects of any given simply segregating factor or combination of segregating factors. In general, the kinds of characteristics that offer the greatest possibilities for taxonomic reliability are those that are dependent upon a multiplicity of genes and gene combinations for their ultimate expression—genes that are not in a single linear sequence of interdependency, but genes in many series whose interaction in a highly complex way results in the final structure or function. It may also be suggested that any given characteristic thus dependent upon a complex genetical system, which is deeply situated within the genotype, becomes protected from radical changes by the build-up of inter-dependencies between it and other characteristics, some of which may be vital to survival. Thus the species phenotype persists over many generations, little altered in basic pattern by the

Reprinted by permission of the author and publisher from
Rhodora, 60, 145–152 (1958).

numerous minor segregations that account for the usual variation present.

At the other end of the scale, characteristics under the control of the simplest gene systems are expected to be least reliable as the basis for classification. Such characteristics would be easily modified or suppressed by repetitious mutations, gene rearrangements or by ordinary segregation. In consequence, it is probably accurate to say that the more simply a character-difference is inherited, the less reliable it is as a criterion of speciation. The converse of this proposition, that the greater the complexity of inheritance of a character-difference the more reliable it is as a criterion of speciation, seems equally tenable. In trying to evaluate a given genetically controlled characteristic, an important attack on the problem is to determine the relative complexity of its inheritance.

One reason that taxonomic characters *per se* have not been frequently subjected to genetic analyses is that this is very time consuming and relatively unrewarding. The results of such experimental work, though answering the specific question regarding the nature of the taxonomic character, often do not have broader implications. Generalizations can only rarely be made because the applicability is or may be restricted to the immediate group under investigation. However, it is important for the long term to have many more cases worked out than are now known. Ultimately these will provide safe guides to proper character-evaluations, which is one of the current needs of taxonomy.

In working with the *Cruciferae* over a period of years, I have often encountered situations where "presence" or "absence" of trichomes appeared to be of trivial significance (1940, 1952). However, without actually testing a given case, it was not possible to know whether the absence of an indument in a given population, in an otherwise pubescent species, was environmentally induced or whether it was under genetic control. An opportunity to experiment with the presence and absence of a dense covering of trichomes on the fruits of *Dithyrea Wislizenii* Engelm. came when a population of this species was found having both glabrous- and pubescent-fruited types growing together near Sacaton, Arizona. The fruits of individual plants of both the glabrous type and the pubescent type were collected

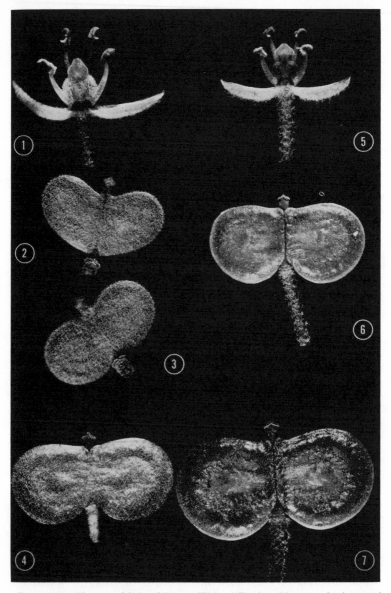

PLATE 1233. Flowers and fruits of *Dithyrea Wislizenii* Engelm. Fig. 1–4, a developmental series from flower to mature fruit of a pubescent-fruited type. In fig. 1, the petals, 2 sepals and the 2 near stamens have been removed to make the ovary visible. The same applies to fig. 5. Fig. 5–7, a developmental series from flower to mature fruit of a glabrous-fruited type.

and kept separate for testing purposes.   The difference between
the glabrous siliques and pubescent siliques is very striking, as
may be seen in Plate 1233.   The objective of the following experiments was to determine the genetic nature of glabrous vs.
pubescent siliques in this species.

THE WILD POPULATION

The species, *Dithyrea Wislizenii*, extends from western Oklahoma and Texas to southern Utah and Nevada, and to Arizona
and northeastern Mexico.   It is common in sandy and loose
granitic soils and often forms large stands composed of several
thousands of individuals.   Up to the present, a single glabrous-
fruited *Dithyrea*, presumably closely related to *D. Wislizenii*, has
been recognized as being of some taxonomic worth.   Wooton
and Standley (1913) originally described it at the species level
as *D. Griffithsii* and it was later reduced to varietal rank by
Payson (1918) under *D. Wislizenii*.   In the Sacaton population,
which provided the material for the following experiments, most
of the plants possessed pubescent fruits, but there was a goodly
number of glabrous-fruited individuals.   Circumstances did not
permit a definite count of pubescent vs. glabrous plants in the
wild population.   However, a rough estimate was recorded suggesting that the pubescent type predominated at least three to
one.   There were no intergrades.   The wild plants possessed
either glabrous fruits or pubescent fruits and none showed a
gradation from one condition to the other.

PROGENY TEST OF SEED PARENTS

Four lots of seeds from the wild population were grown to
provide plants for crossing purposes.   Each seed lot came from
a single wild plant, which had been open pollinated under natural
conditions.   The plants of culture numbers C-1 and C-4 were
produced from glabrous-fruited parents, C-2 and C-3 were from

TABLE I

WILD PLANTS		PROGENIES	
Plant No.	*Siliques*	*No. Glabrous*	*No. Pubescent*
C-1	glabrous	9	3
C-2	pubescent	0	15
C-3	pubescent	0	10
C-4	glabrous	5	9

pubescent-fruited parents.   Table I gives the classification of the
plants of each culture.

It is of some interest that the progenies of both pubescent
plants turned out to be uniformly pubescent even though there
had been no pollen control on the parent plants.

Pollen mother-cell smears were made to reveal the chromosome
number of both glabrous and pubescent plants.   In each case
the number n = 5 was found.

CROSSES AND RESULTS

Three types of crosses were made using various combinations
from the four cultures originally grown from the wild plants
listed in Table 1.   These were glabrous × glabrous, glabrous ×
pubescent, and pubescent × pubescent.   In addition, 14
pubescent plants were placed together in an isolated greenhouse
where interpollination was permitted to be effected by the
insects normally present.   In each of the three types of controlled
crosses, bagging with muslin, emasculation and hand pollination
were practiced.   Controls to check the procedures were carried
along with the experiments.   These showed that pollen control
was effective.   All crosses were carried out reciprocally.   Essentially the same results were achieved regardless of the direction
in which the pollen was carried except for the reciprocal of

TABLE 2. GLABROUS × GLABROUS

CROSS	PROGENY			3:1 RATIO	CHI-SQUARE
	No. plants	No. glabrous	No. pubescent		
C1-1 × C1-3	17	12	5		
reciprocal	7	5	2		
	24	17	7	18:6	.16
C1-4 × C4-9	20	15	5		
reciprocal	6	4	2		
	26	19	7	19.5:6.5	.05
C1-7 × C4-7	12	9	3		
reciprocal	8	7	1		
	20	16	4	15:5	.266
Total	70	52	18		.287
				P = .98–.95	

pubescent C1–5 ♀ ✕ glabrous C1–7 ♂. In this case, the reciprocal did not produce any filled seeds. The significance of this failure was not determined.

In addition to the results shown in Tables 2, 3 and 4, fourteen progenies of pubescent plants open pollinated from pubescent plants were grown. These amounted to 159 plants, all of which possessed pubescent siliques.

TABLE 3. GLABROUS ✕ PUBESCENT

CROSS	PROGENY			1:1 RATIO	CHI-SQUARE
	No. plants	No. glabrous	No. pubescent		
C1–7 ✕ C1–5	0	0	0		
reciprocal	10	3	7		
	10	3	7	5:5	1.60
C1–6 ✕ C4–8	12	3	9		
reciprocal	11	4	7		
	23	7	16	11.5:11.5	3.52
C4–13 ✕ C4–6	6	4	2		
reciprocal	14	5	9		
	20	9	11	10:10	.20
C4–10 ✕ C4–14	17	6	11		
reciprocal	6	3	3		
	23	9	14	11.5:11.5	1.08
Total	76	28	48		6.40

P = .2–.1

Pooled Chi-square (1 df)   5.26

P = .05–.02

Heterogeneity Chi-square (3 df)   1.14

P = .3–.7

The results are easily explainable if it is assumed that a single gene pair is operative in producing the glabrous or pubescent condition of the siliques. From the data, it is obvious that the pubescent plants are homozygous and recessive. Thus the genotype of the pubescent plants may be designated gg. When such a plant is crossed with a glabrous heterozygous individual (Gg), the resulting progeny should show a 1:1 ratio of glabrous to pubescent plants. In table 3, results from four different crosses between glabrous and pubescent plants are given and the Chi-square test for goodness of fit to a 1:1 ratio is provided. The

TABLE 4. PUBESCENT × PUBESCENT

CROSS	PROGENY	
	No. glabrous	No. pubescent
C2–7 × C2–8	0	11
reciprocal	0	1
	0	12
C3–2 × C3–9	0	10
reciprocal	0	8
	0	18
C3–6 × C3–7	0	13
reciprocal	0	28
	0	41
C4–11 × C4–12	0	17
reciprocal	0	30
	0	47
Total	0	118

numbers of plants in the various progenies are small and the possibility of results different from those shown should perhaps not be ruled out completely. However, the evidence strongly favors a 1:1 ratio and the assumption of a heterozygous (Gg) plant as the glabrous parent in each cross seems justified.

If heterozygotes are crossed, a 3:1 ratio of glabrous to pubescent is to be expected. Table 2 gives the data on three glabrous × glabrous crosses and the results show convincingly that a 3:1 ratio of glabrous to pubescent was obtained. It seems perfectly safe to assume that each of the six parents was of the constitution Gg with respect to the genes in control of the glabrous vs. pubescent condition. Evidently no homozygous dominant plants were used in the experiments. Such plants could not be distinguished from the heterozygotes phenotypically.

DISCUSSION

The mechanism of genetic control of glabrous vs. pubescent siliques in Dithyrea Wislizenii is obviously a relatively simple one. For this reason, it is safe to reject the phenotypic characteristic of glabrous siliques as having no significance for taxonomic purposes. Plants with this characteristic are expected to occur without respect to phylogenetic relationship in the populations of the species. In fact, this is exactly what one finds.

Glabrous-fruited plants are found in *D. Wislizenii* proper and in *D. Wislizenii* var. *Palmeri*. Furthermore, glabrous-fruited plants are found more or less throughout the geographical range of the species. On the basis of collections in the Gray Herbarium, the pubescent type appears to be more common than the glabrous. Collectors evidently distinguish between the glabrous and pubescent plants in the field because there are but three mixed collections among 84 different ones available in the herbarium. Six of the collections have glabrous fruits and 75 have pubescent fruits.

In my own field experience, I have examined four different populations of *D. Wislizenii*, one in Texas, two in Arizona and one in New Mexico. In three of these populations, 1 was unable to locate any glabrous-fruited plants. The fourth population yielded the material reported on above. This evidence added to that from herbarium material makes it quite clear that pubescent-fruited plants predominate in the species. If pubescent siliques represent the homogygous recessive condition, as indicated by the analysis of the one population, a more prevalent occurrence of the glabrous type would be expected throughout the species as a whole unless there are positive factors operating to select against it. However, we have no way of knowing about this at the present time. One observation may be pertinent to any ultimate explanation for the prevalence of the pubescent-fruited type. It is that the plants of *D. Wislizenii* are self incompatible. The chances of the accidental establishment of predominantly glabrous-fruited populations through isolation are considerably reduced as compared with a self compatible species.

Conclusions

The glabrous-fruited condition in *Dithyrea Wislizenii*, which provided the chief basis for describing *D. Griffithsii* Wooton and Standley as a separate species, is a simply inherited characteristic under single gene control. Glabrous-fruited heterozygotes when crossed produce a simple mendelian 3:1 ratio of glabrous- to pubescent-fruited plants. Glabrous-fruited heterozygotes crossed with pubescent-fruited plants produce approximately a 1:1 ratio of glabrous to pubescent plants. Pubescent-fruited plants crossed with each other produce only pubescent-fruited offspring. The pubescent plants studied all proved to be homozygous and recessive for the pubescent fruit character. The presence or absence of pubescence on the siliques of *D. Wislizenii* is of no taxonomic significance.

—GRAY HERBARIUM OF HARVARD UNIVERSITY.

LITERATURE CITED

PAYSON, E. B. 1918. Notes on Certain Cruciferae. Ann. Mo. Bot. Gard. **5:** 148.

ROLLINS, REED C. 1940. A Monographic Study of Arabis in Western North America. RHODORA **43:** 299.

———, ———. 1952. Taxonomy Today and Tomorrow. RHODORA **54:** 13.

WOOTON, E. O. AND P. C. STANDLEY. 1913. Contrib. U. S. Nat. Herb. **16:** 124.

SECTION III

Biochemical Systematics

MABRY, T. J., A. TAYLOR, and B. L. TURNER. 1963. The betacyanins and their distribution. Phytochem. **2**: 61–64.

KUPCHAN, S. M., J. H. ZIMMERMAN, and A. AFONSO. 1961. The alkaloids and taxonomy of *Veratrum* and related genera. Lloydia **24**: 1–26.

GELL, P. G. H., J. G. HAWKES, and S. T. C. WRIGHT. 1960. The application of immunological methods to the taxonomy of species within the genus *Solanum*. Proc. Roy. Soc., Ser. B **151**: 364–383.

SMITH, D. M., and D. A. LEVIN. 1963. A chromatographic study of reticulate evolution in the Appalachian *Asplenium* complex. Amer. J. Bot. **50**: 952–958.

MIROV, N. T. 1956. Composition of turpentine of lodgepole X jack pine hybrids. Canad. J. Bot. **34**: 443–457.

ALSTON, R. E., and B. L. TURNER. 1963. Natural hybridization among four species of *Baptisia* (Leguminosae). Amer. J. Bot. **50**: 159–173.

ALSTON, R. E., H. RÖSLER, K. NAIFEH, and T. J. MABRY. 1965. Hybrid compounds in natural interspecific hybrids. Proc. Nat. Acad. Sci. **54**: 1458–1465.

The present decade has seen a dramatic increase of interest in the systematic value of biochemical properties of plants. Chemical information about plants has been accumulating as long as chemistry itself has existed, but it was not until relatively recently that systematists have made extensive use of biochemical data in taxonomic work. It is also only recently that taxonomists have attempted to do the biochemical studies themselves. The papers included in this section deal with the use of various classes of biochemical compounds in systematics of plants at various taxonomic levels. In addition, I have selected papers illustrating the use of different classes of biochemical compounds as well as different methods of extracting and identifying them. In chemotaxonomic studies there is often a large measure of agreement between the distribution of certain compounds in various taxa and the groupings of these taxa based on more traditional methods. The papers presented here also indicate the utility of biochemical characters in solving problems where the information provided by classical methods is equivocal.

The first paper in this section, a brief contribution by Mabry, Taylor, and Turner, is concerned with the distribution of betacyanins in genera belonging to several families included in the order Centrospermae, or allied to it. These authors conclude that betacyanin pigments are characteristic of the Centrospermae and suggest that some families usually placed in this order (e.g., Caryophyllaceae) should be excluded from it. Morphological evidence supporting such an exclusion was not presented in the paper, but I would hope that it played an important role in making this conclusion.

The second paper by Kupchan, Zimmerman, and Afonso concerns alkaloids in relation to the taxonomy of several genera in the tribe Veratreae of Liliaceae. In this study, there is good agreement between alkaloid patterns of various taxa and their taxonomic placement based on morphological characters.

The research by Gell, Hawkes, and Wright deals with immunological studies of proteins in various species of the taxonomically difficult genus *Solanum*. This paper is a sound research contribution to the serological literature, although the methodology is one that is not widely used by plant systematists.

The paper by Smith and Levin presents a chromatographic study of the group of *Asplenium* species whose complex relationships were largely worked out on morphological and cytological evidence by Wagner (see Section II). The chromatographic studies of this group of species and hybrids support Wagner's suggestions concerning the evolutionary relationships within it.

Mirov's paper represents a study of turpentines of lodgepole pine, jack pine, and their artificial hybrids. This information was in turn applied in studies of samples of numerous individuals, collected from a natural population, which exhibited various degrees of intermediacy between the parental species and which were of supposed hybrid origin. Mirov's observations concerning the inheritance of biochemical characters independent of morphological ones are of particular interest.

Alston and Turner's investigation of natural hybridization in the legume *Baptisia* is a good example of the integration of morphological and biochemical studies of plants exhibiting a complex pattern of natural hybridization. These authors demonstrate the value of chromatographic techniques in providing useful data not obtainable by morphological studies alone.

The last paper in this section is a companion piece to the preceding one since it presents a determination of the structure of various biochemical compounds found in many of the *Baptisia* hybrids discussed there. In many other investigations, inheritance of biochemical compounds shows simple dominance or additive relations, but in these *Baptisia* hybrids there are hybrid compounds present as well.

THE BETACYANINS AND THEIR DISTRIBUTION[1]

T. J. MABRY, ANN TAYLOR and B. L. TURNER

Department of Botany and The Plant Research Institute, University of Texas, Austin

(*Received* 12 *October* 1962)

Abstract—Thirty-eight species, including thirteen previously uninvestigated genera, in ten families usually grouped in the Centrospermae were surveyed by electrophoresis and chromatography for the presence of betacyanin and anthocyanin pigments. Betacyanins were observed in all thirty-eight species but no anthocyanins were detected.

THE knowledge[2] that betacyanins, formerly considered to be "nitrogenous anthocyanins", represent a new class of plant pigments of restricted distribution, has stimulated interest in the phylogenetic significance of these compounds. The history of these pigments from the 1860's to 1960 has been reviewed comprehensively by Dreiding.[3] More recently Mabry[1] has discussed the structure of the betacyanins and reviewed their systematic distribution, particularly with respect to phyletic implications.

The formula was deduced[1,2] for betanidin hydrochloride, the aglycone salt of betanin, the betacyanin from *Beta vulgaris*. It is apparent that the betacyanins are unrelated

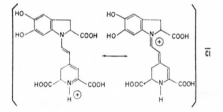

chemically to the well-known flavylium salt structures of the anthocyanins, although the two classes of compound are visually indistinguishable, both having λ_{max} around 540 mμ. The unusual chromophoric polymethylene cyanine group is shown in two resonance structures above.

Distribution of the betacyanins is limited, so far as is known, to ten families usually grouped in the Centrospermae: Chenopodiaceae, Didieraceae, Amaranthaceae, Nyctaginaceae, Stegnospermaceae, Phytolaccaceae, Ficoidaceae, Portulacaceae, Basellaceae and Cactaceae. All of these families but the Stegnospermaceae and Dideraceae had already been known to contain members producing betacyanins. In 1961 Rauh and Reznik[4] observed betacyanins in the Didieraceae and concluded that this family belonged in the

[1] Presented, in part, by T. J. MABRY, *Proceedings of the International Conference on Taxonomic Biochemistry, Physiology and Serology*, Sept. 4–6, 1962, University of Kansas, Lawrence, Kansas. Ronald Press, New York (in press).
[2] T. J. MABRY, H. WYLER, G. SASSU, M. MERCIER, J. PARIKH and A. S. DREIDING, *Helv. Chim. Acta* **45**, 640 (1962).
[3] A. S. DREIDING, *Recent Developments in the Chemistry of Natural Phenolic Compounds*, (Edited by W. D. OLLIS), p. 194, Pergamon Press, London (1961).
[4] W. RAUH and H. REZNIK, *Bot. Jb.* **81**, 95 (1961).

Reprinted by permission of T. J. Mabry, B. L. Turner, and the publisher from PHYTOCHEMISTRY, 2, 61–64 (1963).

Centrospermae. Such an arrangement had been suggested earlier by Radlkofer[5] on morphological grounds (see also Dalla Torre and Harms[6]). We have now found betacyanins in

Table 1. New additions to the list[3] of betacyanin
species

	Voucher numbers*
Chenopodiaceae	
Atriplex barclayana	190314
Atriplex lentiformis	183946
Chenopodium ambrosioides	171885
Chenopodium berlandieria	Mabry 11
Chenopodium glaucum	169317, 169318
Coriospermum nitidum	197422
Cycloloma atriplicifolium	195354
Salicornia perennis	Mabry 12
Suaeda linearis	53586
Amaranthaceae	
Amaranthus acanthocarpa	Mabry 15
Amaranthus palmeri	Mabry 4
Amaranthus pringlei	200689
Froelichia drummondii	Mabry 13
Gomphrena decumbens	193081, 189691
Gomphrena nealleyi	179298
Gomphrena sonorae	190367
Tidestromia lanuginosa	195909
Nyctaginaceae	
Abronia ameliae	178059
Abronia cycloptera	172412
Abronia fragrans	166083
Abronia villosa	54616
Allionia incarnata	174249, 200677
Boerhaavia erecta	193034
Boerhaavia intermedia	200657
Boerhaavia spicata	200655
Cyphomeris gypsophiloides	206819
Mirabilis lindheimeri	Mabry 1
Nyctaginia capitata	Melchert 246
Stegnospermaceae	
Stegnosperma halimifolium	190384
Portulacaceae	
Claytonia linearis	135561
Claytonia megarrhiza	175433
Claytonia virginica	Mabry 16
Montia perfoliata	200438, 200579
Portulaca pilosa	Mabry 7
Spraguea umbellata	175430
Aizoaceae	
Trianthema portulacastrum	Mabry 14
Cactaceae	
Opuntia leptocaulis	Mabry 5
Opuntia lindheimeri	Mabry 6

* Except where otherwise noted, the numbers refer to
accession numbers of the University of Texas Herbarium
where all specimens have been deposited.

[5] L. Radlkofer, *Die naturlichen Pflanzenfamilien*, Vol. III (5), pp. 460–462, A. Engler and K. Prantl,
editors. Wilhelm Engelmann, Leipzig (1896).
[6] D. G. De Dalla Torre and H. Harms, *Genera Siphonogamarum*, p. 606, Sumtibus Guilelmi Engelmann,
Lipsiae (1900).

Stegnosperma halimifolium. The treatment of Stegnospermaceae as a family stems from Hutchinson's[7] elevation of the subfamily Stegnospermatoidiae of the Phytolaccaceae to the rank of family. Hutchinson, however, placed this newly erected family in the order Pittosporales, a woody group, phyletically far removed from the herbaceous Centrospermae. In addition to *Stegnosperma halimifolium* we have examined thirty-seven previously un-investigated taxa, including thirteen genera, among the Centrospermae.

The results of electrophoretic and chromatographic examination of the plants, presented in Table 1, indicate the presence of betacyanins and the absence of anthocyanins.[8] Beta-cyanins and anthocyanins apparently do not co-exist in the same plant or even within the same family, although other classes of flavonoid pigments may occur together with beta-cyanins in the same plant. Our experimental procedure utilized a crude aqueous extract of dried plant material. The pigment extracts were compared by paper electrophoresis and paper chromatography against pure betanin, and a mixture of the pigment extract with pure betanin. In most analyses the pigment migrated slower than the pure betanin standard, but the extract-betanin mixture generally gave only one broad spot which corresponded to the spot observed for the extract alone. Further studies with purified extracts are required but these preliminary results suggest that the number of betacyanins may be fewer than previously suspected. Even purified extracts should be mixed with pure betanin for chromatographic and electrophoretic studies before this type of evidence can be reliably used for identification purposes.

Betanin, the only betacyanin which has been crystallized[9,10], has glucose attached at one of the two phenolic positions[2] in the betanidin structure. Significantly, all betacyanins which have been hydrolyzed produced betanidin as the aglycone.[11] Therefore secondary modifi-cations of the structure shown above, involving the presence of different sugars or esterifi-cation of the carboxyl groups, probably account for the different betacyanins reported.[11]

For many years the correlation between the betacyanins and the Centrospermae was recognized. Reznik,[12] for example, has discussed the systematic value of these pigments, but at a time when these substances were considered to be flavonoid in nature. Ordinarily, major taxonomic importance would not be accorded a single chemical character, but we believe that the totally different structures of the two types of pigments, betacyanins and anthocyanins, which indicate different synthetic pathways, their mutual exclusion, and the limited distribution of the betacyanins make the presence of these latter substances of particular taxonomic significance. It is suggested that the order Centrospermae (Chenopo-diales), as classically constituted, and including the Cactales, be reserved for the betacyanin-containing families, and that those anthocyanin-containing families such as the Caryo-phyllaceae and Illecebraceae be treated as a separate phyletic group whose relationship is close but not within the betacyanin producing order. A more comprehensive analysis of the Centrospermae and the significance of the betacyanins is in progress.

EXPERIMENTAL

The dried plant material was extracted for several hours at room temperature with water. The pigment extracts were concentrated under vacuum and, in most instances,

[7] J. Hutchinson, *Families of Flowering Plants*, Vol. I, II. Clarendon Press, Oxford (1959).
[8] Anthocyanins only were observed in *Rumex, Eriogonum, Antigonon* and *Chorizanthe* of the Polygonaceae, *Paronychia* of the Illecebraceae, *Krameria* of the Krameriaceae and *Hydrocotyle* of the Umbelliferae.
[9] H. Wyler and A. S. Dreiding, *Helv. Chim. Acta* **40**, 191 (1957).
[10] O. Th. Schmidt and W. Schonleben, *Z. Naturforsch.* **12b**, 262 (1957).
[11] H. Wyler and A. S. Dreiding, *Experientia* **17**, 23 (1961).
[12] H. Reznik, *Z. Botan.* **43**, 499 (1955); *Planta* **49**, 406 (1957).

spotted directly on Whatman No. 3 paper strips. With some extracts the pigment was precipitated with aqueous lead acetate, redissolved in methanolic hydrochloric acid and filtered to remove the lead chloride. The filtrate was concentrated before use. The pigments were compared by paper electrophoresis (0·1 M formic acid)[13] and paper chromatography (0·1 M formic acid and 0·1 M pyridine formate) with pure betanin and a mixture of the pigment extract and pure betanin. Frequently, the pigment was eluted from the paper strip with water and rechromatographed. A Lab-line electrophoresis apparatus was used at 450 volts. The descending paper chromatograms were run for about 4 hr.

Acknowledgements—This work was supported by Grant 15890 from the National Science Foundation. We thank Dr. R. E. Alston for helpful discussions.

[13] Betacyanins are present as anions in solutions of about pH 2 or higher and thus migrate towards the anode.

The Alkaloids and Taxonomy of Veratrum and Related Genera[1]

S. Morris Kupchan, James H. Zimmerman, and Adriano Afonso

(Department of Pharmaceutical Chemistry, University of Wisconsin, Madison)

Plants of the *Veratrum* group have been used for medicinal purposes for hundreds of years. Early use in the Middle Ages for sorcery and mystical rites was followed by prescription in the treatment of fevers, as local counter-irritants in neuralgia, as cardiac tonics, as emetics, as crow poisons and as insecticides (1,2). The use of *Veratrum* in the control of hypertension is at least one hundred years old (3). Early results achieved with the plant drug and with crude alkaloid extracts were erratic. Subsequent careful pharmacological investigation of purified alkaloid preparations demonstrated that the alkaloids were suitable for clinical trials. These clinical trials were followed by introduction of veratrum alkaloid preparations into clinical practice in the treatment of certain types of hypertension (4–6).

The alkaloids which have received most attention have been obtained from various species of the genera *Veratrum*, *Schoenocaulon*, and *Zygadenus*. In practice, the compounds isolated from several genera related to *Veratrum* have been classified as "Veratrum alkaloids", and it has been proposed that the latter term be defined as embracing those alkaloids isolated from plants which belong to the tribe *Veratreae* (7). The present paper surveys the occurrence and known structures of alkaloids isolated from the *Veratreae*, the classical botanical taxonomy of the *Veratreae*, and the implications of alkaloid occurrence and structure to the taxonomy of the *Veratreae*.

OCCURRENCE AND STRUCTURES OF THE VERATRUM ALKALOIDS[2]

In table 1 the literature on the occurrence of the veratrum alkaloids is summarized. Alkamines of known structure are listed first, in order of increasing complexity. The three glycosidic alkaloids follow. The ester alkaloids are listed next; the latter are classified in the order of increasing complexity of the parent alkamines. There follow a group of other compounds of known structure and, finally, a group of miscellaneous alkaloids of unknown or partially-elucidated structure. Footnotes to table 1 include the botanical source cited in the references, the geographic origin given, and the supplier where cited. Because of ambiguities in the nomenclature, the geographic location is considered important as a check on identification (see section on taxonomy below).

---

[1]This is Part XLVIII of a series entitled "Veratrum Alkaloids"; Part XLVII, S. M. Kupchan, J. Pharm. Sci., accepted for publication.
[2]S. M. K. and A. A.

Reprinted by permission of S. M. Kupchan, J. H. Zimmerman, and the publisher from Lloydia, 24, 1–26 (1961).

Alkaloids are probably present in all parts of *V. album* and *V. viride* (19,27), but the insecticidal action of dried *S. officinale*, characteristic of cevadine and veratridine, is found only in the seeds (77). The usual sources are the roots and rhizomes of *V. album* and *V. viride* and the seeds of *S. officinale*. The alkaloids

TABLE 1. *Occurrence of Veratrum alkaloids.*

Alkaloid	Formula	Sources	References
Alkamines of known structure			
Veratramine (I)	$C_{27}H_{39}O_2N$	a,b,c,d,e,f,g,h,i	8–16,40
Rubijervine (II)	$C_{27}H_{43}O_2N$	a,c,e,i,j,k,l,m,n,o, p,q,r,s,t,u	8,10,12,15–28,40
Isorubijervine (III)	$C_{27}H_{43}O_2N$	a,c,e,j,k,s,v	8,10,12,16,17,25,29,40
Jervine (IV)	$C_{27}H_{39}O_3N$	a,b,c,d,e,f,g,h,i,j,k, l,m,n,o,p,q,r,s,t,w, x,y,jj	8–10,12–24,26,40,30–34,60
Zygadenine (V)	$C_{27}H_{43}O_7N$	z,aa	35,36
Veracevine (VI) ("protocevine")	$C_{27}H_{43}O_8N$	bb,cc,dd	37–39
Cevine (VII)	$C_{27}H_{43}O_8N$	dd	38
Cevagenine (VIII)	$C_{27}H_{43}O_8N$	dd	38
Germine (IX)	$C_{27}H_{43}O_8N$	c,e,r,aa	10,12,24,36
Protoverine (X)	$C_{27}H_{43}O_9N$	ee	
Glycosidic alkaloids			
Veratrosine (XI)	$C_{33}H_{49}O_7N$	c,ff	8,40,41
Isorubijervosine (XII)	$C_{33}H_{53}O_7N$	ff	8,40
Pseudojervine (XIII)	$C_{33}H_{49}O_8N$	a,c,m,o,p,q,r,s,w,ff	8,19,21–24,30,33,40,41
Ester alkaloids			
a) Esters of zygadenine			
Zygacine (XIV)	$C_{29}H_{45}O_8N$	h,u,gg,hh,ii	14,28,42–44
Angeloylzygadenine (XV)	$C_{32}H_{49}O_8N$	g	13,45
Vanilloylzygadenine (XVI)	$C_{35}H_{49}O_{10}N$	aa,hh	36,43
Veratroylzygadenine (XVII)	$C_{36}H_{51}O_{10}N$	f,l,n,u,w,aa,ff,hh	13,28,30,36,43,46,47
b) Esters of veracevine			
Cevacine (XVIII)	$C_{29}H_{45}O_9N$	bb,cc	37,39
Cevadine (XIX)	$C_{32}H_{49}O_9N$	bb,cc,dd,kk,ll	37–39,48–53
Vanilloylveracevine (XX) ("vanilloylcevine")	$C_{35}H_{49}O_{11}N$	kk	54
Veratridine (XXI)	$C_{36}H_{51}O_{11}N$	bb,cc,dd,kk,ll	37–39,48,51,53
c) Esters of germine			
Germitetrine (XXII) ("germitetrine-B")	$C_{41}H_{63}O_{14}N$	n,mm,nn	55–59
Germitrine (XXIII)	$C_{39}H_{61}O_{12}N$	e,j,k,n,oo,pp	12,16,17,29,61,62
Neogermitrine (XXIV)	$C_{36}H_{55}O_{11}N$	a,j,n,w,ff,gg,hh, oo,pp	8,16,30,40,43,46,56,61–64
Germanitrine (XXV)	$C_{39}H_{59}O_{11}N$	w	30
Germinitrine (XXVI)	$C_{39}H_{57}O_{11}N$	w	30
Germerine (XXVII)	$C_{37}H_{59}O_{11}N$	j,l,m,n,r,t,jj,nn,pp	16,18,19,26,59,62,65,66
Germidine (XXVIII)	$C_{34}H_{53}O_{10}N$	e,j,k,gg,oo	12,16,17,61,63,64
Neogermidine (XXIX) ("Isogermidine")	$C_{34}H_{53}O_{10}N$	c,r,gg,hh	43,62–65
Germbudine (XXX)	$C_{37}H_{59}O_{12}N$	c,j,r	16,62,65
Neogermbudine (XXXI)	$C_{37}H_{59}O_{12}N$	c,j,mm	16,58,62
Protoveratridine (XXXII)	$C_{32}H_{51}O_9N$	o,r,gg	21,24,63,64
d) Esters of protoverine			
Protoveratrine [including		c,j.l,m,n,o,r,t,v, mm,nn,pp,qq	16,18–21,26,27,29,55,57– 59,62,65,67–69
protoveratrine A (XXXIII) ("veratetrine") and	$C_{41}H_{63}O_{14}N$		
protoveratrine B (XXXIV) ("neoprotoveratrine")]	$C_{41}H_{63}O_{15}N$		
Escholerine (XXXV)	$C_{41}H_{61}O_{13}N$	a,ff	8,40,46

TABLE 1. *Continued.*

Alkaloid	Formula	Sources	References
Desacetylprotoveratrine A (XXXVI)...........	$C_{39}H_{61}O_{13}N$	mm	58
Desacetylprotoveratrine B (XXXVII)..........	$C_{39}H_{61}O_{14}N$	c,r,mm	58,62,76
Other alkaloids of known structure			
Zygadenilic acid δ-lactone (XXXVIII)......	$C_{27}H_{41}O_7N$	rr	70,71
Dehydrocevagenine (XXXIX).................	$C_{27}H_{41}O_8N$	dd	38
Cevinilic acid δ-lactone (XL).	$C_{27}H_{41}O_8N$	dd	38
Angeloyl ester of zygadenilic acid δ-lactone (XLI).......	$C_{32}H_{47}O_8N$	i	15
Miscellaneous alkaloids			
Geralbine (XLII)............	$C_{22}H_{33}O_2N$	n	67
Synaine (XLIII).............	$C_{24}H_{39}ON$	ss	72,78
Veratrobasine (XLIV).......	$C_{24}H_{37}O_3N$	n	67
Verine (XLV)...............	$C_{25}H_{39}O_2N$	ss	72,78
Rubiverine (XLVI)..........	$C_{25}H_{39}O_2N$	ss	72,78
Amianthine (XLVII).........	$C_{27}H_{41}O_2N$	x	31
Isojervine (XLVIII).........	$C_{27}H_{39}O_3N$	c	41
Unnamed alkamine (Kupchan's) (XLIX)......	$C_{27}H_{43}O_3N$	j	16
Unnamed alkamine (Jacobs') (L)..............	$C_{27}H_{41}O_4N$	c	41
Unnamed alkamine (Fried's) (LI).............	$C_{27}H_{41}O_5N$	k	17
Sabine (LII)...............	$C_{27}H_{45}O_7N$	dd	73
("neosabadine") Hydroalkamine-S (LIII).....	$C_{27}H_{45}O_8N$	dd	38
Veratralbine (LIV)..........	$C_{28}H_{43}O_5N$	p,q	22,23
Sabadine (LV)..............	$C_{29}H_{47}O_8N$	dd,kk	73–75
("sabatine") Veragenine (LVI)............	$C_{31}H_{53}O_{13}N$	cc	39
Veralbidine (LVII)..........	$C_{37}H_{61}O_{12}N$	n	20,67

(a) *Veratrum eschscholtzii* Gray; Alaska. (b) *V. stamineum* Maxim; Japan. (c) *V. viride* Ait; S. B. Penick and Co. (d) *V. grandiflorum* Loes. fil.; Nopporo, Japan. (e) Verabore, a commerical prep. from *V. viride*; S. B. Penick and Co. ˙ (f) *V. album* var. *oxysepalum*; Hokkaido, Japan. (g) *V. album stamineum* Maxim; Nagano, Japan; Aug., 1956. (h) *V. grandiflorum* Loesen.; Nagano, Japan; 1956. (i) *V. grandiflorum* Loesen.; Hokkaido, Japan; June, 1957. (j) Cryptenamine, a commercial prep. from *V. viride*; Irwin, Neisler and Co. (k) *V. viride*; N. Carolina. (l) *V. viride*; E. Merck, Darmstadt, imported from USA. (m) *V. album* Caesar and Loretz (Suppliers). (n) *V. album.* (o) *V. viride*; Gehe and Co., Dresden. (p) *V. album*; Hopkin and Williams (Suppliers). (q) *V. viride*; Hopkin and Williams. (r) *V. viride* Ait. (s) *V. album* var. *loebelianum*; Eastern Slovakia on "Čerhovskepohon". (t) *V. album*; Yugoslavia. (u) *V. oxysepalum* Turcz.; Hokkaido, Japan; Aug., 1956. (v) *V. viride* Ait.; Quebec; Summer, 1950. (w) *V. fimbriatum* Gray; Northern California; Summer, 1950. (x) *Amianthium muscaetoxicum* Gray. (y) *V. lobelianum*; Poland. (z) *Zygadenus intermedius*; Wyoming. (aa) *Z. venenosus* Wats.; Washington; June, 1950. (bb) Veratrine, a commercial prep. from *Schoenocaulon officinale* S. B. Penick and Co. (cc) Veratrine sulfate, a commercial prep. from *S. officinale*; E. Merck, Darmstadt; Lot No. 54618–4080. (dd) Veratrine, a commercial prep. from *S. officinale*; E. Merck, Darmstradt. (ee) Isolation of the alkamine protoverine has apparently not been reported; inclusion here is based on wide occurrence of protoverine esters in *V.* spp. (ff) *V. escholtzii* Gray; Alaska; Summer, 1950. (gg) *Z. venenosus*; northeastern Oregon; June, 1951. (hh) *Z. paniculatus*; Washington; June, 1951. (ii) *V. album* var. *grandiflorum* Loes. fil. (jj) *V. nigrum*; Botanical gardens, Univ. Wurzburg. (kk) *S. officinale*; S. B. Penick and Co. (ll) Veratrine; commerical.˙ (mm) *V. album*; S. B. Penick and Co. (nn) Protoveratrine, commercial. (oo) *V. viride*; Eastern USA; Summer, 1948 and 1949. (pp) *V. viride*; S. B. Penick and Co.; 1952. (qq) *V. album*; Poland. (rr) *V. album* var. *oxysepalum*; Hokkaido, Japan; Aug., 1956. (ss) *V. album*, Sinaïa, Roumania; 1953.

can be extracted from the appropriate parts of the dried and powdered plants by aqueous or alcoholic acid or by organic solvents, usually with added base in the form of ammonia or triethylamine.   Subsequent separation of the bases from the crude extract has been achieved by fractional crystallization, precipitation or extraction (21–23,41), and by chromatographic separations on alumina (37,56), on silica gel (49,75), on kieselguhr (27), and on Celite (16).   Chromatography on paper has proved invaluable for characterizing the alkaloids (16,27,55).   Perhaps the most useful technique for the isolation of the individual ester alkaloids from amorphous alkaloid mixtures has been liquid-liquid counter-current distribution (e.g., 17,29,55,62).

FIGURE I

ALKALOIDS OF KNOWN STRUCTURE

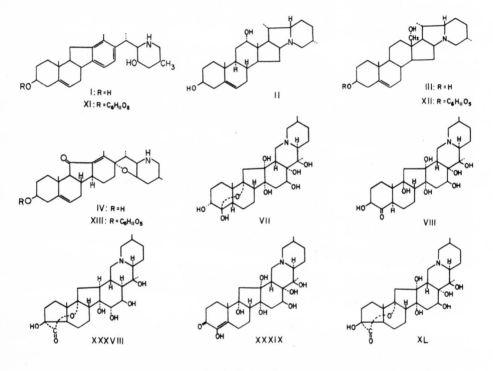

$C_6H_{11}O_5$ = D-glucosyl

The elucidation of the structures of the veratrum alkamines has been summarized in several recent comprehensive reviews (79–81), and the work on the ester alkaloids has also been surveyed in a recently-completed review (82).   Consequently, no detailed account of the structure elucidation is undertaken here. It does appear appropriate, however, to make a few comments concerning the classification and interrelationship of the members of the series.

Figures 1–3 present the constitutions of those alkaloids for which complete structures have been elucidated.   Thus far, only the C_{27} alkamines and their derivatives have received the chemical study necessary for complete structure elucidation.   The C_{27} alkamines fall into two distinct chemical groups: the jerveratrum group, which includes veratramine (I), rubijervine (II), isorubijervine (III), and jervine (IV), and the ceveratrum group, which includes zygadenine (V), veracevine (VI); germine (IX), and protoverine (X) (79).   The jerveratrum

unconjugated alkaloids contain only two or three atoms of oxygen and are found
in unhydrolyzed plant extracts in part as the free alkamines and in part in combination with one molecule of D-glucose as glyco-alkaloids (e.g., XI, XII, XIII).
The ceveratrum bases are highly hydroxylic and contain seven to nine atoms of
oxygen; they usually occur esterified with various acids as ester alkaloids; they
have never been found as glycosides.   Isolation of the free ceveratrum alkamines
has been reported from many laboratories.   However, the fact that the isolation
procedures generallly involved the use of alkaline conditions which may have
led to hydrolysis has left unanswered the question as to the occurrence of free
ceveratrum alkaloids *in the plant.*

FIGURE 2
ALKALOIDS OF KNOWN STRUCTURE

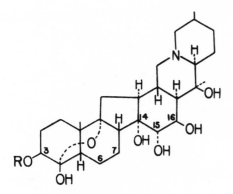 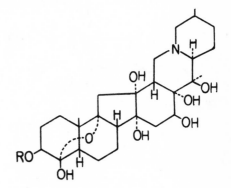

V :	R = H		VI :	R = H	
XIV :	Ac		XVIII :	Ac	
XV :	An		XIX :	An	
XVI :	Va		XX :	Va	
XVII :	Ve		XXI :	Ve	

Ac = acetyl; An = angeloyl; Va = vanilloyl;

Ve = veratroyl.

The jerveratrum alkamines rubijervine (II) and isorubijervine (III) may be
regarded as the simplest of the veratrum alkaloids from a structural point of view.
The latter compounds each have the normal C_{27}-steroid skeleton (e.g., cholesterol),
and the E and F rings may formally be regarded as having been formed by folding
the normal cholesterol side chain around the nitrogen atom.   The positions of
oxygen-bearing carbon atoms 3,12 and 18 are the same as those of several non-
nitrogenous naturally-occurring steroids.   Veratramine (I) and jervine (IV) are
characterized by the C-nor-D-homo ring system, which may formally be regarded
as having originated by migration of the C_{13},C_{14}-bond of a normal steroid to the
C_{12},C_{14}-position.   As noted above, three of the four jerveratrum alkamines also
occur as glycoalkaloids, conjugated with one molecule of glucose.

The four highly hydroxylated native ceveratrum alkamines are veracevine, germine, protoverine and zygadenine. Cevagenine and cevine are known to result from base-catalyzed isomerization of veracevine, and the isolation of the latter alkaloids from veratrine (a commercial alkaloid extract of *Schoenocaulon officinale*) is probably attributable to isomerization during the extraction and isolation procedure. Similarly, dehydrocevagenine is probably formed by auto-

FIGURE 3

ALKALOIDS OF KNOWN STRUCTURE

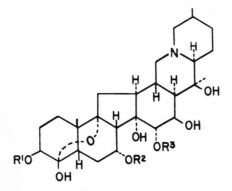 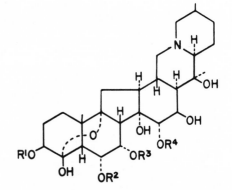

	R¹	R²	R³			R¹	R²	R³	R⁴
IX :	H	H	H		X :	H	H	H	H
XXII :	HMAB	Ac	MB		XXXIII :	HMB	Ac	Ac	MB
XXIII :	MB	Ac	HMB		XXXIV :	t–DMB	Ac	Ac	MB
XXIV :	Ac	Ac	MB		XXXV :	An	Ac	Ac	MB
XXVII :	An	Ac	MB		XXXVI :	HMB	Ac	H	MB
XXVIII :	Ac	H	MB		XXXVII :	t–DMB	Ac	H	MB
XXIX :	H	Ac	MB						
XXX :	t–DMB	H	MB						
XXXI :	e–DMB	H	MB						

Ac = acetyl; An = angeloyl; e-DMB = (*l*)-erythro-2,3-dihydroxy-2-methylbutyryl; t-DMB = (d)-threo-2,3-dihydroxy-2-methybutyryl; HMB = (d)-2-hydroxy-2-methylbutyryl; HMAB = erythro-2-hydroxy-2-methyl-3-acetoxybutyryl; MB = (*l*)-2-methylbutyryl.

oxidation during the extraction and isolation process [cf. (83)]. The four native ceveratrum alkamines have several common structural features. All four possess the modified steroid cevan nucleus. The latter skeletal structure is characterized by the aforementioned C-nor-D-homo arrangement along with an alternate folding of the normal cholesterol side chain around the nitrogen atom. Another characteristic feature of the four native ceveratrum alkamines is the α-ketol hemiketal

system found in rings A and B.   Zygadenine, germine and protoverine have identical structures in rings C,D,E and F.   Protoverine has been degraded to a germine
derivative (84) and germine to a zygadenine derivative (85) by suitable alteration
of ring B.   Veracevine differs appreciably from the other three in the distribution
of functional groups on rings C,D,E and F of cevan skeleton.   On the other
hand, veracevine and zygadenine have identical structures in rings A and B, and
this resemblance may figure in the similar pattern of esterification in the naturally-
occurring ester derivatives of the latter alkamines.   The similarity of the rings
A and B structures of veracevine and zygadenine may account also for the occurrence of analogous lactone derivatives.   Cevinilic acid δ-lactone (XL) [first prepared by chemical oxidation (86)] and the analogous zygadenilic acid δ-lactone
(XXXVIII) have been found, but no analogous derivatives of germine or protoverine have been described to date.

The ester alkaloid derivatives of the ceveratrum alkamines fall into two groups.
All the zygadenine and veracevine esters isolated to date are monoesters with
either acetyl, angeloyl, veratroyl or vanilloyl residues affixed at C_3.   All the naturally-occurring germine and protoverine esters, on the other hand, are polyesters,
with tri- and tertra-esters predominant.   (Protoveratridine, a minor germine
monoester, is probably to be regarded as an artifact which arises by alkaline
hydrolysis of polyesters during the isolation procedure.)

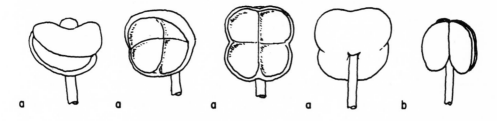

L l mm ⌐   a. V ERATRUM   b. TOFIELDIA

Fig. 4.   *Diagrams illustrating the type of anther found (a) in the tribe Veratreae and (b) in genera
related to, but excluded from, the Veratreae (such as Chamaelirium, Chionographis, Tofeldia,
Helonias).   In Chionographis, the two anther cells are sometimes confluent (106).*

From the chemical point of view, then, zygadenine represents something of a
hybrid structure among the ceveratrum alkaloids.   On the one hand, zygadenine
occurs alongside germine and protoverine in a number of plants, and possesses a
ring C,D,E and F structure identical with those of germine and protoverine.
On the other hand, zygadenine possesses a ring A,B structure identical with that
of veracevine, is a formal precursor for a naturally-occurring δ-lactone derivative
analogous to one formally derived from veracevine, and occurs in monoester conjugates which are closely analogous to the monoester conjugates of veracevine.

CLASSICAL BOTANICAL TAXONOMY OF THE VERATREAE[3]

The tribe *Veratreae* is part of the subfamily *Melanthioideae* of the family
Liliaceae (87–90).   Sometimes this subfamily is treated as a separate family, the
Melanthiaceae (91,92), or the *Colchicaceae* (93).   While some of the other genera
in this subfamily share the separate styles and septicidal capsules found throughout the tribe *Veratreae*, this tribe possesses a unique type of anther (88,94).   Although allied but excluded genera possibly exhibit a transitional anther structure
(fig. 4), the tribe is sufficiently well delimited by its unusual anther that only rarely
(92,95) are its genera apportioned among different tribes.

―――――――

[3]J. H. Z.

Four generic names in common usage provide a convenient subdivision of the tribe into four major groups of species (table 2): *Veratrum* (false hellebore), *Zygadenus* (death camas), *Stenanthium*, and *Schoenocaulon* (Sabadilla). To the vernacular names chosen here (96), may be added many others (89,92,95,99,100, 113,116,118,154). Two other well-known genera, *Amianthium* (crow poison) and *Melanthium* (bunch flower), are here placed under *Zygadenus* and *Veratrum*, respectively, for reasons given below.

TABLE 2. *Botanical definition of the species of the tribe Veratreae*

Information given includes: Name used in this paper[a]; geographic range and habitat; distinguishing morphological features (those unique in the tribe are starred*; legend for abbreviations given below[b]); and names used in selected references (parentheses denote "in part").

VERATRUM. N Hemisphere. Pub* (exc 1); winged seeds* (exc 1); bulb and short to long rhizome.

    ALBOVERATRUM[c]. Circumboreal; mt and tundra (exc Himalayas and N and C Canada). T erose to toothed, usu ascending in fruit; gland V-shaped*; lvs broad (elliptic), usu pub beneath; vegetative pseudoculms tall*; styles central; 2° rac usu compound; ped usu very short; lower fls usu staminate; rhizome stout. Section *Alboveratrum* 94,95; Subgenus *Euveratrum*, Sect. *Alboveratrum* (97,98).

    V. album. Eurasia; W Alaska. Variable; by elimination of other species.

        album. N Portugal E to Poland and Greece; NW Turkey; Caucasus. Mt. meadows. Highly variable in all features; t generally intermediate in size and shape, green to yellow or white. *V. album* L. 93,98–101, 123,(88), ssp. *album* 102,103, ssp. *lobelianum* (Bernh.) Hult. (102,103); *V. lobelianum* Bernh. (88,93,98); *V. bosniacum* Beck 98; *V. croaticum* (Beck) Loes. 98; *V. fluvum* (Griseb.) Loes. 88,98.

---

[a]A few unpublished names or name combinations (such as Section *Eustenanthium*) are used here for convenience in summarizing information only. All names are ranked in the table as follows:
GENUS (In the broad sense)
    SUBGENERIC GROUP (Section; or Genus in the narrow sense)
        Species
            Infraspecific unit (Subspecies or variety)
    [b]Legend for abbreviations: *N*, north, northward, etc.; *C*, central; *mt*, mountain(s); *infl*, inflorescence; *rac*, raceme(s); *2° rac*, secondary (branch) raceme(s); *t*, tepals; *ped*, pedicel(s); *lvs*, leaves; *fl*, flowers or flowering; *pub*, pubescent; *sub*, almost, *mod*, moderately; *usu*, usually; *rel*, relatively; *esp*, especially; *exc*, except; *lat*, latitude; *alt*, altitude.
    [c]Section *Alboveratrum* is interpreted as follows: *V. stamineum*, *V. insolitum*, and *V. dahuricum* rate full specific rank by virtue of constancy of their unique features despite sympatry with other *Alboveratra*. All seven American *Alboveratra* rate specific rank because of the relative stability of their distinguishing features or combinations of them. The Eurasian *V. album*, in contrast, forms a complex of broad geographic clines to which there are many striking local exceptions in all regions [such as long ped and internodes and subglabrous lvs (95, "*V. patulum*") in S Japan; local variability in Kamtchatka (102)]. The Asian cline is arbitrarily separated into two subspecies (*grandiflorum* to the south; *oxysepalum* to the north) in the zone where intermediate and heterogeneous populations prevail, in Manchuria, N Korea, Ussuri Region of SE Siberia, Far East (Maritime Terr.), Sakhalin, and Hokkaido (89,95,104,107,108). The populations in Arctic Europe are placed with ssp. *oxysepalum* because of weak morphological tendencies and Hulten's interpretation (103,113) of the history of *V. album*. The remaining heterogeneous assortment of populations is grouped under ssp. *album* in the table. The green flowered forms, often called *V. lobelianum* (or *V. album* var. *lobelianum*), include a great diversity of forms and reach all the geographic boundaries given for ssp. *album*. Typical *V. album* (large, broad white tepals) is less widely distributed; it prevails in Hungary, E Austria and parts of Yugoslavia, and grades into smaller-flowered and more variable forms toward W Austria and S Germany. Sometimes green and white (and even yellow) forms are locally juxtaposed (99). Because *V. album* not only shares the phenotypic variability common to most *Alboveratra* but in addition appears to be genotypically diverse and perhaps heterozygous, it is especially essential in this species that a complete voucher specimen, with notes on exact geographic location and local ecology, be preserved for each lot of rhizomes dug, in order to insure uniformity and comparability of medical and chemical results.
    The E American *V. viride*, superficially at least, appears to be an extensive, relatively stable (uniform) population similar (through history or coincidence) to a few of the thousands of diverse local populations of *V. album* in Eurasia. But in general *V. viride* has longer and more numerous branches than the green-flowered forms of *V. album*.

TABLE 2.   *Continued*

grandiflorum. C and SW China (Yunnan, E Sikang, Szechuan, Hupeh, N Kiangsi); C and S Japan; C and S Korea; mt meadows and forests. T very large (8–18 mm long), broad, greenish white; ovary always woolly; lvs usu pub. *V. grandiflorum* (Maxim.) Loes. 98,104,105,(95); *V. album* L. 110, 116, var. *grandiflorum* Maxim. 93,106; *V. patulum* Loes. 95,98,105,107; *V. puberulum* Loes. 98; *V. sikokianum* Nakai 95; *V. dahuricum* (Turcz.) Loes. (98).

oxysepalum. Woods and swamps, mt of N Korea and Hokkaido, N in meadows, shores, brush and tundra to Arctic Coast from N Norway E to Nome, Alaska. T mod to small, narrow, green or yellowish or whitish green; ovary and lvs often subglabrous. *V. oxysepalum* Turcz. 89,93,95,98,104,105; *V. album* L. 108, var. *oxysepalum* (Turcz.) Miyabe and Kudo 109, var. *viride* Baker 110, ssp. *oxysepalum* (Turcz.) Hult. 102,103,111–114, ssp. *lobelianum* (Bernh.) Hult. (102,103); *V. lobelianum* Bernh. 89,115,(88,93,98), var. *asiaticum* Loes. 98,104; *V. misae* (Sirjaev.) Loes. 89,98,103; *V. dolichopetalum* Loes[d] 98,107; *V. calycinum* Komarov 89; *V. alpestre* Nakai 95,107; *V. grandiflorum* Loes. (95).

V. dahuricum. Marshes and brushy slopes in Siberia, from Tomsk (85° E long) E to mouth of Amur R., S to mt of N Korea. Upper lvs and ovary densely white-woolly; t small, yellowish white, glabrous on the conspicuously paler margins. *V. dahuricum* (Turcz.) Loes. 88,89,107,115,(98).

V. viride. Wet woods, Gulf of St. Lawrence, Quebec, S to Md. and NE Ohio; S in high mt meadows to SW N. C. T rather large, often lanceolate, green; infl robust, crowded; ovary and usu lvs mod pub; fl early summer. *V. viride* Aiton 88,91–93,98,100,101,109, 117–121,123,(121).

V. eschscholtzii. Moist slopes, sea level to timberline, Alaska Peninsula and Mt. McKinley, Alaska, E to SE Yukon, S to higher mt of N Calif., C Idaho and SW Mont. T rather small, greenish, often oblanceolate; upper lvs finely white-woolly between veins; 2° rac strongly pendent, not crowded, with ped turning upward *as soon as flowers open*; ovary often mod pub; fl late summer. *V. eschscholtzii* Gray 91, 93,100,101,109,112,114,120,122,123; *V. eschscholtzianum* (Schult.) Rydb. 124,125; *V. escholtzianum* (Schult.) Loes. 88,98; *V. viride* Aiton 126–129, 133, 134, (121), var. *escholtzianoides* Loes. 98; *V. speciosum* Rydb. (125?,126); *V. californicum* Durand (91), (131?); *V. unidentified* 101?

V. tenuipetalum. Wet meadows, high mt of Colo. and N New Mexico. Tall; 2° rac much-branched; t small, narrow, yellowish white, translucent; upper lvs subglabrous to mod pub (esp. toward apex); ovary glabrous. *V. tenuipetalum* Heller 91,98,124, 125; *V. californicum* Durand 132, (91,93,131), var. *watsoni* Baker (93); *V. speciosum* Rydb. (126).

V. jonesii. Rather dry, low-elevation meadows or prairies, W Idaho or C Ore. and C Wash. T small (7.5–10.0 mm long), rel broad, creamy white; upper lvs finely white-woolly between veins; 2° rac much-branched; seeds very large (12–19 mm long); ovary glabrous. *V. jonesii* Heller 91, 98, 124; *V. speciosum* Rydb. (122,125,126); *V. californicum* Durand (127,130,131,133).

V. caudatum. Low elevation swamps from Cascade Mts to coast in Ore. and Wash. Sparingly branched; terminal rac very long; t large, rel very narrow, greenish white; lvs mod pub on veins to glabrous; ovary glabrous. *V. caudatum* Heller 91,98,124, 127,130,134,135; *V. californicum* Durand (52?,91?,131).

V. californicum. Common in low to high mt meadows from N Idaho, S Ore. and W Wyo. S to S Calif., S New Mexico, and N Mexico. T large, broad, creamy white; lvs usu mod pub on veins; ovary rarely pub; mod branched. *V. californicum* Durand 98,100,101,124,128,129,134,136–139,(91,120,125,127,130,131,133), var. *watsoni* Baker (93); *V. speciosum* Rydb. 98, (122,126); *V. caudatum* Heller var. *tenuipetaloides* Loes. 98; *V. af. californicum* 140.

V. insolitum Mt slopes (serpentine and diorite of NW Calif. and W Ore. Much-branched infl and ovaries densely woolly; t white, thin, small (5–9 mm long) rel broad, often fringed; ped long, spreading; lvs pub on veins; capsule pub; seeds large. *V. insolitum* Jepson 128–130,134.

V. stamineum. Mt marshes, C and N Japan. T very small (about as long as stamens), rel broad, white; ped very long, spreading; infl and lvs small; ovary glabrous; lvs glabrous toward N. *V. stamineum* Maxim. 93,95,98,104,105,106,141; *V. nipponicum* Nakai (apparently a hybrid with *V. album grandiflorum*) 142.

---

[d]The status of these forms needs further clarification.

TABLE 2. *Continued*

FUSCOVERATRUM[e]. E Asia; 1 species W to C Europe. T oblong, narrowed convexly at base, entire, reflexed in fruit; gland dark, covering most of basal ⅔ to ½ of t; anthers open early, fall soon; styles diverge from outer corners of glabrous truncate ovary; ped usu rel long, divergent; leaf blades glabrous; rhizome mod to short; 2° rac mostly unbranched. Section *Fuscoveratrum* 94,(95); Subgen. *Euveratrum*, Sect. *Fuscoveratrum* 98,(97); Subgen. *Pseudoanticlea* (97,98); Section *Alboveratrum* (97).

V. nigrum. Asia: Siberia from Altai down Yenisei R. to 67° N lat, E to mouth of Amur R., S to S Korea, Quelpaert I. and Sado I.; China from Jehol SW to E Sikang and W Hupeh. Europe: SW Switzerland and C Italy to SW Ukraine and Yugoslavia; Kursk. Mt slopes, forest openings, meadows, Robust; lvs elliptic; rac many, long, many-fld, usu white-woolly; t purple, usu dark. *V. nigrum* L. 88,89,93,94,98,99, 110,(108), var. *japonicum* Baker (110), var. *ussuriense* Loes. 98,115; var. *microcarpum* Loes. 98; *V. bracteatum* Batalin 98,110; *V. schindleri* Loes. (98); *V. sadoense* Nakai 95; *V. ussuriense* Nakai 107.

V. maackii. SE Siberia and N Japan S to SW China. Variable but generally smaller, slenderer, narrower-leaved and less pubescent than *V. nigrum.*

maackii. Amur. R. between cities of Blagoveshchensk and Khabarovsk, S to S Korea and Shantung; low meadows, brushy slopes, woods. Lvs lanceolate; t usu purple; ped and rac usu long; capsules usu slender; in S Korea tend to be yellow-green fld and have short terminal and compound 2° racemes. *V. maackii* Regel 89,94,115, (93,98,107,110); *V. mandschuricum* Loes. 98,107; *V. bonhofii* Loes. 88,98,107; *V. coreanum* Loes. (98,107); *V. oblongum* Loes. (98), var. *macrantha* Loes. 98; *V. versicolor* Nakaid[d] 107; *V. nigrum* L. (108).

japonicum. Japan: forests, meadows, mt of S Hokkaido and extreme N Honshu. Lvs elliptic; t purple; ped and rac mod length. *V. japonicum* (Baker) Loes. 94, 98,104,105(95); *V. nigrum* L. var. *japonicum* Baker 93; *V. maximowiczii* Baker 104?

maximowczii. Japan: forests and meadows, mt of N and C Honshu. Lvs elliptic (rarely linear); t yellow-green; ped mod length; rac often long. *V. maximowczii* Baker 93,94,98,105,106,(95); *V. angustipetalum* Loes. (98); *V. warburgii* Loes. (98); *V. coreanum* Loes. (98).

reymondianum. Japan: mt forests and alpine meadows, C Honshu and Sado. Lvs elliptic to lanceolate; 't purple; ped mod length; rac variable. *V. reymondianum* (Loes.) Zimmerman 94; *V. nigrum* L. var. *japonicum* Baker 106, var. *reymondianum* Loes. 97; *V. japonicum* (Baker) Loes 105 var. *reymondianum* Loes. 98, (95); *V. warburgii* Loes. (98).

maackioides. Japan: mt forests and meadows from C Honshu to Kyushu. Lvs narrowly lanceolate to linear; t purple; ped long; rac variable in length. *V. maackioides* Loes 94,98,(95); *V. maackii* Regel 105 (93,95,107); *V. japonicum* (Baker) Loes. (143), var. *reymondianum* Loes. (95); *V. maximowiczii* Baker (95); *V. coreanum* Loes. (107).

coreanum. Korea: Alpine meadows, Quelpaert I. Lvs linear; t yellow-green; ped and rac mod length; 2° rac simple; plant small. *V. coreanum* Loes. 94,107,(98); *V. maximowiczii* Baker (95).

oblongum. C China: moist meadows, W Hupeh, E Szechuan. Lvs elliptic, papillate on veins; t purplish, at least on gland; ped and infl long; lower rac compound; bracteoles woolly: tall plant. *V. oblongum* Loes. 94,116,(98); *V. maackii* Regel (110); *V. maximowiczii* Baker (110).

kiulingianum. C China: moist woods, S Anhwei, N Kiangsi, N Kwangsi. Lvs elliptic to lanceolate, large; t yellow-green with reddish gland; ped mod length, infl long with many very short compound 2° rac; bracteoles woolly; tall plant. *V. kiulingianum* Zimmerman 94; *V. maximowiczii* Baker (110); *V. oblongum* Loes. (98); *V. warburgii* Loes. (98); *V. angustipetalum* Loes. (98); *V. cavaleriei* Loes. (98); *V. schindleri* Loes[d]. 94,116,(98).

---

[e]Section *Fuscoveratrum* is interpreted as follows: The entities are all very closely related. Most of them form a network of geographically-replacing populations joined to each other by steep places in the over-all morphological gradients extending from SW China to the Amur R. and N Japan. The points of steepest clines and greatest heterogeneity are E–C China, Korea, and C Honshu. Most of the entities are here treated as subspecies of *V. maackii.* *V. nigrum* rates specific rank because it appears to maintain uniformity and distinctness [Maximowicz (108) to the contrary] where its range overlaps that of *V. maackii* from the Amur R to S Korea; moreover, it appears to be polyploid (155–157).

TABLE 2. *Continued*

formosanum. China: mt meadows; from NE Kweichow and N Chekiang S to Hong
Kong; Taiwan; Okinawa.   Often stout; lvs linear, stiff, bracteoles and purple t
usu woolly; ped mod length; rac often long, even the lower ones usu fertile. ˈ*V.
formosanum* Loes. 88,94,98; *V. chingianum* Zimmerman[d] 94; *V. nigrum* L. var.
japonicum Baker 110; *V. warburgii* Loes. (98); *V. kudoi* Masamune 143; *V. japonicum*
(Baker) Loes. 143; *V. maackii* Regel 110?).

   atroviolaceum. SW China: wet meadows, W Yunnan.   Slender; lvs linear, flaccid;
bracteoles and purple t very woolly; peds and rac mod length.   *V. atroviolaceum*
Loes. 94,98.

V. longebracteatum[d].   Japan: alpine meadows, N and C Honshu.   Like *V. m. maximowiczii* except: t more pointed, ascending; rac short; either bracteoles or bracts
often long; sometimes subglabrous.   *V. longebracteatum* Takeda 94,95,97,98,105; *V.
maximowiczii* Baker (95,98).

V. micranthum[d].   C China: E Szechuan.   Lvs lance-elliptic, papillate; fls very small;
plant small.   *V. micranthum* Wang and Tang 144; *V. minutiflorum* Zimmerman 94.

TELANDRIUM.   Centering in the two Arcto-tertiary refugia (145), the mt of SW China
and E USA.   Stamens inserted on base of t*; t entire, narrowed concavely toward base;
glands paired, central (exc 1); ovary usu usu as in *Fuscoveratrum* but sometimes pub.;
leaf blades glabrous; rhizome usu poorly developed; 2° rac. sometimes branched.   Sect.
Telandrium 94; Subgen. *Pseudoanticlea* (97,98) Subgen. *Pseudomelanthium* 97, 98; Sec.
Fuscoveratrum (95); Genus *Melanthium* 97.

V. shanense.   SW China.   T green, with small single basal gland; lvs linear to lanceolate, sometimes papillate.

   shanense.   Lower elevation thickets and wet ground, S Sikang, N Yunnan, N Burma.
Lvs and rac long; bracteoles short; ped mod. length; t small, spreading.   *V.
shanense* W. W. Smith 88,98, var. *shanense* 94; *V. yunnanense* Loes. 88,98,146.

   stenophyllum.   High alpine meadows and forest edges, S Sikang.   Rac and ped
short; lvs short, blunt; bracteoles long; t large, ascend.   *V. shanense* W. W. Smith
var. *stenophyllum* (Diels) Zimmerman 94; *V. stenophyllum* Diels 88,98,146.

V anticleoides.   Far E USSR: Damp barrens and coniferous forest, Sakhalin and
adjacent mainland.   Small, glabrous; t greenish yellow, with soon-obscure slender
purple glands; lvs linear; rhizome often long.   *V. anticleoides* (Trautv. and Meyer)
Takeda 94,95,98,104; *Acelidanthus antileoides* Trautv. and Meyer 89,93,115.

V. woodii.   E USA: Deciduous forest, S Iowa and E Okla. E to W Ohio and C Ky.;
local, SW N. C. to N Fla.   Lvs elliptic; ovary woolly; to dark purple.   *V. woodii*
Robbins 88,91,93,94,98,101,117–119,121,147; *V. intermedium* Chapm. 88,91–93,98,117.

V. parviflorum E USA: High elevation deciduous forest, Va.   S to NE Ga., W into
Tenn. and Ky.   Lvs elliptic; ovary glabrous; stamen inserted well out on narrow
green t; glands obscure.   *V. parviflorum* Michx. 88,91–94,98,117,121; *Melanthium
parviflorum* (Michx.) S. Wats. 118.

V. taliense.   SW China: Edge of pine forest, mt of Yunnan and S Sikang.   Like *V.
parviflorum* but lvs linear; plant very large; glands definite.   *V. taliense* Loes. 94,98,
146; *V. cavaleriei* Loes. 94,(98).

V. mengtzeanum.   SW China: Dry meadows and pine or mixed forest, mt of Yunnan
and S Sikang (and SW Kweichow?).   Lvs linear; t large, obovate, thick, white;
glands large, fleshy; ovary usu glabrous.   *V. mengtzeanum* Loes. 94,98,146; *V.
wilsonii* C. H. Wright ex Loes. 97,98,148.

V. hybridum.   E USA: Open or rocky woods, in upland, Conn. and Pa. S to S. C. and
Ga.   Lvs oblanceolate; t white (turning green); slender claw bears stamen at or below
middle; thick short obcoradate acuminate blade bears fan-shaped fleshy glands;
ovary often mod pub.   *V. hybridum* (Walt.) Zimmerman 94; *Melanthium hybridum*
Walt. 91,93,118,121; *M. latifolium* Desr. 92,117.

V. virginicum.   E USA: Moist Meadows and bogs, S New York to N Fla., W to E
Texas, N to NE Iowa.   Lvs linear; t white (turning green or reddish); slender claw
bears stamen at or above middle; thick oblong-obovate blade bears oval fleshy glands;
ovary often mod pub.   *V. virginicum* (L.) Aiton 94; *Melanthium virginicum* L. 88,91–
93,117–119,121,147,149; *M. dispersum* Small 92,117; *M. monoicum* Walt. 91.

MELOVERATRUM.   W Coast, USA: Mendocino and Sonoma Counties, Calif.   Section
Meloveratrum 94; Subgen. *Euveratrum*, Sect. *Alboveratrum* (97,98).

V. fimbriatum.   T large, white, fringed; glands central, paired, large, fleshy; styles
central; ovary sometimes pub.; capsule paper-thin, lobed, with sunken apex*; seeds
few, large, green; leaves elliptic, sometimes pub.; ped divergent; 2° rac often long and
branched; bulb large; rhizome short but stout.   Marshes and shaded rivers on coast.
V. fimbriatum Gray 91,93,94,98,100,101,120,124,128,129,134.

TABLE 2. *Continued*

STENANTHIUM. C and N America; one reaching E Asia. T lanceolate-acuminate*; capsule ⅛–¼ inferior; bulb; rhizome small or absent.
    EUSTENANTHIUM. E USA: Pa. to W Fla., W to E Texas and NW Mo.
      S. gramineum. Slender; branches and fls many, the lower wholly staminate; t small, greenish to yellowish white; gland small, obscure; slender stolons* among roots; lvs linear. Moist meadows. *Stenanthium gramineum* (Ker) Morong 91,92,100,117,118, 121,147,150; *S. robustum* S. Wats. 91,92,100,117,147; *S. angustifolium* Kunth 93.
    STENANTHELLA. Pacific region. Fls few, large, bisexual; gland large, bilobed (obscure when dried).
      S. occidentalis. W N America: Mossy stream banks in mt, W Mont. and N Calif. to Vancouver, B. C., and Banff, Alberta. E Asia: rocky places, Sakhalin. Small, slender; perianth greenish to reddish or purplish, campanulate; t tips reflexed*; sometimes a few branches; lvs often oblanceolate. *Stenanthella occidentalis* (Gray) Rydb. 88,91,125,126; *S. sachalinensis* (F. Schmidt) Rydb.[d] 88,126; *Stenanthium occidentale* Gray, 93,100,127–130,133,134; *S. sachalinense* F. Schmidt 89,93,104,115; *S. rhombipetalum* Suks. 151.
      S. frigida. Mexico: Open pine forests in mts E and W of Mexico City. Stout to slender, often branched; t dark purple; lvs linear. *Stenanthella frigida* (C and S) Gates 91, *Stenanthium frigidum* (C and S) Kunth 88,93,139.
ZYGADENUS. C and N America; one in Asia. By elimination of the other genera. Lvs linear; bulb (exc 1); rhizome small or absent (exc 1). (Note: The original spelling, *Zigadenus,* technically has priority; see 100,152).
    AMIANTHIUM. E USA. To oblong, creamy white (to yellow or pink?), convexly narrowed at base, about as long as stamens; gland single, basal; ped long, crowded. Sect. *Oceanoros* (excluding *A. muscaetoxicum*) 152.
      A. muscaetoxicum. Low sandy grounds, bogs, open woods, Fla W to S Mo. and Okla., N in mt to Pa. and on Coastal Plain to E N. Y. Rac unbranched; carpels broad, their tips separate*; seeds few, large, with fleshy reddish coat; t firm, turning green; gland obscure when dried; lvs rel broad, blunt. *Amianthium muscaetoxicum* (Walt.) Gray 88,91,93,118,121; *Chrosperma muscaetoxicum* (Walt.) Kuntze 92,117.
      Z. densus. Damp pineland and bogs, mostly on Coastal Plain, Fla. W to La., N to SE Va. Like *A. muscaetoxicum* but carpels very slender, their erect tips united up to the styles; seeds tiny, many; gland often visible when dried; lvs slender. *Zigadenus densus* (Desr.) Fern. 118,121,152; *Amianthium angustifolium* Gray 91,93; *Tracyanthus angustifolius* (Michx.) Small 88,92,117.
      Z. leimanthoides. Sandy pine-land and boₜs, Coastal Plain and upland, local; C Ga. and W N. C. W to La. and N to Va.; N. J. and environs; E Texas. Like *Z. densus* but branched; gland thickened and distinct when dried. *Zigadenus leimanthoides* Gray 93, 118,121,152; *Amianthium texanum* (Small) Gates 91; *Oceanoros leimanthoides* (Gray) Small 88,91,92,117.
TOXICOSCORDION. Mt and plains of C and W N. America. T thin, white or yellowish, often narrowed to a short claw, usu about as long as stamens; gland single, central; ped long. Sect. *Chitonia* 152.
    Z. venenosus. NW Mexico N to SW Canada. T usu shorter than 6 mm, and sometimes shorter than stamens; sepals acute to obtuse, clawed; infl elongate, seldom cymose, sometimes branched.
      venensosus. Coast, Sierra Nevada, and Cascade Mts., from extreme NW Baja Calif. N to SE British Columbia, E in moist meadows to E Idaho. Ped ascend to spread; sepal claw about as well developed as petal claw; lower leaf sheaths usu lacking; exposed (upper) sheaths usu open, exposing slender stem; very rarely a branch or two. *Zigadenus venenosus* S. Wats. 100,122, 125,128–130,134,136,(127, 131), var, *venenosus* 133,152; *Toxicoscordion venenosum* (S. Wats.) Rydb. 91,125,153; *T. arenicola* Heller 91; *T. salinum* (Nelson) Gates 91.
      gramineus. Grassland and *Pinus ponderosa* forest, mostly NE of range of *Z. v. venenosus,* from Colo. and E Nebr. N to S Sask. and S British Columbia, and W to Cascade Mts. in Wash. Like *Z. v. venenosus* but sepal claw poorly developed (to 0.5 mm long); lower sheaths distinct; exposed sheaths elongate, enclosing the stout stem; sometimes a 2° rac or two. *Zigadenus venenosus* S. Wats. (127,131), var. *gramineus* (Rydb.) Walsh ex Peck 130,133,152; *Z. gramineus* Rydb. 100,126,131,132,(122); *Z. intermedius* Rydb. 126,134; *Z. acutus* Rydb. 126; *Z. falcatus* Rydb. 126; *Toxicoscordion gramineus* Rydb. 119,125,153; *T. intermedium* Rydb. 88,91,153; *T. acutum* Rydb. 119,125,153; *T. falcatum* Rydb. 91,125,153.
      micranthus. Serpentine and olivine hills, Klamath mts and NW Sierra and coast mt of Calif. Like *Z. v. venenosus* but ped sparser, longer and spread horizontally; t may be shorter than stamens. *Zigadenus venenosus* S. Wats. var. *micranthus*

TABLE 2. *Continued*

(Eastw.) Jepson 128,129,152; *Z. micranthus* Eastw. 130,134; *Toxicoscordion micranthus* (Eastw.) Heller 91.
  fontanus. Serpentine springs and marshes, C and W Calif. Like *Z. v. micranthus* but larger plant; t always as long as stamens. *Zigadenus venenosus* S. Wats. var. *fontanus* (Eastw.) Preece 152.
  Z. paniculatus. Dry foothills, esp in sagebrush, from NW New Mexico and SW Mont. W to Cascade Mts. of Wash. and Ore. and to Sierra Mts. of Calif. and S Nev.; W into N–C Calif. Like *Z. venenosus* but sepals often acuminate and scarcely clawed; few to many 2° rac always present; plant usu large. *Zigadenus paniculatus* (Nutt.) S. Wats. 93,100,126–134,136–138,152,(122); *Toxicoscordion paniculatum* (Nutt.) Rydb. 91,125,153.
  Z. exaltatus. Wooded W slopes of Sierra Mts in C Calif. Like *Z. paniculatus* but still larger plant with larger t (6–10 mm long). *Zigadenus exaltatus* Eastw. 128,129,134, 152; *Toxicoscordion exaltatum* (Eastw.) Heller 91.
  Z. nuttallii. Prairies, E Kans., Tenn. and S Mo. to S Texas. Like *Z. Venenosus* but claw indistinct on all t; rac usu cymose, sometimes branched; lvs stout, falcate. *Zigadenus nuttallii* Gray ex S. Wats. 118,121,126,149,152,(93); *Toxicoscordion nuttallii* (Gray) Rydb. 88,91,92,117,119,153; *T. texense* Rydb. 91, 117.
  Z. brevibracteatus. Mojave Desert, S Calif. T 6 mm or more long; ped very sparse, very long, spread horizontally from zig-zag axis; bracteoles up to 5 mm long; branched. *Zigadenus brevibracteatus* (M. E. Jones) Hall 128,129,134,152; *Toxicoscordion brevibracteatum* (Jones) Gates 91.
  Z. fremontii. Slopes, esp in chaparral, on Pacific Coast and in coast mt from extreme NW Baja Calif. N to SW Ore. T very large (6–12 mm long), longer than stamens, with large gland; rac often branched. Variable. *Zigadenus fremontii* Torr. ex S. Wats. 91,93,100,128–130,134,152; *Toxicoscordion fremontii* (Torr.) Rydb. 88,153.
ANTICLEA. C and N America; one in Asia. Generally at high alt and N lat. T thick, white to green, concavely narrowed to base, ascending to fruit; gland single, central, fleshy, bilobed; capsule about ⅙ inferior: ped mod long, sparsely spaced. Sect. *Anticlea* 152.
  Z. elegans. N and C America, in dry to wet meadows, often near coniferous forest; t large (7–10 mm long), broad-ovate.
    elegans. Western: NW Alaska and Yukon S to N Dak., S in mts to W Texas and NW Mexico. T usu yellowish white; rac often unbranched. *Zigadenus elegans* Pursh 88,100,112,114,118,121,125–127,130–134,137,138, var. *elegans* 152; *Z. coloradensis* Rydb. 91,125,126; *Z. mohinorensis* Greenm. 139; *Z. volcanicus* Benth.137,139; *Anticlea elegans* (Pursh) Rydb. 91,119,153; *A. chlorantha* (Rich.) Rydb. 125,153; *A. glauca* Kunth 93; *A. alpina* (Blankinship) Heller 125; *A. gracilenta* (Greene) Gates 91; *A. longa* Heller, 91; *A. mohinorensis* (Greenm.) Gates 91; *A. coloradensis* Rydb. 153.
    glaucus. Eastern: Gaspé Peninsula, Quebec, and S Ohio W to E N. Dak.; in mt of Va. and N. C. and S Mo. T more often greenish and bronze-tinged; rac usu branched; plant more often glaucous. *Zigadenus elegans* Pursh var. *glaucus* (Nutt.) Preece 152; *Z. glaucus* Nutt. 100,118,121,147; *Anticlea chlorantha* (Rich.) Rydb. 91,92,119. (Note: the type of *Z. chloranthus* Richards belongs with the western form, *Z. e. elegans*; see 118,152.)
  Z. vaginatus. W USA: Wet sandstone, SE Utah. Like *Z. elegans* but t usu under 7 mm long, white. *Zigadenus vaginatus* (Rydb.) Macbride 152; Anticlea vaginata .Rydb. 91,125.
  Z. volcanicus. Alpine meadows, Guatemala. Like *Z. vaginatus* but t green-streaked; upper bracteoles longer; robust. *Zigadenus volcanicus* Benth. 152; *Anticlea volcanica* Baker 91,93.
  Z. sibiricus. Asia: Open forests and rocky places; Siberian Arctic coast from 85° to 155° E long, S to Oirot, N Outer Mongolia, N Korea, Maritime Terr. (Far E USSR), and Riishiri I. (N Japan); C China (E Szechauan, W Hupeh). T narrowly ovate (1–3 mm wide) greenish, reflexed at anthesis; plant slender, often glaucous. *Zigadenus sibiricus* (L.) A. Gray ex Wats. 89,110,115,152; *Z. makinoanus* Miyabe and Kudo[d] 104,105,152; *Anticlea sibirica* (L.) Knuth 91,93,153; *A. japonica* (Makino) Gates 91.
  Z. virescens. Mt. forests; Mexico, Ariz., New Mexico. T ovate, small (5–7 mm long), on nodding ped. *Zigadenus virescens* (HBK) Macbride 91,138,139,152; *Anticelea virescens* (HBK) Rydb. 153; *A. porrifolia* (Greene) Rydb. 91,125,153; *A. mexicana* Kunth 93.
EUZYGADENUS. SE USA on Coastal Plain, SE Va. to S Miss. Sect. *Euzigadenus* 152.
  Z. glaberrimus. T thick, white, clawed, ascending in fruit; glands paired, central, fleshy; rac branched; ped sparse; bulb lacking*; rhizome elongate. Bogs, pineland. *Zigadenus glaberrimus* Michx. 91–93, 100,117,118,121,152,153; *Z. bracteatus* R and S 91.

TABLE 2. *Continued*

SCHOENOCAULON. C America and adjacent N and S America, in mt grassland, pine and
oak woods, barrens, prairies, Rac spicate*, unbranched; fls often crowded; t ligulate to
elliptic, very small, greenish; stamens often colored, usu exceeding t; gland usu obscure;
lvs linear; bulb; rhizome small or absent.
    GROUP I. T elliptic to ovate; margins finely denticulate.
      S. drummondii. SE Texas from Bexar and Fayette Cos.); N Mexico. By elimination of
        others in group. *Schoenocaulon drummondii* Gray 154,(91,93,100,117); *Sabadilla drum-
        mondii* (Gray) B and R (88).
      S. yucatanense. Mexico: Yucatan. Long filaments. *Schoenocaulon yucatanense*
        Brinker 154.
      S. tenuifolium. Mexico: Oaxaca. Large t; seeds few, large; lvs rel broad. *Schoeno-
        caulon tenuifolium* (Mart. and Gal.) Robins and Greenm. 139,154.
    GROUP II. T ligulate, entire, but often with a pair of conspicuous hyaline-scarious flanges
      along part of their length.
      S. comatum. Mexico: Oaxaca, Puebla, San Luis Potosi. Flange absent. *Schoeno-
        caulon comatum* Brinker 154.
      S. dubium. Florida. Flange absent; smaller than *S. comatum.* *Schoenocaulon dubium*
        (Michx.) Small 91,92,100,117,154; *S. gracile* Gray 93; *Sabadilla gracile* (Gray) B and
        R 88.
      S. pringlei. Mexico: Hidalgo, D. F., Nayarit, Puebla. Flange extends along ⅔ of
        t length; stamens barely exserted. *Schoenocaulon pringlei* Greenm. 139,154.
      S. texanum. Mexico, S Texas (W from Travis and Bexar Cos.), SE New Mexico. One
        distinct hyaline tooth on each side. *Schoenocaulon texanum* Scheele 154; *S. drum-
        mondii* Gray (91,93,100,117); *Sabadilla drummondii* (Gray) B and R (88).
      S. related species[d]. Similar to *S. texanum,* differing slightly in size or shape of t, sta-
        mens, infl, or capsules 93,139,154. (*Schoenocaulon calcicola* Greenm.; *S. caricifolium*
        (Schlecht) Gray; *S. conzattii* Brinker; *S. coulteri* Baker; *S. intermedium* Baker; *S.
        jaliscense* Greenm.; *S. macrocarpum* Brinker; *S. megarhiza* Jones; *S. mortonii* Brinker;
        S. obtusum Brinker; *S. regulare* Brinker; *S. tenue* Brinker).
      S. ghiesbrechtii. Mexico: Chiapas. Two hyaline teeth or jags per side; faint t gland
        suggests relationship to Group III; filaments very long, curved. *Schoenocaulon
        ghiesbrechtii* Greenm[d]. 139,154.
    GROUP III. T ligulate, entire; gland dark, near base, bilobed on sepal, smaller on
      petal; plant robust; lvs rel broad.
      S. officinale. Costa Rica, El Salvador, Guatemala, Honduras, Mexico, Peru, Venezuela.
        Schoenocaulon officinale (C and S) Gray 93,100,154; *Sabadilla officinale* (Schlecht)
        B and R 88.

Schoenocaulon is the most distinctive and homogeneous group, set off by its
unbranched, spicate inflorescence, crowded flowers, very small tepals[4] and exserted
stamens. Though unique in the tribe, this striking bottle brush-shaped inflorescence is shared by other liliaceous genera, such as *Chamaelirion* and *Chionographis* (88). A major variable among the species of *Schoenocaulon* is the tepal
shape (fig. 5), of which the three main types are designated by the unnamed
groups described in table 2. Brinker's monograph (154) suffered from insufficient
herbarium material for unraveling the Mexican complex of entities related to
S. texanum in Group II. More work is needed to determine which of these forms
deserve specific rank.

The species of *Stenanthium,* in contrast, are few and diverse in aspect. The
group is defined by its unique lanceolate, acuminate tepal shape (fig. 5) and by its
partially inferior ovary. However, the latter feature (121, fig. p. 405) is shared
with one group (*Anticlea*) of *Zygadenus* (121, fig. p. 408; 89, fig. 3b)[5]. Rydberg
(126) erected a new genus, *Stenanthella,* for *S. occidentale,* because it differs in

    [4]"Tepal" is a shorthand term for "perianth segment" in the lily family, where petals and
sepals are very much alike.
    [5]Many illustrations of the *Veratreae* are unreliable because of errors in labelling or in
incomplete or incorrect drawing. For example, the good drawing of *Melanthium hybridum* in
Small (92) is referred to as *M. virginicum,* while the drawing of *M. hybridum* in Gleason (121)
omits the prominent glands and is placed less closely to the name than is the drawing of
Veratrum viride flowers.

appearance and habit (plant much smaller, flowers much larger with reflexed campanulate perianth) from the first-named species, *S. gramineum*. The third species, *S. frigidum*, was then placed in *Stenanthella* by Gates (91) because, in its large, uniformly bisexual flowers, it more closely resembles *S. occidentale* than it does *S. gramineum*. While the two *Stenanthellae* appear to be quite uniform, *S. gramineum* exhibits considerable variability (in flower color and size, leaf morphology, plant size, and flowering phenology). This variation appears to be partly geographically clinal (118,150) and partly locally bimodal (147).

Veratrum has been delimited from the rest of the *Veratreae* by the presence of pubescence (at least in the inflorescence) and by broadly-winged seeds (94). In the other genera, the plants are wholly glabrous and the seeds wingless or only slightly winged or tailed. Two partial exceptions were included in *Veratrum* on the basis of other shared features, the glabrous *V. anticleoides* because of its rhizome and the shapes of its ovary and its obscure gland, and the wingless-seeded *V. fimbriatum* because of its rhizome, broad leaves and pubescence. Although unique in their incurving filaments (149) and slender abrupt tepal claws, the two species of *Melanthium* were included in *Veratrum*, (*V. hybridum* and *V. virginicum* in table 2), not only because of their pubescence and winged seeds, but also because they form the climax in a progressive series in tepal shape, gland development, and stamen adnation peculiar to those species of *Veratrum* in which the stamen is inserted on the tepal a short distance away from the ovary. For this group, which well illustrates variation on a theme (fig. 5), the section *Telandrium* was erected (94).

Zygadenus, thus defined as what is left of the *Veratreae* after carving off *Veratrum*, *Schoenocaulon* and *Stenanthium*, is a heterogeneous grouping. It has received careful treatment by Preece (152), who presents good grounds, such as differing chromosome numbers, for treating the four sections as separate genera, according to the subgeneric section characteristics given in table 2. Though he did not include *Amianthium muscaetoxicum* in his study, his work points to the grouping under the name *Amianthium* of *A. muscaetoxicum* and the two species of his section *Oceanoros* (as done in table 2). It may also be pointed out that one of the supposed oddities which set *A. muscaetoxicum* apart (few, very large seeds) also appears (homologously or analogously) in two very diverse groups, in *Veratrum fimbriatum* and *Schoenocaulon tenuifolium*. Though the three *Amianthia* are more closely similar to each other than are the three *Stenanthia*, they are still very distinct species; their sympatry implies the presence of breeding barriers. They exhibit very little variability, with the possible exception of *Z. leimanthoides*.

Of the remaining *Zygadeni*, *Z. glaberrimus* is even more uniform and distinct (note lack of synonymy in table 2); hence it is easy to defend monotypic generic status for it. Its well-developed rhizome without a bulb is unique in the tribe; and it shares several features (tepal shape, texture, and glands) with diverse groups in *Zygadenus* and *Veratrum* (fig. 5). At the other extreme are the species clusters comprising sections *Anticlea* and *Toxicoscordion*. These groups are distinct from each other and from other groups, but within them most of the entities are very similar to each other, and the discontinuities are not always sharp. Because of geographic clines and frequent allopatry, some of them were reduced by Preece to infraspecific rank, the two confluent forms of *Z. elegans* and the four of *Z. venenosus*. One could go farther and consider all of the large-flowered *Anticleae* (*Z. elegans*, *Z. vaginatus*, and *Z. volcanicus*) to be on the borderline between species and subspecies. Similarly, in *Toxicoscordion*, one is almost tempted to consider a series of subspecific relationships among *Z. nuttallii*, *Z. venenosus*, *Z. paniculatus*, and *Z. exaltatus*, at least. However, little would be gained by thus further adding to the burdensome synonymy, since local variants (some named, some not) vastly complicate the actual picture, as Preece notes (152) under *Z. elegans* and *Z. venenosus*.

Parallelling *Zygadenus, Veratrum* is a heterogeneous group in the same two ways. First, it is composed of four subgroups, of which section *Alboveratrum,* at least, stands well apart as a good genus, on account of its unique sub-marginal, V-shaped tepal glands (fig. 5) and other features. On this dark gland, which appears neither fleshy nor juicy, one finds, in most of the *Alboveratra* (but not in every specimen nor every flower), the conspicuous, bluish-white deposit described by Loesener (97, p. 115–6).

Secondly, the subgeneric sections in *Veratrum* differ in kind, just as they do in *Zygadenus.* The counterpart of *Z. glaberrimus* is the equally distinctive *V. fimbriatum,* which likewise shares certain features with diverse groups (precocious anthers with *Fuscoveratrum;* succulent paired glands with part of section *Telandrium;* central styles with *Alboveratrum*) as well as having unique features, such as papery, emarginate ovary. Hence, the section *Meloveratrum* was erected for it (94). The counterpart of the *Amianthium* group is *Telandrium,* in which similarly there is a progressive development of a characteristic type of gland among the species [the paired central glands (fig. 5) on which Loesener partly based his subgenus *Pseudoanticlea* (97, fig. 7c)]. Though the *Telandria* share many other features, they are all very distinct species, and some of them are sympatric. Furthermore, they are all very uniform, with the exception of *V. shanense,* whose poorly-differentiated single basal gland is also an exception to this group. The latter species forms a bimodal complex (morphologically, phenologically and altitudinally) in the climatically diverse steep mountains of Southwestern China (94).

Finally, the sections *Fuscoveratrum* and *Alboveratrum* comprise species clusters comparable to those of *Anticlea* and *Toxicoscordion.* That is, because of close similarity, clinal and local variability, and frequent allopatry, most of them are on the borderline between species and subspecies, as their extensive snyonymy in table 2 indicates. Close relationship is also suggested by the uniformity in chromosome numbers within each of the four groups (94,101,152,155–157). In figure 5, *Zygadenus venenosus* would occupy a position next to the diagrams for *Z. nuttallii* and *Z. paniculatus; Veratrum album* between *V. californicum* and *V. eschscholtzii.* It is of interest that these two phytochemically intensively investigated species in the tribe, *Z. venenosus* and *V. album,* are morphologically the most variable species, and that each comprises the center of a complex of closely-related forms. An unhappy result of the great difficulty of identification has been the imprecise application of names in these groups. Fortunately, however, information on the precise locality, elevation and plant association can often substitute for experience in identification (table 2).

EXPLANATION OF FIGURE 5

FIG. 5. *Diagrams of representative tepal and gland types in the tribe Veratreae, drawn to scale In most cases, the distances between the species and groups in the figure are roughly proportional to the number of morphological differences between them. (However, to avoid crowding, the vertical spacing is on a larger scale than the horizontal). The following symbols indicate the location of a few of these differences: — — —, (1) pubescence (the others are wholly glabrous); – – – – –, (2) leaves lanceolate to elliptic (the others are linear-leaved, except sometimes in S. occidentalis); x x x x, (3) mature seeds broadly winged (in the rest they are very narrowly or not winged); ' ' ' ', (4) polygamous and usually much-branched (in the others, functional pistils usually appear on all branches, when branch racemes are present); . . . . ., (5) perianth adnate to basal portion of capsule (in the others, the capsule is wholly superior or nearly so); ←, (6) insertion of filament on base of tepal in Sect. Telandrium (in the other groups, the adnation is slight or none).*
NOTE: The tepal shapes are distorted by flattening, such as in V. fimbriatum. The shapes shown are usually rough averages between the slightly longer petal and the broader, blunter sepal. Extremes of variation are shown by replicate figures for the same species; for the others, an average flower was usually chosen.

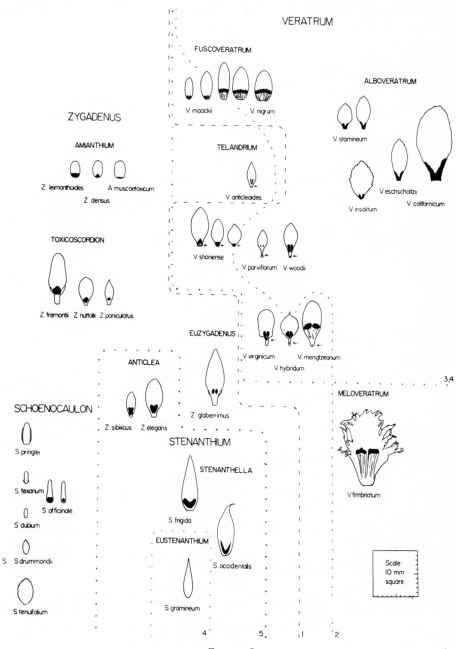

FIGURE 5

221

A summary of the botanical relationship between and within groups in the *Veratreae* should be as independent as possible of the practical but sometimes arbitary generic categories used in naming them. Earlier attempts (91,97) at the ambitious task of relating the species in this tribe were often hampered by the lack of quantitative material for distinguishing large (or constant) from small (or variable) discontinuities between the species. The arrangement given in table 2 and in figure 5, which grew out of the need to define *Veratrum* (94), is based on a large sample, about 5,000 herbarium sheets, including all of the entities recognized in table 2 and almost all of the described species in the *Veratreae*; in addition, fresh material of a number of them was studied. The herbarium material examined, summarized in table 3, was distributed approximately as follows: *Veratrum*, 3,500 sheets; *Zygadenus*, 800; *Stenanthium*, 400; *Schoenocaulon*, 150.

TABLE 3.   *Source material on which table 2 and figure 5 are based.*

Genus	Geographic Area	Herbaria Supplying Most of Material[1]
Veratrum (including *Melanthium*)	Europe	B DAO F G GH IA M MICH MO NY PH TENN US W WIS WU
	Asia	B CAL DAO E F FU G GH HK K LE M MO NA NY PH S SAP TNS UC US W WIS WU
	W North America	BRY COLO DAO F GH IA MICH MO MSC NA NO PH SMU UC UTC WIS
	E North America	DAO F FLAS GA GH IA MICH MO MSC NA PH SMU TENN UARK WIS
Stenanthium (including *Stenanthella*)	Asia	G GH LE NY
	Central America and W North America	F FLAS GH MICH MO MSC NA PH UTC WIS
	E North America	COLO F FLAS GA GH IA MICH MO MSC NA PH SMU TENN UARK WIS
Zygadenus (including *Amianthium*)	Asia	B CAL E F G GH K LE MO NY S TNS US
	Central America and W North America	F MO SMU TENN UTC WIS
	E North America	F FLAS MO MSC NA SMU TENN UARK UTC WIS
Schoenocaulon	Central America and North America	F FLAS MO NA WIS

[1]The symbols are those of Lanjouw and Stafleu (158). Grateful acknowledgment is expressed to the curators of these herbaria for their generous loan of the *Veratreae* material.

In only a few instances (such as the ranges of some *Zygadeni* and *Schoenocaula*), was supplementary information added second-hand from the literature. The synonymy given in table 2 is based on examination of the same collections cited by the authors given, where possible, and otherwise where the geographic range or species description left no doubt of the identity.

The construction of figure 5 attempts to indicate the number of features shared by, and the number of discontinuities found between, each species or group and each of the others. Some degree of objectivity was attained by listing in the squares of a correlation table an estimate of the numer of differences observed between each possible pair among the representative species illustrated, and using those numbers to measure distances between the species before locating them on the figure.   However, the subjective judgments required in weighing major against minor differences undoubtedly were an important source of bias.   In addition to this necessary compromise between objectivity and experience, the limitations of a two-dimensional figure contributed to distortion.   For example, in the correlation table, *V. fimbriatum* was actually found to be closer to section *Fuscoveratrum* than to section *Alboveratrum*.

A further handicap is the sole reliance on gross morphological features.   Comparative anatomical work, such as that of Youngken (101,123) needs to be extended in order to test these relationships on the microscopic level.   The features chosen for constructing fig. 5 were the types or relative development of: underground parts (rhizomes, bulbs, fibrillose leaf-bases); leaf shapes and leaf-reduction series; pubescence of inflorescence and leaves; branching of inflorescence and length and position of pedicels; distribution of pistils; tepals (size, shape, color, margin, gland, position); stamen-tepal adnation, length of filament, and time of opening and falling of anther; ovary shape; seed shape; adnation of perianth to ovarv; and unique features.

These features may be plotted on the figure as it now stands.   For example, large succulent tepal glands occupy the region from *Zygadenus* section *Anticlea* to *Veratrum mengtzeanum* and *V. fimbriatum*.   Clines in the shape, position and development of the tepal glands can be traced in several directions—starting from *V. shanense:* (a) to section *Amianthium;* (b) to section *Toxicoscordion;* (c) to section *Fuscoveratrum* and, through section *Telandrium*, to *V. fimbriatum;* and (d) also through *Telandrium* to *Z. glaberrimus*, *Z.* section *Anticlea, Stenanthella*, and even to *Schoenocaulon officinale*.   Similar relationships may be observed in tepal shape, such as the similarity of *Amianthium* to *Fuscoveratrum*, and the difference between their oblong tepal shape and the type which narrows concavely near the base, found in sections *Alboveratrum, Meloveratrum, Telandrium, Euzigadenus, Anticlea*, and *Toxicoscordion*.   Another feature shared by adjacent species in the figure is the truncate type of ovary, well developed in section *Fuscoveratrum* and most of section *Telandrium*.

In certain other features one can think of the figure as a spindle-shaped continuum formed between two very unique groups each placed a little apart from the rest: At one end is section *Alboveratrum*, with stout rhizomes, broad pubescent leaves, tall stout leafy stems, pubescent and much-branched racemes, large tepals, functional pistils confined to the upper racemes, and numerous broadly-winged seeds.   At the opposite end is genus *Schoenocaulon*, with bulbs alone, glabrous linear basal leaves, slender glabrous spicate inflorescence, much-reduced tepal size, uniformly bisexual flowers, and relatively few unwinged seeds.   Each of these features changes somewhere between these poles, among the heterogeneous central groups of *Veratrum, Stenanthium* and *Zygadenus*, as a few lines drawn in figure 5 suggest.   There are, of course, some irregularities in the gradient.   The leaves of *Stenanthella occidentalis* tend to be oblanceolate.   Functional pistils are found in almost all the flowers in *V. fimbriatum* and *V. maackii formosanum*, while they are lacking on the lower branches in *Stenanthium gramineum*, and often in *Z. leimanthoides* and *Z. paniculatus*.   Persistent fibrillose leaf-bases curiously are most conspicuous at the two ends, in *Schoenocaulon* and *Veratrum*.   It is hoped that this figure may be useful as a basis for further refinement as additional information comes to light.

COMPARISON BETWEEN ALKALOID CONTENT AND BOTANICAL TAXONOMY OF THE VERATREAE

It is evident from table 4 that only a small proportion of the plants which belong to the *Veratreae* have received phytochemical study.   Furthermore, it must be stressed that some of the plants which do appear in table 4 have received very little chemical investigation. Consequently, the absence of a report of isolation of a given alkaloid from a given plant should not necessarily be taken as evidence for the absence of the alkaloid from the plant. Considerable additional phytochemical work will be necessary before any appreciable number of firm chemical taxonomic correlations will be possible. For the present, one can only formulate some preliminary generalizations. It is hoped that these generalizations will point the way to additional phytochemical studies designed to further evaluate the potential significance of alkaloid occurrence in chemical taxonomy [cf. (159)].

TABLE 4. *Distribution of alkaloids isolated from the tribe Veratreae*

Plant name used in this paper	Jerveratrum alkaloids	Ceveratrum alkaloids	Unclassified alkaloids
Veratrum album album (including var. *lobelianum*).........	II;III;IV; XIII.	XVII;XXII;XXIII;XXIV; XXVII;XXXI;XXXIII; XXXIV;XXXVI;XXXVII.	XLII;XLIII; XLIV;XLV;XLVI; LIV;LVII.
V. album oxysepalum...	I;II;IV.	XIV;XVII;XXXVIII.	
V. album grandiflorum..	I;II;IV.	XIV;XLI.	
V. viride..............	I;II;III;IV; XI;XIII.	IX;XVII;XXIII;XXXIV; XXVII;XXVIII;XXIX;XXX; XXXI;XXXII;XXXIII; XXXIV;XXXVII.	XLVIII;XLIX;L; LI;LIV.
V. eschscholtzii........	I;II;III;IV; XI;XII;XIII.	XVII;XXIV;XXXV.	
V. stamineum..........	I;IV.	XV.	
V. fimbriatum..........	IV;XIII.	XVII;XXIV;XXV;XXVI.	
V. nigrum.............	IV.	XXVII.	
Amianthium muscaetoxicum.......	IV.		XLVII.
Zygadenus venenosus venenosus............		V;IX;XIV;XVI;XVII;XXIV; XXVIII;XXIX;XXXII.	
Z. venenosus gramineus.		V.	
Z. paniculatus........		XIV;XVI;XVII;XXIV;XXIX.	
Schoenocaulon officinale.		VI;VII;VIII;XVIII;XIX;XX; XXI;XXXIX;XL.	LII;LIII;LV;LVI.

The most significant generalization apparent from the data assembled herein is that the alkaloid studies to date strongly support the botanical classification made along classical lines. The fact that *Veratrum* and *Schoenocaulon* elaborate different alkaloids (table 4) is entirely in accord with the wide botanical separation between the two genera (see fig. 5). Assignment of the genus *Zygadenus* to a position intermediate between *Veratrum* and *Schoenocaulon* is supported by a number of considerations. Thus, while all members of the genus *Veratrum* studied to date elaborate low-oxygen jerveratrum alkaloids as well as high-oxygen ceveratrum alkaloids, *Zygadenus* and *Schoenocaulon* appear to elaborate only ceveratrum derivatives.   Careful paper chromatographic analysis of the mixed alkaloids from *Z. venenosus venenosus* in this laboratory (with S. D. Levine) indicated the absence of jerveratrum alkaloids.   *S. officinale* is one of the few plants of the tribe which has received extensive scrutiny in many laboratories; in no case has the presence of jerveratrum derivatives been reported.   It has been noted above that zygadenine and germine esters have been isolated both from *Veratrum* and *Zygadenus* species.   The relative proportion of zygadenine esters appears to be higher in *Zygadenus* species than in *Veratrum* species.   In view of the "hybrid" chemical nature of zygadenine and its esters, discussed above, the relatively high zygadenine ester concentration in *Zygadenus* represents another factor which supports the intermediate taxonomic position assigned to *Zygadenus*.   Apparently, no protoverine derivative has been isolated to date from *Zygadenus*, and one might be tempted to speculate as to the possible significance of the latter fact.   However, the exceedingly close relationship between the structures and physical properties of germine and protoverine derivatives lead us to feel that it is likely that protoverine derivatives may occur in *Zygadenus* and may be isolated as more intensive phytochemical studies are undertaken.

A second preliminary generalization which characterizes the data summarized in table 4 concerns the nature of the 5-carbon acids in the ceveratrum ester alkaloids of different plants.   Within the relatively small sampling of species and subspecies included in table 4, certain plants elaborate ester alkaloids containing only mono- or dihydroxymethylbutyrate residues, while others elaborate only angelate or tiglate esters.   Thus, *V. album album*, *V. viride* and *V. nigrum* have yielded ester alkaloids which contain 2-hydroxy-2-methylbutyrate and 2,3-dihydroxy-2-methylbutyrate residues but none with angelate or tiglate residues.[6]   On the other hand, *V. album grandiflorum*, *V. eschscholtzii*, *V. stamineum*, *V. fimbriatum* and *S. officinale* have yielded angelate and tiglate esters, but no esters of the hydroxylated methylbutyric acids.   It may be noteworthy that the former group consists of species which grow in areas adjacent to the Atlantic Ocean, whereas the latter group occurs in areas bordering the Pacific Ocean.   This information, if substantiated by further work, may prove useful in tracing the origin, evolution, and migration of the *Veratreae*.   Because of the small sampling examined to date, it must be emphasized that any generalization must be qualified, pending the accumulation of more data.   Nevertheless, it would seem worth while to further examine the possibility that the apparent difference noted is a significant factor of potential taxonomic value.   It is of incidental interest to note, in this connection, that the angelate ester, escholerine. (XXXV), has thus far been isolated only from *V. eschscholtzii*, and that angeloylzygudenine (XV) has thus far been isolated only from *V. stamineum*.   Also, *V. fimbriatum*, assigned a unique position in the botanical classificiation (fig. 5), elaborates two unique angelate esters, germanitrine (XXV) and germinitrine (XXVI, a monoangelate monotiglate).

Finally, the occurrence of jervine in *A. muscaetoxicum* may be noteworthy.   Classical taxonomy has assigned *Amianthium* to a position between *Veratrum* and *Zygadenus*, but a closer affinity to *Zygadenus* has generally been assumed.   The fact that *A. muscaetoxicum* elaborates jervine may suggest a closer proximity to *Veratrum* than heretofore believed.   Perhaps the structure elucidation of amianthine (XLVII) and other alkaloid constituents of *Amianthium* will provide additional taxonomically useful data.

---

[6]An early paper reported that "cevadic" acid ("doubtless identical with tiglic acid") had been detected among the products of alkaline saponification of the alkaloids of *V. viride* (23). However, the saponification involved heating with alcoholic potash for twenty-four hours and distillation with dilute sulfuric acid, conditions which would undoubtedly lead to dehydration of 2-hydroxy-2-methylbutyric acid with consequent formation of tiglic acid (cf. footnote 25 in 17b.)

This survey has collected available data on the occurrence and structures of the veratrum alkaloids and on the classical botanical taxonomy of the *Veratreae*. The data have been examined seeking possible generalizations concerning the relationship between alkaloid content and botanical taxonomy of the *Veratreae*. It is apparent that, although the quanity of information concerning alkaloid occurrence is exceedingly small, certain preliminary patterns may be emerging. It is hoped that further phytochemical studies of the *Veratreae* may yield results which may be significant for their potential contribution to the understanding of the course of plant evolution, as well as for their taxonomic utility.

Received 15 February 1961.

LITERATURE CITED

1. **Goodman, L. S.** and **A. Gilman.** 1955. The pharmacological basis of therapeutics, 2nd ed. The MacMillan Co., New York, pp. 747–754.
2. **Krayer, O.** 1958. Veratrum alkaloids, pp. 515–524. *In* **V. A. Drill,** Pharmacology in medicine, 2nd ed. McGraw-Hill Book Co., Inc., New York.
3. **Baker, P. D.** 1859. *Veratrum viride* in chorea and other convulsive diseases. Southern Med & Surg. **15:** 4.
4. **Meilman, E.** and **O. Krayer.** 1950. Clinical studies on veratrum alkaloids. I. Action of protoveratrine and veratridine in hypertension. Circulation **1:** 204.
5. **Hoobler, S. W., R. W. Corley, T. C. Kabza** and **H. G. Loyke.** 1952. Treatment of hypertension with oral protoveratrine. Ann. Int. Med. **37:** 465.
6. **Currens, J. H., G. S. Myers** and **P. D. White.** 1953. Use of protoveratrine in treatment of hypertensive vascular disease. Am. Heart J. **46:** 576.
7. **Kupchan, S. M.** 1956. Recent developments in the chemistry of the veratrum alkaloids. Baskerville Chem. J. **7:** 27–32.
8. **Klohs, M. W., F. Keller, S. Koster** and **W. Malesh.** 1952. Hypotensive alkaloids of *Veratrum eschscholtzii.* J. Am. Chem. Soc. **74:** 1871.
9. **Tsukamoto, T.** and **Y. Kishimoto.** 1954. Alkaloids of Japanese *Veratrum* species. I. Alkaloids from *Veratrum stamineum* Maxim. J. Pharm. Soc. Japan **74:** 729–731.
10. **Jacobs, W. A.** and **L. C. Craig.** 1945. The veratrine alkaloids. XXV. The alkaloids of *Veratrum viride.* J. Biol. Chem. **160:** 555–565.
11. **Saito, K.** 1940. Alkaloids of white hellebore. IV. Veratramine, a new alkaloid of white hellebore (*Veratrum grandiflorum* Loes. fil.). Bull. Chem. Soc. Japan **15:** 22–27.
12. **Shimizu, B.** 1955. The chemical composition of veratrum alkaloid preparation, Verabore (A preliminary report). Ann. Rept. Takamine Lab. **7:** 30–35; Chem. Abs. **50:** 15026.
13. **Suzuki, M., B. Shimizu, Y. Murase, R. Hayashi** and **N. Sanpei.** 1957. Isolation of of zygadenine ester from *Veratrum album* var. *oxysepalum* and *Veratrum album staminium* Maxim. J. Pharm. Soc. Japan **77:** 1050.
14. **Shimizu, B.** and **R. Hayashi.** 1959. Studies on the constituent of domestic *Veratrum* plants. II. Constituent of *Veratrum grandiflorum* Loesen. J. Pharm. Soc. Japan **79:** 615–618.
15. **Tsukamoto, T.** and **A. Yagi.** 1959. Alkaloids of Japanese *Veratrum* genus plants. III. Alkaloids from *Veratrum grandiflorum* (Maxim.) Loesener fil. J. Pharm. Soc. Japan **79:** 1102–1106.
16. **Kupchan, S. M.** and **N. Gruenfeld.** 1959. The hypotensive principles of cryptenamine, a *Veratrum viride* alkaloid preparation. J. Am. Pharm. Assoc., Sci. Ed. **48:** 727–730.
17. **Fried, J., H. L. White** and **O. Wintersteiner.** (a) 1949. Germidine and germitrine, two new ester alkaloids from *Veratrum viride.* J. Am. Chem. Soc. **71:** 3260–3261. (b) 1950. The hypotensive principles of *Veratrum viride.* J. Am. Chem. Soc. **72:** 4621–4630.
18. **Auterhoff, H.** and **F. Gunther.** 1955. Beiträge zur Kenntnis verschiedener Veratrum-Drogen und ihrer Alkaloide. 7-Mitteilung: Veratrin-Veratrum-Alkaloide. Arch. Pharm. **288:** 455–465.
19. **Poethke, W.** 1937. Die Alkaloide von *Veratrum album.* I. Mitteilung: Darstellung der Alkaloide und ihre Verteilung in Rhizomen, Wurzeln und Blattbasen.-germerin, ein neues Alkaloid von *Veratrum album.* Arch. Pharm. **275:** 357–379.
20. **Stoll, A.** and **E. Seebeck.** 1952. Veralbidine, a new alkaloid from *Veratrum album.* Science **115:** 678.
21. **Salzberger, G.** 1890. Über die Alkaloide der weissen Nieswurz (*Veratrum album*). Arch. Pharm. **228:** 462–483.
22. **Wright, C. R. A.** and **A. P. Luff.** 1879. XLVI—The alkaloids of the *Veratrums.* Part II. The alkaloids of *Veratrum album.* J. Chem. Soc. **35:** 405–420.
23. **Wright, C. R. A.** XLVII—The alkaloids of the *Veratrums.* Part III. The alkaloids of *Veratrum viride.* J. Chem. Soc. **35:** 421–426.
24. **Seiferle, E. J., I. B. Johns** and **C. H. Richardson.** 1942. Alkaloids of American hellebore and their toxicity to the American cockroach. J. Econ. Entomol. **35:** 35–44.

25. **Tomko, J., B. Dvorakova, S. Bauer** and **J. Mokry.** 1957. Alkaloids of *Veratrum album* var. *lobelianum.* II. Rubijervine and isorubijervine. Chem. zvesti **11:** 542–546; Chem. Abs. **52:** 8464.
26. **Poethke, W.** 1938. Amorphous alkaloids of *Veratrum album.* Sci. Pharm. **9:** 110–111; Chem. Abs. **33:** 807.
27. **Hegi, H. R.** and **H. Flück.** 1956. Alkaloids of the above-ground parts of *Veratrum album.* Pharm. Acta Helv. **31:** 428–447; Chem. Abs. **51:** 3087.
28. **Shimizu, B.** and **M. Suzuki.** 1959. Studies on the constituent of domestic *Veratrum* plants. I. Constituent of *Veratrum oxysepalum* Turcz. J. Pharm. Soc. Japan **79:**609–615.
29. **Klohs, M. W., R. Arons, M. D. Draper, F. Keller, S. Koster, W. Malesh** and **F. J. Petracek.** 1952. The isolation of neoprotoveratrine and protoveratrine from *Veratrum viride* Ait. J. Am. Chem. Soc. **74:** 5107–5110.
30. **Klohs, M. W., M. D. Draper, F. Keller, S. Koster, W. Malesh** and **F. J. Petracek.** 1953. The alkaloids of *Veratrum fimbriatum* Gray. J. Am. Chem. Soc. **75:** 4925—4927.
31. **Neuss, N.** 1953. A new alkaloid from *Amianthium muscaetoxicum* Gray. J. Am. Chem. Soc. **75:** 2772–2773.
32. **Saito, K., H. Suginome** and **M. Takaoka.** 1934. On the alkaloids of white hellebore. I. Isolation of constituent alkaloids. Bull. Chem. Soc. Japan **9:** 15–23.
33. **Tomko, J., B. Dvorakova, S. Bauer** and **J. Mokry.** 1956. Alkaloids in *Veratrum album* var. *lobelianum.* I. Isolation and separation. Chem. zvesti **10:** 642–648; Chem. Abs. **51:** 7655.
34. **Maj, J.** and **J. Hano.** 1956. *Veratrum lobelianum.* I. Jervine. Dissertationes Pharm. **8:** 9–18; Chem. Abs. **51:** 10766.
35. **Heyl, F. W., F. E. Hepner** and **S. K. Loy.** 1913. Zygadenine. The crystalline alkaloid of *Zygadenus intermedius.* J. Am. Chem. Soc. **35:** 258–262.
36. **Kupchan, S. M.** and **C. V. Deliwala.** 1952. Zygadenus alkaloids. I. Veratroyl zygadenine and vanilloyl zygadenine, two new hypotensive ester alkaloids from *Zygadenus venenosus.* J. Am. Chem. Soc. **74:** 2382.
37. **Kupchan, S. M., D. Lavie, C. V. Deliwala** and **B. Y. A. Andoh.** 1953. Schoenocaulon alkaloids. I. Active principles of *Schoenocaulon officinale.* Cevacine and protocevine. J. Am. Chem. Soc. **75:** 5519–5524.
38. **Auterhoff, H.** 1955. Sabadilla-Nebenalkaloide 8. Mitt. Veratrin-Veratrum-Alkaloide. Arch. Pharm. **288:** 549–560.
39. **Vejdelek, Z. J., K. Macek** and **B. Kakac.** 1956. Veratrum alkaloide. III. Über die inhaltsstoffe der varatrins. Collection Czechoslov. Chem. Commun. **21:** 995–1002.
40. **Klohs, M. W., M. D. Draper, F. Keller, W. Malesh** and **F. J. Petracek.** 1953. Alkaloids of *Veratrum eschscholtzii* Gray. I. The glycosides. J. Am. Chem. Soc. **75:** 2133–2135.
41. **Jacobs, W. A.** and **L. C. Craig.** 1944. The veratrine alkaloids. XXII. On pseudojervine and veratrosine, a companion glycoside in *Veratrum viride.* J. Biol. Chem. **155:** 565–572.
42. **Kupchan, S. M., D. Lavie** and **R. D. Zonis.** 1955. Zygadenus alkaloids. V. Active principles of *Zygadenus venenosus.* Zygacine. J. Am. Chem. Soc. **77:** 689–691.
43. **Kupchan, S. M., C. V. Deliwala** and **R. D. Zonis.** 1955. Zygadenus alkaloids. VI. Active principles of *Zygadenus paniculatus.* J. Am. Chem. Soc. **77:** 755.
44. **Shimizu, B.** 1958. Isolation of zygadenine ester from *Veratrum album* var. *grandiflorum* Loes. fil. J. Pharm. Soc. Japan. **78:** 443–444.
45. **Suzuki, M., Y. Murase, R. Hayashi** and **N. Sanpei.** 1959. Studies on the constituent of domestic *Veratrum* plants. III. Constituent of Veratrum album staminium Maxim. J. Pharm. Soc. Japan **79:** 619–623.
46. **Klohs, M. W., M. Draper, F. Keller, S. Koster, W. Malesh** and **F. J. Petracek.** 1954. Alkaloids of *Veratrum eschscholtzii* Gray. II. The ester alkaloids. J. Am. Chem. Soc. **76:** 1152–1153.
47. **Stoll, A.** and **E. Seebeck.** 1953. Veratroyl-zygadenin aus *Veratrum album.* Helv. Chim. Acta. **36:** 1570–1575.
48. **Poetsch, C. E.** and **L. M. Parks.** 1949. Sabadilla alkaloids. II. Alkaloidal components of the petroleum ether extract. J. Am. Pharm. Assoc., Sci. Ed. **38:** 525–530.
49. **Svoboda, G. R.** and **L. M. Parks.** 1954. Sabadilla alkaloids. IV. Separation of veratridine and cevadine by partition chromatography. J. Am. Pharm. Assoc., Sci. Ed. **43:** 584–588.
50. **Ringel, S. J.** 1956. A note on sabadilla alkaloids. Cevadine. J. Am. Pharm. Assoc., Sci. Ed. **45:** 433.
51. **Mitchner, H.** and **L. M. Parks.** 1956. Sabadilla alkaloids. VI. Separation of veratridine and cevadine by countercurrent distribution. pH vs. partition coefficients. J. Am. Pharm. Assoc., Sci. Ed. **45:** 549–555.
52. **Ikawa, M., R. J. Dicke, T. C. Allen** and **K. P. Link.** 1945. The principal alkaloids of sabadilla seed and their toxicity to *Musca domestica* L. J. Biol. Chem. **159:** 517–524.
53. **Bräuniger, H.** and **G. Borgwardt.** 1955. Trennung von Alkaloiden durch gegenstromverteilung. Pharmazie **10:** 591–596.
54. **Stuart, D. M.** and **L. M. Parks.** 1956. Sabadilla alkaloids. V. Vanilloylcevine. J. Am. Pharm. Assoc., Sci. Ed. **45:** 252–256.

55. **Nash, H. A.** and **R. M. Brooker.** 1953. Hypotensive alkaloids from *Veratrum album* protoveratrine A, protoveratrine B and germitetrine B. J. Am. Chem. Soc. **75**: 1942–1948.

56. **Kupchan, S. M.** and **C. V. Deliwala.** 1953. The isolation of crystalline hypotensive veratrum ester alkaloids by chromatography. J. Am. Chem. Soc. **75**: 4671–4672.

57. **Glen, W. L., G. S. Myers, R. Barber, P. Morozovitch** and **G. A. Grant.** 1952. Hypotensive alkaloids of *Veratrum album.* Nature **170**: 932.

58. **Myers, G. S., W. L. Glen, P. Morozovitch, R. Barber, G. Papineau-Couture** and **G. A. Grant.** 1956. Some hypotensive alkaloids from *Veratrum album.* J. Am. Chem. Soc. **78**: 1621–1624.

59. **Levine, J.** and **H. Fischbach.** 1957. Determination of protoveratrine. II. Separation of protoveratrines A and B from associated alkaloids. J. Am. Pharm. Assoc., Sci. Ed. **46**: 191–192.

60. **Saito, K.** and **H. Suginome.** 1936. On the alkaloids of white hellebore. II. Isolation of alkaloids from the so called resinous matters. Bull. Chem. Soc. Japan **11**: 168–171.

61. **Fried, J., P. Numerof** and **N. H. Coy.** 1952. Neogermitrine, a new ester alkaloid from *Veratrum viride.* J. Am. Chem. Soc. **74**: 3041–3046.

62. **Myers, G. S., P. Morozovitch, W. L. Glen, R. Barber, G. Papineau-Couture** and **G. A. Grant.** 1955. Some new hypotensive ester alkaloids from *Veratrum viride.* J. Am. Chem. Soc. **77**: 3348–3353.

63. **Kupchan, S. M.** and **C. V. Deliwala.** 1952. Zygadenus alkaloids. II. The occurrence of hypotensive germine esters in *Zygadenus venenosus.* J. Am. Chem. Soc. **74**: 3202.

64. **Kupchan, S. M.** and **C. V. Deliwala.** 1954. Zygadenus alkaloids. IV. Active principles of *Zygadenus venenosus.* Germine esters. J. Am. Chem. Soc. **76**: 5545–5547.

65. **Myers, G. S., W. L. Glen, P. Morozovitch, R. Barber** and **G. A. Grant.** 1952. Germbudine, isogermidine and veratetrine, three new hypotensive alkaloids from *Veratrum viride.* J. Am. Chem. Soc. **74**: 3198–3199.

66. **Poethke, W.** 1937. Alkaloids of *Veratrum album.* Pharm. Monatsh. **18**: 77.

67. **Stoll, A.** and **E. Seebeck.** 1952. Veratrobasine and geralbine, two new alkaloids isolated from *Veratrum album.* J. Am. Chem. Soc. **74**: 4728–4729.

68. **Stoll, A.** and **E. Seebeck.** 1953. Über protoveratrin A und protoveratrin B. Helv. Chim. Acta **36**: 718–723.

69. **Pijewska, L.** 1958. Isolation of protoveratrine from native species of *Veratrum album.* Acta Polon. Pharm. **15**: 219–221; Chem. Abs. **52**: 20893.

70. **Shimizu, B.** 1958. Isolation of zygadenillic acid δ-lactone from *Veratrum album* var. *oxysepalum.* J. Pharm. Soc: Japan **78**: 444.

71. **Shimizu, B.** 1959. Studies on the constituents of domestic *Veratrum* plants. IV. Isolation of zygadenillic acid δ-lactone from *Veratrum album* var. *oxysepalum.* J. Pharm. Soc. Japan **79**: 993–997.

72. **Cionga, E.** and **V. Cucu.** 1957. Investigations·on alkaloids of *Veratrum.* I. Synaine, verine and rubiverine—three new alkaloids isolated from *Veratrum album.* Acta Polon. Pharm. **14**: 73–76; Chem. Abs. **52**: 12882.

73. **Auterhoff, H.** and **H. Möhrle.** 1958. Über Neosabadin-ein neues Sabadilla-Alkamin. Arch. Pharm. **291**: 299–298.

74. **Merck, E.** 1891. Neue Alkaloide aus Sabadilla samen. Arch. Pharm. **229**: 164–169.

75. **Hennig, A., T. Higuchi** and **L. M. Parks.** 1951. Sabadilla alkaloids. III. Chromatographic separation of the water soluble fraction. Isolation of a new crystalline alkaloid, sabatine. J. Am. Pharm. Assoc., Sci. Ed. **40**: 168–172.

76. **Klohs, M. W., M. D. Draper, F. Keller, W. Malesh** and **F. J. Petracek.** 1953. The isolation of desacetylneoprotoveratrine from *Veratrum viride* Ait. J. Am. Chem. Soc. **75**: 3595–3596.

77. **Allen, T. C., R. J. Dicke** and **H. H. Harris.** 1944. Sabadilla, *Schoenocaulon* spp., with reference to its toxicity to houseflies. J. Econ. Entomol. **37**: 400–408.

78. **Cionga, E.** and **V. Cucu.** 1958. Veratrum alkaloids. III. Presence of synaine, verine and rubiverine in roots and rhizomes of *Veratrum album.* Ann. Pharm. franc. **16**: 511–517; Chem. Abs. **53**: 5590.

79. **Fieser, L. F.** and **M. Fieser.** 1959. Steroids. Reinhold Publishing Corp., New York. pp. 867–895.

80. **Morgan, K. J.** and **J. A. Barltrop.** 1958. Veratrum alkaloids. Quart. Rev. **12**: 34–60.

81. **Jeger, O.** and **V. Prelog.** 1960. Steroid alkaloids: Veratrum group, pp. 363–417. *In* R. H. F. Manske, The alkaloids, vol. VII, Academic Press Inc., New York.

82. **Kupchan, S. M.** 1961. Hypotensive veratrum ester alkaloids. J. Pharm. Sci., accepted for publication.

83. **Barton, D. H. R.** and **J. F. Eastham.** 1953. Steroidal alkaloids. Part I. The functional groups of cevine. J. Chem. Soc. 424–428.

84. **Kupchan, S. M., C. I. Ayres, M. Neeman, R. H. Hensler, T. Masamune** and **S. Rajagopalan.** 1960. Veratrum alkaloids. XXXVIII. The structure and configuration cf protoverine. J. Am. Chem. Soc. **82**: 2242–2251.

85. **Kupchan, S. M.** 1959. Veratrum alkaloids. XXX. The structure and configuration of zygadenine. J. Am. Chem. Soc. **81**: 1925–1928.

86. **Kupchan, S. M.** and **D. Lavie.** 1955. Schoenocaulon alkaloids. III. The bismuth oxide oxidation of veracevine, cevagenine and cevine. J. Am. Chem. Soc. **77:** 683–686.
87. **Dalla Torre, C. G. de** and **H. Harms.** 1900–1907. *Genera siphonogamarum.* W. Engelmann, Leipzig, pp. 60–61.
88. **Engler, A.** and **K. Prantl.** 1930. *Melanthioideae,* in die natürlichen pflanzenfamilien. W. Engelmann. Leipzig. **15a:** 260–266.
89. **Kuzneva, O. I.** 1935. *Veratreae,* p. 733. *In* **Komarov, V. L.** [ed.], Flora U. R. S. S. Bot. Inst., Acad. Nauk., Leningrad **4:** 1–2; 6–14; tab. 1; Addend. 3.
90. **Willis, J. C.** 1955. A dictionary of the flowering plants, 6th ed. Univ. Press, Cambridge, England.
91. **Gates, R. R.** 1918. A systematic study of the North American *Melanthaceae.* J. Linnean Soc. London, Botany **44:** 131–172.
92. **Small, J. K.** 1933. Manual of the southeastern flora. Science Press Printing Co., Lancaster, Pa., pp. 273–280.
93. **Baker, J. G.** 1879 (1880). Synopsis of the *Colchicaceae* and aberrant tribes of the *Liliaceae.* J. Linnean Soc. London, Botany **17:** 405–413; 469–485.
94. **Zimmerman, J. H.** 1958. A monograph of *Veratrum.* Ph.D. Thesis. University of Wisconsin, Madison.
95. **Nakai, T.** 1937. Japanese species of *Veratrum.* J. Jap. Bot. **13:** 631–645; 701–713.
96. **Kelsey, H. P.** and **W. A. Dayton.** 1942. Standardized plant names. 2nd ed. J. Horace McFarland Co., Harrisburg, Pa.
97. **Loesener, O.** 1926. Studien über die gattung *Veratrum* und ihre verbreitung. Verh. Bot. Vereins. Prov. Bradenburg **68:** 105–166.
98. **Loesener, O.** 1927–1928. Übersicht über die arten der gattung *Veratrum.* Fedde's Repert. Spec. Nov. Reg. Veg. **24:** 61–72; **25:** 1–10.
99. **Hegi, G.** 1939. Illustrierte flora von Mittel-Europa, vol. 2. Rev. ed. C. Hanser, München. pp. 241–244.
100. **Dayton, W. A.** 1960. Notes on western range forbs: *Equisetaceae* through *Fumariaceae.* U. S. Dept. Agr. Forest Serv. Agric. Handb. 161. U. S. Govt. Printing Office, Washington. pp. 42–55.
101. **Youngken, H. W.** 1952. A pharmacognostical study of roots of different species of *Veratrum.* J. Am. Pharm. Assoc., Sci. Ed. **41:** 356–361.
102. **Hultén, E.** 1927 (1928). Flora Kamtchatka. K. Svenska Vetenskapsakad. Handl. Stockholm. Ser. 3. **5:** 233–235.
103. **Hultén, E.** 1937. Outline of the history of Arctic and boreal biota during the quaternary period. Bokförlags Aktiebolaget Thule, Stockholm. pp. 111–113.
104. **Miyabe, K.** and **Y. Kudo.** 1932. Flora of Hokkaido and Saghalien. J. Fac. Agr. Hokkaido Imp. Univ. **26:** 310–313.
105. **Ohwi, J.** 1953. Flora of Japan. Shibundo, Tokyo. pp. 286–288.
106. **Makino, T.** 1951. Illustrated flora of Japan, rev. ed. The Hokuryukan Co., Tokyo. pp. 756–757.
107. **Nakai, T.** 1937. *Species generis veratri in regions manshurico-koreano sponte nascentes.* Rep. Inst. Sci. Res. Manchouko **1:** 325–344; XI pl.
108. **Maximowicz, C. J.** 1859. *Primitiae florae amurensis.* Mem. Acad. Imp. Sci. St. Petersburg **9:** 289–290.
109. **Boivin, B.** 1948. Veratrum. Naturaliste Can. **75:** 224–226; 1960. **87:** 48.
110. **Forbes, F. B.** and **W. B. Hemsley.** 1905. Enumeration of the plants known from China. Part 3. J. Linnean Soc. London, Botany **36:** 147–148.
111. **Hultén, E.** 1937. Flora of the Aleutian Islands. Bokförlags Aktiebolaget Thule, Stockholm. p. 37, 43, 130.
112. **Hultén, E.** 1942. Flora of Alaska and Yukon. C. W. K. Gleerup, Lund, Sweden. **3:** 449–452; maps pp. 357–359.
113. **Hultén, E.** 1950. Atlas över växternas utbredning i norden. Generalstabens litografiska anstalts förlag, Stockholm. Map p. 120.
114. **Anderson, J. P.** Flora of Alaska. Iowa State Univ. Press, Ames, Ia., pp. 152–153.
115. **Komarov, V. L.** and **E. N. Klobukova-Alisova.** 1931. Key for the plants of the far eastern region, U. S. S. R. Acad. Sci., U. S. S. R., Leningrad **1:** 356–361; tab. 110.
116. **Steward, A. N.** 1958. Manual of vascular plants of the lower Yangtze valley. (Oregon State College, Corvallis, Ore.) International Printing Co., Tokyo. pp. 510–512.
117. **Small, J. K.** 1903. Flora of the southeastern United States. Pub. by the author; N. Y. Botanical Garden. pp. 248–253.
118. **Fernald, M. L.** 1950. Gray's manual of botany, 8th ed. American Book Co., New York. pp. 423–428.
119. **Rydberg, P. A.** 1932. Flora of the prairies and plains. (N. Y. Botanical Garden.) Science Press Printing Co., Lancaster, Pa. pp. 202–205.
120. **Taylor, C. A.** 1956. The culture of false hellebore, and alkaloid yields of *Veratrum fimbriatum.* Econ. Botany **10:** 155–173.
121. **Gleason, H. A.** 1952. The new Britton and Brown illustrated flora of the northeastern United States and adjacent Canada, vol. 1. Lancaster Press, Lancaster, Pa. pp. 407–411.

122. **St. John, H.** 1956. Flora of southeastern Washington and adjacent Idaho. Rev. ed. Students Book Corp., Pullman, Wash. pp. 93–94.
123. **Youngken, H. W.** 1953. Studies on *Veratrum*. II. J. Am. Pharm. Assoc., Sci. Ed. **42**: 39–45.
124. **Heller, A. A.** 1904–1905. The western *Veratrums*. Muhlenbergia **1**: 39: 119–125.
125. **Rydberg, P. A.** 1917. Flora of the Rocky Mountains and adjacent plains. Reprinted 1954 by Hafner Publishing Co., New York. pp. 146–149.
126. **Rydberg, P. A.** 1900. The Rocky Mountain species of *Melanthaceae*. Bull. Torr. Bot. Club **27**: 528–538; 650.
127. **Piper, C. V.** 1906. Flora of the state of Washington. Contr. U. S. Nat. Herb., U. S. Govt. Printing Office, Washington. **11**: 196–198.
128. **Jepson, W. L.** 1922. A flora of California, vol. 1(6). Assoc. Students Store, University of California, Berkeley. pp. 263–266.
129. **Jepson, W. L.** 1925. A manual of the flowering plants of California. Assoc. Students Store, University of California, Berkeley. pp. 211–213.
130. **Peck, M. E.** 1941. A manual of the higher plants of Oregon. Binfords and Mort. Portland, Ore. pp. 189–191.
131. **U. S. Forest Service.** 1937. Range plant handbook. U. S. Dept. Agr. Supt. of Documents, Washington. p. W201, W209, W213.
132. **Harrington, H. D.** 1954. Manual of the plants of Colorado. Sage Books, Denver, Colo. pp. 156–157.
133. **Davis, R. J.** 1952. Flora of Idaho. W. C. Brown, Dubuque, Iowa. pp. 198–201.
134. **Abrams, L.** 1923. Illustrated flora of the pacific states. University Press, Stanford, Calif. **1**: 374–379.
135. **Heller, A. A.** 1899. *Veratrum caudatum*. Bull. Torr. Botan. Club. **26**: 588.
136. **Train, P., J. R. Henrichs** and **W. A. Archer.** 1941. Medicinal uses of plants by the Indian tribes of Nevada. Contr. Flora Nevada, U. S. Dept. Agr., Washington. **33**: (3) 147–150.
137. **Tidestrom, I.** and **Sister T. Kittell.** 1941. Flora of Arizona and New Mexico. Catholic Univ. Press, Washington. p. 739.
138. **Kearney, T. H.** and **R. H. Peebles.** 1942. Flowering plants and ferns of Arizona. U. S. Dept. Agr. Misc. Pub. 423, U. S. Govt. Printing Office, Washington. pp. 187–188.—1951. Arizona flora. Univ. of California Press, Berkeley. pp. 176–177.
139. **Conzatti, C.** 1947. *Flora taxonomica Mexicana*. Soc. Mex. Hist. Nat., Mexico City. **2**: 60–63.
140. **Martínez, M.** 1957. Una especie de *Veratrum* en Durango. Bol. Soc. Bot. Mex. **20**: 14–15.
141. **Satake, Y.** 1942. *Veratrum stamineum* var. *micranthum*. J. Jap. Bot. **18**: 661.
142. **Nakai, T.** 1938. *Veratrum nipponicum*. J. Jap. Bot. **14**: 741.
143. **Masamune, G.** 1932. *Veratrum*. J. Soc. Trop. Agric. **4**: 193–194; 309.
144. **Wang, F. T.** and **T. Tang.** 1949. *Veratrum micranthum*. Contr. Inst. Bot. Nat. Acad. Peiping. (Reimpr.) **6**: 215.
145. **Li, Hui-Lin.** 1952. Floristic relationships between eastern Asia and eastern North America. Trans. Am. Phil. Soc. **42**: 371–429.
146. **Loesener, O.** *Veratrum* identifications. In Handel-Mazzetti, H. 1936–1937. *Symbolae Sinicae*. J. Springer, Wien. **7**: 1193.
147. **Dean, C. C.** 1940. Flora of Indiana. Wm. B. Burford, Indianapolis. pp. 303–308.
148. **Rendle, A. B.** 1938. *Veratrum wilsonii*. Curtis Bot. Mag., London. **147**:pl. 8925.
149. **Stevens, W. C.** 1948. Kansas wild flowers. Univ. Kansas Press, Lawrence. pp. 37–41.
150. **Fernald, M. L.** 1946. *Stenanthium* in the eastern United States. Rhodora **48**: 148–152; pl. 1037–1041.
151. **Suksdorf, W. N.** 1923. *Stenanthium rhombipetalum*. Werdenda **1**: 6.
152. **Preece, S. J., Jr.** 1956. A cytotaxonomic study of the genus *Zigadenus*. Ph.D. thesis, State College of Washington, Pullman.
153. **Rydberg, P. A.** 1903. Some generic segregations. Bull. Torr. Botan. Club. **30**: 271–273; pl. 13.
154. **Brinker, R. R.** 1942. Monograph of *Schoenocaulon*. Ann. Missouri Botan. Garden **29**: 287–315.
155. **Miller, E. W.** 1930. A preliminary note on the cytology of the *Melanthioideae* section of the *Liliaceae*. Proc. Univ. Durham Phil. Soc. **8**: 261–274.
156. **Matsuura, H.** and **T. Suto.** 1935. Contribution to the idiogram study in phanerogamous plants. J. Fac. Sci. Hokkaido Univ., Ser V. **5**: 33–75.
157. **Sato, D.** 1942. Karyotype alteration and phylogeny in the *Liliaceae* and allied families. J. Jap. Bot. **12**: 57–161.
158. **Lanjouw, J.** and **F. A. Stafleu.** 1959. *Index herbariorum*, part 1. Regn. Veg. **15**. 4th ed. Internat. Bur. Plant Tax. and Nomen., Utrecht.
159. **Erdtman, H.** 1956. Organic chemistry and conifer taxonomy. *In* **A. Todd**, Perspectives in organic chemistry. Interscience Publishers, Inc., New York. pp. 453–494.

The application of immunological methods to the taxonomy of species within the genus *Solanum*

By P. G. H. Gell*, J. G. Hawkes† and S. T. C. Wright*

* *Department of Experimental Pathology, University of Birmingham*
† *Department of Botany, University of Birmingham*

(*Communicated by K. Mather, F.R.S.—Received* 24 *March* 1959)

[Plates 9 to 12]

The application of immunological analysis to plant taxonomy has been made practicable by the development of gel-diffusion methods, both by the Elek-Ouchterlony technique and by the more recent immuno-electrophoretic technique of Grabar & Williams. By these means individual proteins in plant extracts may be differentiated and a number of components in the extracts compared individually with those from related species. A modification of these methods has been applied to the investigation of the genus *Solanum*, with particular reference to the inter-relationships of certain Mexican species of potato with one another and with *S. tuberosum*, the domestic potato.

Antisera were raised in rabbits to crude saps from *S. tuberosum* and *S. ehrenbergii* (a Mexican species), using a combination of Freund's adjuvant technique with courses of intravenous injections. With both antisera well-marked precipitation lines developed against extracts from all the thirty-eight species examined; and by comparison of the direct 'line-spectra' and those obtained after cross-absorption of an antiserum, it was possible to divide the species into groups. The results show in their main outline a remarkably close agreement with those obtained from the classical taxonomic methods, and with the general conclusions arrived at from cytological and genetical studies.

The value and the limitations of these immunological techniques as applied to taxonomic studies are discussed.

Introduction

Serological methods were systematically used in plant taxonomy first by Metz and his school, and later by a few other groups of workers who were stimulated by his results, at a time when studies on the gross morphology, anatomy and geographical distribution of the families and orders of flowering plants had been found to be, by themselves, insufficient to establish evolutionary relationships. This work up to 1937 has been fully reviewed by Chester (1937). That it was largely unsuccessful in contributing to the subject was due to two factors: first, to the comparatively crude serological methods available at that time, and to a sometimes uncritical use even of these; and secondly, to the absence of any third criterion for deciding between the results of serological and morphological-anatomical methods, when there was disagreement between them. Taxonomists naturally, and rightly, tended to prefer tried and classical methods of study to the novel one of relying on the antibody-forming mechanism of a mammal to make their distinctions for them. The great advantage of the serological method is its power of distinguishing antigenic substances which are indistinguishable by chemical means. An antiserum, or rather the rabbit antibody-forming mechanism, is certainly capable of distinguishing between proteins of similar anatomical source derived from different species within a single genus as, for instance, between the various somatic and flagellar antigens of the bacilli of the genus *Salmonella*—the basis for their classification in the 'Kauffman-White' scheme (Wilson & Miles 1946)—or, among higher animals, between the serum proteins of horses, mules and asses.

However, when considering the use of such phenomena for purposes of taxonomy, various points have to be borne in mind. First, an antibody against a given protein derived from one species in a group may either precipitate with a protein derived from another species in that group, in a way which is qualitatively and quantitatively identical, which is *prima facie* evidence that the two proteins are actually themselves identical; or it may 'cross-react', that is, precipitation may occur, but more antibody will be required to produce a given amount of precipitate, and the inter-reaction may be less efficient in other ways. The currently accepted explanation for this is that the population of antibody molecules is not homogeneous, some being capable of combining only with the 'homologous' protein (the one used for the original immunization of the rabbit), while some can also combine with a similar but not identical protein. When antisera which contain antibodies against a number of unrelated antigens are used 'cross-reactions' of this type cannot readily be distinguished from 'homologous' reactions; and in the work described below the analysis has been based upon the presence or absence of any reaction at all, no attempt being made to measure the amount of precipitate produced.

There is, in fact, a serious risk of error if taxonomic conclusions are based upon measurements of the total bulk of the precipitate produced when crude plant extracts, containing many different antigenic proteins, react with their corresponding antisera. It has often been assumed that, if an antiserum against an extract from species A gives more precipitate with an extract from species B than with one from species C, then species B must be more closely 'related', in an evolutionary sense, to A than C is. This is an unsafe assumption; it may well be the case that, say, 50 % of the maximal precipitate with A, 90 % of that with B, and 10 % of that with C may be due to a single identical protein, while C may contain three or four other proteins which are present in A and absent from B, being there represented by other, non-cross-reacting substances. If this were so A and C might reasonably be considered the more closely related species, their real similarity being obscured by the overriding quantitative effect of the shared antigen in the total reaction.

It is thus of some importance to be able to distinguish between different antigens in our extracts; and the more antigens we can differentiate, the more data for determining relationship we have, the firmer our conclusions. For this it is necessary to use serological methods which can distinguish between different antigen-antibody systems in the same total reaction. Such methods have recently been developed through the use of gels in place of liquid media, in which to bring about precipitation.

These methods, which in the present studies are applied for the first time to higher plant material (Gell, Hawkes & Wright 1956) depend on the fact that different antigen-antibody systems in a mixture form separate bands of precipitate when allowed to diffuse towards one another in a thin sheet of agar gel. Thus, a characteristic 'spectrum' of precipitin lines or bands is formed for every species or group of species, and further, one species may be directly compared with another by observing how many of these lines join up when protein extracts of each are placed side by side and allowed to diffuse towards a common antiserum. One can then make a comparison by noting how many antigens common to a pair or group of species are present, and how many antigens are not common to the pair or group. Further information may be obtained by noting the density of individual lines.

Where there are a number of identical proteins shared among a group of species, these common lines may overlie and obscure those more useful lines by which the differences between the species can be analyzed. A standard serological technique for overcoming this difficulty is to 'absorb' the antiserum, that is to mix it with an appropriate amount of the extract derived from a species which shows the lines which all have in common, and discard the resulting precipitated antigen-antibody complex. The result is that the common and non-informative lines are eliminated. If the absorption has been efficient the 'absorbed' antiserum does not react at all with the species supplying the extract used for 'absorption', but reacts in varying degrees with species more closely related to the homologous one.

Taxonomic conclusions reached in this way can be compared with those obtained by classical methods; and when they agree they may serve to reinforce one another. If, however, the results from the two kinds of investigation disagree (as was sometimes the case with the earlier serological work mentioned above) and no further techniques are available we clearly arrive at an *impasse*. When dealing with the higher taxonomic categories such as families and orders there is indeed no further method of deciding which of two conflicting results is correct, since cytogenetical methods are ruled out owing to the presence of complete sterility barriers, whilst palaeontological evidence is almost invariably lacking where it is required most. When, however, we work at the species level, we can further cross-check our results by bringing in data on species crossability, fertility of F_1 and F_2 hybrids, chromosome pairing in hybrids, and other tests of this kind. Of recent years it has been customary to use these criteria at the species level, when at least some of the species are interfertile. Such studies have progressed quite satisfactorily in the tuber-bearing solanums, where owing to their established or prospective value as sources of genes conferring resistance to potato diseases, a large number of species has been under observation in the living state by plant breeders, geneticists and cytologists. In consequence, we possess a considerable body of data, in addition to morphological and phytogeographical information, which can be used for cross-checking results gained from serological techniques. However, until the work dealt with here was started there had been no serological studies on *Solanum* species.

The results described below obtained by these methods show in their main outlines a remarkably close agreement not only with those obtained from the classical taxonomic methods but also with the general conclusions arrived at from cytogenetical studies. There are, nevertheless, certain discrepancies, the significance of which will be discussed later: and there are still considerable numbers of species, notably all those from South America, on whose detailed inter-relationships the gel-diffusion techniques, as at present used, throw little light, since the antisera used by us were unable to distinguish between them.

MATERIALS AND METHODS

(a) *Botanical—tuber collection and propagation*

The potato tubers used in the present work were derived from plants grown at Birmingham in a glasshouse whose opening vents and doors were covered with nylon gauze to prevent the entrance of virus-transmitting insects. As an additional precaution against infection by viruses weekly nicotine fumigations were made. All plants were raised in 7 in. pots under standard conditions in sterilized John Innes compost.

The plants were harvested in September to October when fully mature, the normal practice being to allow the pots to dry off thoroughly under the greenhouse staging after the haulms had withered. It should be mentioned here that the species used in this work mature in the 12 to 13 hour days of tropical latitudes and will not form tubers under the longer 16 to 18 hour summer days in England. They continue to grow vegetatively until September, when the natural day length becomes short enough for tuber formation to begin. When grown out of doors the temperatures are then too low for proper tuberization, and consequently the yields obtained are very low indeed. Under glass, however, where the thermostatically controlled electric heaters prevent the temperature from falling below 50 °F, the heat is sufficient for good yields of apparently normal tubers. Care was taken to delay planting of the tubers until May, so that the growing season of 4 to 5 months was roughly similar to that obtaining under natural conditions in Mexico. Thus in respect of photo-period, temperature and growing season the plants were grown under conditions not very dissimilar to those to which they were accustomed in their native country.

The Mexican potato material used in the present work is listed in table 1 and its provenance is shown in the Appendix (p. 382). Since it is not our intention in the present work to give detailed information on the South American potato material in view of the as yet inconclusive nature of the results we merely list the species examined (see table 2). Of the Mexican potatoes some lines were collected in the form of tubers in 1949 and have been propagated vegetatively from then on. Others were collected in the form of seed and a number of seedlings raised at a later date. Such lines are shown here by means of a stroke '/' followed by a figure which respresents the seedling number. Almost all the material was collected by one of us (J.G.H.) for the Commonwealth Potato Collection, formerly housed at Cambridge and now situated at the John Innes Horticultural Institution, Bayfordbury, Hertfordshire. Duplicates of these lines have been grown in Birmingham since 1952, and it was on this latter material that the present series of tests were made. Some few samples, of which the accession number is prefixed by the letter 'H', represent part of the Birmingham collection which is not duplicated in the Bayfordbury series.

The taxonomy of the species dealt with follows the treatment proposed by Hawkes (1956, 1958) in which the tuber-bearing solanums are divided into seventeen series, according to their presumed affinities. Only the Mexican species, belonging to seven series, are dealt with here, together with the originally South

American cultivated species *S. tuberosum*. The species are referred to in the plates and diagrams, for reasons of space, by a standard three-letter code abbreviation (see table 1).

TABLE 1. MEXICAN POTATO SPECIES TESTED

series	name	code	accession no.
III. Morelliformia	*S. morelliforme*	*MOR*	2262
IV. Bulbocastana	*S. bulbocastanum*	*BUL*	2242
			2281
V. Cardiophylla	*S. cardiophyllum*	*CPH*	2244
			2269
			2271
			2283
	S. ehrenbergii	*EHR*	2297
			2299
			2302
			2304
			2309
	S. sambucinum	*SMB*	2312
			2313/1
VI. Pinnatisecta	*S. pinnatisectum*	*PIN*	2300
	S. jamesii	*JAM*	1394
XII. Demissa	*S. demissum*	*DEM*	2095
			2449
	S. guerreroense	*GRR*	2475
	S. semidemissum	*SEM*	2
	S. spectabile	*SPT*	2433
			H 75/2
			H 77/1
	S. verrucosum	*VER*	2246
			2247
XIII. Longipedicellata	*S. polytrichon*	*PLT*	2305
			2310
			2311
			2450
	S. stoloniferum	*STO*	2282/2
			2331
			9/1
			9/2
XIV. Polyadenia	*S. polyadenium*	*POL*	2408
			2409

TABLE 2. SOUTH AMERICAN POTATO SPECIES TESTED

S. acaule	*S. microdontum*
S. bukasovii	*S. neohawekesii*
S. canasense	*S. neoweberbauerii*
S. capsicibaccatum	*S. oplocense*
S. chacoense	*S. raphanifolium*
S. chaucha	*S. sanctae-rosae*
S. gourlayi	*S. simplicifolium*
S. infundibuliforme	*S. tarijense*
S. lapazense	*S. toralapanum*
S. macolae	*S. tuberosum* subsp. *andigena*
S. megistacrolobum	*S. vernei*

(b) Biochemical

(i) Protein extraction of tubers

Thin slices of carefully washed tubers of each species were soaked in sodium hydrosulphite (7 g/l.) for 30 min and then rinsed for a similar time in distilled water. The juice was expressed by crushing the slices, supported within folded strips of moist calico, through stainless-steel rollers. After centrifugation to clarify (15000 g for 20 min), the extracts were stored at 2 °C prior to protein-nitrogen determination.

(ii) Protein-nitrogen estimation and standardization of the extracts

Total nitrogen was estimated by the micro-Kjeldahl technique of Ma & Zuazaga (1942). Non-protein-nitrogen was estimated after precipitation of the protein by the addition of an equal volume of 20 % trichloroacetic acid (w/v). The standard conversion factor of 6·25 was adopted to calculate the protein concentration.

For three species (*S. morelliforme*, *S. bulbocastanum* and *S. guerreroense*) there was insufficient extract to carry out a micro-Kjeldahl protein estimation and therefore the Biuret test was resorted to, using the method described by Wolfson, Cohn, Calvary & Ichiba (1948). The protein concentration of the extracts was obtained from a standard curve based on dilutions of a *S. tuberosum* extract of known protein content.

Before comparing the crude juices serologically the protein concentration, which varied from 0·13 to 1·25 %, was adjusted to approximately 0·5 %, either by diluting with distilled water or concentrating by freeze drying. The extracts were stored until required at 2 °C with sodium azide as a preservative.

(c) Serological

(i) Preparation of antisera

An 'adjuvant' emulsion (of the kind extensively used to improve antibody responses: cf. Freund & Bonanto 1944) was prepared by grinding together in a mortar two parts of light paraffin containing 1 % of killed moist tubercle bacilli, one part of Eucerin (Herts Pharmaceuticals Ltd.) and one part of crude tuber extract (protein concentration *ca.* 1 %). One millilitre of this mixture was injected into each thigh of a pair of sandy-lop rabbits three times, at weekly intervals. After 2 weeks they were given four intravenous injections of the crude extract (not the emulsion), two of 1 ml. and two of 2 ml. at daily intervals. Five days after the last of these injections they were bled from the ear, 60 to 80 ml. of blood being taken. The blood was allowed to clot and the resulting serum centrifuged to clear.

A second course of intravenous injections of crude extracts was given after an interval of 4 months. These injections were given every second day, two of 1 ml., two of 2 ml. and two of 5 ml. After a further 5 days the animals were again bled from the ear, and the serum prepared as before.

Both these batches of antisera were satisfactory, the latter one being very strong indeed.

(ii) *Absorption of antisera*

The absorption was carried out by adding a 0·5 % protein solution to an equal volume of antiserum and incubating at 37 °C for 4 h; the precipitate was removed by centrifugation and the absorbed antiserum tested with the same antigen solution, to ensure that the antibodies reacting with it had been completely removed. If necessary more protein was added and the procedure repeated.

(iii) *Gel-diffusion technique*

The horizontal gel-diffusion technique evolved by Ouchterlony (1948) and Elek (1948) was used in a modified form as described below for analyzing the proteins of the potato species.

New Zealand agar (0·6 %; w/v) in veronal buffer, pH 8·6 (sodium diethyl-barbiturate, 0·1 M; diethylbarbituric acid, 0·02 M), with sodium azide (1:10000) as a preservative was poured to a depth of 2 mm on a photographic emulsion-free '$\frac{1}{2}$ plate' (6$\frac{1}{2}$ in. × 4$\frac{3}{4}$ in.) glass sheet held in a Perspex frame.

Using a Perspex mask, to ensure even and standard spacing, sixteen cups were cut in the agar with a $\frac{3}{16}$ in. cork borer, arranged in two rows of eight on opposite sides of a central trough 5 mm wide. The tuber extracts (0·15 ml.) were placed in the cups and undiluted antiserum (0·1 ml. per 1 cm length of trough) was added to the trough. (The tuber extracts (antigen) were separated from the antiserum (antibody) by 7 mm of agar and from each other by 6 mm of agar.) The plate was transferred to a water-saturated atmosphere and incubated at 25 °C for 42 h (for *S. ehrenbergii* antiserum), or 37 °C for 18 h (for *S. tuberosum* antiserum). The times and temperatures mentioned here were found to give the most sharply defined precipitin lines in each case. During this time the reagents diffused towards one another, and lines of precipitation formed, each line corresponding to an antigen-antibody system. The precipitin lines were photographed by reflected light for record purposes.

(iv) *Immuno-electrophoretic technique*

The technique of Grabar & Williams (1953) was modified as described below to suit our requirements.

Sheets of buffered agar were prepared as before except that they were on 3$\frac{1}{4}$ in. square lantern slides held in Perspex frames. Contact was made with the electrolyte by means of two strips of Whatman No. 4 filter-paper which were clamped on opposite sides, between the lantern slide and the Perspex frame, prior to pouring on the agar.

The electrolyte (veronal buffer pH 8·6 as above) was contained in a Perspex box which was divided into five compartments (figure 5, plate 9). The agar plates were placed so that they bridged the central compartment, their filter-paper connecting strips dipping into the adjoining electrolyte reservoirs. These two reservoirs were connected with the two outermost, containing the platinum electrodes, by agar bridges, and with each other by a piece of capillary tube to keep the fluid levels equal. The four reservoirs shared 2·5 l. of buffer.

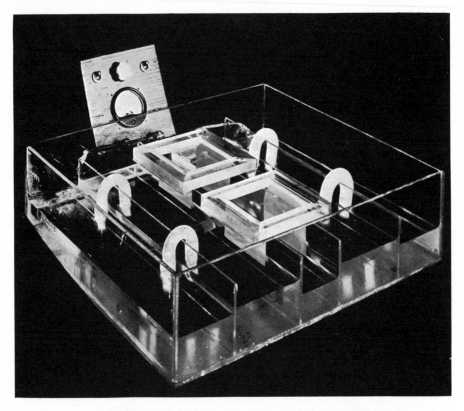

FIGURE 5. Immuno-electrophoresis apparatus.

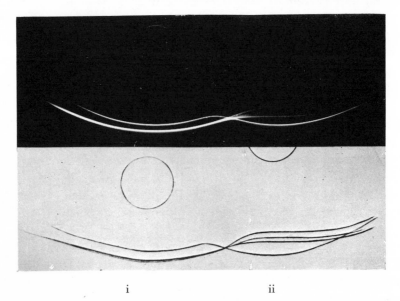

i   ii

FIGURE 6. *S. tuberosum* tuber extract reacting with homologous antiserum: (i) without electrophoresis the antigen shows only two lines of precipitate; (ii) after electrophoresis the relative positions of the lines have changed and one of them has split into three.

4 lines	2 lines	1 line
Series IV	Series V	Series III
BUL	*CPH*	*MOR*
Series XII	*SMB*	
VER	*EHR*	
SEM	Series VI	
DEM	*JAM*	
GRR	*PIN*	
SPT		
Series XIII		
PLT		
STO		
Series XIV		
POL		
Series XVII		
TUB		

FIGURE 7. Separation of the species into three divisions with *S. tuberosum* antiserum.

BUL = *S. bulbocastanum*   *POL* = *S. polyadenium*
VER = *S. verrucosum*   *TUB* = *S. tuberosum*
SEM = *S. semidemissum*   *CPH* = *S. cardiophyllum*
DEM = *S. demissum*   *SMB* = *S. sambucinum*
GRR = *S. guerreroense*   *EHR* = *S. ehrenbergii*
SPT = *S. spectabile*   *JAM* = *S. jamesii*
PLT = *S. polytrichon*   *PIN* = *S. pinnatisectum*
STO = *S. stoloniferum*   *MOR* = *S. morelliforme*

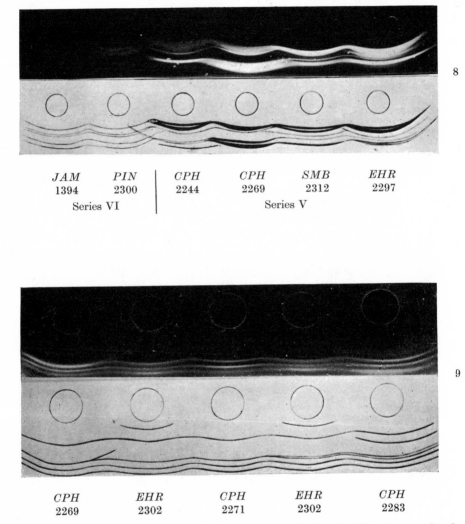

8

JAM	PIN	CPH	CPH	SMB	EHR
1394	2300	2244	2269	2312	2297

Series VI | Series V

9

CPH	EHR	CPH	EHR	CPH
2269	2302	2271	2302	2283

FIGURES 8 & 9. Precipitin line patterns obtained using *S. ehrenbergii* antiserum absorbed with *S. tuberosum* protein extract.

(8) Separation of Series V from Series VI.

(9) Range of precipitin line patterns exhibited by three strains within *S. cardiophyllum*.

JAM = *S. jamesii*   SMB = *S. sambucinum*
PIN = *S. pinnatisectum*   EHR = *S. ehrenbergii*
CPH = *S. cardiophyllum*

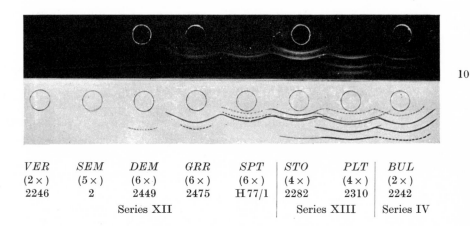

10

VER	SEM	DEM	GRR	SPT	STO	PLT	BUL
(2×)	(5×)	(6×)	(6×)	(6×)	(4×)	(4×)	(2×)
2246	2	2449	2475	H 77/1	2282	2310	2242
		Series XII			Series XIII		Series IV

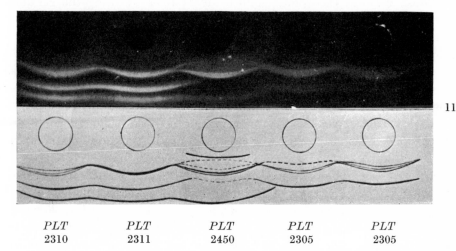

11

PLT	PLT	PLT	PLT	PLT
2310	2311	2450	2305	2305

FIGURES 10 & 11. Precipitin line patterns obtained using *S. ehrenbergii* antiserum absorbed with *S. tuberosum* protein extract.

(10) The precipitin line patterns of species in Series XII, XIII and IV.

(11) Range of precipitin line patterns exhibited by four strains of *S. polytrichon*. Extracts of tubers from different plants are shown for one strain (PLT 2305).

VER	= S. verrucosum	SPT	= S. spectabile
SEM	= S. semidemissum	STO	= S. stoloniferum
DEM	= S. demissum	PLT	= S. polytrichon
GRR	= S. guerreroense	BUL	= S. bulbocastanum

Cold water was passed through the central compartment to cool the agar plates during early experiments, but was later dispensed with when it was found that very little heating occurred.

The tuber extracts (0·15 ml.) to be compared were put into cups cut in the agar as described above, usually four cups side by side, with 10 mm of agar between each. The current was then switched on; 7 mA per plate (200 V, d.c. supply) were passed until a control spot of bromophenol blue (0·2 % in veronal buffer) moved 1·5 cm towards the positive electrode (usually a period of about 4 h).

The agar plates were removed from the electrolyte box and a trough 5 mm wide was cut at right angles to the direction of the current, with 12 mm of agar separating it from the antigen cups. The antiserum was added and the lines of precipitate allowed to develop as described above.

Experimental results

(a) Preliminary experiments

Antisera raised in the way described contain antibodies to most or all of the proteins (antigen) present in the extracts in adequate concentration. One can distinguish between these antigen-antibody systems by using the gel-diffusion technique as described above. In this technique the antigens are allowed to diffuse towards their homologous antibodies in an agar medium. Where the reagents meet at 'optimal' proportions a line of precipitate will form. If several antigen-antibody systems are present several lines may develop, each corresponding to a single antigen-antibody system. Exactly where in the intervening space the lines will form will depend upon the concentrations and diffusion rates of the reactants; clearly two or more systems may coincide and appear as a single line.

Such a phenomenon occurred when a *S. tuberosum* extract (antigen) was allowed to diffuse towards its homologous antiserum, for it was found that only two precipitin lines could be resolved satisfactorily. In order to try to improve the separation, the antigen was first subjected to a range of short periods of electrophoresis from 2 to 5 h using a current of 7 mA per plate as described above, before the antiserum was added. A 4 h period of electrophoresis gave the best separation and resulted in the splitting of one of the precipitin lines into three components as shown in figures 6, plate 9.

(b) Analysis of species and strains of various species with Solanum tuberosum antiserum

Using this immuno-electrophoretic method tuber extracts from various species were each tested side by side with that of *S. tuberosum* extract. Where lines from extracts of different species joined end-to-end they were assumed to belong to identical or cross-reacting proteins and this was taken as evidence for genetic relationship of the species concerned. On the other hand, when fewer lines developed, a lack of homology in the proteins of such species and a corresponding remoteness, from the evolutionary point of view, was assumed. This assumption was justified by the close similarity of the results obtained by the gel-diffusion

242

methods to those obtained from morphological and cytological studies (Hawkes 1956), as will be seen later. The relative positions of the precipitin lines in the agar when compared with the corresponding ones of *S. tuberosum* extract were sometimes different; this is likely to result from differences in the relative amounts of each protein present, since the higher the concentration of antigen the further from its source will 'optimal proportions' occur with respect to antibody.

The results indicated that the Mexican species and their strains (table 1) could be divided into three groups; the first gave four precipitin lines, similar to those of *S. tuberosum* itself, the second gave two lines and the third only one: figure 7, plate 10 shows the species placed in each group. The leading line of all species examined (except *S. morelliforme*) was found to be resolvable into two under special circumstances; but this is not relevant to the points at issue. All the South American species (listed in table 2) were found to give reactions practically identical with those of *S. tuberosum*; consequently only the results with the Mexican species will be considered in detail.

To investigate whether any of the apparent differences between species might be due to virus antigens in the tuber extracts, an extract of 'virus-free tubers' (var. Majestic) was compared with the non-virus-free *S. tuberosum* extract used to raise the antiserum, by the immuno-electrophoretic technique. No difference in the precipitin lines was observed and it was therefore concluded that antibodies against viruses were absent. No such test was carried out on the *S. ehrenbergii* antiserum (see below), but great care was taken to grow tubers under virus-free conditions. The fact that the results obtained were largely in agreement with those of classical taxonomy would suggest that virus precipitin lines, if any, were not an important source of error. Nevertheless, it is as well to bear in mind that some of the finer differences, particularly in the series Demissa and Longipedicellata, might conceivably be due to virus antigens.

(c) Analysis of species and strains of species with Solanum ehrenbergii *antiserum*

As a means of cross-checking the grouping of the species obtained with the *S. tuberosum* antiserum, a further series of tests was carried out by producing an antiserum against *S. ehrenbergii* (Accession No. 2302), a representative species of the group giving only two precipitin lines with the original antiserum.

The new antiserum was tested against its homologous antigen using the gel-diffusion technique and was found to give a complex pattern of at least ten lines. A short period of electrophoresis, so successful with *S. tuberosum* antiserum, was detrimental to the separation of the precipitin bands with this antiserum.

To simplify the analysis the antiserum was absorbed out with an extract of *S. tuberosum*, a species giving only three precipitin lines against the new antiserum. All the species were subsequently tested with this absorbed antiserum using the gel-diffusion technique. Figures 8 to 11, plates 11 and 12 represent some of the results. It will be seen that the species can be placed in a sequence, ranging from those species with many lines (and therefore closely related to *S. ehrenbergii*), figure 8, to those with few or no lines (most distant from *S. ehrenbergii*), figure 10.

It was found that although strains of the same species gave identical results when tested against *S. tuberosum* antiserum, this was not so with *S. ehrenbergii* antiserum. Some examples of differences within species are shown in figures 9 and 11. It is clear that in certain cases, notably with the strains of *S. polytrichon*, differences within species may be greater than those between species.

From the results of the two analyses the Mexican species could be classified on serological evidence alone as follows:

First, there is the aberrant ecological species, *S. morelliforme*, which, because of its paucity of precipitin lines with both antisera, is considered to be only distantly

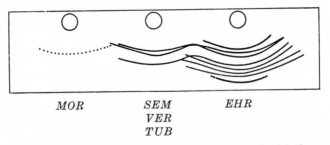

FIGURE 1. The precipitin line pattern of *S. morelliforme* compared with those of certain other species using unabsorbed *S. ehrenbergii* antiserum.

MOR = *S. morelliforme*   TUB = *S. tuberosum*
SEM = *S. semidemissum*   EHR = *S. ehrenbergii*
VER = *S. verrucosum*

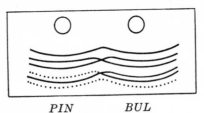

FIGURE 2. The precipitin line patterns of *S. pinnatisectum* (*PIN* 2300) and *S. bulbocastanum* (*BUL* 2242) with *S. ehrenbergii* antiserum absorbed with *S. tuberosum* protein extract.

related to all the other species tested (figure 7, plate 10, and figure 1). As figure 1 shows it shares only one of the three antigens of *S. tuberosum*, used for the absorption of the *S. ehrenbergii* antiserum, and it shows no precipitin lines with the absorbed *S. ehrenbergii* antiserum. In this latter feature it agrees with *S. verrucosum* and *S. semidemissum*. But these species differ in having three precipitin lines instead of one in common with *S. tuberosum* and are accordingly shown in figure 10 (results for absorbed antiserum) as a group that does not include *S. morelliforme*.

S. cardiophyllum, *S. sambucinum* and *S. ehrenbergii* group themselves with *S. jamesii* and *S. pinnatisectum* by possessing two precipitin lines in common with *S. tuberosum* (figure 7), whereas with absorbed *S. ehrenbergii* antiserum they are found to form a separate well-defined group sharing several lines not possessed by these species. Furthermore, these shared lines are denser, suggesting a close

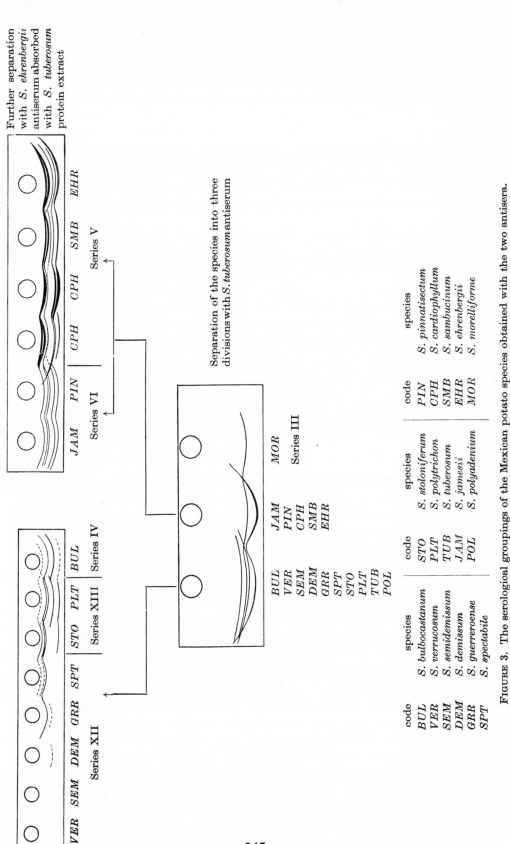

Further separation with *S. ehrenbergii* antiserum absorbed with *S. tuberosum* protein extract

Series XII

VER   SEM   DEM   GRR   SPT | STO   PLT | BUL

Series XIII | Series IV

JAM   PIN | CPH   CPH   SMB   EHR

Series VI | Series V

Separation of the species into three divisions with *S. tuberosum* antiserum

code	species	code	species	code	species
BUL	*S. bulbocastanum*	STO	*S. stoloniferum*	PIN	*S. pinnatisectum*
VER	*S. verrucosum*	PLT	*S. polytrichon*	CPH	*S. cardiophyllum*
SEM	*S. semidemissum*	TUB	*S. tuberosum*	SMB	*S. sambucinum*
DEM	*S. demissum*	JAM	*S. jamesii*	EHR	*S. ehrenbergii*
GRR	*S. guerreroense*	POL	*S. polyadenium*	MOR	*S. morelliforme*
SPT	*S. spectabile*				

BUL
VER
SEM
DEM
GRR
SPT
STO
PLT
TUB
POL

JAM
PIN
CPH
SMB
EHR

MOR   Series III

FIGURE 3. The serological groupings of the Mexican potato species obtained with the two antisera.

245

relationship between them (figure 8). There are small differences in line patterns between the species, but these are no greater than are found within species with this antiserum (figure 9).

As stated above, *S. jamesii* and *S. pinnatisectum* group themselves with *S. cardiophyllum*, *S. sambucinum* and *S. ehrenbergii* when tested with *S. tuberosum* antiserum, whereas with absorbed *S. ehrenbergii* antiserum they show precipitin line patterns similar to *S. bulbocastanum*, *S. stoloniferum* and *S. polytrichon* (figures 2 and 3). They would therefore appear to be a linking group between these other two groups.

S. bulbocastanum, *S. stoloniferum*, *S. polytrichon*, *S. guerreroense*, *S. spectabile*, *S. demissum*, *S. semidenissum*, *S. verrucosum* and *S. tuberosum* are all grouped together when tested against *S. tuberosum* antiserum. With absorbed *S. ehrenbergii* antiserum, however, only *S. tuberosum*, *S. verrucosum* and *S. semidemissum*—the three species showing no precipitin lines—could be placed together. *S. tuberosum* is not shown in figure 10 but it gave no precipitin bands since it had been used to absorb out the *S. ehrenbergii* antiserum. *S. bulbocastanum*, *S. stoloniferum*, *S. polytrichon*, *S. guerreroense*, *S. spectabile* and *S. demissum* showed a range of precipitin line patterns (figure 10) and possessed considerable differences within species (figure 11). One must, therefore, conclude that they represent a very heterogeneous group which on serological evidence would be difficult to subdivide.

Discussion

(a) *Analysis with* Solanum tuberosum *antiserum*

As we have already mentioned, three distinct reaction types were obtained when the complete range of Mexican and South American potatoes were tested against *S. tuberosum* antiserum, using the immuno-electrophoresis method described above (figure 7, plate 10).

All the South American species (see table 2) showed a four-line spectrum, similar to that of *S. tuberosum* itself. In addition, four Mexican series, namely, Bulbocastana (Series IV), Demissa (Series XII), Longipedicellata (Series XIII), and Polyadenia (Series XIV) also gave the same four-line spectrum. The serological tests would indicate therefore some rather close relationship between all these species.

Leaving aside for a moment series Bulbocastana and discussing the other three Mexican series together with the South American species, there is one important morphological feature which most of them possess in common. This is the rotate or wheel-shaped corolla, in which the free lobes are very short in comparison with the joined portions. We can contrast this with the species which show the other two reaction types (series Pinnatisecta (Series VI), Cardiophylla (Series V), and Morelliformia (Series III)), characterized by a stellate corolla, in which the narrow lobes are joined together only at the base. We should, however, mention that the corolla of Polyadenia is somewhat intermediate in form ('semi-stellate'), whilst the South American series Commersoniana and the Mexican series Bulbocastana are both anomalous, since although the corolla in both is stellate the serological tests place them with the rotate corolla series. Morphological considerations then, indicate a rough correlation with the serological tests, though some exceptions can be noted.

The serological tests and the data shown on the Crossability Chart (Figure 4) yield the same general picture. Thus crosses between series Demissa, Longipedicellata and Tuberosa can be made, even though there is difficulty in some cases and the progeny is often of reduced fertility. Furthermore, crosses between the various South American series are quite possible. Series Polyadenia forms hybrids with series Tuberosa with considerable difficulty, but nevertheless such hybrids

series	♀ \ ♂	S. tuberosum	S. verrucosum	S. semidemissum	S. demissum	S. guerreroense	S. spectabile	S. stoloniferum	S. polytrichon	S. bulbocastanum	S. jamesii	S. pinnatisectum	S. cardiophyllum	S. sambucinum	S. ehrenbergii	S. morelliforme	S. polyadenium
Tuberosa	S. tuberosum	+	×	×	(×)	.	.	×	.	—	—	.	—	.	.	.	(+)
Demissa	S. verrucosum	—	+	.	—	.	(×)	—	.	.	—	.	.	.	—	.	.
	S. semidemissum	×	—	.	×	.	.	—	.	.	.	.	.	.	.	.	.
	S. demissum	×	(×)	+	+	.	×	×	.	—	.	—	.	.	.	.	.
	S. guerreroense	.	.	.	×	+	×	.	.	.	.	.	.	.	.	.	.
	S. spectabile	—	—	.	×	.	+	—	.	.	.	—	.	.	.	.	.
Longipedicellata	S. stoloniferum	(×)	.	—	×	.	.	+	+	.	.	.	.	.	.	.	.
	S. polytrichon	.	.	.	(×)	.	.	×	+	.	.	.	.	.	.	.	.
Bulbocastana	S. bulbocastanum	—	.	.	.	.	.	.	.	.	.	.	.	.	.	.	.
Pinnatisecta	S. jamesii	.	.	.	.	.	.	.	.	.	+	+	—	.	.	.	+
	S. pinnatisectum	.	.	.	.	.	.	.	.	(+)	+	+	(+)	+	.	.	(+)
Cardiophylla	S. cardiophyllum	—	.	.	—	.	.	.	.	—	.	+	+	.	+	.	.
	S. sambucinum	.	.	.	.	.	.	.	.	.	.	.	+	+	.	—	.
	S. ehrenbergii	—	.	.	.	.	.	.	.	.	.	.	+	—	+	.	.
Morelliformia	S. morelliforme	.	.	.	.	.	.	.	.	—	.	.	.	.	.	+	.
Polyadenia	S. polyadenium	.	.	.	.	.	.	.	.	.	×	.	.	.	.	.	+

+ Cross easy; F_1 fertile. (+) Cross difficult; F_1 fertile.
× Cross easy; F_1 with reduced fertility. (×) Cross difficult; F_1 with reduced fertility.
— Cross impossible. ☐ Groups of reasonably interfertile species.

FIGURE 4. Species crossability chart.

when formed are of reasonable fertility. Series Bulbocastana again forms a complete exception, in that, although it belongs to the four-line serological group it will not form hybrids with any other series within that group. We should point out, nevertheless, that series Bulbocastana has only been hybridized once with any other series. This was a cross between *S. bulbocastanum* and *S. pinnatisectum*, using a special technique (Swaminathan 1955); no descriptions of the progeny resulting from this cross have been published.

The second reaction type to *S. tuberosum* antiserum is the two-line spectrum, exhibited exclusively by the two Mexican series Pinnatisecta and Cardiophylla. As we have already mentioned, the species belonging to these two series have a markedly stellate corolla and also differ from other species in leaf and hair type and in stigma form.

Reference to the Crossability Chart (figure 4) will show that the species in series Pinnatisecta and Cardiophylla are fairly inter-fertile both within and between the two series. With the group possessing a four-line spectrum, i.e. Tuberosa, Demissa,

Longipedicellata and Polyadenia, they only form hybrids with Polyadenia. The only known species, *S. polyadenium*, has been hybridized with *S. jamesii* and *S. pinnatisectum*, both in series Pinnatisecta. We have already drawn attention to the hybridization of *S. polyadenium* with species in Tuberosa. The series Polyadenia seems, therefore, to lie as a linking or bridge series between the four-line and the two-line spectrum series, even though serologically it lies within the four-line group.

With the exception of the linking series Polyadenia and the possibly linking series Bulbocastana, the serological results follow quite closely those obtained from crossability and morphological studies.

The third reaction type to *S. tuberosum* antiserum is provided by the species *S. morelliforme* (Series Morelliformia), which gives a spectrum of only one line. This species was once (Rydberg 1924) grouped with *S. bulbocastanum* in series Bulbocastana, but was later removed (Hawkes 1956) owing to its very distinctive epiphytic habit, very small stellate corolla, small berry, and glabrous simple leaves. The comparatively long narrow anthers in *S. morelliforme* are another feature quite alien to the rest of the tuber-bearing solanums. Very few attempts have, unfortunately, been made to hybridize this species with any other, owing to its very late flowering season in Europe, when other species have already finished. The few attempts that have been made gave entirely negative results. The serological tests confirm our previous views, based on morphology, that this species is far removed from any of the other wild potatoes.

Up to this point then, the results obtained from the immunological method with *S. tuberosum* antiserum agree fairly well with our views of species relationships gained from morphological and crossability studies. The three apparent exceptions to this are the Mexican series Bulbocastana (Series IV), Polyadenia (Series XIV) and the South American series Commersoniana. The position of the first two series may be readily explained by assuming that they are linking groups, which have evolved together with Tuberosa and the other four-line series in respect of their serological reactions, but still retain morphological or fertility links with the more primitive stellate flowered series Pinnatisecta and Cardiophylla. As regards the third exception, the South American series Commersoniana, its stellate corolla may possibly be a feature derived fairly recently from the rotate corolla of Tuberosa, since hybrids between these two series are highly fertile and the chromosomes pair regularly. This genetic relationship is in accordance with the similar four-line spectra of the two series. In these circumstances, therefore, when both cyto-genetical and serological evidence conflict with morphological evidence we should consider that the phylogenetic views based on the latter only are probably incorrect.

(b) *Analysis with* Solanum ehrenbergii *antiserum absorbed with* S. tuberosum *tuber extract*

We saw in the previous section that *S. ehrenbergii* was apparently rather distantly related to *S. tuberosum*. The former species was therefore selected to test the validity of the results discussed above. However, instead of a simple test it was considered that more information might be forthcoming if the antigen-antibody systems which *S. ehrenbergii* possesses in common with *S. tuberosum* were first removed by precipitation. It follows that the species now tested against this absorbed *S. ehrenbergii* antiserum will show no precipitin lines at all if their antibody-antigen systems are completely similar to those of *S. tuberosum*, whilst more and more lines will appear when antigen-antibody systems similar to those of *S. ehrenbergii* but not represented in *S. tuberosum* are developed.

The general results on species in Demissa (Series XII), Longipedicellata (Series XIII) and Bulbocastana (Series IV) are shown in figures 10 and 11. From this it appears that *S. verrucosum* and *S. semidemissum* agree entirely in their protein spectrum with *S. tuberosum*, whilst *S. demissum* with one faint line, is very little removed from it. However, the other two hexaploid species, *S. guerreroense* and *S. spectabile*, are rather more removed from *S. tuberosum* and show certain affinities with *S. stoloniferum*.

In the next series, Longipedicellata, *S. stoloniferum* seems to show more affinities to *S. spectabile* from the serological data than it does to *S. polytrichon*, the other member of this series to be examined. This latter species is remarkably similar to *S. bulbocastanum* in its serological spectrum.

These results agree only partially with the morphological groupings and hardly at all with the crossability data. There is certainly no hard and fast boundary dividing the series from each other, and we must therefore re-examine our criteria for classifying the species in the ways that have been accepted up to now.

It has been pointed out by Marks (1955) on the basis of chromosome pairing at meiosis in a number of artificial hybrids between the various species in Demissa (Series XII) that the diploid species *S. verrucosum* has probably contributed one set of twenty-four chromosomes to all the hexaploid species. However, since *S. verrucosum* gives no precipitin spectrum in the tests under discussion we cannot suppose that its influence would show in the serology of the hexaploid species to which it has supposedly contributed its whole set of twenty-four chromosomes. Morphologically *S. verrucosum* is very similar to certain diploid species in series Tuberosa from South America (e.g. *S. andreanum* from Colombia); furthermore, it can be hybridized fairly easily with these species, and cytological examination shows that chromosome pairing in the F_1 of such hybrids is remarkably regular, and that they are quite fertile. These facts outlined above indicate that *S. verrucosum* may possibly be a very recent immigrant to Mexico from South America (Hawkes 1958). The serological results confirm this hypothesis of a close relationship between *S. verrucosum* and South American diploid species.

A further hypothesis (Hawkes 1958) as to the origin of the hexaploid species in Demissa (Series XII) is that they may have been formed from initial hybridizations of *S. verrucosum* with existing Mexican tetraploid species in Longipedicellata (Series XIII) followed by chromosome doubling. On the contribution made by *S. verrucosum* the serological evidence has little to say, since this species shows no precipitin lines with the absorbed *S. ehrenbergii* antiserum (figure 10). The fact that the precipitin spectra of the hexaploid *S. guerreroense* and *S. spectabile* are closely similar to that of the tetraploid *S. stoloniferum* would agree perfectly with the view that the Longipedicellata tetraploids were involved in their origin. For *S. demissum*, however (or at least for the two clones tested here), there appears to be no serological similarity either to the other two hexaploids or to the Longipedicellata tetraploids. Perhaps *S. demissum* is the product of hybridization between *S. verrucosum* and some other tetraploid species such as *S. oxycarpum*. It might also perhaps have originated as an autotetraploid from diploid ancestors in a manner suggested by von Wangenheim, Frandsen & Ross (1957). Morphologically, *S. demissum* is much more similar to *S. verrucosum*, whilst *S. spectabile* is morphologically close to *S. stoloniferum*, and this similarity is indeed reflected by their serological spectra, whatever theories we hold to as to their true relationships and modes of formation.

The position of the pentaploid hybridogenic 'species' *S. semidemissum* is of interest here. Although it stands serologically very close to *S. verrucosum*, Bukasov (1939) considered it to be a hybrid of *S. demissum* and *S. stoloniferum* (as *S. antipoviczii*). If this were so we should expect to see in its line spectrum much more evidence of *S. stoloniferum*. Later, however, Bukasov stated (1956, verbal communication) that *S. semidemissum* might be a hybrid between the normal hexaploid *S. demissum* and some as yet undiscovered tetraploid form of this species. This view would certainly accord better with our present results, but one should note that no tetraploids such as Bukasov postulates have yet been discovered amongst the many collections of *S. demissum* known to cytologists and plant breeders. We should like to put forward here an alternative hypothesis for the formation of *S. semidemissum*, namely, that it resulted from the hybridization of *S. demissum* and *S. verrucosum*, the latter species having furnished a diploid gamete. In support of this we may point out that both species are found growing in close proximity and that *S. demissum*, when crossed with diploid species in series Tuberosa, seems not infrequently to induce the functioning of unreduced gametes, thus giving a pentaploid progeny. Although no pentaploid hybrids between *S. demissum* and *S. verrucosum* have yet been produced artificially it would be of considerable theoretical interest to make this attempt, even though the two species cross together with some difficulty. This latter hypothesis would agree well therefore with the serological spectrum of this rather sterile hybridogenic pentaploid species *S. semidemissum*.

The position of the tetraploid species *S. polytrichon* (Longipedicellata (Series XII)) is no less interesting. In its corolla form and chromosome number it shows close similarities to *S. stoloniferum*, and was for those reasons included in Series Longipedicellata. Reference to figure 10 indicates that sample 2310 shows a much closer serological similarity to *S. bulbocastanum* than to *S. stoloniferum*. Figure 11 shows that there is some variation between different strains of *S. polytrichon* and that one of these strains (2305) shows a rather closer similarity to *S. stoloniferum* than strain 2310. Thus from the results shown in figure 11 we must conclude that *S. polytrichon* and possibly other species also, may show a wider range of intraspecific variability than we at first realized. We must therefore be prepared to regard as tentative the results obtained from other species on the basis of only one sample.

Figure 8 shows the results of serological tests on the individual species in Series Pinnatisecta and Cardiophylla. The very high intensity of precipitin lines in Cardiophylla (Series V) is to be expected, since *S. ehrenbergii* itself, from which the original antiserum was produced, is to be found in this series. The spectra for the species in Series Cardiophylla contrast strongly with the very much weaker and fewer lines in Pinnatisecta (Series VI). Within each group there are differences but they are not consistent as between different species. Indeed different strains of the same species may differ from each other as widely as do the species themselves (see figure 9). The serological results, however, certainly agree with the general arrangement of the species into series deduced on morphological grounds.

When one compares the spectra for *S. jamesii* and *S. pinnatisectum* (Series Pinnatisecta) on the one hand with those for *S. polytrichon* (Longipedicellata), and *S. bulbocastanum* (Bulbocastana) on the other, it is possible to recognize about six lines in each case. In figure 2 the two species *S. pinnatisectum* and *S. bulbocastanum* are compared side by side, with the six lines clearly following through from one to the other, though with the relative positions of two pairs of lines reversed. Although this result gives evidence of great similarity between the species mentioned at the beginning of this paragraph we must not forget that *S. bulbocastanum* and *S. polytrichon* possessed four antigen-antibody systems in common with *S. tuberosum*, whilst *S. pinnatisectum* had only two of such systems, and that presumably these differentials had already been eliminated by precipitation before the test started. *S. polyadenium* shows two precipitin lines in common with *S. jamesii*, *S. pinnatisectum*, *S. bulbocastanum*, *S. polytrichon*, *S. stoloniferum* and *S. spectabile*, but it also possesses other lines which are absent from all these species. With *S. tuberosum* antiserum it is placed in the four-line group, and from this result it would seem to be more closely related to *S. tuberosum*. More work is clearly needed to resolve these discrepancies.

We may conclude from these results that the simple testing of species against *S. tuberosum* antiserum gives a clear division of the species into three main groups. These accord fairly well with morphological and crossability data, though there are certain exceptions. Further subdivision by means of *S. ehrenbergii* antiserum absorbed with *S. tuberosum* extract gives results which are rather more difficult to interpret. The anomalous position of *S. bulbocastanum*, and to a lesser extent that of *S. polyadenium*, have yet to receive completely satisfactory explanations, whilst there are undoubtedly a number of problems connected with their inter-relationships.

Apart from the value of serological evidence to plant taxonomists it may also be of some practical use to plant-breeders. Thus, *S. bulbocastanum* is of interest by virtue of its immunity to blight (*Phytophthora infestans*), but has so far resisted all attempts at crossing it with *S. tuberosum* or related species. Yet the present serological results indicate that it may be more related to series Tuberosa than its gross morphology suggests. Furthermore, in the series of tests conducted with absorbed *S. ehrenbergii* antisera it shows close similarities to the spectra of *S. polytrichon*, *S. jamesii* and *S. pinnatisectum*. Intensive attempts at hybridizing *S. bulbocastanum* with those three species are therefore probably worth while.

(c) General discussion

That the serological methods discussed here indicate a scheme of relationships between species which is on the whole rather similar to that already postulated on the basis of morphological and cytogenetical studies, argues well for the inclusion of these gel-diffusion methods in modern taxonomic studies. That the results do not agree in every detail with those obtained by either or both of the other disciplines mentioned is not surprising. Indeed the discrepancies are of some value in calling attention to points which need re-examination. The importance of the serological method lies in the fact that it represents another way of measuring differences between species and groups of species which can be used together with other data in making a final appraisal of the probable course of evolution in the group concerned.

The evidence produced here shows that some proteins may be confined to a species, or to a closely related group of species, while some may be found throughout a genus. However, some proteins seem to be identical or at least cross-reacting, throughout a wider botanical range than this. Serological studies by Hammond (1955) on the seed proteins of genera of the families Ranunculaceae and Solanaceae, using a nephelometric method which does not distinguish between individual proteins in the extracts, have shown that a nexus of inter-generic relationships may be constructed which is consistent with current ideas in their taxonomy; he indicates as well a number of interesting points for future research, as, for instance, the position of *Paeonia* and *Hydrastis* within the Ranunculaceae. There is indeed suggestive evidence that some proteins may be similar or identical throughout much of the plant kingdom, as may be the case with the 'chloro-plastin' of green leaves (Dorner, Kahn & Wildman 1957). At the other extreme, some may depend on *intra-specific* single gene differences, such as those which are responsible for inter-strain sterility barriers in *Oenothera* (Lewis 1952). In animals this extreme specificity is paralleled by the antigens responsible for 'graft-rejection' (Billingham, Brent & Medawar 1956) which may also be the product of a single gene or gene-set.

A priori it would be reasonable to expect some correlation between the serological specificities of plant-derived antigens and their functions. There well might be great similarity throughout a wide range of plants between the proteins involved in such a generalized function as photosynthesis, while storage proteins from seeds or tubers might be less different from one another than proteins from the same or other sources more actively responsible for specific characters. Thus the selection of appropriate organs and tissues and the serological characterization of the proteins in extracts from them may help to elucidate genetic relationships from the widest to the most minute.

The authors wish to express their thanks to the late Professor E. J. Maskell, F.R.S., for his interest in this work and for discussions on its presentation, and to Professor K. Mather, F.R.S., and Professor J. R. Squire for their encouragement in the early stages of the investigations. We are also grateful for the valuable technical assistance given by Miss A. Hudson.

One of us (S.T.C.W.) is indebted to the Nuffield Foundation for a Research Fellowship under which a great part of this work was carried out.

The 'virus-free' tubers of *S. tuberosum* were kindly supplied by Dr J. C. Cullen, of the National Institute of Agricultural Botany, Cambridge.

APPENDIX

species	accession no.	collector and no.	locality (Mexico, unless otherwise stated)
S. morelliforme	CPC 2262	Hawkes 1063	Vera Cruz State, La Joya
S. bulbocastanum	CPC 2242	Hawkes 1004	Distrito Federal, Pedregal de Tizapán
	CPC 2281	Hawkes 1029	Puebla State, Cholula, Teocali
S. cardiophyllum	CPC 2244	Hawkes 1006	Distrito Federal, Pedregal de Tizapán
	CPC 2269	Hawkes 1010	Mexico State, near Texcoco, Chapingo
	CPC 2271	Hawkes 1012	Mexico State, near Texcoco, Chapingo
	CPC 2283	Hawkes 1032	Puebla State, near Tehuacán
S. ehrenbergii	CPC 2297	Hawkes 1086	Querétaro State, San Juan del Rio
	CPC 2299	Hawkes 1089	Querétaro State, S.E. of Querétaro
	CPC 2302	Hawkes 1095	Jalisco State, Guadalajara to S.L. Potosí, km. 201.
	CPC 2304	Hawkes 1097	San Luís Potosí State, South of S.L. Potosí
	CPC 2309	Hawkes 1102	Zacatecas State, South of Zacatecas
S. sambucinum	CPC 2312	Hawkes 1105	Guanajuato State, 12 km. South of Dolores Hidalgo
	CPC 2313/1	Hawkes 1106	Guanajuato State, 9 km. South of Dolores Hidalgo
S. pinnatisectum	CPC 2300	Hawkes 1092	Guanajuato State, near León
S. polyadenium	CPC 2408	—	(E.B.S. 50/205) locality unknown
	CPC 2409	—	(PI. 161728) Michoacán State, Matujeo
S. jamesii	CPC 1394	—	Unknown, probably U.S.A.
S. demissum	CPC 2095	—	Unknown, probably Mexico
	CPC 2449	Hawkes 1134	Durango State
S. guerreroense	CPC 2475	Correll 14410*a*	PI. 161730. Guerrero State, Chilpancingo
S. semidemissum	CPC 2	Balls 4246	Mexico State, Popocatapetl, Paraje Provincial
S. spectabile	CPC 2433	Correll 14340	PI. 161726. Colima State, Volcán de Nevada
	H 75/2	Correll 14340	PI. 161726. Colima State, Volcán de Nevada
	H 77/1	Correll 14340	PI. 161740 × PI. 161726
S. verrucosum	CPC 2246	Hawkes 1046	Hidalgo State, Real del Monte
	CPC 2247	Hawkes 1047	Hidalgo State, Real del Monte
S. polytrichon	CPC 2305	Hawkes 1098	San Luís Potosí State, Canoas
	CPC 2310	Hawkes 1103	Zacatecas State, near Zacatecas
	CPC 2311	Hawkes 1104	Zacatecas State, near Zacatecas
	CPC 2450	—	Guanajuato State, León
S. stoloniferum	CPC 2282/2	Hawkes 1031	Puebla State, road from Puebla to Orizaba
	CPC 2331	Hawkes 1107	Distrito Federal, above Contreras, Cuatro Dinamos
	CPC 9/1	Balls 4843	Tlaxcala State, Tizatlán
	CPC 9/2	Balls 4843	Tlaxcala State, Tizatlán

REFERENCES

Billingham, R. E., Brent, L. & Medawar, P. B. 1956 *Phil. Trans.* B, **239**, 387.

Boyden, A. 1942 *Physiol. Zool.* **15**, 109.

Bukasov, S. M. 1939 *Physis. B. Aires*, **18**, 41.

Chester, K. S. 1937 *Quart. Rev. Biol.* **12**, 19, 165, 294.

Dorner, R. W., Kahn, A. & Wildman, S. G. 1957 *Plant Physiol.* **32**, Suppl. xii.

Elek, S. D. 1948 *Brit. med. J.* i, 493.

Freund, J. & Bonanto, M. V. 1944 *J. Immunol.* **48**, 325.

Gell, P. G. H., Hawkes, J. G. & Wright, S. T. C. 1956 *Nature, Lond.* **177**, 573.

Grabar, P. & Williams, C. A. 1953 *Biochim. biophys. Acta*, **10**, 193.

Hammond, H. D. 1955 *Serol. Mus. Bull.* **14**, pp. 1, 3.

Hawkes, J. G. 1956 *Ann. Rep. Scot. Soc. Res. Pl. Breed.* p. 37.

Hawkes, J. G. 1958 in Kappert, H. & Rudorf, W. *Handbuch der Pflanzenzüchtung*, 2nd ed., vol. III, 1–43.

Lewis, D. 1952 *Proc. Roy. Soc.* B, **140**, 127.

Ma, T. S. & Zuazaga, G. 1942 *Industr. Engng Chem. (Anal.)*, **14**, 280.

Marks, G. E. 1955 *J. Genet.* **53**, 262.

Ouchterlony, O. 1948 *Acta. path. microbiol. scand.* **25**, 186.

Rydberg, P. A. 1924 *Bull. Torrey Bot. Club*, **51**, 145, 167.

Swaminathan, M. S. 1955 *Nature, Lond*, **176**, 887.

Wangenheim, K. H. Frh. V., Frandsen, N. O. & Ross, H. 1957 *Z. Pflanzenz.* **37**, 41.

Wilson, G. S. & Miles, A. A. 1946 in Topley and Wilson's *principles of bacteriology and immunity*, pp. 712–715. London: Edward Arnold and Co.

Wolfson, W. O., Cohn, C., Calvary, E. & Ichiba, F. 1948 *Amer. J. clin. Path.* **18**, 723.

A CHROMATOGRAPHIC STUDY OF RETICULATE EVOLUTION IN THE APPALACHIAN ASPLENIUM COMPLEX[1,2]

DALE M. SMITH AND DONALD A. LEVIN

Department of Botany, University of Illinois, Urbana, Illinois

ABSTRACT

SMITH, DALE M. and DONALD A. LEVIN. (U. Illinois, Urbana.) A chromatographic study of reticulate evolution in the Appalachian Asplenium complex. Amer. Jour. Bot. 50(9): 952–958. Illus. 1963.—The reticulate relationships of the members of the Appalachian *Asplenium* complex were studied by means of paper chromatography. Substances could be observed with ultraviolet light in the presence of ammonia vapor in all the taxa of the complex. The diploid species (*A. montanum*, *A. platyneuron* and *A. rhizophyllum*) had characteristic biochemical substances. Interspecific hybrids and/or their allotetraploid derivatives showed a complete complementation of all the substances of their known or presumed diploid ancestors. A combination of all the substances of the 3 diploids was found in the hybrids *A.* × *kentuckiense* and *A.* × *gravesii*. The results agree in all respects with the concept of reticulate evolution in the group which was advanced by Wagner on the basis of comparative morphology, hybridization and karyology.

QUESTIONS of the origin and taxonomic treatment of polyploid taxa have received much attention, but the difficulties involved in carrying out detailed morphological comparisons, cytogenetic analyses, crossing experiments, and other pertinent investigations are so great that the ancestry of a polyploid taxon is rarely ever fully established. Furthermore, with respect to some polyploids, the data often do not allow one to differentiate between closely related members of a species group, any one of which might logically be considered ancestral to a particular polyploid.

The use of paper chromatography of certain biochemical constituents to study interspecific hybridization may be extended to an investigation of the problems associated with polyploidy, since polyploids are frequently of hybrid origin. An important generalization emerging from biochemical studies of hybridization is the idea of complementation of species-specific constituents of the parental species in interspecific hybrids (Alston and Turner, 1962); that is, the detectable substances of the parental species are found together in their hybrids. The implication of this fact for the study of polyploidy is that if one knows what substances occur in the diploid species which are presumed basic to a polyploid series, it should be possible to postulate the ancestry of a polyploid species on the basis of its complement of species-specific chemical constituents.

The Appalachian *Asplenium* complex (Wherry, 1925; Wagner, 1954) offers an excellent opportunity to test the validity of a chemical approach

to the study of polyploidy. The interrelationships of these ferns have been worked out in great detail by more conventional studies. Wagner (1954) postulated that *Asplenium montanum*, *A. platyneuron*, and *A. rhizophyllum* (*Camptosorus rhizophyllus*) are the diploids basic to this complex, and genomic allotetraploids derived from these species are *A. bradleyi* (*A. montanum-platyneuron*), *A. pinnatifidum* (*A. montanum-rhizophyllum*), and *A. ebenoides* (*A. platyneuron-rhizophyllum*). The latter taxon is known in the form of a sterile diploid hybrid as well as the fertile allotetraploid. Only tetraploids are known of *A. bradleyi* and *A. pinnatifidum*. In addition to the plants mentioned above, there are several natural and artificial hybrids which provide further insight into this complex (Darling, 1957; Smith, Bryant and Tate 1961a,b,c; Wagner, 1954, 1956, 1958; Wagner and Boydston, 1958, 1961; Wagner and Darling, 1957; Wagner and Whitmire, 1957). Named hybrids include *A.* × *gravesii* (*A. bradleyi* × *pinnatifidum*), *A.* × *kentuckiense* (*A. pinnatifidum* × *platyneuron*), *A.* × *trudellii* (*A. montanum* × *pinnatifidum*), and *A.* × *wherryi* (*A. bradleyi* × *montanum*). Of this group, *A.* × *kentuckiense* is especially interesting since it combines equal numbers of chromosomes from each of the diploids (Smith et al., 1961c). Other known natural and/or artificial hybrids between members of this complex are *A. bradleyi* × *platyneuron*, *A. ebenoides* × *platyneuron*, *A. ebenoides* × *rhizophyllum*, and *A. ebenoides* × *pinnatifidum*.

Most of these taxa were available to us, and the collection presented an unusual opportunity to test a number of facets of biochemical systematics as well as an opportunity to gain new insight into the problems of the interrelationships of the Appalachian spleenworts. First, it was essential to know whether or not these taxa could be identified by means of chromatography. Individual variation could be studied from population samples and by comparing individuals from one population to

[1] Received for publication March 20, 1963.

[2] The authors wish to express their thanks to Professor Warren H. Wagner, Jr., of the University of Michigan, for many helpful comments and for supplying material of *A. ebenoides*, *A.* x *wherryi*, and *A.* x *gravesii*, and to Professor Ralph E. Alston, of the University of Texas, for many helpful suggestions and comments during an earlier phase of this work. Thanks are also due those collectors whose specimens were used in this study, especially Mr. T. R. Bryant and Mr. D. E. Tate.

TABLE 1. *Presumed or demonstrated relationships and genome designation of Appalachian Asplenium species and hybrids*

Taxon	Relationship	Somatic chromosome number	Genome designation
A. montanum Willd.	ancestral diploid	72	MM
A. platyneuron (L.) Oakes	ancestral diploid	72	PP
A. rhizophyllum L.	ancestral diploid	72	RR
A. ebenoides R. R. Scott	A. platyneuron × rhizophyllum	72	PR
A. ebenoides R. R. Scott	A. platyneuron–rhizophyllum amphidiploid	144	PPRR
A. bradleyi D. C. Eaton	A. montanum–platyneuron amphidiploid	144	MMPP
A. pinnatifidum Nutt.	A. montanum—rhizophyllum amphidiploid	144	MMRR
A. × kentuckiense McCoy	A. platyneuron × pinnatifidum	108	MPR
A. × gravesii Maxon	A. bradleyi × pinnatifidum	144	MMPR
A. × trudellii Wherry	A. montanum × pinnatifidum	108	MMR
A. × wherryi Smith, Bryant, Tate	A. bradleyi × montanum	108	MMP

another. Differences between living plants and herbarium specimens could also be studied. Certain of these taxa occur in different habitats, a factor which might also contribute to variability. Our material also allowed us to determine the combination of substances in a hybrid at the diploid level, in the case of A. × ebenoides. The effect of tetraploidy could be checked by comparing this diploid with the fertile allotetraploid derivative. The presumed allotetraploids, A. bradleyi and A. pinnatifidum, could then be compared with A. ebenoides, whose origin has been demonstrated experimentally. The effect of genome "dosage" could also be tested, since the triploid "backcross" hybrids, A. × trudellii and A. × wherryi, theoretically consist of 2 sets of A. montanum chromosomes in combination with one from A. rhizophyllum in the case of A. × trudellii, and one from A. platyneuron in the case of A. × wherryi. The interaction of 3 whole and distinctive genomes could be determined in A. × kentuckiense, while the additional effect of dosage could be determined from A. × gravesii.

The genome designations and the presumed or demonstrated relationships of all the taxa used in this study are shown in Table 1.

METHODS AND MATERIALS—Our plants were obtained from several habitats scattered through the ranges of the species. Most of the analyses were carried out using herbarium specimens which had been accumulated over a period of approximately 8 years, although some analyses of fresh plants from the field, or greenhouse transplants, were also used. No significant differences between fresh and dried materials were detectable within the limits of the experimental procedure outlined below. This is especially significant with this group of ferns, since some of the critical taxa are exceedingly rare, and all are rather difficult to grow under greenhouse conditions. Data about each plant from which chromatograms were made are given in Table 2.

Each chromatogram was prepared from 1 plant, and wherever possible a portion of the specimen was saved to serve as a voucher. These vouchers are in the University of Illinois Herbarium. The age and condition of the specimen were noted in each case. Some chromatograms were prepared from strictly vegetative fronds, others from fronds with young sporangia, others from fronds with mature spores, and some were even made from moribund material. Occasionally it was necessary to combine all the fronds from one plant to get sufficient material for a good chromatogram. Extracts were prepared by powdering the whole dried frond and soaking the material for 36 hr in 2 ml of absolute methanol. The chromatograms were run in 2 dimensions by the ascending method. The first-dimension solvent system consisting of n-butanol: glacial acetic acid: water (4:1:1, v/v) was employed for 24 hr, and this was followed by distilled water for 2½ hr in the second dimension. This simple procedure gave excellent separation with little spreading or streaking of individual components.

The dried chromatograms were examined in ultraviolet light, ultraviolet light in the presence of ammonia vapor, and in visible light in the presence of ammonia vapor. Certain chromatograms were also treated with diazotized p-nitraniline, or diazotized sulphanilic acid, which are general reagents for detecting phenols (Smith, 1958). Ultraviolet light in the presence of ammonia vapor proved to be most useful, and most of the conclusions are drawn from those substances which were detected by this means.

Every detectable spot was marked on each chromatogram. The spots were grouped as follows: (1) frequent spots readily recognizable by their color in ultraviolet light and having a characteristic position on the chromotograms, and (2) spots which occur with low frequency, and/or which are usually too faint to be characterized accurately.

TABLE 2. *Asplenium taxa used in chromatography and their sources*

Taxon	Date collected	Substratum	Locality	Collector
A. bradleyi	11–7–59	Sandstone	Lee Co., Ky.: Bear Track Lookout	T. R. Bryant & D. E. Tate 235
A. bradleyi	12–29–59	Sandstone	Menifee Co., Ky.: Wolfpen Creek	T. R. Bryant & D. E. Tate 258
A. bradleyi	3–9–61	Potted plant	Powell Co., Ky.: High Rock Lookout	D. M. Smith
A. bradleyi	9–22–62	Sandstone	Powell Co., Ky.: High Rock Lookout	D. M. Smith
A. bradleyi	5–23–59	Sandstone	Powell Co., Ky.: Slade Hill	T. R. Bryant & D. E. Tate 176
A. bradleyi	9–22–62	Sandstone	Powell Co., Ky.: Natural Bridge State Park	D. M. Smith
A. bradleyi	5–2–59	Sandstone	Wolfe Co., Ky.: Rock Bridge	T. R. Bryant & D. E. Tate 161
A. bradleyi	5–23–59	Sandstone	Wolfe Co., Ky.: Pine Ridge Lookout	T. R. Bryant & D· E. Tate 175
A. ebenoides	1959	Potted plant	Hale Co., Ala.: Havana Glen	W. H. Wagner
A. ebenoides	3–9–61	Potted plant	Hale Co., Ala.: Havana Glen	W. H. Wagner
A. × *ebenoides*	3–9–61	Potted plant	Jessamine Co., Ky.: Brooklyn Bridge	D. M. Smith
A. × *ebenoides*	3–30–59	Limestone	Mercer Co., Ky.: near Shakertown	T. R. Bryant & D. E. Tate 127
A. × *gravesii*	3–9–61	Potted plant	Lee Co., Ky.: Bear Track Lookout	D. M. Smith
A. × *gravesii*	3–9–61	Potted plant	Powell Co., Ky.: High Rock Lookout	D. M. Smith
A. × *gravesii*	10–31–59	Sandstone	Powell Co., Ky.: High Rock Lookout	T. R. Bryant & D. E. Tate 211
A. × *gravesii*	3–31–59	Sandstone	Powell Co., Ky.: Natural Bridge State Park	D. E. Tate, D. M. Smith 6
A. × *gravesii*	3–9–61	Potted plant	Powell Co., Ky.: Natural Bridge State Park	D. M. Smith
A. × *gravesii*	2–5–56	Potted plant	Synthetic hybrid, Parents from near Front Royal, Va.	T. Darling
A. × *gravesii*	4–29–56	Potted plant	Dade Co., Ga. (Topotype?)	T. Darling
A. × *kentuckiense*	3–9–61	Potted plant	Floyd Co., Ky.: near Prestonsburg	D. E. Tate 12–20–60
A. montanum	11–7–59	Sandstone	Lee Co., Ky.: Bear Track Lookout	T. R. Bryant & D. E. Tate 241
A. montanum	4–18–59	Sandstone	Menifee Co., Ky.: near Sky Bridge	T. R. Bryant & D. E. Tate
A. montanum	11–4–62	Sandstone	McCreary Co., Ky.: Natural Arch	D. M. Smith
A. montanum	9–22–62	Sandstone	Powell Co., Ky.: Natural Bridge State Park	D. M. Smith
A. montanum	3–31–59	Sandstone	Powell Co., Ky.: Near Nada Tunnel	T. R. Bryant & D. E. Tate 132
A. montanum	10–3–59	Sandstone	Wolfe Co., Ky.: Parched Corn Creek	T. R. Bryant & D. E. Tate 190
A. montanum	11–3–62	Sandstone	Wolfe Co., Ky.: Sky Bridge	D. M. Smith
A. pinnatifidum	7–9–58	Sandstone	Breathitt Co., Ky.: Robinson Forest	D. M. Smith 1828
A. pinnatifidum	11–7–59	Sandstone	Lee Co., Ky.: Bear Track Lookout	T. R. Bryant & D. E. Tate 235
A. pinnatifidum	7–18–59	Sandstone	Lee Co., Ky.: 10 mi. W. Beattyville	T. R. Bryant & D. E. Tate 179
A. pinnatifidum	4–11–59	Sandstone	Menifee Co., Ky.: near Sky Bridge	Z. B. Carothers, T. R. Bryant, D. M. Smith 7
A. pinnatifidum	4–18–59	Sandstone	Menifee Co., Ky.: Wolfpen Creek	T. R. Bryant & D. E. Tate
A. pinnatifidum	9–22–62	Sandstone	Powell Co., Ky.: Natural Bridge State Park	D. M. Smith
A. pinnatifidum	9–22–62	Sandstone	Powell Co., Ky.: High Rock	D. M. Smith
A. pinnatifidum	3–9–61	Potted plant	Powell Co., Ky.: High Rock	D. M. Smith
A. pinnatifidum	3–31–59	Sandstone	Powell Co., Ky.: near Nada Tunnel	Z. B. Carothers, D. E. Tate, T. R. Bryant, D. M. Smith 4

TABLE 2. *Continued*

Taxon	Date collected	Substratum	Locality	Collector
A. pinnatifidum	11–3–62	Sandstone	Wolfe Co., Ky.: Sky Bridge	D. M. Smith
A. pinnatifidum	5–23–59	Sandstone	Wolfe Co., Ky.: Pine Ridge Lookout	T. R. Bryant & D. E. Tate 171
A. platyneuron	11–10–62	Forest Soil	Jefferson Co., Ind.: near Deputy	D. M. Smith
A. platyneuron	5–30–59	Limestone	Anderson Co., Ky.: near Lawrenceburg	T. R. Bryant & D. E. Tate 177
A. platyneuron	7–21–58	Sandstone	Breathitt Co., Ky.: Robinson Forest	D. M. Smith 1830
A. platyneuron	6–23–56	Sandstone	Breathitt Co., Ky.: Robinson Forest	B. Barbour 38
A. platyneuron	5–10–60	Limestone	Fayette Co., Ky.: 5 mi. S. Lexington	D. M. Smith
A. platyneuron	11–7–59	Sandstone	Lee Co., Ky.: Bear Track Lookout	T. R. Bryant & D. E. Tate 236
A. platyneuron	11–4–62	Limestone	Mercer Co., Ky.: Shaker's Bend	D. M. Smith
A. platyneuron	3–30–59	Limestone	Mercer Co., Ky.: near Shakertown	T. R. Bryant & D. E. Tate 125
A. platyneuron	11–4–62	Sandstone	McCreary Co., Ky.: Natural Arch	D. M. Smith
A. platyneuron	9–30–61	Shale	Powell Co., Ky.: near Clay City	D. M. Smith
A. platyneuron	5–2–59	Sandstone	Wolfe Co., Ky.: Rock Bridge	T. R. Bryant & D. E. Tate 162
A. rhizophyllum	9–22–62	Limestone	Jefferson Co., Ind.: near Deputy	D. M. Smith
A. rhizophyllum	3-14-59	Limestone	Boyle Co., Ky.: Spear's Creek	T. R. Bryant & D. E. Tate 111
A. rhizophyllum	3–30–59	Sandstone	Breathitt Co., Ky.: Robinson Forest	C. Martin 28
A. rhizophyllum	3–16–59	Limestone	Jessamine Co., Ky.: Indian Falls	J. Cornett 4
A. rhizophyllum	11–7–59	Sandstone	Lee Co., Ky.: Bear Track Lookout	T. R. Bryant & D. E. Tate 238
A. rhizophyllum	4–11–59	Sandstone	Menifee Co., Ky.: near Sky Bridge	T. R. Bryant & D. M. Smith 151
A. rhizophyllum	11–4–62	Limestone	Mercer Co., Ky.: Shaker's Bend	D. M. Smith
A. rhizophyllum	9–22–62	Limestone	Powell Co., Ky.: Natural Bridge State Park	D. M. Smith
A. rhizophyllum	9–22–62	Sandstone	Powell Co., Ky.: near Nada Tunnel	D. M. Smith
A. rhizophyllum forma *auriculatum* R. Hoffm.	4–4–59	Sandstone	Wolfe Co., Ky.: near Sky Bridge	T. R. Bryant & D. E. Tate 140
A. × trudellii	11–7–59	Sandstone	Lee Co., Ky.: Bear Track Lookout	T. R. Bryant & D. E. Tate 239
A. × trudellii	3–9–61	Potted plant	Lee Co., Ky.: Bear Track Lookout	D. M. Smith
A. × trudellii	10–10–59	Sandstone	Powell Co., Ky.: High Rock Lookout	D. M. Smith & T. R. Bryant 210
A. × trudellii	3–9–61	Potted plant	Powell Co., Ky.: High Rock Lookout	D. M. Smith
A. × trudellii	3–31–59	Sandstone	Powell Co., Ky.: near Nada Tunnel	Z. B. Carothers, D. E. Tate, T. R. Bryant, D. M. Smith 1
A. × trudellii	10–3–59	Sandstone	Wolfe Co., Ky.: Parched Corn Creek	T. R. Bryant & D. E. Tate 191
A. × trudellii	3–9–61	Potted plant	Wolfe Co., Ky.: Parched Corn Creek	D. M. Smith
A. × trudellii	5–2–59	Sandstone	Wolfe Co., Ky.: Rock Bridge	T. R. Bryant & D. E. Tate 163
A. × wherryi	8–17–62	Rock outcrop	Giles Co., Va.: South end of Peters Mountain	W. H. Wagner 62321.5

TABLE 3. *The occurrence of biochemical constituents on chromatograms of species and hybrids of Asplenium*

Taxon	*Detected substances and their percentage occurrence																Number of plants chromatographed
	M-1	M-2	M-3	M-4	M-5	M-6	M-7	P-1	P-2	P-3	P-4	P-5	R-1	R-2	R-3	R-4	
A. bradleyi	83	83	100	100	100	100	100	92	100	100	100	100					12
A. ebenoides								100	100	100	100	100	100	100	100	100	2
A. × ebenoides								100	100	100	100	100	100	100	100	100	2
A. × gravesii	100	62	100	100	75	100	100	88	88	88	88	100	88	75	88	62	8
A. × kentuckiense	100	100	100	100	100	100	100	100	100	100	100	100	100	100	100	100	1[a]
A. montanum	100	100	100	100	100	100	100										7
A. pinnatifidum	91	82	100	100	55	100	91						91	82	100	91	11
A. platyneuron								100	100	100	100	94					16
A. rhizophyllum													95	40	100	80	10
A. × trudellii	100	100	100	88	100	100	100						100	75	88	100	8
A. × wherryi	100	100	100	100	100	100	100	100	100	100	100	100					1[a]

[a] Only single plants of A. × kentuckiense and A. × wherryi were available. Replications from the same extracts gave identical results.

RESULTS AND DISCUSSION—The results of our chromatographic analyses are reported in Table 3. A summary diagram of the chromatographic pattern presented by each taxon is given in Fig. 1–10. These data show that the diploid species (*A. montanum*, *A. platyneuron*, and *A. rhizophyllum*) have groups of species-specific substances. The uniformity of results within each taxon was striking. The number of distinguishing substances differs in each species, ranging from 4 in *A. rhizophyllum*, through 5 in *A. platyneuron*, and up to 7 in *A. montanum*. It is possible that with more efficient techniques additional substances will be detected. For instance, a few compounds showed with a high frequency, but were so faint that their recognition was extremely difficult; consequently, they were not included among the "species-specifics." Other additional substances were very prominent, but not constant in their appearance. Nevertheless, the chromatographic distinctiveness of these 3 taxa was clearly established.

While the diploids may be identified by this technique, it is also apparent that certain other taxa yield quite similar chromatograms. This is true of the pairs *A. bradleyi* and *A. × wherryi*; *A. × ebenoides* (2n) and *A. ebenoides* (4n); *A. pinnatifidum* and *A. × trudellii*; and the pair, *A. × gravesii* and *A. × kentuckiense*. Thus, as a tool in identification, the technique has limitations. But, this is predictable when one considers the genomic constitutions of the pairs, and in light of Wagner's postulates (1954), the similarities are of great evolutionary interest.

A result which is equally as significant as the high degree of distinctiveness of the individual diploid species is the near absence of variation in chromatograms of a given taxon. Only minor variations were encountered in general. The principal exception was in *A. rhizophyllum*, where the substances designated R-2 and R-4 were either faint or absent in several chromatograms, giving a lowered confidence level for these substances as species-specifics. The presence or absence of these substances could not be significantly correlated with any known variables. The uniformity of results is especially remarkable when one considers that our material was selected so as to include several individuals from one population, individuals of the same taxon from different geographically distributed populations, living and dried material, recently collected material and older herbarium specimens, young fronds and mature fronds, and plants from different habitats which grew on different substrata and which were collected at various times during the growing season. The uniformity of results under these highly varied conditions suggests that these compounds are rather stable, and that herbarium collections as used here may be of significance to taxonomists.

Complementation of the biochemical constituents of parental species in interspecific hybrids of *Asplenium* is clearly evident in the results of this investigation. The hybrid *A. × ebenoides* provides the example of complementation at the diploid level. This hybrid combines all the substances from its parents, *A. platyneuron* and *A. rhizophyllum*. Furthermore, as mentioned above, the chromatograms of *A. × ebenoides* and its fertile allotetraploid derivative are indistinguishable, showing that polyploidy, per se, has no detectable effect.

The tetraploids *A. bradleyi* and *A. pinnatifidum* are considered by Wagner (1954) to be allotetra-

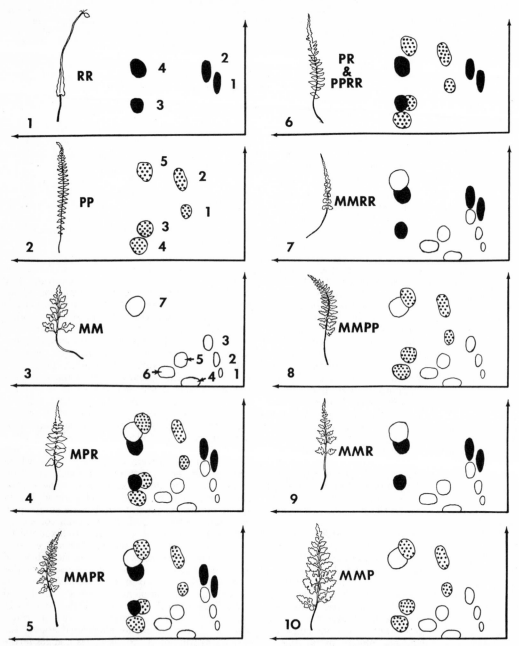

Fig. 1–10. Diagrammatic representations of 2-dimensional chromatograms of *Asplenium* species and hybrids. Each diagram is accompanied by a representative frond and the appropriate genome designation.—Fig. 1. *Asplenium rhizophyllum.*—Fig. 2. *A. platyneuron.*—Fig. 3. *A. montanum.*—Fig. 4. *A.* x *kentuckiense.*—Fig. 5. *A.* x *gravesii.*—Fig. 6. *A.* x *ebenoides* (2n) and *A. ebenoides* (4n).—Fig. 7. *A. pinnatifidum.*—Fig. 8. *A. bradleyi.*—Fig. 9. *A.* x *trudellii.*—Fig. 10. *A.* x *wherryi.*

ploids derived from *A. montanum* × *platyneuron* and *A. montanum* × *rhizophyllum*, respectively. Accordingly, we should expect complementation analogous to that seen in *A. ebenoides* in both *A. bradleyi* and *A. pinnatifidum*. This is precisely the case. The diploid hybrids ancestral to these 2 allotetraploids have never been recognized in nature or synthesized in the laboratory, but this chemical evidence, coupled with Wagner's (1954) morphological, anatomical, and cytological evidence, confirms their postulated ancestry.

It is evident from the foregoing discussion that the interaction of 2 distinctive genomes represented in equal amounts gives equal complementation of the parental attributes. The effect of having 1 genome represented once and another genome represented twice is manifested in the hybrids *A.* × *trudellii* and *A.* × *wherryi*. Eight plants of *A.* × *trudellii* were chromatographed, but only one of the exceedingly rare *A.* × *wherryi* was available. In both hybrids, the *A. montanum* substances were brighter and more easily recognized. However, the fluorescing substances usually appeared brighter in *A. montanum*, whether in combination with other species or not.

The rare hybrid, *A.* × *kentuckiense*, apparently combines in equal numbers all the chromosomes of all 3 of the diploid species (Smith et al., 1961c). This taxon presents a rare opportunity to see the effect of the simultaneous interaction of 3 genomes (MPR). We were unfortunate in having but 1 plant to study; however, an excellent chromatogram was obtained and the results indicated complete complementation of all the substances of all 3 diploid species. Another hybrid, *A.* × *gravesii*, gives indistinguishable chromatograms. This plant is a tetraploid hybrid of *A. bradleyi* × *pinnatifidum* whose genome formula is presumably MMPR. We were able to examine 8 plants of this hybrid, including an artificial hybrid and another obtained from the vicinity of the type collection.

The fact that our chromatographic studies corroborate the results obtained by other methods suggests that the technique has significant potential for evolutionary studies involving polyploidy. The work also confirms an important point made by Wagner (1954) that predictability can be a part of taxonomic investigations. Our work not only corroborates Wagner's observations, but goes farther, by lending direct evidence to postulates which he made about the ancestry or interrelationships of this group of spleenworts. The study of biochemical constituents provides a new dimension in which one may offer predictions. It is not a replacement for cytological or morphological studies, but might allow one to formulate hypotheses about relationships at a much earlier point in his studies.

LITERATURE CITED

ALSTON, R. E., AND B. L. TURNER. 1962. New techniques in analysis of complex natural hybridization. Proc. Natl. Acad. Sci. (U.S.) 48: 130–137.

DARLING, T., JR. 1957. In search of the rock-fern hybrid *Asplenium gravesii*. Amer. Fern Jour. 47: 55–66.

SMITH, D. M., T. R. BRYANT, AND D. E. TATE. 1961a. *Asplenium x gravesii* in Kentucky. Brittonia 13: 69–72.

———, ———, AND ———. 1961b. Another *Asplenium* hybrid from Kentucky. Amer. Fern Jour. 51: 70–73.

———, ———, AND ———. 1961c. New evidence on the hybrid nature of *Asplenium kentuckiense*. Brittonia 13: 289–292.

SMITH, I. 1958. Chromatographic techniques: Clinical and biochemical application. William Heinemann Medical Books, Ltd., London.

WAGNER, W. H., JR. 1954. Reticulate evolution in the Appalachian Aspleniums. Evolution 8: 103–118.

———. 1956. *Asplenium ebenoides x platyneuron*. A new triploid hybrid produced under artificial conditions. Amer. Fern Jour. 46: 75–82.

———. 1958. Notes on the distribution of *Asplenium kentuckiense*. Amer. Fern Jour. 48: 39–43.

———, AND K. E. BOYDSTON. 1958. A new hybrid spleenwort from artificial cultures at Fernwood and its relationship to a peculiar plant from West Virginia. Amer. Fern Jour. 48: 146–159.

———, AND ———. 1961. A new hybrid showing homology between *Asplenium ebenoides* and *A. pinnatifidum*. Brittonia 13: 286–289.

———, AND T. DARLING, JR. 1957. Synthetic and wild *Asplenium gravesii*. Brittonia 9: 57–63.

———, AND R. S. WHITMIRE. 1957. Spontaneous production of a morphologically distinct, fertile allopolyploid by a sterile diploid of *Asplenium ebenoides*. Bull. Torr. Bot. Club 84: 79–89.

WHERRY, E. T. 1925. The Appalachian Aspleniums. Amer. Fern Jour. 15: 47–54.

COMPOSITION OF TURPENTINE
OF LODGEPOLE × JACK PINE HYBRIDS[1]

By N. T. Mirov

Abstract

Chemical composition of turpentines in lodgepole–jack pine hybrids was studied. When the two pines were artificially crossed, the F_1 generation possessed turpentine in which the bicyclic terpenes of jack pine dominated over the simpler, monocyclic terpene—phellandrene—of lodgepole pine. Trees in a natural hybrid swarm also tended towards a predominance of the jack pine bicyclic terpenes.

Very little is known about the inheritance of chemical characters in plants. If one parent "A" has a chemical compound "a" and another parent "B" has instead a compound "b" of the same class of compounds (e.g. terpenes, organic acids, or any other class), what kind of compound may be expected to be present in the hybrid between "A" and "B" ? What kind of compound would be found in a hybrid swarm, when the "A" plant and the "B" plant meet and cross under natural conditions ?

This paper attempts to shed some light on these two questions. The plants under consideration are lodgepole pine (*Pinus contorta* Dougl.) and jack pine (*Pinus banksiana* Lamb.). The investigated compounds belong to the class of unsaturated predominantly cyclic compounds—terpenes.

Range and Taxonomy of Lodgepole and Jack Pines

Both lodgepole pine and jack pine belong to the group *Insignes* of the subgenus *Diploxylon* genus *Pinus* (25). Lodgepole pine has a wide range, being found from lower California to Alaska and Yukon territory, and from the sea level of the Pacific to an elevation of 11,000 ft. in the Rocky Mountains.

Lodgepole pine was first collected in 1826 by Mertens near Sitka, Alaska, during his voyage as a botanist and zoologist of Captain Lütke's around-the-world expedition (15). The specimens were studied by Bongard (4) and the pine was described as *Pinus inops* Ait., which is a synonym for *Pinus virginiana* Mill. Comparing his material with the drawing of *P. inops* in Lambert's *Description of genus Pinus* (11), Bongard, apparently not sure of the identity of his Alaskan pine, made a note that "spinae squamarum parum breviores, quam in iconae Lamberti laudata."

Some botanists distinguish coastal and inland forms of lodgepole pine. The Pacific coast form is sometimes designated as *Pinus contorta* Dougl., whereas the inland form, both of the Sierra Nevada of California and the

[1]*Manuscript received December 19, 1955.*
Contribution from the Institute of Forest Genetics, California Forest and Range Experiment Station, Forest Service, U.S. Department of Agriculture, maintained at Berkeley, California, in co-operation with the University of California.
The work reported in this paper was aided through a grant from the Rockefeller Foundation. Thanks are due to the public foresters of Alberta, and to Professor E. H. Moss, Chairman, Department of Botany, University of Alberta, for their assistance in the field work.

American Rockies, is known as *P. contorta* var. *latifolia* Engelm., as *P. contorta* var. *murrayana* (Grev. & Balf.) Engelm., or as *Pinus murrayana* Grev. & Balf. A scrubby form of the pine found on the Pacific coast of California is called *P. contorta* var. *bolanderi* Parl.

In British Columbia the coastal form and the inland form merge, and farther north both go under the name of *P. contorta*. In Alberta, lodgepole pine descends somewhat from the eastern slope of the Rockies to the adjacent plains.

Jack pine, or Banks pine, is named after Sir Joseph Banks, once President of the Royal Society of London. It is a northeastern pine occupying an enormous range from Nova Scotia and Maine westward to Minnesota, Ontario, Manitoba, Saskatchewan, northeastern Alberta, northeastern British Columbia, and the Mackenzie and the Yukon regions. Halliday and Brown (8) state that jack pine and lodgepole pine "meet along the eastern foothills of the Rocky Mountains overlapping in the Peace river districts." More accurately, in Alberta, in an area located between Edmonton on the south, Peace River on the north, Grande Prairie on the west, and a point not far from Athabaska on the east, there are numerous groves where the two pines are intermingled. Here one may observe trees possessing morphological characters intermediate between the characters of lodgepole pine and jack pine. These intermediate forms in the "overlap" area were thoroughly studied in 1947 and 1948 by Moss (18), who arrived at the conclusion that they are hybrids between the two species.

In 1939, Righter (22) succeeded in crossing lodgepole pine and jack pine. Pollen was collected from a jack pine in the Eddy Arboretum, Institute of Forest Genetics, Placerville, California, grown from seed obtained from Michigan. The seed parent was a wild lodgepole pine growing at an elevation of 5700 ft. in El Dorado County, California. The resulting hybrid possessed morphological characters intermediate between the parents.

Morphological differences between lodgepole pine, jack pine, and an artificial F_1 hybrid are largely of a comparative nature. Lodgepole pine cones are spreading or reflexed, each scale carrying a strong recurved spine. Jack pine cones are predominantly erect, recurved towards the apex of the shoot— seldom spreading, but always unarmed. The hybrid cones generally resemble those of lodgepole pine, but armed with slender inconspicuous prickles.

Ecological Aspects of Natural Hybridization

In the overlap area lodgepole pine grows on the heavier soils and is associated with white spruce (*Picea glauca* (Moench) Voss), quaking aspen (*Populus tremuloides* Michx.), and balsam poplar (*Populus balsamifera* L.). Jack pine occupies poorer sites on sandy areas where it grows together with scrubby quaking aspen and paper birch (*Betula papyrifera* Marsh.). The patches of forest trees in the overlap area alternate with stretches of grassland and cultivated fields.

During the Wisconsin glaciation, the jack pine forests of Canada were completely destroyed. When forest trees reinvaded Canada, jack pine came as a component of the eastern forest centered on the Appalachian land mass, that is, it approached Alberta from the east. Lodgepole pine migrated southward, probably from the Yukon Valley (9), even before the Wisconsin glaciation and may have persisted in ice-free areas close to the ice front during at least the late Wisconsin glaciation when the land located both eastward and westward was still covered with ice.

In early postglacial times what is today the overlap area probably was an extensive grassland, or perhaps a parkland or grove area. The black soils now found frequently in the area could not have developed under postglacial conifer forests. Moss (19) concluded that the forest is gradually encroaching upon the grassland. Fires and cultivation have retarded this encroachment. All investigators agree that the area has been greatly disturbed by fires, which became more frequent with the advent of primitive man. Although Moss (19) considers the disturbing influence of bison and domestic animals only of local importance, nevertheless, judging by the information available for other grassland regions (3), the influence of once-numerous hoofed wild animals in disturbing the prehistoric grasslands should not be disregarded. We may visualize the Alberta overlap area since the retreat of the ice as having been repeatedly disturbed by fires, by wild cattle, and by possible subsequent surface erosion especially in sandy places. The area offered conditions favorable to the appearance of lodgepole × jack pine hybrid swarm (1). It might be possible that the two pines never overlapped, but merely approached each other when hybrids were first formed. The hybrid swarm then might have originated in a disturbed area not previously occupied by either parent.

There is no botanical evidence at present of a preglacial hybridization between the two pines. Apparently there had been no preglacial contact between lodgepole pine and jack pine; at least no fossil records are available that would indicate such contact. No signs of hybridization between these two pines have been reported in any part of their respective ranges other than the Alberta overlap area.

A slight variability in the cone morphology of jack pine was mentioned by Moss (19, p. 228). Moss suggested that the horizontal cones of jack pine occasionally found as far east as Manitoba might be the result of a "postglacial union of lodgepole and typical jack pine" although he was cautious to add that the occurrence "seems to make a considerable demand upon a migration hypothesis." In later correspondence Dr. Moss informed the author that jack pine possessing horizontal cones has been found as far east as northern Michigan. In the author's opinion, the straight-cone jack pine may be considered as a variant within the species, developed without any introgression of lodgepole pine genes. Racial variability of jack pine throughout its range, described by Schantz-Hansen and Jensen (23), is strictly infraspecific; there also is no evidence of introgression of lodgepole pine genes. At the Institute of Forest Genetics, Placerville, California, there is a jack pine from Connecticut whose otherwise typical cones are horizontal, with the tips curved down.

Pines of an intermediate character are found occasionally west of and beyond the overlap area, as for instance near Seebe, between Calgary and Banff. There are also reports of intermediate forms in Saskatchewan. Both of these localities are not too far from the overlap area of Alberta.

Chemical Composition of Turpentines

When the trunk of a pine is cut, the wound yields a quantity of oleoresin. The oleoresin consists of a part that is volatile with steam, called turpentine, and of a non-volatile part, called rosin. Commonly turpentine is composed of terpenes. Terpenes offer certain advantages over other plant constituents in a study of inheritance of chemical characters: terpenes are an end product of metabolism (12) and once formed, they are apparently not used by the plant; turpentine composition in all but a few pine species is very simple; and enough material can be obtained from an individual tree for chemical analysis.

The chemical composition of turpentine is specific. It may vary considerably within a species, but the variability is quantitative rather than qualitative in character. The chemical variability is reflected in a variability of physical characters of pine turpentine: its density, index of refraction, and optical rotation. Variability of the rotatory power, for instance, may be caused by varying amounts of different terpenes or by the presence of levo- and dextro-antipodes of the same terpene in varying amounts. A pure dextrorotatory antipode of alpha-pinene rotates the plane of polarized light to about $+40°$. The rotation of a mixture of the two antipodes may vary all the way from $+40°$ to $-40°$. Again, the variability of optical rotation of a turpentine may be caused by presence of two different terpenes, one dextro- and the other levorotatory, as in jack pine.

Optical rotation of jack pine turpentine fluctuates considerably. This fluctuation is caused both by varying amounts of levo-β-pinene and by varying amounts of dextrorotatory and levorotatory antipodes of α-pinene. Some samples of jack pine turpentine from Ontario and from Wisconsin are levorotatory. All jack pine turpentine samples from Alberta were dextrorotatory.

Lodgepole pine turpentine from all localities, except Sierra Nevada mountains of California, is levorotatory. It consists almost entirely of levo-β-phellandrene. The Sierra Nevada lodgepole turpentine contains about 10% of a dextrorotatory sesquiterpene-ketone. This semisolid compound apparently is not found in the Canadian lodgepole pine in appreciable quantity. Thus, jack pine turpentine consists of a mixture of dextro- and levo-α-pinene, with an admixture of levo-β-pinene, both terpenes being of bicyclic structure. No phellandrene is present (7, 16). Canadian lodgepole turpentine consists almost entirely of a monocyclic terpene, levo-β-phellandrene (24). The structure of α-pinene, β-pinene, and β-phellandrene is shown in Fig. 1. There are thus clear chemical differences between the turpentines of lodgepole and jack pines. What, then, is the nature of the turpentine in the hybrid between these two pines?

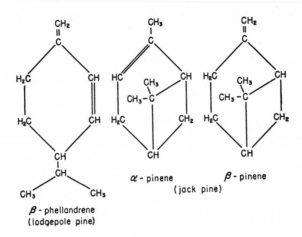

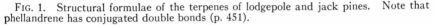

FIG. 1.   Structural formulae of the terpenes of lodgepole and jack pines.   Note that phellandrene has conjugated double bonds (p. 451).

Source of Experimental Material

Several samples of turpentine from typical lodgepole pine from California, Idaho, and Colorado were analyzed by the writer before the present study. Samples analyzed for this study were from Kananaskis Forest Experiment Station near Calgary, Alberta; from Kamloops, British Columbia; and from trees planted in New Zealand.   Turpentine samples of typical jack pines were obtained from Minnesota, Wisconsin, and Ontario.[2]

Samples of turpentine from the artificial lodgepole pine × jack pine hybrid were obtained at the Institute of Forest Genetics, Placerville, California, where the hybrid was developed (22).   Six F_1 trees, 12 years old, about 6 in. in diameter at the base, and 20 ft. tall, were tapped in 1952; a small quantity of oleoresin was obtained, not sufficient to analyze the sample individually but enough for a composite sample.   The turpentine was dextrorotatory ($\alpha_{578 \text{ m}\mu} = +7.00°$), had an index of refraction, $n_D^{25} = 1.4713$, and a density, $d_4^{25} = 0.8520$.   Fractional distillation and identification of the compounds revealed the presence of 75 to 78% pinenes and 20 to 22% phellandrene.   The conclusion was that the F_1 generation of an artificially produced (and thus authentic) hybrid between lodgepole pine and jack pine possessed turpentine of a mixed nature.

Oleoresin of 73 individual trees intermediate between lodgepole and jack pines was obtained from the overlap area near Edmonton, Alberta, where these two pines meet and apparently cross (Fig. 2).   In the summer of 1952 the writer visited the Edmonton area and with the kind assistance of Dr. Moss collected oleoresin samples from two localities, one northeast of Edmonton,

[2]*Thanks are due to the members of the Kananaskis Forest Experiment Station, to the members of the Provincial Forest Service of British Columbia, to the Forest Officers of Ontario, and to the Lake States Forest Experiment Station, U.S. Forest Service, for their assistance in procuring the oleoresin samples.*

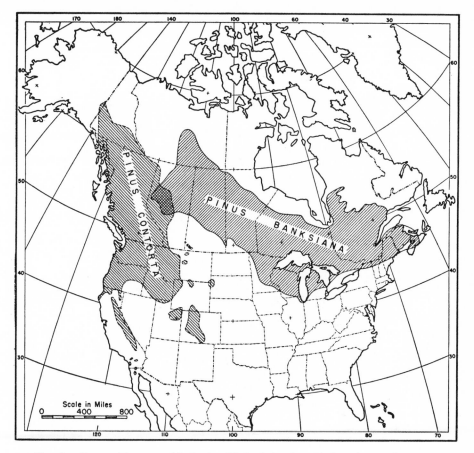

FIG. 2.   Geographic range of jack pine (*P. banksiana*) and lodgepole pine (*P. contorta*) showing the Alberta overlap area.

near Bruderheim, designated in this paper as Station M, and another northwest of Edmonton, designated as Station N.   In the summer of 1954, oleoresin samples from 10 other localities between Edmonton and the Rockies were collected under the supervision of Dr. Moss (Fig. 3).   All these samples furnished experimental material used in the present study (Table I).

Experimental Technique

Oleoresin samples were collected from the pines by cutting V-shaped grooves $\frac{1}{2}$ in. deep into the sapwood.   The exuded oleoresin was collected in glass jars and kept in cold storage until used.

The turpentine was obtained by heating oleoresin *in vacuo*, so that, at the end of the operation, when all turpentine was distilled off, the pot temperature was increased to 180° C. and pressure was reduced to 1 mm. of mercury.   The distilled turpentine samples then were dried over anhydrous sodium sulphate

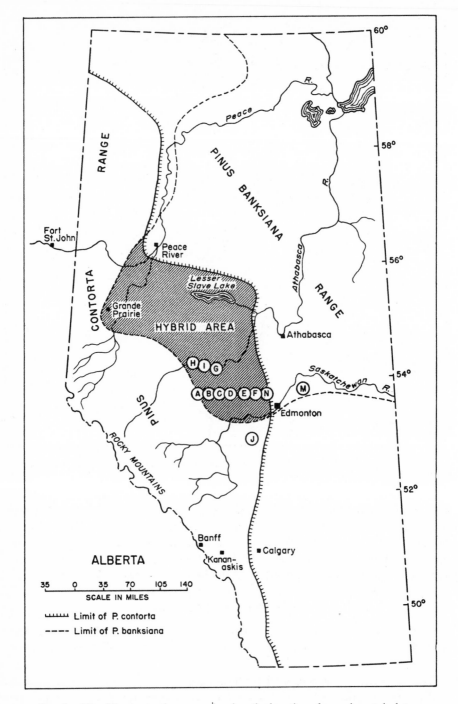

FIG. 3.   The Alberta overlap area, showing the location of experimental plots.

TABLE I

SOURCE OF TURPENTINE SAMPLES

Location	Plot symbol	No. trees in plot	No. trees from which turpentine samples were obtained*	Classification of trees on morphological characters†
Lodgepole—jack pine overlap area				
Bruderheim, 30 mi. NE. of Edmonton	M	11	9	Typical jack pine
Heatherdown, 35 mi. NW. of Edmonton	N	10	9	Lodgepole, hybrids, and typical jack pine
21 mi. SW. of Edson (140 mi. W. of Edmonton)	A	11	10	Typical lodgepole
19 mi. SW. of Edson	B	7	5	Typical lodgepole
10 mi. SW. of Edson (130 miles W. of Edmonton)	C	9	7	Typical lodgepole
Near Leaman, 80 mi. W. of Edmonton	D	11	7	All but one tree typical lodgepole
Near Evansburg, 60 mi. W. of Edmonton	E	10	1	Mixture of hybrids and typical lodgepole
Near Seebe, 50 mi. W. of Edmonton	F	10	1	All typical jack pine
95 mi. NW. of Edmonton (4 miles E. of White Court)	G	10	8	Jack pine and hybrids
125 mi. NW. of Edmonton (30 miles W. of White Court)	H	6	3	Typical lodgepole
15 mi. W. of White Court (110 miles NW. of Edmonton)	I	8	3	Lodgepole and hybrids
Near Rocky Mt. House, about 100 miles SW. of Edmonton	J	12	10	Typical lodgepole with an admixture of possible hybrids
Total for hybrid area		115	73	
Other areas				
Artificial hybrid *P. contorta* × *P. banksiana* (Institute of Forest Genetics, Calif.)		1 composed sample		Cones with weak spines
P. contorta (including *P. murrayana*) from California, British Columbia, and Alberta		12 composed samples		Cones with strong spines
P. banksiana from Minnesota, Wisconsin, and Ontario		4 composed samples		Cones smooth (without spines)

Not all trees yielded enough oleoresin for chemical analysis.
†*Based on description of Dr. Moss and on herbarium specimens.*

and kept in a refrigerator.   Altogether, 90 turpentine samples were prepared and investigated: 4 samples from jack pine, 12 samples from lodgepole pine, 1 sample from the artificial hybrid between these two pines, and 73 samples from the individual trees of the Alberta hybrid area.   For each sample the following characters were determined: density, d_4^{25}; index of refraction, n_D^{25}; specific rotation, $[\alpha]_{578m\mu}^{23}$.

Density of the turpentine, d_4^t was determined by means of a pycnometer of 0.4 cc. capacity.   A factor of 0.0008 per degree was used to correct the reading to 25° C.   Index of refraction n_D^t was determined by means of Abbe refractometer and corrected to 25° C. by using a factor 0.00045 per degree.[3] Optical rotation was observed with a polarimeter, using a standard 1-decimeter long tube. The specific rotation was calculated by dividing the observed optical rotation of the sample by its density. The rotation measurements were made in the mercury yellow, using Corning glass filters Nos. 3480 and 4303. The resultant wavelength was 578 mμ.

Phellandrene (in its levo-β-form) was identified by preparation of phellandrene nitrosite, according to the method suggested by Baker and Smith (2); α-pinene was identified by its nitrosochloride (28).

Thirty-nine samples of turpentine were subjected to an ultraviolet ray analysis.[4] Presence of conjugated double bonds in the lodgepole pine phellandrene and absence of conjugation in the jack pine turpentine permitted an easy differentiation between the turpentines of the two pines by this method.

Pure β-phellandrene has an absorption maximum at 232 mμ in the ultraviolet and the ϵ value is 19,300 (5). This ϵ value was used to calculate the percentage of phellandrene by use of Beer's law. Since the validity of Beer's law (13) for solutions of phellandrene in 95% ethanol has not been checked, the percentages of phellandrene calculated are to be regarded not as highly accurate measurements but as indices of the relative amount present.

The transmission values were measured at 232 mμ for solutions of the turpentine in 95% ethanol, mostly at a dilution of 10^{-4} molar. A dilution of 10^{-3} or 10^{-2} molar was used for samples having a low absorption value. The values were determined on a Beckman DU model spectrophotometer.

Results

The indices of refraction and the densities of the 73 individual trees of the overlap area were plotted by a method adopted from the work of Sutherland (27). This diagram (Fig. 4) shows that the chemical composition of turpentine of the individual trees was far from uniform. Some points for individual trees are concentrated along the α-pinene–β-pinene line where points for pure jack pine samples from the eastern part of the continent are located. On the lower right end of the diagram are located pines possessing lodgepole pine characteristics. The values for true lodgepole pines from outside the hybrid swarm are scattered much more than the values for the jack pines. This scattering is probably caused mostly by the varying sesquiterpene fraction of the lodgepole pine turpentine, but the position of the two composed samples from Kananaskis, Alberta (between Calgary and Banff), may possibly be caused by the presence of pinenes from jack pine. Between these two extremes of the diagram are scattered the individual trees that possess turpentines intermediate between that of lodgepole and jack pine. Turpentine from the artificial F_1 hybrid also had characteristics like those of the intermediate group.

[3]*Correction of readings to 25° C. was necessary for preparation of Sutherland diagram (Fig. 4).*
[4]*Thanks are due to Dr. P. M. Iloff, Jr., for furnishing the spectrophotometric data for the turpentine samples.*

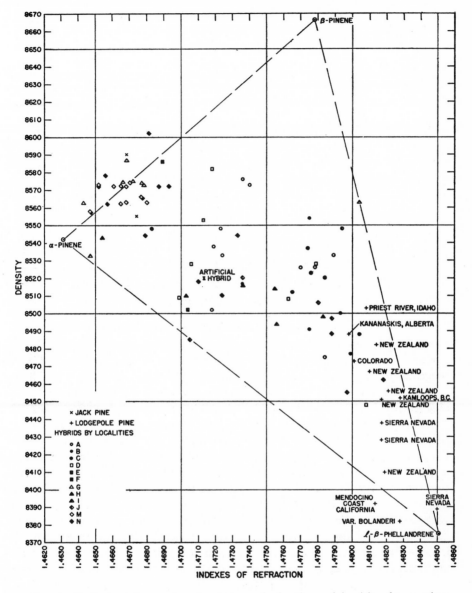

FIG. 4.   Sutherland diagram based on indexes of refraction and densities of turpentines of experimental trees.

271

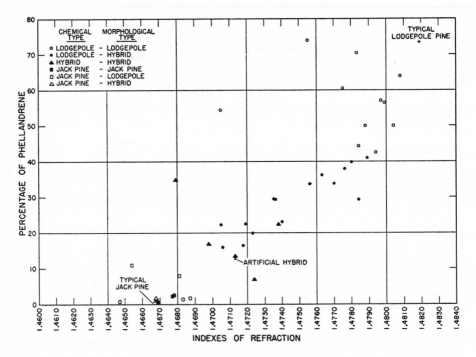

Fig. 5. Phellandrene content of experimental trees and the indexes of refraction.

Results of photospectrometric determination of phellandrene (Fig. 5) suggest that turpentine obtained from 39 individual trees in the Alberta overlap area had rather low 1-β-phellandrene content; even the pure lodgepole pine turpentine contained only 73%. This relatively low figure may be explained by inaccuracies of spectroscopic determination and possibly by polymerization of phellandrene, which is a very unstable terpene; nevertheless, the position of the pure lodgepole pine turpentine on the diagram may serve as a criterion for estimating the relative content of phellandrene in the individual trees of the hybrid swarm. Of these, the presumably pinene (that is, jack) pines are clustered at the lower left end of the diagram. At the upper right part are located apparently pure phellandrene (that is, lodgepole) pines. These are much more scattered than the pinene pines. The artificial hybrid is located closer to the pinene pines and probably actually contains 20 to 22% of phellandrene, judging from the previously mentioned fractional distillation.

Specific rotation was plotted (Fig. 6) with the trees arranged in the same order as they appeared on the Sutherland diagram; that is trees possessing dextrorotatory turpentine, characteristic of jack pine, to the left and trees possessing levorotatory turpentine, characteristic of lodgepole pine, to the right. It is apparent from this diagram that the trees in the overlap area are to a larger extent dextrorotatory, possessing the physical character of jack pine turpentine. Data on morphological and chemical characters are presented in Table II.

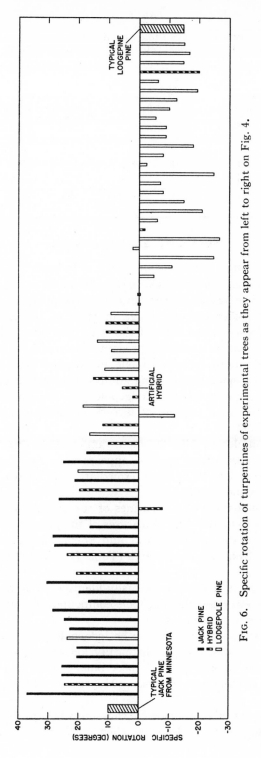

Fig. 6.   Specific rotation of turpentines of experimental trees as they appear from left to right on Fig. 4.

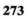

TABLE II

DISTRIBUTION OF EXPERIMENTAL TREES FROM THE ALBERTA LODGEPOLE–JACK PINE OVERLAP
AREA, BY MORPHOLOGICAL AND CHEMICAL CHARACTERS

Morphological character	Chemically jack pine		Chemically intermediate forms		Chemically lodgepole pine		Total	
	No.	%	No.	%	No.	%	No.	%
Jack pine	21	28.8	0	0	0	0	21	28.8
Intermediate	3	4.1	14	19.2	0	0	17	23.3
Lodgepole pine	3	4.1	17	23.3	15	20.5	35	47.9
All	27	37.0	31	42.5	15	20.5	73	100.0

Summary and Discussion

Results of our findings may be summarized as follows:

1. Lodgepole pine turpentine consisted largely of levo-β-phellandrene with varying amounts of dextrorotatory sesquiterpene compounds. (Sesquiterpenes amounted to a considerable percentage in trees of the Sierra Nevada of California and almost none in trees of the coast and the Rocky Mountains.)

2. Jack pine turpentine consisted predominantly of a mixture of dextro- and levo-α-pinene (more dextro-antipode in Alberta than in Ontario and Lake States), with a small and varying admixture of levo-β-pinene.

3. The artificial hybrid between lodgepole pine and jack pine possessed turpentine consisting of a mixture of levo-β-phellandrene (20 to 22%) and pinenes (75 to 78%).

4. The pines sampled in Alberta where ranges of the two species overlap were of a heterogeneous morphological appearance. Some looked like jack pine; others appeared to be of an intermediate type; trees that resembled lodgepole pine were most numerous.

5. Chemical composition of turpentines of the overlap area pines did not always correspond to morphological features of the pines.

From analysis of the morphological and chemical characters of the 73 experimental trees from the overlap area (Table II), the following conclusions can be drawn:

1. None of the pines that could be easily identified morphologically in the field as jack pines possessed the lodgepole compound, phellandrene. Nearly 30% of the 73 trees were of this type.

2. Pines that externally appeared to be lodgepole pines were found to be either phellandrene pines, that is, chemically lodgepole (20% of the total); or chemical hybrids, possessing both jack pine pinenes and lodgepole pine phellandrene in different proportions (23%); or chemically pure jack pines (4%).

3. Pines that possessed morphological characters intermediate between jack pine and lodgepole pine were also often chemically intermediate (about 20%

of the total). Of the morphologically intermediate pines 4% were chemically pure jack pines; none in this morphologically intermediate group was chemically pure lodgepole.

The present investigations of inheritance of terpenes in lodgepole–jack pine hybrids show that when the two pines were artifically crossed, the F_1 generation possessed turpentine in which the bicyclic terpenes of jack pine dominated over the simpler monocyclic terpene—phellandrene—of lodgepole pine. The ratio was about 3 to 1. Trees in the natural hybrid swarm around Edmonton, Alberta, also tended toward a predominance of the jack pine pinenes. Morphologically, however, more trees in the hybrid swarm looked like lodgepole pines than like jack pines.

Dominance of complicated turpentine components over simpler ones has been previously found in turpentine of the hybrid between *Pinus ponderosa* (containing a mixture of bicyclic terpenes) and *Pinus jeffreyi* (containing a saturated straight chain hydrocarbon of the methane series, *n*-heptane) (14).[5] This trend also seems apparent in the natural cross of *Pinus montezumae* and *Pinus pseudostrobus* encountered by the author in Chiapas, Mexico (10, 17).

A similar phenomenon has been observed in a study of inheritance of essential oil components in *Ocimum* by Nilov (20). There are indications, although not expressed, of the same nature in the works of Penfold and his associates (21) with Australian Myrtaceae and in Sievers' experiments with hybridization of species of the genus *Mentha* (26).

The present study is admittedly of a preliminary character. It was concerned with only one group of chemical substances found in plants— terpenes. To study other classes of organic compounds seems highly advisable. If a gradual disappearance of simpler compounds in natural or in artificial hybrids is of widespread occurrence in nature, this phenomenon might be important in the study of evolution of chemical substances in plants.

References

1. ANDERSON, E. Introgressive hybridization. John Wiley & Sons, Inc., New York. 1949.
2. BAKER, R. T. and SMITH, H. G. A research on the Eucalypts, especially in regard to their essential oils. Technol. Museum, New South Wales. Tech. Educ. Ser. No. 13. 1902. p. 262.
3. BERG, L. S. Natural regions of the U.S.S.R. The MacMillan Co., New York. 1950. p. 105.
4. BONGARD, H. G. Observations sur la végétation de l'ile de Sitcha. Mem. Imp. Acad. Sci. St. Petersburg, 6th Ser. No. 143. 2 : 163. 1833.
5. DAVENPORT, J. B., SUTHERLAND, M. D., and WEST, T. F. 'β-phellandrene' from Canada-Balsam oil. J. Appl. Chem. 1 : 527-528. 1951.
6. GUENTHER, E. The essential oils. Vol. 2. D. Van Nostrand Company, Inc., New York. 1949.
7. HAAGEN-SMIT, A. J., REDEMANN, C. T., WANG, T. H., and MIROV, N. T. Composition of gum turpentines of pines. A report on *P. ponderosa*, *P. banksiana*, *P. canariensis* and *P. washoensis*. J. Am. Pharm. Assoc. Sci. Ed. 39 : 260-265. 1950.[6]

[5] *The U.S. Forest Products Laboratory Report on which this information was based gives a ratio of 25% heptane and 75% terpenes.*
[6] *In the last column of Table III of this article the first two figures should have a plus sign instead of the minus. The α-pinene in P. banksiana is predominantly dextrorotatory.*

8. HALLIDAY, W. E. D. and BROWN, A. W. A. The distribution of some important forest trees in Canada. Ecology, 24 : 353-373. 1943.
9. HANSEN, H. P. Postglacial forests in West Central Alberta, Canada. Bull. Torrey Botan. Club, 76 : 278. 1949.
10. ILOFF, P. M. and MIROV, N. T. Composition of gum turpentines of pines XVII. A report on *P. montezumae* from Chiapas and *P. oocarpa* var. *trifoliata* and *P. durangensis* from Durango, Mexico. J. Am. Pharm. Assoc. Sci. Ed. 42 : 46-49. 1953.
11. LAMBERT, A. B. A description of the genus *Pinus*, etc. 2nd ed. Vol. 1. Weddell, London. 1828.
12. LVOV, S. D. Signification physiologique du process de la formation des essences pour la plante. Acad. Sci. Bot. Soc. U.S.S.R. Essays Botan. Moscow, 2 : 561-676. 1954.
13. MELLON, M. G. Analytical absorption spectroscopy. John Wiley & Sons, Inc., New York. 1950.
14. MIROV, N. T. A note on Jeffrey and Western Yellow pines. J. Forestry, 30 : 93-94. 1932.
15. MIROV, N. T. Lodgepole pine discovered and misnamed. Madroño, 12 : 156-157. 1954.
16. MIROV, N. T. Chemical composition of gum turpentines of pines of the United States and Canada. J. Forest Products Research Soc. 4 : 107. 1954.
17. MIROV, N. T. Composition of turpentines of Mexican pines. Unasylva, 8 : 167-173. 1954.
18. MOSS, E. H. Natural pine hybrids in Alberta. Can. J. Research, C, 27 : 218-229. 1949.
19. MOSS, E. H. Grassland of the Peace River region, Western Canada. Can. J. Botany, 30 : 98-124. 1952.
20. NILOV, V. I. Chemical changes in plant hybridization. All-Union Acad. Agr. Sci. Nikitskii Botan. Garden, 171-192. 1939.
21. PENFOLD, A. R. Researches on essential oils of the Australian flora. Museum Technol. Appl. Sci. Sydney, 1948-1953.
22. RIGHTER, F. I. and STOCKWELL, W. P. The fertile species hybrid *Pinus murraybanksiana*. Madroño, 10 : 65-69. 1949.
23. SCHANTZ-HANSEN, T. and JENSEN, R. A. The effect of source of seed on growth of jack pine. J. Forestry, 50 : 539-544. 1952.
24. SCHORGER, A. W. Contribution to the chemistry of American conifers. Wisc. Acad. Sci. Trans. Pt. 2. 1919.
25. SHAW, G. R. The genus *Pinus*. Publs. Arnold Arboretum No. 5, Cambridge, Mass. 1914.
26. SIEVERS, A. F., LOWMAN, M. S., and RUTTLE, M. L. Investigations of the yield and quantity of the oils from some hybrid and tetraploid mints. J. Am. Pharm. Assoc. Sci. Ed. 34 : 225-231. 1945.
27. SUTHERLAND, M. D. A review of densities and refractive indices of terpenes. Univ. Queensland Papers, Dept. Chem. 1 : 1-21. 1948.
28. WALLACH, O. Zur Kenntniss der terpenen. Ann. 245 : 253. 1888.

NATURAL HYBRIDIZATION AMONG FOUR SPECIES OF BAPTISIA (LEGUMINOSAE)[1]

R. E. Alston and B. L. Turner

The Plant Research Institute and Department of Botany, The University of Texas, Austin, Texas

ABSTRACT

Alston, R. E., and B. L. Turner. (U. Texas, Austin.) Natural hybridization among four species of Baptisia (Leguminosae). Amer. Jour. Bot. 50(2): 159–173. Illus. 1963.—Interspecific hybridization involving 4 species of Baptisia (B. leucophaea, B. sphaerocarpa, B. nuttalliana, and B. leucantha) has been studied by means of extensive field work and subsequent morphological and chromatographic analyses. As a result of these studies, numerous hybridizing populations involving any 2, 3 and, in 1 instance, 4 species have been located. Near Dayton, Texas, all 4 species and all 6 of the possible 2-way hybrid combinations have been found in a single field. Approximately 125 different chemical compounds have now been detected in the 4 species. Many of these compounds serve as species specific markers useful in the validation of specific hybrid types. Hybrids between B. leucophaea and B. sphaerocarpa and between B. leucophaea and B. nuttalliana are numerous, and in these large hybrid swarms a chromatographic and morphological analysis of population structure is possible. The former combination provides an excellent opportunity for the utilization of chemical markers as criteria for introgressive hybridization. The hybrid B. leucantha × B. sphaerocarpa is frequently encountered and contains a large number of compounds species-specific for one or the other parental species. The other 3 hybrid types have been found infrequently. Certain hybrid types are generally similar morphologically (e.g., B. leucantha × B. sphaerocarpa as opposed to B. leucantha × B. nuttalliana), and chromatographic techniques are of great value in the absolute identification of such plants, especially in complex populations where backcrossing further complicates the interpretation of the background of a plant from exomorphic features alone.

The 5 species of Baptisia native to Texas are B. minor, B. leucophaea (including B. laevicaulis), B. nuttalliana, B. leucantha, and B. sphaerocarpa (including B. viridis) (Turner, 1959).[2] Although B. minor apparently hybridizes with B. leucophaea

[1] Received for publication July 12, 1962.
Supported by National Science Foundation Grant 15890.
The authors wish to express their appreciation for the technical assistance of Mrs. Virginia Findeisen.
[2] Baptisia laevicaulis and B. viridis, treated as species in the author's earlier papers, are now believed to be better treated as infraspecific categories under the older names B. leucophaea and B. sphaerocarpa.

and possibly with others, hybrids involving B. minor have not been studied by the present workers, and the species is omitted from consideration at this time. Baptisia leucophaea and B. leucantha are widely distributed in the central United States; B. sphaerocarpa and B. nuttalliana, more restricted in their distribution, are found in only 4 or 5 states in the south central United States (Fig. 1, 2). These species are morphologically unlike and may be readily distinguished even at great distances, yet they hybridize without apparent sterility or other incompatibility, as do many other species of Baptisia.

TABLE 1. *Locations of specific hybrid combinations*

A. *B. leucophaea* × *B. nuttalliana*

1. Sebastian Co., Ark., U.S. 71, 3 miles N.W. of Greenwood
2. Evangeline Pa., La., Dirt road between Mamou and Chantaignier
3. Choctaw Co., Okla., U.S. 70, 5 miles east of Hugo
4. Freestone Co., Tex., Farm Rd. 488, 1.6 miles south int.ᵃ Farm Rd. 2548
5. Grimes Co., Tex., State Hwy. 30, 4.5 miles east of Brazos Co. line
6. Grimes Co., Tex., State Hwy. 158, 2 miles west of Roan's Prairie
7. Hardin Co., Tex., State Hwy. 326, 0.5 miles north of Pine Island Bayou
8. Hardin Co., Tex., Farm Rd. 105, 200 yds. north int. Farm Rd. 770
9. Harris Co., Tex., Farm Rd. 2100, 2 miles south of Huffman
10. Hopkins Co., Tex., U.S. 30, ¼ mile west int. State Hwy. 19
11. Leon Co., Tex., U.S. 79 just east of Jewett
12. Liberty Co., Tex., U.S. 90, 2 miles west of Dayton
13. Madison Co., Tex., U.S. 75, 3.2 miles north of Madisonville
14. Newton Co., Tex., State Hwy. 63, 4 miles east of Burkeville
15. Van Zandt Co., Tex., State Hwy. 19, 3.3 miles north int. State Hwy. 64
16. Van Zandt Co., Tex., State Hwy. 19, between Rds. 858 and 1256
17. Walker Co., Tex., U.S. 190, 0.6 miles east int. Farm Rd. 405
18. Walker Co., Tex., U.S. 190, just east int. Farm Rd. 2296
19. Walker Co., Tex., State Hwy. 30, 6.9 miles east of Shiro
20. Walker Co., Tex., U.S. 75, 3.0 miles north of Crabb's Prairie
21. Walker Co., Tex., U.S. 19, 6 miles north of Huntsville, scattered to Trinity River

B. *B. leucantha* × *B. sphaerocarpa*

1. Jefferson Davis Pa., La., int. State Hwys. 99 and 380
2. Hardin Co., Tex., State Hwy. 105, 1.3 miles east of Sour Lake
3. Harris Co., Tex., Farm Rd. 2100 north of Crosby
4. Harris Co., Tex., int. U.S. 90 and 90A, Houston
5. Jefferson Co., Tex., State Hwy. 326 just south of Pine Island Bayou
6. Jefferson Co., Tex., U.S. 90, 200 yds. west int. Farm Rd. 364, Beaumont
7. Jefferson Co., Tex., U.S. 90, 4.7 miles east of China
8. Liberty Co., Tex., Farm Rd. 1960, 0.2 miles west of int. Farm Rd. 686
9. Liberty Co., Tex., U.S. 90, 2.7 miles west of Nome
10. Liberty Co., Tex., U.S. 90, 2 miles west of Dayton

C. *B. leucophaea*ᵇ × *B. sphaerocarpa*

1. Sebastian Co., Ark., U.S. 71, 10.4 miles N.W. of Greenwood
2. Acadia Pa., La., U.S. 90 just east of Mementau
3. Bryan Co., Okla., U.S. 69, 7 miles N.E. of Colbert
4. Brazoria Co., Tex., Farm Rd. 1301, just north of West Columbia
5. Fannin Co., Tex., State Hwy. 121, 2 miles south of Bonham
6. Galveston Co., Tex., State Hwy. 146, 3 miles N.W. Texas City near Moses Lake
7. Hardin Co., Tex., State Hwy. 105, 1.3 miles east of Sour Lake
8. Hardin Co., Tex., State Hwy. 105 just north of int. Farm Rd. 770
9. Harris Co., Tex., int. U.S. 90 and 90-A, Houston
10. Harris Co., Tex., Farm Rd. 2100 north of Crosby
11. Jackson Co., Tex., State Hwy. 111, 2.3 miles east of Edna
12. Liberty Co., Tex., Farm Rd. 1960, 0.2 miles west of Farm Rd. 686
13. Liberty Co., Tex., State Hwy. 61, 2 miles east of Devers
14. Liberty Co., Tex., 2 miles west of Dayton

D. *B. nuttalliana* × *B. sphaerocarpa*ᵇ

1. Houston Co., Tex., State Hwy. 21, 1 mile north of Farm Rd. 304
2. Liberty Co., Tex., U.S. 90, 2 miles west of Dayton
3. San Jacinto Co., Tex., State Hwy. 150, 0.4 miles east of Evergreen
4. Walker Co., Tex., U.S. 75, 2 miles north of Huntsville

E. *B. leucantha* × *B. nuttalliana*

1. Jefferson Davis Pa., La., U.S. 196, 6 miles south of Kinder
2. St. Landry Pa., La., U.S. 190, just west of Lawtell
3. Hardin Co., Tex., State Hwy. 326, north of Pine Island Bayou
4. Jefferson Co., Tex., State Hwy. 326, south of Pine Island Bayou
5. Liberty Co., Tex., U.S. 90, 2 miles west of Dayton

TABLE 1. *Continued*

F. *B. leucantha* × *B. leucophaea*

    1. Allen Pa., La., U.S. 190, 4 miles west of Reeves
    2. Hardin Co., Tex., State Hwy. 162, 1 mile west of Batson
    3. Harris Co., Tex., Farm Rd. 2100 between Huffman and Crosby
    4. Liberty Co., Tex., U.S. 90, 2 miles west of Dayton

  [a] int. = intersection.
  [b] Numerous hybridizing populations may be found to the west and southwest of Houston, in the coastal prairie, to Jackson Co.

Despite the fact that all 4 species are geographically broadly sympatric in Texas, they are adapted to quite different ecological conditions, and consequently one rarely encounters the 4 species together in a single population. Two species commonly occur together and less frequently 3 species may be found together, generally in disturbed areas (Fig. 3). The authors have been engaged in extensive field work in Texas and parts of Louisiana, Arkansas and Oklahoma. One objective has been to determine the extent and characteristics of natural hy-

bridizing populations involving *Baptisia* in these areas. Figures 4–9 show the distribution of various hybrid individuals or hybridizing populations which have been observed. Exact locations of the hybrid sites are listed in Table 1. Prior to this study, only 2 of the 6 possible hybrid combinations were certainly known. Larisey (1940a) reported the hybrid combination, *B. leucantha* × *B. sphaerocarpa* (treated as *B. viridis*), and Turner and Alston (1959) reported details of the combination *B. leucophaea* × *B. sphaerocarpa*. Larisey (1940b), in her mono-

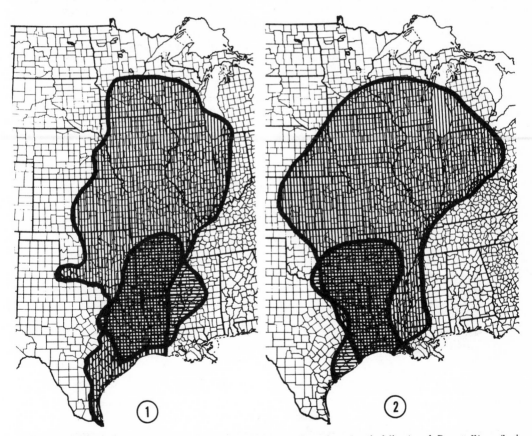

Fig. 1, 2.—Fig. 1. Approximate natural distribution of *Baptisia leucophaea* (vertical lines) and *B. nuttalliana* (horizontal lines); region of sympatry cross-hatched.—Fig. 2. Approximate natural distribution of *B. leucantha* (vertical lines) and *B. sphaerocarpa* (horizontal lines); region of sympatry cross-hatched. Areas of recent local introductions are not included in the maps.

graphic treatment, described apparent hybrids between *B. leucophaea* and *B. nuttalliana* or *B. leucantha* and *B. leucophaea* as new species. Her inability to recognize these hybrids from herbarium specimens underscores the wide morphological separation of the species (i.e., the hybrid is distinctive itself as a "good species"), and is also indicative of the difficulty in deducing hybridity from morphological evidence without familiarity with the natural populations.

Now, all 6 of the hybrid combinations have been validated by both morphological and chromatographic data. Details of each combination are given in a later section. The frequency with which hybrids of different origins occur varies greatly. An actual count of parental species and hybrids has been obtained in only 1 instance: in a population within Houston, Texas (intersection of U.S. 90 and U. S. 90A), 2 acres of plants contained: 162 *B. sphaerocarpa*, 64 *B. leucophaea*, 49 *B. leucantha*, and 33 hybrid types. Estimates of a larger population at Sour Lake, Texas, including the same 3 species, indicate a lower percentage of hybrids. The frequency of hybrids in a particular population is dependent upon a number of variables which affect, collectively, the population structure.

In some areas it is impossible to maintain a simple concept of discrete populations of *Baptisia*. The pattern may be very complex. For example, except where interrupted by towns and especially by the Trinity River bottomland, roughly 75 miles of U. S. 90 between Houston and Beaumont is a linear mosaic of *Baptisia* populations consisting of 1, 2, 3 and, in 1 instance, 4 species and assorted hybrids (Fig. 3). Along this highway 2 miles west of Dayton, Texas, all 6 hybrid combinations plus the 4 parental species have been identified with certainty in a single pasture.

OBSERVATIONS AND RESULTS—*Morphological attributes of the individual species*—Although the 4 species considered here differ greatly in their general form and gross appearance, one must rely, in addition, upon a group of specific key characters in the detection and validation of hybrids. In general, hybrids are intermediate in their morphological characters, and *Baptisia* hybrids are not exceptional. Table 2 presents a summary of the distinguishing features of the 4 species. Figures 10, 11 illustrate the 4 species and the 6 hybrids.

Chromatographic attributes of the individual species—We have analyzed the constituents of these and other *Baptisia* species intensively by 1- and 2-dimensional chromatography utilizing many solvent combinations and extraction techniques. Many plant parts have been investigated, including stems, leaves, petals, fruits, sepals and even the stamens. Compounds such as free amino acids, the lupine alkaloids and

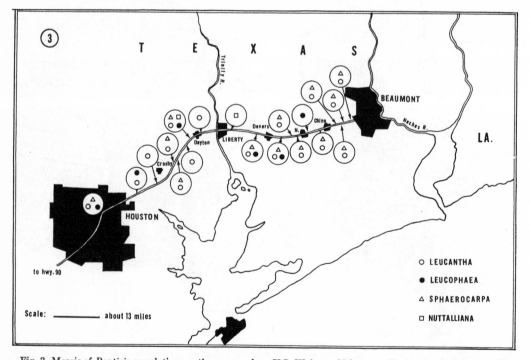

Fig. 3. Mosaic of *Baptisia* populations as they occur along U.S. Highway 90 between Houston and Beaumont, Texas. Sympatry at any one site is shown by the symbols included in the circles.

TABLE 2. *Morphological characters which distinguish the species of Baptisia being considered*[a]

| Character | Species | | | | List of all 6 possible 2-way hybrids between the species |
	B. sphaerocarpa	B. leucophaea	B. nuttalliana	B. leucantha	
Ovary					
Pubescence	glabrous	densely villous	densely villous	glabrous	B. leucophaea × sphaerocarpa
Ovary shape	globose	ovoid-elliptic	ovoid to sub-globose	obovoid	B. nuttalliana × sphaerocarpa
Ovary wall	thick, indurate	thin, fragile	thin, fragile	thin, firm	B. leucantha × sphaerocarpa
Ovules per ovary	2–5	11–15	6–10	16–24	B. leucophaea × nuttalliana
Flower color	bright yellow	pale yellow	bright yellow	white	B. leucantha × leucophaea
Stipules	absent	conspicuous persistent (20–40 mm long)	absent or caducous	conspicuous persistent (10–15 mm long)	B. leucantha × nuttalliana
Pedicel length	1–5 mm	25–40 mm	2–4 mm	10–15 mm	(So far as known, when the characters are combined in the F₁ the resulting characters are intermediate or nearly so.)
Flower arrangement	in racemes, evenly disposed	in racemes, secund	single in leaf axil	in racemes, whorled at nodes	
Petiole length	2–7 mm	3–6 mm	0.5–1 mm	8–15 mm	
Raceme condition	stiffly erect	abruptly reflexed	racemes absent (flowers single)	erect, elongate, lax	

[a] Ten selected characters which serve, singly or in combination, to identify the 4 *Baptisia* species in this study. At least 20 additional characters could be added to the list.

anthocyanins, although useful in other ways, have not proven to be of much practical value in the documentation of hybrids. We have concentrated upon miscellaneous substances extractable in 0.5% HCl in methanol. These extracts were chromatographed in 2 solvents: (1) 22 hr in t-butanol: acetic acid: water (3:1:1); and (2) 4 hr in 15% acetic acid. The substances visible in ultraviolet light with and without ammonia and after spraying with dinitroaniline are recorded in these investigations. Many of these substances are adjudged to be phenolic or polyphenolic, but the group may be quite heterogeneous. For example, spot #23 (Table 3), one of the few substances identified thus far, is the coumarin, scopoletin.

The chromatographic results are summarized in tabular form (Table 3) and graphically (Fig. 14). There is no need to discuss further the nature of the biochemical criteria. The chromatographic "profiles" are essentially a composite. Rare indeed is the single plant which exhibits every one of the major and minor spots. Yet, the general pattern of basic components is so reliable that one can identify a species from these patterns as rapidly and with as much accuracy as could be done from a living specimen in full flower. The work of Brehm (1962) may be consulted for documentation of the nature and extent of variation in chromatographic constituents in one of the species, *B. leucophaea*. Although the data of Table 3 and Fig. 14 represent, as accurately as possible, our present knowledge of the chromatographic patterns in these species, it is obvious that some further modifications, mostly in the nature of additions, can be expected. For example, Brehm (1962) has recently added 2 components to the profile of *B. leucophaea* which were detected in a chemical race growing along the Gulf Coast. Had these substances appeared first in a hybrid they might have been considered tentatively to be "hybrid substances."

The following sections contain brief descriptions of the 6 hybrid combinations with notes on the frequency of hybridization and methods of validating the hybrids.

Baptisia leucophaea × *B. sphaerocarpa*—Extensive hybridization of these taxa occurs in

TABLE 3. *Characteristics of components illustrated in Fig. 14*[a]

Number in Fig. 14	Appearance in various treatments				Occurrence and characteristics			
	Daylight (NH₃)	U.V.	U.V. (NH₃)	Dinitro-aniline	B. leucophaea	B. nutt.	B. sphaer.	B. leucantha
1	Y	D	bY	Y → lBr	3-A	3-A	3-A	
2	Y	D	bY	Y → lBr	3-D	3-D		
3	Y	D	Y	pY → lBr	3-A	3-A	1-F	
4	—	D	pY	lY	3-E	3-E		
5	—	D	pCr	slGyGr	3-B	3-B		
6	—	D	YGr	slBr	3-B	3-B	3-B	
7	—	D	D	slBr	3-B	3-B	3-B	{1-B, 2-A}
8	—	lB	bBGr	—	3-E	3-E	2-A	
9	—	W	W	—	3-F			
10	—	lB	BGr	—	3-A	3-A	3-A	3-A
11	—	lB	BGr	—	1-F	1-F		3-F
12	—	lB	bB	—	3-E	1-E		
13	—	CrO	bCr	—	1-E	3-E		
14	—	lB	lB	—	3-F	3-F		
15	—	GoY	GoY	—	1-F	1-E		
16	—	l	l	—	3-F	1-F		
17	—	—	—	L	3-B	3-B	3-B	3-B
18	Gy	pBrGr	pBrGr	P	3-A	3-A		3-A
19	—	pBrGr	pBrGr	P	3-D	3-D		3-D
20	—	—	—	P	1-F			
21	—	—	—	P	3-F			1-F
22	—	l	l	—	3-E	3-E		3-E
23	—	dkB	dkB	—	1-E			
24	—	dkB	dkB	—	1-E			
25	—	Y	Y	—	1-E			
26	—	pB	pB	Br/L[b]	1-F	3-F	1-F	3-F
27	—	—	—	pP	1-F			
28	—	—	—	P/P[b]	3-D			1-D
29	—	D	pY	P	3-F	1-D		
30	—	D	pY	—	2-F			
31	—	—	—	P	2-F			2-F
32	—	—	—	P	2-F			
33	—	—	—	P	2-F			2-F
34	—	D	D	Gy → BrO		3-A		
35	—	D	D	—		3-A		
36	—	D	D	Pk → PkO		3-A		
37	—	D	D	R → RB		3-A		
38	—	D	D	pGyP		3-E		
39	—	D	pYBr			3-F		
40	—	D	Pk	—		1-F		
41	—	D	—	—		1-E		
42	—	D	—	—		1-F		
43	—	—	bBGr	—		1-E		
44	—	—	BBlGr	—		1-E		
45	—	B	B	—		3-F		
46	—	—	pB	—		1-E		
47	—	bBl	bB	—		1-E		
48	—	D	D	—		2-E		
49	—	D	D	Br		2-E	3-E	
50	—	D	D	Br		2-E		
51	—	B	B	—		2F		
52	—	B	B	—		2-F		
53	—	—	B	—		2-F		
54	—	—	bB	PkL		2-F	2-F	
55	—	D	D	pY		2-F		
56	—	pD	Y	—		2-E		
57	—	—	lBr	—			1-F	
58	slPkO	D	D	RBr → bR		3-A		

TABLE 3. *Continued*

| Number in Fig. 14 | Appearance in various treatments | | | | Occurrence and characteristics | | | |
	Daylight (NH₃)	U.V.	U.V. (NH₃)	Dinitro-aniline	B. leucophaea	B. nutt.	B. sphaer.	B. leucantha
59	—	D	D	BrG			1-E	
60	—	—	—	B			1-E	
61	—	—	—	B			1-F	
62	—	D	D	slBr			1-F	
63	—	D	D	PkO			3-F	
64	—	D	D	PkO			1-F	
65	—	D	D	—				1-F
66[b]	Y	D	YGr	R			3-A	
67	—	l	l	—			2-F	
68	—	Y	YO	lBr			2-A	
69	—	Y	YO	lBr			2-A	
70	—	D	Y	—		2-E	2-E	
71	—	D	Y	—			2-E	
72	—	B	B	—			2-F	
73	—	l	l	—			2-F	
74	—	—	—	B			2-C	
75	Y	D	dkYGr	G → lBr				1-A 2-B
76	Y	D	Y	brY				1-A 2-B
77	dull Y	D	dkYGr	Go → lBr				1-A 2-B
78	Y	D	Y	pY → lBr				1-A 2-B
79	dull Y	lBr	lBr	Gr → lBr				1-A
80	—	D	D	pGr → pGyB				3-B
81	Y	D	Y	slYBr → pPkO				3-E
82	—	GoY	GoY	lBr				3-A
83	—	GoY	GoY	lBr			2-B	3-E
84	—	GoY	GoY	—				3-E
85	—	l	l	—				1-F
86	—	l	lBGr	—				3-F
87	—	Cr	Cr	—				1-F
88	—	—	—	Bl				1-F
89	—	D	OY	—				1-F
90	—	D	dkY	—				1-F
91	—	GoY	GoY	—				3-F
92	—	D	D	—				1-F
93	—	D	D	—				1-F
94	—	B	B	—				1-F
95	—	D	D	GoBr				1-E
96	—	l	l	—				3-F
97	—	D	D	Br				2-F
98	—	lB/Gr	—	—				2-E
99	—	—	—	Pk				2-F
100	—	—	—	Bl				3-F
101	—	—	—	Bl				3-F
102	—	—	Cr	sldkBl	3-F			
103	—	B/Gr	bB/Gr	—	2-D			
104	—	D	pY	—			2-B	
105	—	D	D	R → RB			1-F	
106	—	—	—	L			1-B	

[a] *Colors*: B = blue; Br = brown to tan; Cr = cream; D = dark (absorbing UV); Go = gold; Gr = green; Gy = grey; L = lavender; O = orange; P = purple; Pk = pink; R = red; W = white; Y = yellow; BrGo = rust; PkO = salmon; RBr = burnt red.

Occurrence: 1 = leaf; 2 = flower; 3 = leaf and flower.

Descriptive terms: b = bright; dk = dark; l = light; p = pale (weak); sl = slow color development.

Characteristics: A = major, constant spot; B = medium, constant spot; C = minor, constant spot; D = major, variable spot; E = medium, variable spot; F = minor, variable spot.

[b] double spot: right side br.Y in NH₃; left side Y-Gr in NH₃-UV.

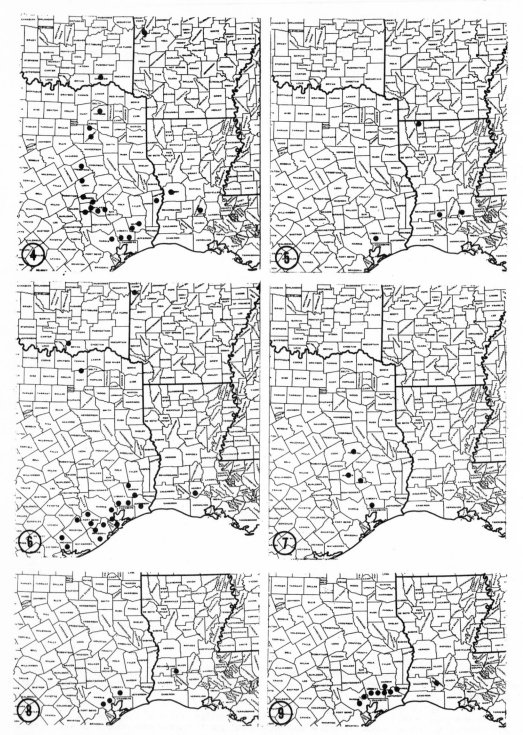

Fig. 4–9. Locations of *Baptisia* hybrids studied. All 6 possible combinations involving the 4 species are shown.—Fig. 4. *B. leucophaea* × *B. nuttalliana.*—Fig. 5. *B. leucantha* × *B. nuttalliana.*—Fig. 6. *B. leucophaea* × *B. sphaerocarpa.*—Fig. 7. *B. nuttalliana* × *B. sphaerocarpa.*—Fig. 8. *B. leucantha* × *B. leucophaea.*—Fig. 9. *B. leucantha* × *B. sphaerocarpa.* (For specific sites see Table 2.)

scattered areas in northeast Texas, Oklahoma, and especially in southeast Texas where large sympatric populations are present. Although no extensive analysis of these populations by chromatography has been attempted, it is evident that backcrossing and more complex genetic exchange occurs in these large hybrid swarms. Since hybridization has apparently been in progress in certain areas for a long period, the periphery of areas of hybridization would be an excellent place to search for biochemical evidence of introgressive hybridization.

Hybrids of *B. leucophaea* × *B. sphaerocarpa* are easily distinguished morphologically, since they are intermediate between the parental types in most characteristics. The reflexional angle of the raceme, bract size, pedicel length, the pattern of pubescence of the ovary, and fruit characters are among the salient features of this hybrid. *Baptisia leucophaea* × *B. nuttalliana* may be distinguished only with difficulty from the hybrid *B. leucophaea* × *B. sphaerocarpa* by one unfamiliar with the various hybrid types.

Chromatographically, the hybrid *B. leucophaea* × *B. sphaerocarpa* is readily identified since a number of major species-specific substances (for this combination) occur together in the hybrid. The hybrid chromatographic pattern is essentially a summation of the parental patterns with some quantitative reduction of individual components. Components especially useful in validating the *B. leucophaea* × *B. sphaerocarpa* hybrids are: 2, 3, 4, 5, 23, 24; 18 and 19 from *B. leucophaea*; and 29, 49, 58, 66, 68, 69, 70, 71 and 83 from *B. sphaerocarpa*.

Baptisia leucophaea × *B. nuttalliana*—These species hybridize in scattered locations over a large area of east Texas, western Louisiana, southwest Arkansas and southeast Oklahoma, but the most extensive area of hybridization centers around Huntsville, Texas. Little information is available at this time on the population structure of these hybrid swarms, but it is unlikely that chromatographic techniques alone will be able to provide adequate data for the analysis of backcrossing or related events.

Hybrids of *B. leucophaea* × *B. nuttalliana* may comprise 10% or more of a population in which both species are equally represented. The hybrids are readily distinguished morphologically when

Fig. 10. Photographs of the 4 species of *Baptisia*: (A) *B. leucophaea*; (B) *B. leucantha*; (C) *B. nuttalliana*; and (D) *B. viridis*.

only the 2 species are involved. However, when
B. sphaerocarpa is present, as noted above, it
may be difficult in some instances to distinguish
the hybrid *B. leucophaea* × *B. nuttalliana* from
the hybrid *B. leucophaea* × *B. sphaerocarpa*.
Shorter racemes and a more pubescent foliage
are characteristic of the former hybrid.

Validation of a *B. leucophaea* × *B. nuttalliana*
hybrid by chromatography is possible, but analysis must be made from stem material. Although
a number of leaf components of *B. nuttalliana* are
absent from *B. leucophaea*, this latter species has
no reliable leaf or flower components absent
from *B. nuttalliana*, on the basis of present

Fig. 11. Photographs of the six 2-way hybrid types: (A) *B. leucantha* × *B. leucophaea*; (B) *B. leucantha* × *B. nut-talliana*; (C) *B. leucophaea* × *B. nuttalliana*; (D) *B. nuttalliana* × *B. sphaerocarpa*; (E) *B. leucophaea* × *B. sphaero-carpa*; and (F) *B. leucantha* × *B. sphaerocarpa*.

knowledge. Components 23 and 24 of *B. leuco-phaea* are potentially useful, but they may be reduced or absent, especially in young plants. However, in the stems of mature hybrid plants, components 23 and 24 of *B. leucophaea* are reliable and distinct. Additionally, components 43 and 44 of *B. nuttalliana* are present in this hybrid. A few other minor distinctions of the hybrid's stem extract added to data from leaves and flowers allow a reasonably certain identification of *B. leucophaea* × *B. nuttalliana* hybrids by chromatography. Components 34, 35, 36, 37, 43 and 44, which are specific for *B. nuttalliana* (in this combination) and which represent major components, often appear reduced and sometimes even absent from hybrids. Since the behavior of these components in the individual hybrids is rather inconsistent, no exact description of these substances in the hybrid is possible at present. There is no difficulty in determining by means of chromatography whether a putative hybrid is derived from *B. leucophaea* × *B. nuttalliana* or *B. leucophaea* × *B. sphaerocarpa*.

Baptisia leucantha × *B. leucophaea*—Thus far, only 4 definitive hybrids involving these species have been discovered, each in a separate population in 3 counties in Texas and 1 in Louisiana (Table 1). Since sympatric populations of these 2 species have been examined carefully without yielding any clear evidence of hybridization, it may be assumed that such hybrids are rare. It is significant that of the known hybrids, none was found in large sympatric populations of the 2 parental species; 1 hybrid was found in the complex Dayton site described earlier; 1 was found with a single member of each parental species, 1 was found along a roadside with only a few *B. leucantha* individuals in the adjacent woods and no *B. leucophaea* in the immediate area, and 1 was found in an area with only a few members of each species present.

Hybrids between *B. leucophaea* and *B. leucantha* are morphologically distinctive by virtue of the pale-yellowish flowers, definitely reflexed racemes, and bract and fruit characters. Color of inflorescence, presence of bracts, and fruit form serve to distinguish this hybrid from hybrids of *B. leucantha* × *B. nuttalliana*, but with superficial examination the 2 hybrids may appear similar.

Chromatographically, the hybrid *B. leucantha* × *B. leucophaea* is easily validated since numerous species-specific components are contributed from each parent. Yet, in an area where hybrids of *B. leucantha* × *B. nuttalliana* were also present, as at the Dayton site, chromatographic data alone would not serve to distinguish the 2 types of hybrids. In such combinations, combined morphological and biochemical data rae required. Components useful in validating the hybrid of *B. leucantha* × *B. leucophaea* are: 1, 2, 3, 4, 5, 6, 7, 23, 24 from the former, and 75, 76, 77, 78, 79, 80, 81, 82, 83, and 85 from the latter.

Baptisia nuttalliana × *B. sphaerocarpa*—Relatively few hybrids of this origin have been fully validated. One definite hybrid from the Dayton population and 1 from Huntsville, Texas, have been found, and 2 other probable hybrids have been collected. In each instance, except for the plant collected in the complex Dayton population, the hybrid was found together with 1 or a very few individuals of *B. sphaerocarpa*, apparently introduced, among a larger population of *B. nuttalliana*. Large sympatric populations of these 2 species have not yet been found, although they probably exist.

This hybrid is intermediate morphologically between the parents for individual characters but is slightly more *B. sphaerocarpa*-like in gross appearance. The inflorescence is a shortened raceme, and some single axillary flowers occur. The fruit is distinctive in the hybrid, *B. sphaerocarpa*-like in form, but pubescent when young and darkening with age as in *B. nuttalliana*. This hybrid could be confused with backcrosses of *B. leucophaea* × *B. sphaerocarpa* to *B. sphaerocarpa* but is otherwise rather easily recognized.

Chromatographically, this hybrid is easily validated, provided that flowers are available, although there is the usual problem of ascertaining the presence of *B. nuttalliana* rather than *B. leucophaea*. This is best done by means of components 43 and 44 of *B. nuttalliana* and, to some extent, with components 34–37. Flowers provide the *B. sphaerocarpa*-specific substances 70, 71, 69 and 104. It is possible that components 68 (*B. sphaerocarpa*) and 15 (*B. nuttalliana*) are identical. When only *B. nuttalliana* and *B. sphaerocarpa* occur together in an area, hybrids may be identified by components 58, 66, 69, 70, 71 and 104 from *B. sphaerocarpa* and components 2, 3, 4, 43, 44, 18, 19, 34, 35, 36, and 37 (the last 4 with less reliability) from *B. nuttalliana*. Component 29, a major constant spot in *B. sphaerocarpa*, is sometimes present in *B. nuttalliana*.

Baptisia leucantha × *B. nuttalliana*—Only a few hybrid plants involving this combination have been identified with certainty. Small sympatric populations of these 2 species occur in several areas of Texas and Louisiana with little evidence of hybridization. These situations, in which relatively little hybridization occurs in sympatric populations, are partly explicable by differences in the times of flowering of the species involved.

This hybrid is distinguished by pale-yellow flowers and much shorter racemes, but it is not greatly different in its general appearance from hybrids of *B. leucantha* × *B. sphaerocarpa*. It is not likely to be easily confused with other hybrid types.

Chromatographically, this hybrid is rather similar to the *B. leucantha* × *B. leucophaea* hybrid, and when all 3 species occur together, a combined morphological and chromatographic analysis is required to prove the identity of a particular plant. Otherwise, the hybrid is quite distinctive and numerous species-specific components are introduced with each parental genome. Components useful in validating this hybrid are 1, 2, 3, 4, 5, 6, 7, 29, 43, and 44 from *B. nuttalliana* and 75, 76, 77, 78, 79, 80, 81, 85, 86, 82, 83 and 84 from *B. leucantha*. Components 34–37, from *B. nuttalliana*, tend to be somewhat obscured in the hybrid and appear to be present in lesser amounts. All hybrids involving *B. leucantha* are potentially useful in the chromatographic analysis of the population structure of hybrid swarms, but only in the instance of *B. leucantha* × *B. sphaerocarpa* hybrids is the incidence of hybrids in the population high enough to warrant an intensive population study.

Baptisia leucantha × *B. sphaerocarpa*—Numerous hybrids of this type have been found in southeast Texas and southwestern Louisiana. In sympatric populations, the hybrid may comprise only a small percentage of the total population, but such populations are quite numerous. This hybrid is perhaps the most distinctive of those discussed here. It is a robust plant, more like *B. leucantha* in general habit but having more numerous racemes and intermediate yellow flowers. The fruit is intermediate between the light-brown, small, globose, thick-walled type of *B. sphaerocarpa* and the large, inflated, thin-walled black fruit of *B. leucantha*. It is possible that one unfamiliar with the hybrid types would confuse this hybrid with the *B. leucantha* × *B. nuttalliana* hybrid.

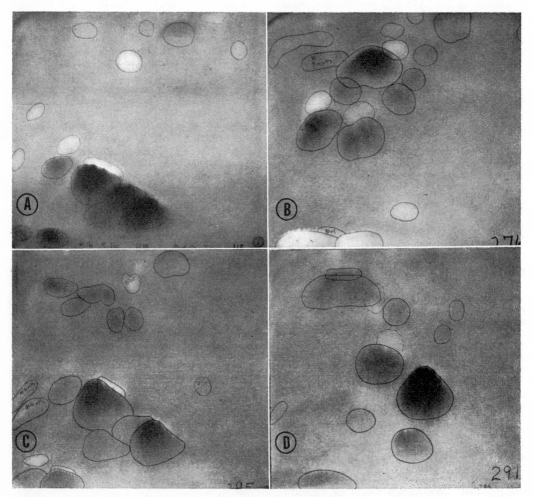

Fig. 12, 13. Chromatograms of leaf extracts photographed in ultraviolet light. Most of the dark spots (absorbing ultraviolet) fluoresce with characteristic color in presence of ammonia vapor. The placement of these chromatograms matches the placement of the corresponding plants of Fig. 10, 11.

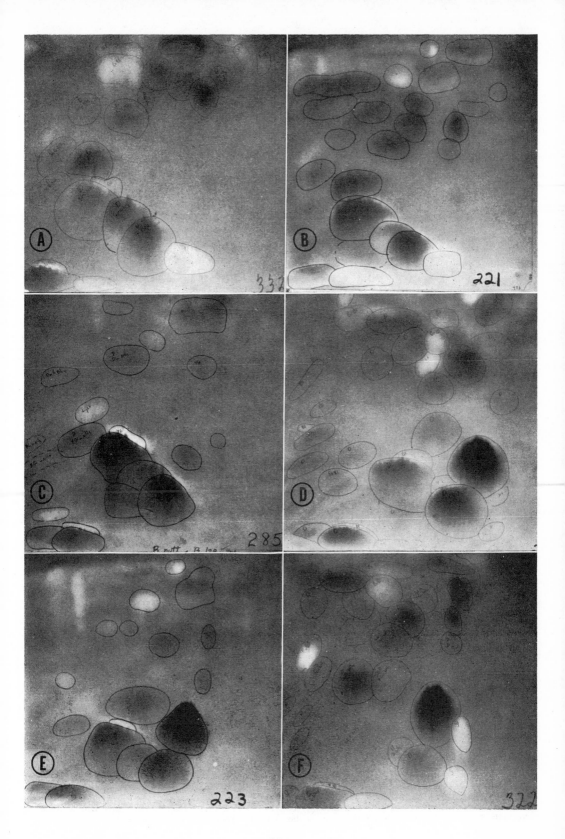

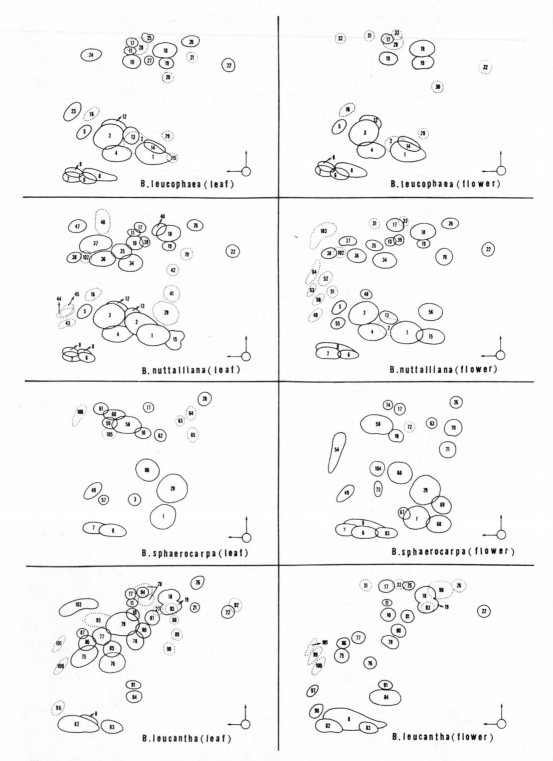

Fig. 14. Composite chromatographic maps of the components of the leaves and the flowers of the 4 species of *Baptisia*. Table 3 contains a description of certain of the properties of the compounds illustrated. Dotted lines refer to compounds which have been selected arbitrarily as inconsistently present following examination of chromatograms of numerous individuals of each species. Absence of one or more of this group of substances may be insignificant.

This hybrid is the easiest of all known *Baptisia* hybrids to validate chromatographically, since almost all of the major components are limited to one or the other parental species. Such a large number of species-specific components is available in this hybrid that analysis of backcrossing patterns is quite feasible. At least 1 probable backcross type (to *B. leucantha*) has now been collected. In this hybrid combination the components 68, 69, 70, and 71, which are found in flowers only of *B. sphaerocarpa*, occur in the leaves as well as in the flowers (Alston and Simmons, 1962). These components had previously been considered as "hybrid specific" substances (Alston and Turner, 1962). Components which are useful in the study of this hybrid are 1, 6, 7, 29, 49, 58, 66, 68, 69, 70, 71, and 104, from *B. sphaerocarpa*, and 18, 19, 75, 76, 77, 78, 79, 80, 81, 82, 83, 84, 85 and 86, fro ᛃ *B. leucantha*. This hybrid is so distinctive chromatographically that even a part of 1 leaflet is sufficient to establish its identity with certainty.

CONCLUSIONS—It has been shown that the documentation of natural hybridization by chromatographic techniques is not only a new approach to an old problem but also provides certain types of data not obtainable by morphological criteria alone. The technique is particularly useful in determining the composition of complex hybridizing populations and in the accurate determination of a specific putative hybrid in appropriate circumstances. Or even,

in some instances, as a corollary, there is provided a method for the analysis of introgression in populations peripheral to areas of hybridization. When qualitative intraspecific chemical variation occurs (as in the species *B. nuttalliana* involving particularly component 29, Table 3), this technique allows further population analysis at the species level.

LITERATURE CITED

ALSTON, R. E., AND JANIECE SIMMONS. 1962. A specific and predictable biochemical anomaly in interspecific hybrids of *Baptisia viridis* × *B. leucantha*. Nature 195: 825.

———, AND B. L. TURNER. 1962. New techniques in analysis of complex natural hybridization. Proc. Natl. Acad. Sci. (U.S.) 48: 130–137.

BREHM, B. G. 1962. The distribution of alkaloids, free amino acids, flavonoids and certain other phenolic compounds in *Baptisia leucophaea* Nutt. var. *laevicaulis* Gray and their taxonomic implications. Ph.D. Dissertation. Univ. of Texas, Austin, Texas.

LARISEY, MAXINE M. 1940a. A monograph of the genus *Baptisia*. Ann Missouri Bot. Gard. 27: 119–258.

———. 1940b. Analysis of a hybrid complex between *Baptisia leucantha* and *Baptisia viridis* in Texas. Amer. Jour. Bot. 27: 624–628.

TURNER, B. L. 1959. Legumes of Texas. Univ. of Texas Press, Austin.

———, AND R. E. ALSTON. 1959. Segregation and recombination of chemical constituents in a hybrid swarm of *Baptisia laevicaulis* × *B. viridis* and their taxonomic implications. Amer. Jour. Bot. 46: 678–686.

HYBRID COMPOUNDS IN NATURAL INTERSPECIFIC HYBRIDS*

By R. E. Alston, H. Rösler,† K. Naifeh, and T. J. Mabry

CELL RESEARCH INSTITUTE AND DEPARTMENT OF BOTANY, UNIVERSITY OF TEXAS

Communicated by Wilson S. Stone, September 9, 1965

Since the more recent applications of chemical methods to the study of natural interspecific hybridization, there has been considerable interest in the theoretical question of whether or not new structural configurations occur in such hybrids; i.e., hybrid-specific products formed by the combined enzymatic complements of the parents. Many years ago, Reichert[1] called attention to the fact that hybrids occasionally exhibited unexpected flower colors. The appearance of new compounds has been suggested from chemical analyses of interspecific hybrids. Alston and Turner[2] described four hybrid-specific flavonoids in the leaves of the hybrid *Baptisia leucantha* × *B. sphaerocarpa*, but the compounds were later shown to occur in the flower petals of the latter species.[3] Other sporadic suggestions of the occurrence of such hybrid-specific substances have not been followed by definitive experimental proof of their existence. Diverse genetic studies of flavonoid compounds (the only such extensively investigated plant secondary compounds) have invariably shown that simple mendelian mechanisms govern qualitative differences in these compounds.[4] From current knowledge of the types of flavonoid compounds which are widely distributed in plants, it is possible to predict a large number of ways in which hybrid substances might occur. This question is important to systematic studies utilizing variability in the patterns of secondary compounds as systematic criteria.

We are concerned here with a number of hypothetical compounds which could be expected to exist in the following natural hybrids of *Baptisia: B. leucantha* × *B. sphaerocarpa; B. alba* × *B. tinctoria;* and *B. alba* × *B. perfoliata.* Other hybrid-type molecules may be predicted to occur in other known *Baptisia* hybrid combina-

Reprinted by permission of T. J. Mabry and the National
Academy of Sciences (Washington) from PROCEEDINGS OF THE
NATIONAL ACADEMY OF SCIENCES, **54**, 1458–1465 (1965).

tions, but in these other situations the necessary chemical investigations have not yet been completed. Since we are concerned at this time only with flavonol glycosides of the kaempferol and quercetin series, the numbering system assigned to the flavonol nucleus should provide sufficient information to follow the discussion (Fig. 1).

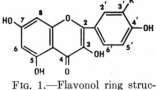

FIG. 1.—Flavonol ring structure and numbering system. Kaempferol, R = H; quercetin, R = OH.

Identification of Flavonoids.—Chromatographic methods for the crude plant extracts and for the detection of the flavonoids were similar to those reported in our previous work.[5] Complete characterization of the glycosidic moieties of compounds 74, 75, and 77 has not been achieved, but it is known that 74 is a 3-monoglycoside of quercetin, and 75 and 77 are 3-mono- and diglycosides of kaempferol, respectively. The complete chemical characterization of these compounds is not central to the present discussion.

Compound 76 is rutin; (quercetin 3-[6-0-(α-L-rhamno)-β-D-glucoside] i.e., quercetin 3-β-rutinoside). It has been isolated from *Baptisia alba* and identified, utilizing such chemical criteria as NMR spectroscopy and by comparison with authentic material.

The details of the structure elucidation of compounds 68–71 of *Baptisia sphaerocarpa* will be reported elsewhere;[6] therefore, the different techniques required will only be summarized here. Compounds 70 and 71 were obtained crystalline and their structures were determined primarily by NMR spectroscopy of the trimethylsilyl ethers.[7a] Independent confirmation of the glucosyl moieties was effected by enzyme hydrolysis with emulsin.[8] In addition, acid hydrolysis of all the glycosidic linkages followed by gas chromatographic analysis of the trimethylsilylated sugars[7b] determined the nature of the individual sugars present. Compound 71 is quercetin 3-β-D-glucosyl-7-β-rutinoside, and compound 70 is quercetin 3,7-di-β-D-glucoside. Compound 71 was converted to a 5,3',4'-trimethyl-ether whose NMR spectrum was identical in all respects with the spectrum of the compound obtained by oxidation of hesperidin (5,3'-dihydroxy-4'-methoxy-flavanone-7-β-rutinoside) to the corresponding flavonol, glucosylation at the 3-position, and finally methylation of the phenolic hydroxyl groups. This confirms the identification of compound 71 as quercetin 3-β-D-glucosyl-7-β-rutinoside. Compound 69, a product of partial hydrolysis of 71 with 10 per cent acetic acid, is quercetin 7-β-rutinoside; 3-glycosyl groups are units known to be rapidly hydrolyzed by acid treatment relative to the 7-glycosyl group. Compound 68, a product obtained by partial acid hydrolysis of quercetin 3,7-di-β-D-glucoside (70), is quercetin 7-β-D-glucoside.

A compound designated as 71a occurs in *Baptisia alba* and chromatographs the same as compound 71. However, it yields rutin (76), upon hydrolysis by emulsin. Thus, compound 71a is quercetin 3-β-rutinoside-7-β-D-glucoside and differs from compound 71 only in the position of attachment of the sugar moieties to the quercetin nucleus. Quercetin 3-β-rutinoside-7-β-D-glucoside was subsequently synthesized from rutin, and the synthetic material ran at the same chromatographic position as compound 71a isolated from *B. alba*, thus providing additional proof of the identification of compound 71a.

Kaempferol 7-β-neohesperidoside was obtained from the flavanone glycoside naringin by standard methods. Partial hydrolysis of the neohesperidoside afforded

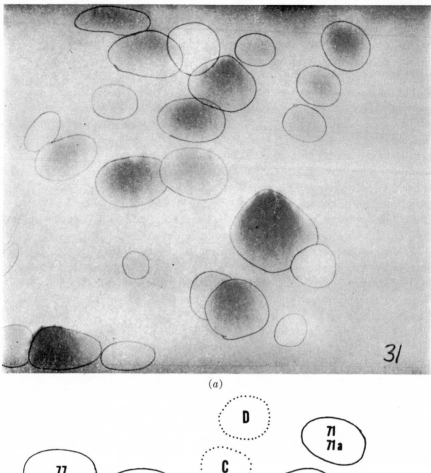

(a)

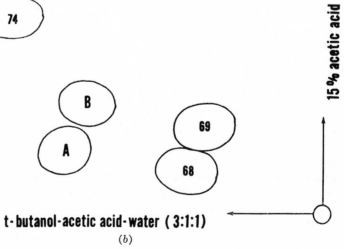

15 % acetic acid

t-butanol-acetic acid-water (3:1:1)

(b)

kaempferol 7-β-glucoside. Kaempferol glycosides of the duckweed, *Wolffia punctata*,[9] were utilized to establish the probable locations of kaempferol analogues of compounds 70 and 71a.

Figure 2 illustrates the positions of the various compounds which have been discussed above as they occur in the two-dimensional solvent system used for screening purposes. The actual chromatogram is derived from a natural hybrid.

Results.—Table 1 indicates the known flavonol compounds found in the four species now being considered. The yellow-flowered species (*B. perfoliata, B.*

TABLE 1

FLAVONOLS OF *Baptisia* SPECIES

	B. leu.		B. alba		B. sphaerocarpa		B. tinctoria		B. perfoliata	
	L	F	L	F	L	F	L	F	L	F
Quercetin 3-glycoside 74	+	tr	+	tr	0	+	0	0	0	0
Quercetin 3-rutinoside 76	+	tr	+++	+	0	tr	0	0	0	0
Kaempferol 3-glycoside 75	+	tr	0	0	0	0	0	0	0	0
Kaempferol 3-diglycoside 77	+	tr	+	tr	0	0	0	0	0	0
Quercetin 7-β-D-glucoside 68	0	0	0	0	0	+	0	+	0	0
Quercetin 7-β-rutinoside 69	0	0	0	0	0	+	0	+	0	0
Quercetin 3,7-di-β-D-glucoside 70	0	0	tr	tr	0	+	0	+	0	0
Quercetin 3-β-D-glucosyl-7-β-rutinoside 71*	0	0	0	0	0	+	0	+	0	0
Quercetin 3-β-rutinosyl-7-β-D-glucoside 71a*	0	0	+	+	0	0	0	0	0	0

* Originally considered to be a single compound.
+++, The major flavonoid component; +, present in moderate concentration; tr, trace; 0, not detected.

sphaerocarpa, and *B. tinctoria*) produce either no flavonols at all or 7- or 3,7-glycosides of quercetin. The white-flowered species (*B. leucantha* and *B. alba*) produce flavonol 3-mono- and 3-diglycosides of both kaempferol and quercetin. *B. leucantha* produces no 7-glycosides, but *B. alba* produces certain 3,7-glycosides of quercetin only. Figure 3a–c illustrates the compounds of the groups discussed here which are present in the combinations of parental species and their hybrids.

By consulting the data of Table 1 and Figure 3 it may be seen that in certain

FIG. 2.—(*a*) Two-dimensional chromatogram of leaf extract of natural hybrid between *Baptisia leucantha* and *B. sphaerocarpa* showing compounds of interest to the present study. (*b*) Compounds of the hybrid shown in (*a*) which are relevant to the present discussion: (*68*) quercetin 7-β-D-glucoside; (*69*) quercetin 7-β-rutinoside; (*70*) quercetin 3,7-di-β-D-glucoside; (*71*) quercetin 3-β-D-glucosyl-7-β-rutinoside; (*71a*) quercetin 3-β-rutinosyl-7-β-D-glucoside; (*74*) quercetin 3-glycoside; (*75*) kaempferol 3-glycoside; (*76*) quercetin 3-β-rutinoside; (*77*) kaempferol 3-diglycoside. The following compounds do not appear in the hybrid, but theoretically could have occurred in the hybrid: (*A*) kaempferol 7-β-D-glucoside; (*B*) kaempferol 7-diglycoside; (*C*) kaempferol 3,7-diglycoside; and (*D*) kaempferol triglycoside.

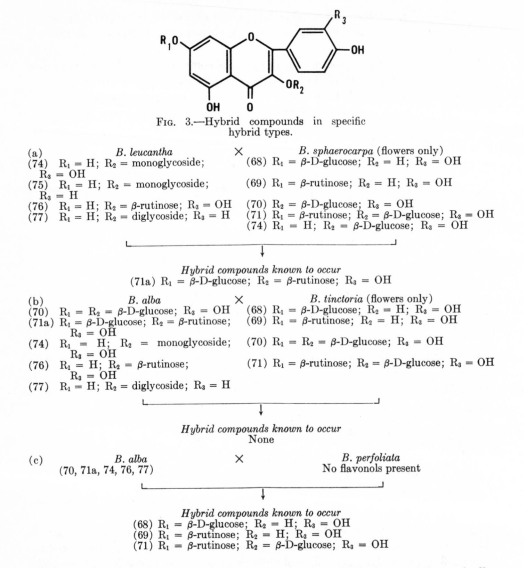

Fig. 3.—Hybrid compounds in specific
hybrid types.

(a)   *B. leucantha* $\times$ *B. sphaerocarpa* (flowers only)

(74) $R_1 = H$; $R_2 =$ monoglycoside;   (68) $R_1 = \beta$-D-glucose; $R_2 = H$; $R_3 = OH$

      $R_3 = OH$

(75) $R_1 = H$; $R_2 =$ monoglycoside;   (69) $R_1 = \beta$-rutinose; $R_2 = H$; $R_3 = OH$

      $R_3 = H$

(76) $R_1 = H$; $R_2 = \beta$-rutinose; $R_3 = OH$ (70) $R_2 = \beta$-D-glucose; $R_3 = OH$

(77) $R_1 = H$; $R_2 =$ diglycoside; $R_3 = H$ (71) $R_1 = \beta$-rutinose; $R_2 = \beta$-D-glucose; $R_3 = OH$

                                          (74) $R_1 = H$; $R_2 = \beta$-D-glucose; $R_3 = OH$

$\downarrow$

Hybrid compounds known to occur

(71a) $R_1 = \beta$-D-glucose; $R_2 = \beta$-rutinose; $R_3 = OH$

(b)   *B. alba* $\times$ *B. tinctoria* (flowers only)

(70) $R_1 = R_2 = \beta$-D-glucose; $R_3 = OH$ (68) $R_1 = \beta$-D-glucose; $R_2 = H$; $R_3 = OH$

(71a) $R_1 = \beta$-D-glucose; $R_2 = \beta$-rutinose;   (69) $R_1 = \beta$-rutinose; $R_2 = H$; $R_3 = OH$

        $R_3 = OH$

(74) $R_1 = H$; $R_2 =$ monoglycoside;   (70) $R_1 = R_2 = \beta$-D-glucose; $R_3 = OH$

        $R_3 = OH$

(76) $R_1 = H$; $R_2 = \beta$-rutinose;   (71) $R_1 = \beta$-rutinose; $R_2 = \beta$-D-glucose; $R_3 = OH$

        $R_3 = OH$

(77) $R_1 = H$; $R_2 =$ diglycoside; $R_3 = H$

$\downarrow$

Hybrid compounds known to occur

None

(c)   *B. alba* $\times$ *B. perfoliata*

    (70, 71a, 74, 76, 77)   No flavonols present

$\downarrow$

Hybrid compounds known to occur

(68) $R_1 = \beta$-D-glucose; $R_2 = H$; $R_3 = OH$

(69) $R_1 = \beta$-rutinose; $R_2 = H$; $R_3 = OH$

(71) $R_1 = \beta$-rutinose; $R_2 = \beta$-D-glucose; $R_3 = OH$

hybrid combinations a number of hybrid structural configurations are theoretically
possible. As noted in previous reports,[3] the flavonoid chemistry of *Baptisia* hybrids
is typically the summation of the compounds present in the two parental species.
This report concerns only the presence or absence of those compounds of Table 1 in
the appropriate hybrid type.

Since smaller quantities of the hybrids were available, all of the analyses of
specific compounds in hybrid types were conducted by means of paper chromatography. In certain situations, wherein a mixture of compounds 71 and 71a was
theoretically possible, the material was eluted from the paper chromatogram, purified over polyamide, and then subjected to acid hydrolysis and enzyme hydrolysis
with emulsin. Figure 4 illustrates the result of enzymatic hydrolysis of the material
from the position on the chromatogram of compound 71 in the hybrid, *B. alba* $\times$

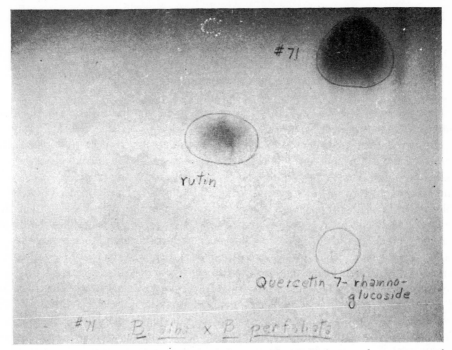

FIG. 4.—Results of enzyme hydrolysis of the area of spot 71 from a chromatogram of leaf extract of natural hybrid between *Baptisia alba* and *B. perfoliata*. Evidence of the presence of the hybrid compound, 71a, is provided by the appearance of rutin as a hydrolysis product.

B. perfoliata. Products of this hydrolysis were rutin and quercetin 7-β-rutinoside.

Following is a brief summary of the results of analyses of the three hybrid combinations.

Baptisia leucantha × *B. sphaerocarpa*: No kaempferol glycosides were detected in the hybrids analyzed. In a few hybrids, traces of yellow-fluorescing compounds were present at similar positions. There was no evidence of any increase in these compounds in the hybrid. The hybrid compound, quercetin 3-β-rutinoside-7-β-D-glucoside, was definitely present but in lesser amounts than the corresponding triglycoside isomer, compound 71.

Baptisia alba × *B. tinctoria*: The only theoretically possible hybrid compounds in this combination are the kaempferol glycosides but none were produced. However, all four flavonols found only in the flowers of *B. tinctoria* were also present regularly in the leaves of this hybrid. The area of spot 71 also contained a mixture of about equal quantities of 71 and 71a. Thus, this situation is similar to that of the hybrid, *B. leucantha* × *B. sphaerocarpa*.

Baptisia alba × *B. perfoliata*: Since *B. perfoliata* produces no flavonols in either its flowers or leaves, no hybrid types are theoretically to be expected. However, this hybrid contained all of the compounds present in the hybrid, *B. alba* × *B. tinctoria* in approximately the same amounts. Again, the area of spot 71, upon hydrolysis, was shown to consist of a mixture of compounds 71 and 71a. We conclude from these results that three hybrid-specific compounds are formed in this instance (compound 70 was already present in the *B. alba* parent).

Discussion.—The distributions of the series of quercetin 7-glycosides and querce-tin 3,7-di- and triglycosides (compounds 68–71) among the three yellow-flowered species, *B. tinctoria*, *B. sphaerocarpa*, and *B. perfoliata*, and in hybrids involving these species, illustrate two modes of formation of hybrid compounds. As noted, *B. tinctoria* and *B. sphaerocarpa* produce compounds 68–71 in their flowers but not in their leaves, while *B. perfoliata* does not produce these substances at all. The fact that compounds 68–71 are found in leaves only in certain hybrid combinations in-volving *B. sphaerocarpa*, indeed in those combinations which on other grounds would be regarded as wide crosses, led us to speculate that in such hybrids a regu-latory mechanism which normally restricted the presence of such compounds to the leaves was interrupted.[10] We interpret the situation involving *B. perfoliata* similarly except that in this species the four compounds are not produced in detect-able amounts either in leaf or flower. If this interpretation is correct, then the series of hybrid compounds in the cross *B. alba* × *B. perfoliata* is synthesized by an enzyme system latent in *B. perfoliata* but activated in the simultaneous presence of the *B. alba* genome. This hypothesis cannot be proved by the evidence presented here, but it is strongly suggested, however, since *B. alba* does not apparently produce any flavonol or flavone 7-β-rutinosides while *B. perfoliata* makes mostly 7-rutinosides of flavones. Genetic tests designed to breed out the regulating system of *B. perfoliata* in reciprocal backcrossings to that parent might succeed, but in this ma-terial such a program is relatively slow. Now that some success has been achieved *in vitro* with enzymatic flavonoid glycosylation,[11] it may be more efficient to at-tempt *in vitro* glycosylation at the 7 position to yield quercetin 7-β-rutinoside, or to resort to sterile tissue culture of the hybrid and parents under a wide range of con-ditions of growth with the objective of placing enough physiological stress on the system to interrupt the regulatory mechanism. As an alternative explanation, compounds 68, 69, and 71 of the hybrid *B. alba* × *B. perfoliata* could be synthesized in part by enzymes provided specifically by either parent. This is the interpreta-tion we propose to explain the existence of compound 71a in the hybrid *B. leucantha* × *B. sphaerocarpa*. At this time, we favor the position that the two occurrences of hybrid-specific compounds involve different mechanisms.

This work suggests that there is generally a high degree of enzyme specificity con-trolling the production of flavonoid types. It is especially notable in the lack of production of 7-β-D-glycosides of kaempferol, although the kaempferol nucleus is synthesized by one parent in three different situations. Even the hybrid com-pound, 71a, in the hybrid *B. leucantha* × *B. sphaerocarpa*, is produced in much less quantity than is compound 71.

We conclude from this work that truly hybrid compounds may be produced in interspecific hybrids, and that considerable enzyme specificity governing even these secondary compounds may be expected.

* This work was supported by a grant (GM-11111-03) from the National Institutes of Health.

† Present address: Organic Chemistry Institute, University of Zurich, Zurich, Switzerland.

[1] Reichert, E. T., *Carnegie Inst. Wash. Publ. 270*, part I, 1–376; part II, 377–834 (1919).

[2] Alston, R. E., and B. L. Turner, these Proceedings, **48**, 130–137 (1962).

[3] Alston, R. E., and B. L. Turner, in *Taxonomic Biochemistry and Serology*, ed. C. A. Leone (New York: Ronald Press, 1964), pp. 225–238.

[4] Alston, R. E., in *The Biochemistry of Phenolic Compounds*, ed. J. B. Harborne (New York: Academic Press, 1964), pp. 171–204.

[5] Alston, R. E., and B. L. Turner, *Am. J. Bot.*, **50**, 159–173 (1963).

[6] Rösler, H., J. Kagan, and T. J. Mabry, in preparation.

[7] (a) Mabry, T. J., J. Kagan, and H. Rösler, *Phytochemistry*, **4**, 177–183 (1965); (b) Kagan, J., and T. J. Mabry, *Anal. Chem.*, **37**, 288–289 (1965).

[8] Harborne, J. B., *Phytochemistry*, **4**, 107–120 (1965).

[9] McClure, J. W., Ph.D. dissertation, The University of Texas, Austin, 1964.

[10] Alston, R. E., and J. Simmons, *Nature*, **195**, 825 (1962).

[11] Barber, G. A., *Biochemistry*, **1**, 463–468 (1962).

SECTION IV

Field and Garden Studies

KRUCKEBERG, A. R. 1951. Intraspecific variability in the response of certain native plant species to serpentine soil. Amer. J. Bot. **38**: 408–419.

ERICKSON, R. O. 1945. The *Clematis Fremontii* var. *Riehlii* population in the Ozarks. Ann. Mo. Bot. Gard. **32**: 413–460.

BRADSHAW, A. D. 1959. Population differentiation in *Agrostis tenuis* Sibth. I. Morphological differentiation. New Phytol. **58**: 208–227.

LEWIS, H., and C. EPLING. 1959. *Delphinium gypsophilum*, a diploid species of hybrid origin. Evolution **13**: 511–525.

ANDERSON, E., and B. R. ANDERSON. 1954. Introgression of *Salvia apiana* and *Salvia mellifera*. Ann. Mo. Bot. Gard. **41**: 329–338.

GRANT, K. A., and V. GRANT. 1964. Mechanical isolation of *Salvia apiana* and *Salvia mellifera* (Labiatae). Evolution **18**: 196–212.

The present role of ecological and phytogeographic studies in plant systematics is not as influential as it should be. The pioneering work of Turesson, Gregor, and of the Carnegie group at Stanford demonstrates the great value of simple transplant studies in assessing morphological characters and relating them to environmental factors. The recent development of growth chambers of moderate cost now enables systematists to grow plants from diverse sources under either standard conditions or a variety of controlled conditions at any time of the year. In addition, many systematists neglect field studies in their own work, even though such studies can easily be made and could provide insights into some of the variation patterns of plants upon which they are working. Although systematists have been quick to interest themselves in the complexities of numerical taxonomy and chemotaxonomy, they are at the same time largely ignoring the possible contributions of ecological studies to their work, though these studies often involve considerably simpler techniques.

Several problems have arisen in selecting the papers for this section of the book. One problem is that many of the "ecosystematic" classics are rather lengthy. Another problem is that authors have not stressed the value of many ecological studies to systematics largely because they were either unaware of these implications or unconcerned with them. Because of the breadth and eclecticism of ecology, this section includes some strange bedfellows, although in general these papers contain at least a strong ecological flavor. They represent various aspects of ecological studies of relevance to systematics, but space permits only a portion of the wide variety of techniques and approaches of interest to systematists to be represented here.

The first paper, by Kruckeberg, deals with intraspecific variability in the ability of certain plant species to tolerate the peculiar conditions of soils derived from serpentine rocks. He demonstrates the presence of genetically determined serpentine-tolerant and serpentine-intolerant races within these species. One important taxonomic implication of this work is the demonstration that the division of a species into edaphic ecotypes does not necessarily segregate its component populations into the same groupings that would be formed by a subdivision of the species into climatic ecotypes. This indicates that the term *ecotype* cannot be applied meaningfully without an indication of the environmental condition to which the plant races are adapted since they are simultaneously adapted to diverse facets of their complex environment. The unqualified use of the word *ecotype* without a defining adjective is of little value. Secondly, Kruckeberg's work demonstrates the impracticality of using the term *ecotype* as a formal intraspecific designation which some workers have suggested should replace the term *subspecies*.

The second paper in this section by Erickson is a rather long one, but I have included it because of its emphasis on field studies as a source of information about plants, because of its strong ecological orientation, and particularly because of its biometrical approach to characterizing plant variation. Few taxa of plants have been subjected to such careful and thorough study in the field, as has *Clematis Fremontii* var. *Riehlii*.

The next study by Bradshaw has many points of similarity and contrast with those of Kruckeberg and Erickson. It is a detailed study of a single taxon in a small part of its range. In this case the plant is the grass *Agrostis tenuis* in Great Britain. Unlike Erickson, Bradshaw largely studied variation of plants collected from the field and grown under garden conditions. Bradshaw relates many patterns of variation in this grass to environmental features and interprets the adaptive significance of much of this variation. One conclusion he draws from his study is that the variation of *A. tenuis* is gradual and is in response to graded spatial differences in environmental factors. It is thus impossible to satisfactorily classify the intraspecific variation into discrete classes either by formal taxonomic terms or by those of experimental taxonomy. In these respects, *A. tenuis* offers some contrasts to the discontinuous edaphic ecotypes recognized by Kruckeberg.

The fourth paper by Lewis and Epling would be at home in the section of the book describing cytogenetic studies of plants, but since it has a strong ecogeographic theme I have included it here. These authors postulate that *Delphinium gypsophilum* of California is of hybrid orgin between two other species in the region. The apparent hybrid-derived species is morphologically, ecologically, and geographically intermediate between its reputed parents. The paper presents a sound, integrated approach to substantiating speculations concerning the origin of *D. gypsophilum*. Two particularly noteworthy features of this study are the comparisons of artificial hybrids with the naturally occurring entity of supposed hybrid origin and the argument in favor of recognizing *D. gypsophilum* as a distinct species despite its high interfertility with its relatives. This taxonomic treatment of *D. gypsophilum* is at variance with the treatment it would be given by adherents to a strict biological species concept.

Anderson's paper on *Salvia* is one of his many contributions to the study of introgression in the Andersonian manner. It presents a largely morphological analysis of two Salvias and their hybrid derivatives in which Anderson relates the hybridization between the two species to ecological disturbances. Recently, Anderson has written me that "this same area was reexamined in 1957 after it had begun to recover from one of the most destructive fires in many years. This had resulted in an explosion of *S. mellifera* and segregates resembling it (including two pure albinos) spreading way down the slope. A series of collections made at that time between Pomona and Palm Springs demonstrated the increasing importance of introgression into *S. apiana* from *S. apiana* var. *compacta* Munz, as one approached the desert. In such sites as pastures at Riverside (now part of the [University of California's] new campus) the plants of *S. apiana* were all gray-white and lower than on the mountainsides above Pomona or in the nearby washes." Despite the suggestion that *S. apiana* and *S.*

mellifera were easily hybridizable, natural hybrids between them are uncommon even though the two species are sympatric over a large area.

The Grants interested themselves in determining the nature of the isolation barriers separating these two interfertile *Salvia* species. They studied various aspects of the species' phenology and reproductive biology and concluded that a number of different interspecific isolating mechanisms were operating, among them barriers related to the different pollination systems of the two species.

INTRASPECIFIC VARIABILITY IN THE RESPONSE OF CERTAIN NATIVE PLANT SPECIES TO SERPENTINE SOIL [1]

Arthur R. Kruckeberg

EVENTS OF the Jurassic era have exerted a profound influence on the evolution of certain elements of the Californian flora. Towards the end of the deposition of Jurassic Franciscan sediments, extensive intrusions of ultrabasic igneous magma took place (Taliaferro, 1943). Later these magnesium-rich intrusive rocks became serpentinized. Many of these Franciscan sedimentary and ultrabasic rocks are exposed today in the central Coast Ranges where they have given rise to a vast array of soil types. One of these is the soil derived from serpentine rock. As in many other parts of the world, this soil in California, though considered infertile by the agriculturalist, supports a rich flora, many members of which are narrow endemics. Some of these endemic species are restricted to but one or a few small patches of serpentine.

Upon encountering such a unique and highly restricted flora as that on serpentine soils, the botanist is presented with this challenging problem: What has been the origin and evolution of such a flora? To offer only one explanation for such a complex soil-plant interrelationship would be a gross oversimplification of the problem. Undoubtedly there have been several ways in which the endemic status of serpentine species has come about. However various may have been the means, the end results—the endemic species—appear to be of two major types (Stebbins, 1942). The first consists of *depleted species*, ". . . those which formerly were widespread and genetically diverse, but have lost many or most of their biotypes." His second class consists of *insular species*, ". . . those which have developed on an island or an isolated

ecological habitat on a continent, . . ." presumably from but one or a few individuals of an ancestral species. It seems probable that both these types of endemic species are represented on the serpentine outcrops of California.

The three best-known indicator species for the serpentine habitat, *Quercus durata*, *Ceanothus Jepsoni*, and *Cupressus Sargentii*, may be interpreted as good examples of the *insular* type of endemic. Possible examples of the *depleted species* type of endemic may be found in the section Euclisia of the cruciferous genus *Streptanthus*. As defined by Morrison (1941), all of the sixteen entities in this section occur on serpentine, and the majority of them are wholly restricted to these ultrabasic outcrops. However, the distribution of at least two entities of the section Euclisia is not confined solely to serpentine. It is the distribution pattern of these two "facultative" endemics that favors the "biotype-depletion" hypothesis as a likely explanation for the serpentine endemism in this section of *Streptanthus*. A test of this hypothesis has been made on the basis of soil-tolerance studies with *Streptanthus glandulosus typicus* and *S. glandulosus secundus*; this subject is taken up in greater detail below.

Not all of the problems presented by the vegetation of serpentine areas concern the "narrow endemics" of this soil type. In California, intricate soil patterns that are a direct manifestation of the lithological complexity of the Franciscan formation are often compressed within regions of similar climate. Of course, the vegetation along a transect through this mosaic of soil types may vary considerably from one soil to the next. Certain species, however, are common to both serpentine and many of the neighboring non-serpentine soils. The occurrence on serpentine of numerous species found on other, more fertile soil types, raises the question of the genetic and physiological homogeneity of such species. Exploratory studies led to the belief that many such species were divisible into serpentine-tolerant and serpentine-intolerant races. If this could be demonstrated experimentally, such intraspecific variability in response to soil types

[1]Received for publication June 12, 1950.

A portion of a thesis presented to the Faculty of the College of Letters and Science, University of California, in partial fulfillment of the requirements for the degree of Doctor of Philosophy.

The writer is grateful to Professors L. Constance, H. L. Mason, and G. L. Stebbins, Jr. for their help and criticism during the preparation of the manuscript. To Dr. W. M. Hiesey and Dr. R. B. Walker sincere acknowledgment is given for their interest and assistance throughout the course of this study.

would afford ideal examples of edaphic ecotypes as defined by Turesson (1922) and Gregor (1944). Numerous serpentine and non-serpentine seed collections of several different species with this "bodenvag"[2] type of distribution were grown reciprocally on serpentine and non-serpentine soils at the University of California Botanical Garden. Results of some of these soil-tolerance studies will be outlined in this paper.

[2]One of two contrasting terms coined by Unger (1836). Those species requiring a specific chemical substance from the soil he termed "bodenstet," while those not restricted to a specific chemical medium were called "bodenvag."

METHODS.—*Seed collections.*—Of the several different species subjected to growth tests on serpentine soil, only the results from three will be presented in this paper. Seeds for these tests were collected by the author (except for three collections by V. Grant) in comparable, arid sites throughout the central Coast Range Area, from Santa Clara County north to Lake County. Table 1 lists the species studied, together with the collection data for the various strains of each species tested.

Cultural methods.—Each of the strains listed in Table 1 was grown from seed on both a serpentine soil and, in the case of *Gilia* and *Achillea*, on a

TABLE 1. *Origin of the strains tested for tolerance reaction to serpentine soil.*

Species and strain	Locality	Parent material of soil
Streptanthus glandulosus secundus		
S-2	Roadcut along dirt road between Guerneville and Cazadero, Sonoma County.	Sandstone
S-9	Above Mount Jackson quicksilver mine, Sonoma County.	Distintegrating serpentine
S-28	Roadcut talus, west end of Knights Valley. Sonoma County.	Shale
S. glandulosus typicus		
S-5	Talus slide at head of Russian Gulch, Sonoma County.	Sandstone
S-36	Talus slide, upper Stevens Creek, Santa Clara County.	Saussuritized gabbro
S-20	On bare areas in chaparral below Big Geysers, Sonoma County.	Serpentine
S. glandulosus typicus		
1494	Slide in upper Weldon (Mix) Canyon, Solano County.	Shale
Gilia capitata capitata		
S-108	On bare areas in chaparral, 4 miles east of Middletown, Lake County.	Serpentine
S-124	Talus below massive outcrop in Los Alamos Creek canyon, Sonoma County	Basalt
S-134	In chaparral below Conn Dam, Napa County.	Serpentine
S-180	Head of Lucas Valley, Marin County.	Serpentine
VG-7702	Near Vichy Springs, Mayacama Mountains, Napa County. (V. Grant)	Non-serpentine
VG-8246	Douglas fir-yellow pine forest near Hatchet Creek, Shasta County. (V. Grant)	Non-serpentine
G. capitata Chamissonis		
VG-8033	Sand hills, Golden Gate Park, San Francisco. (V. Grant)	Non-serpentine
Achillea borealis		
S-125	Spring Mountain road, Sonoma County.	Tuff
S-135	In chaparral below Conn Dam, Napa County.	Serpentine
S-142	Pope Creek canyon, Napa County.	Serpentine
S-161	Mill Creek, above Mission San Jose, Santa Clara County.	Shale
S-164	1 mile east of Highway 101 on Metcalf Road, Santa Clara County.	Serpentine
S-184	Head of Lucas Valley, Marin County.	Serpentine
S-198	Berkeley Hills, Alameda County.	Basalt
S-206	Bluffs above San Rafael ferry slip, Contra Costa County.	Shale

contrasting, fertile, non-serpentine soil. Growth on the latter medium served as a control by which comparisons in relative growth on serpentine soil could be made. Both the serpentine soil and the "control" soil were obtained in large quantities (2 tons of each) from open range on the Skaggs Bar X Ranch, 4 mi. east of Middletown, Lake County, California. That these two primary soils have formed under similar conditions of weathering is seen by their close proximity to one another (fig. 1). Though separated by only 200 yd., the two soils differ markedly in the vegetation they support. The serpentine soil supports a chaparral vegetation dominated by such serpentine-endemic shrubs as *Ceanothus Jepsonii* Greene, *Quercus durata* Jepson, and *Garrya Congdonii* Eastwood, as well as by the non-endemics, *Adenostema fasciculatum* H. & A., *Photinia arbutifolia* Lindl., and *Pinus Sabiniana* Dougl. The flora of the nearby non-serpentine soil consists of wide-spread annuals and the usual blue oak-and-grass vegetation typical of the inner Coast Ranges. Though much more replete with variety, the serpentine-barren vegetation nowhere exists in such dense stands as does the neighboring non-serpentine flora. This is particularly true of the annual species which are sparsely scattered over the serpentine outcrops, and the members of which are separated by completely barren areas in the serpentine community.

No exact data are available on the differences between the two soils as regards such physical factors as water-holding-capacity, wilting percentage, *etc.* However, from observations on the two soils in the field and in the garden cultures, it is apparent that the non-serpentine soil is of a finer texture and has a higher water-holding-capacity than the serpentine soil. The textural differences between the two soils become apparent when they are compared in fig. 3 and 5. In addition, the two soils can be readily contrasted in terms of chemical soil analyses. Table 2 presents some of the chemical differences between the two soil types. The data are based on cation exchange analyses of the 2 mm. fractions of oven dry soils.[3] The non-serpentine soil, mapped as Konockti gravelly clay loam, is derived from Franciscan sandstone. It differs from the serpentine soil principally in its significantly greater proportion of exchangeable calcium (71 per cent) as against 25 per cent magnesium. Of the several features which distinguish the two soils, the difference in calcium: magnesium ratios seem to be the most critical for plant growth. In this regard, Walker (1948) found that tomato and lettuce plants attained normal growth on serpentine soil only when the exchangeable-calcium level of the soil was raised to values of 25 per cent or greater. Nitrate, phosphate, and potassium amendments alone at the lower calcium levels were ineffective in decreasing the marked deficiency symptoms of plants grown on serpentine.

The various strains of *Gilia* and *Achillea* were

[3] Soils were analyzed following procedures outlined by Johnson and Epstein (1948). Data for the serpentine soil from Walker (1948).

Fig. 1. Contrast between a non-serpentine and a serpentine habitat in Lake County, California.—A. Blue oaks and annual grasses on sandstone soil.—B. Chaparral and digger pines on serpentine soil across meadow. Actual distance between the two sites is 200 yd.

TABLE 2.

Soil type	pH	Ca	Mg	K	Na	Sum	Cation-exchange capacity me./100 dry g.	Ca/Mg Ratio
		Exchangeable cations (Me./100 g. of 2 mm. dry soil)						
Serpentine	6.8	2.76	15.7	0.14	0.06	18.66	18.4	0.18
Non-serpentine	6.2	21.6	7.6	0.81	0.35	30.36	28.0	2.84

started from seed in 3-in. pots, using six pots of serpentine and six pots of non-serpentine soil for each strain. In the case of *Gilia*, 120 seeds per strain were sown, 60 to each of the two soils with 10 seeds to each pot. With *Achillea* the same procedure was followed. As soon as they were old enough the seedlings were transplanted to the same type of soil in which they had been started. The soil containers used here were large wooden crates (78 × 32 × 8 in.), the inner surfaces of which had been coated with black asphaltum varnish. These soil bins were set out at the foot of a sunny, south-facing slope at the University of California Botanical Garden. The cultures were regularly (but sparingly) watered until the end of the experiment.

The *Streptanthus* material was grown from seed to rosette stage on a smaller scale, using metal baking pans (10 ×6 × 3 in.) coated with black asphalt paint. Serpentine was the only soil used in this soil-tolerance test, good growth of *Streptanthus* on a control soil of higher fertility having been demonstrated in a previous test. The surface of each of these small culture pans containing serpentine soil was divided in half by a shallow glass strip placed on edge. A serpentine strain was then sown on one side of the glass strip and a non-serpentine strain on the other (fig. 2). These pan cultures were watered with distilled water.

Photographs, herbarium vouchers, dry weight of plant material, and other pertinent data were taken from the species in question. The herbarium specimens are deposited in the University of California herbarium.

RESULTS.—*Streptanthus glandulosus Hook.*—Certain plant groups have undergone extensive speciation on the serpentine barrens of California. Of these, the section Euclisia of the cruciferous genus *Streptanthus*, has been most thoroughly documented in its close restriction to these ultrabasic outcrops (Morrison, 1938, 1941; Stebbins, 1942; Mason, 1946). All but one of the species in this group appear to be wholly restricted to serpentine. This exception, *S. glandulosus*, is widely—but sporadically— distributed throughout the Coast Ranges of California and occurs primarily on serpentine. However, non-serpentine localities for at least two of the infraspecific units of this species recognized by Morrison (1941)—*S. glandulosus typicus* and *S. glandulosus secundus* — are occasionally encountered. Except for the parent material, these localities are quite similar ecologically to the typical ser-

pentine site: Dry, south-facing slopes with very shallow, loose soil, or, even more commonly, talus slides and road-cuts are typical for such non-serpentine collections. The soils of these non-serpentine sites are usually derived from shales and sandstones of the Franciscan formation. Since the other entities of the *S. glandulosus* complex—*S. glandulosus niger*, *S. glandulosus pulchellus*, and *S. glandulosus albidus*—as well as other closely related species are wholly restricted to serpentine, it might be supposed that the few non-serpentine forms are merely migrants from serpentine populations and have soil-tolerance ranges like those of the serpentine forms. However, such is not the case. All the non-serpentine strains of this species complex tested on serpentine proved to be serpentine-intolerant. Fig. 2 shows the response of five races to serpentine. Seed germination was not indicative of any segregation into tolerant and intolerant types. Nevertheless, in each case the subsequent growth of the non-serpentine race is much inferior to that of the serpentine race. These results were obtained from a small-scale test, using asphaltum-coated baking pans containing serpentine soil. Earlier large-scale cultures of this species in soil bins showed essentially the same reaction in seedling and later stages. Unfortunately, the species is very susceptible to aphid and fungal infections and for this reason the larger cultures had to be abandoned.

This differentiation into serpentine-tolerant and serpentine-intolerant races led to the hypothesis that many of the species common to both serpentine and non-serpentine areas would exhibit the same bipartite soil-tolerance reactions. Of the numerous species that demonstrate this edaphic differentiation, only the tests of two typical examples—*Gilia capitata* and *Achillea borealis*—will be presented here.

Gilia capitata Dougl.—*Gilia capitata* has recently been treated as a species complex by Grant (1949). In this combined cytogenetic and taxonomic study, Grant recognized six ecogeographic subspecies, all members of this common foothill annual species complex. Of these several subspecies, at least three occur on both serpentine and non-serpentine sites in the Coast Ranges. Both because of the ubiquity of the species and because of the well-founded taxonomic basis of the several subspecies, numerous seed collections of *G. capitata* were made for the purpose of testing its range of tolerance to serpentine soil. Five strains of *G. capitata capitata*—three

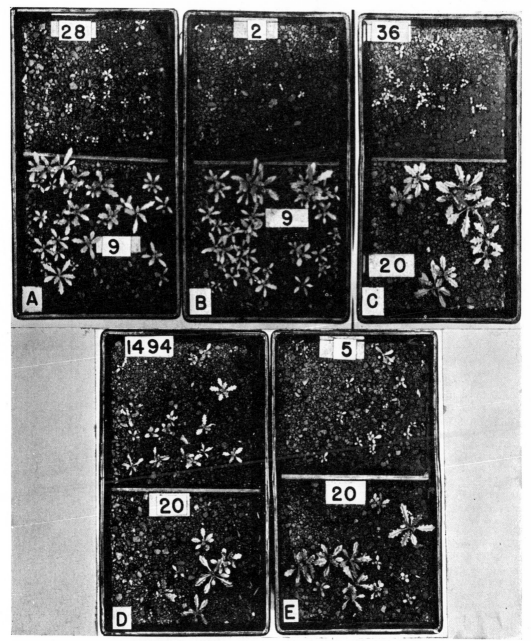

Fig. 2. Response of serpentine and non-serpentine strains of *Streptanthus glandulosus secundus* (A, B) and *S. glandulosus typicus* (C, D, E) to serpentine soil. In each case, the non-serpentine strain is in the upper half of the soil container. About one-third natural size. The numbers refer to strains as listed in table 1.

from serpentine and two from non-serpentine localities—as well as one strain of *G. capitata Chamissonis* from a non-serpentine locality, were grown reciprocally on serpentine and non-serpentine soils, following the large-scale soil bin technique outlined

above. From Table 3 it is apparent that even in the germination stages, segregation into serpentine-tolerant and serpentine-intolerant races does occur in *Gilia*. The non-serpentine strains gave an average germination of only 31 per cent while germina-

TABLE 3. *Gilia capitata.*

Locality (strain) Soil [b]	Number germinated		Per cent germinated		Average Heights (cm.)		Dry Weights (g.) [a]	
	S	NS	S	NS	S	NS	S	NS
S-108—Lake County (Serp.)	28	38	46	63	56.5	50	5.25	5.4
S-134—Napa County (Serp.)	33	43	53	72	55.5	65	3.2	4.15
S-180—Marin County (Serp.)	31	37	52	62	43	44	4.45	5.25
S-124—Sonoma County (Non-serp.)	7	28	12	46	12	54	0.42	5.45
VG-7702—Napa County (Non-serp.) [c]	29	42	48	70	7.5	35	0.32	3.51
VG-8033—San Francisco (Non-serp.)	28	55	46	93	4	18	0.11	0.95
VG-8246—Shasta County (Non-serp.)	11	43	18	72	1.7	25	0.15	0.95

[a] Yield expressed as oven dry weight for three largest plants (less roots) of a given strain/soil type.
[b] "S" and "NS" stand for "serpentine" and "non-serpentine" test soils, respectively.
[c] "VG" denotes collections by V. Grant.

tion of the strains from serpentine localities was 51 per cent. On the non-serpentine ("control") soil the germination of both serpentine and non-serpentine strains was uniformly higher (66 per cent and 70 per cent, respectively). The subsequent results of the soil-tolerance test with these two subspecies are shown in fig. 3. Table 3 presents quantitatively the striking differences between serpentine and non-serpentine strains in their response to serpentine soil. These differences can also be brought out graphically in terms of relative yields (fig. 4). The photographs (fig. 3) reveal an apparent difference in performance among the various strains when grown on the fertile control soil. These are merely differences in growth form of the two subspecies as well as differences in stage of development of the various strains. A more critical comparison can be made by noting the relative growth made by the various strains on serpentine soil. Beginning with the seedling stage, the reaction of serpentine and non-serpentine strains of *Gilia capitata* diverges into two distinct classes: serpentine-tolerant and serpentine-intolerant types. By maturity only the serpentine strains are seen to be doing well on the serpentine medium. Usually, even a serpentine strain fares better on the more fertile, non-serpentine soil than on its native serpentine substratum. However, with *Gilia*, there is no such diminution of vigor. From fig. 4 it is seen that the yields of a serpentine-tolerant type on serpentine are quite similar to its yield of dry matter on the more fertile non-serpentine soil. In *Gilia*, then, the case for serpentine and non-serpentine races on even an infraspecific level is clearly demonstrated.

Achillea borealis Bong.—Perhaps no other native plant in California shows the ecological amplitude that characterizes the distribution of the herbaceous perennial *Achillea borealis* and its relatives. Although well-known for its ecotypic responses to climatic gradients (Clausen *et al.*, 1948), its wide range of edaphic situations suggests further ecotypic differentiation. It occurs on serpentine throughout the central inner Coast Range area, as well as on soils of almost all possible lithological origins. It seemed likely, then, that this species would show the same sort of differentiation into serpentine-tolerant and serpentine-intolerant races as has been demonstrated for *Streptanthus* and *Gilia.*

In order to test this line of reasoning, seeds of several strains of *A. borealis* from both serpentine and non-serpentine localities were grown reciprocally on serpentine and non-serpentine soils as a test of their soil tolerance. Consistent with the results presented above for the two annuals, the *Achillea* strains can be readily separated into serpentine-tolerant and serpentine-intolerant types. Fig. 5 shows the typical reaction of a series of *Achillea borealis* strains to serpentine soil. As with *Streptanthus* and *Gilia*, strains from serpentine localities are far more successful than non-serpentine strains when grown on the serpentine medium.

One feature of the serpentine-tolerance tests not evident in the previous tests comes to light here. Some non-serpentine strains of *A. borealis* show a partial tolerance to serpentine, in that a few scattered individuals are able to perform just as well on serpentine as do the plants of a serpentine-tolerant strain (fig. 6). This sporadic tolerance of certain non-serpentine individuals suggests that some populations of *A. borealis* are more variable than others: That is, they may include biotypes that are potentially adapted to the more severe, selective serpentine habitat. Even more striking is the case of a coastal strain, S-206 from Contra Costa County. This population shows an even greater (uniform) tolerance to serpentine, a fact whose explanation is yet to be found.

Demonstrating the existence of these serpentine and non-serpentine races offered an enticing opportunity for exploration into the problems of the comparative physiology of these races. The differences between the two soil types used for these serpentine tolerance studies are undoubtedly physical as well as chemical. Ultimately, plant responses to the two soil types must be observed in terms of both these types of edaphic factors. As the initial step in this direction, the chemical approach was taken. It

Fig. 3. Response of seven strains of *Gilia capitata* to serpentine (above) and non-serpentine soil (below). The serpentine strains are S-108, S-134, and S-180 (table 1). Reduced about ten times.

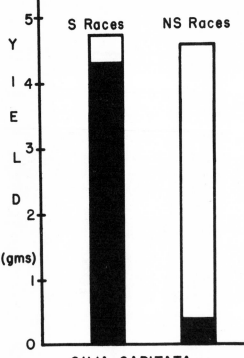

GILIA CAPITATA

·Fig. 4. Comparison of growth between serpentine and non-serpentine races of *Gilia capitata*. Black bars represent yield on serpentine soil; white bars, yield on non-serpentine soil. Average yield is expressed for three serpentine and two non-serpentine races as oven-dry weight for three plants (less roots) of each race. Serpentine races are S-108, S-134, and S-180; non-serpentine races are S-129 and VG-7702.

seemed likely that mineral-nutrition studies could point to some of the physiological differences between serpentine-tolerant and serpentine-intolerant races of a given species. To follow up this aspect of the problem, serpentine soils were reconstituted with varying amounts of calcium, a nitrate-phosphate-potassium mixture, and molybdenum. Of these (added singly to serpentine soil), only calcium was able to bring about "normal" growth of a non-serpentine strain on serpentine soil. A complete analysis of these nutritional studies, as well as further tolerance tests, are to be presented elsewhere (Kruckeberg, in manuscript).

DISCUSSION.—Many botanists have now become conditioned to think of the majority of species populations as having a vast store of actual and potential variability. Though often expressed morphologically, the more fundamental aspects of this variability are physiological. In many cases the effects of the constellations of genes that exist in a species are displayed only through physiological

channels. Thus the species becomes elaborated into ecotypes, races, *etc.*, through selection from the genotypic reservoir by the environment of a particular area. Early in the development of this concept of genotype-environment interaction, Turesson (1922) demonstrated the response of plant species on an infra-specific level to discontinuities of edaphic conditions. Awareness of the ecotypic response of plants enables us to examine the results presented in this paper in terms of the ecotype concept.

In 1948, Clausen *et al.* summarized their extensive work with climatic races of western North American species of *Achillea*. Based on the transplant technique, they demonstrated that the Achilleas of the seacoast-to-High Sierra transect exemplify a sequence of ecotypes.

One of their climatic ecotypes, the inner Coast Range-Sierran foothill race (*Achillea borealis* subsp. *californica* of the Clayton-Knights Ferry type) was used for a part of the current soil-tolerance studies. This Clayton-Knights Ferry type may be interpreted as a *single* climatic ecotype. What then is the biosystematic status of the serpentine-tolerant and serpentine-intolerant races of this single climatic ecotype? It seems wholly consistent with the general concept of the ecotype to consider the serpentine-tolerant race, at least, to be an edaphic (serpentine) ecotype. With the great edaphic diversity in California, it is reasonable to suppose that other such edaphic ecotypes adapted for some other extreme soil situation may be turned up as investigation along these lines proceeds. Eventually, such a climatic ecotype as this foothill example would have to be considered a complex of ecological variants, responsive to edaphic as well as to climatic factors, rather than a simple and indivisible climatic ecotype. Whether or not these serpentine-tolerant strains should be called races or ecotypes is not the prime issue of this discussion. Rather, the existence of such edaphically adapted types emphasizes the soil as a potent selective factor of the environment. In areas of unusual edaphic discontinuity throughout the world, the selective pressure of extreme soil types may often be a prime factor to be reckoned with when accounting for any concomitant floristic diversity.

The evidence presented in this paper that a single climatic race of *Achillea borealis* may be divisible into two or more edaphic races serves to emphasize the complexity and diversity of the elements within an ecotype. The ecotype is defined as "all the members of a species that are fitted to survive in a particular kind of environment within the total range of the species." (Clausen *et al.*, 1945) In light of the case of *Achillea borealis* where edaphic races appear to be superimposed upon climatic races, this definition of an ecotype seems appropriate only when a single environmental factor is under scrutiny. The complexes of factors that make up the over-all environment of a particular habitat

Fig. 5. Response of eight strains of *Achillea borealis* to serpentine (above) and non-serpentine soil (below). The serpentine strains here are S-142, S-164, S-184, and S-135. Note the unusual (vigorous) response of S-206, a non-serpentine strain, to serpentine soil. Reduced about thirty times.

preclude the existence of a single uniform ecotypic response to that habitat. Within a given area, discontinuities and gradients of all possible magnitudes for certain environmental factors (topography, soil, *etc.*) may be superimposed upon and act independently of some other factor (such as climate) that is uniform throughout the same area. The individuals constituting the ecotype for this single constant factor are then, at the same time, responding adaptively to each of the other factors whose ranges are *confined within* the area of the single uniform factor. Furthermore, other factors which *overlap* the area in question will also be a part of the environment of this population; they too will elicit an adaptive response, the limits of which

will extend beyond those of the area in question. Under many environmental situations, such an appraisal of habitat responses would render the term "ecotype" synonymous with either a local population or a small segment of a population. With this interpretation, it seems more realistic to think of many natural populations less in terms of discreet ecotypes. Rather, natural populations might best be visualized as consisting of a continuous or discontinuous array of *ecotypic variation* in response to the sum total of the environmental factors in an area.

Another important observation stems from the results of these soil tolerance studies. From the data presented in Table 3 and from fig. 4 and 5, it is evi-

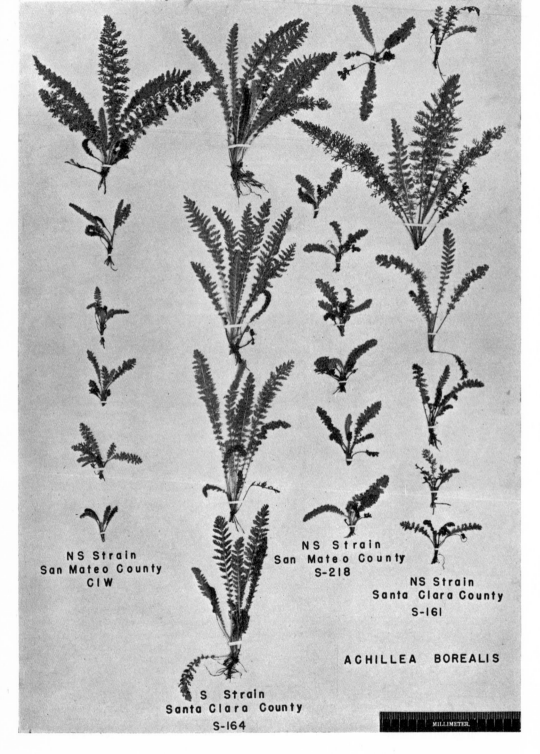

NS Strain
San Mateo County
CIW

NS Strain
San Mateo County
S-218

NS Strain
Santa Clara County
S-161

ACHILLEA   BOREALIS

S Strain
Santa Clara County
S-164

MILLIMETER.

dent that the growth of *all* strains of *Gilia* and *Achillea* is better on non-serpentine than on serpentine soil. Though not taken up in this paper, the author can report similar responses for both the obligate and the facultative serpentine endemic species in *Streptanthus*. This superior growth of *all* the species tested suggests, at least, that the serpentine endemics are not restricted to serpentine merely because of some specific requirement uniquely provided by serpentine. How, then, do we account for the restriction?

In studying these "narrow endemic" types of distribution, it is always tempting to look for the solution to the ultimate conundrum just posed: That is, how did such a pattern of restriction become established? It was pointed out earlier that it is possible to apply certain results presented in this paper to the "biotype-depletion" hypothesis as it relates to the origin of serpentine endemics. The serpentine-tolerance tests with strains of the facultative serpentine endemic, *Streptanthus glandulosus*, demonstrated the existence of two distinct types: one serpentine-tolerant, the other serpentine-intolerant. These results can be used to support the idea of "biotype depletion." First, we may think of the ancestors of such obligate serpentine endemics as *Streptanthus Breweri*, *S. barbiger*, and *S. hesperidis* as being the sole surviving biotypes of pre-existing species with greater biotype diversity and hence wider ecological tolerance. Then the case of *S. glandulosus* with its two facultative non-serpentine biotypes and its three serpentine restricted biotypes may be regarded as a closing stage in the elimination of all but the serpentine-adapted biotypes; that is, with the eventual elimination of the non-serpentine biotypes it will have attained the status of a true serpentine endemic. Elaboration of new types restricted to serpentine may then ensue; any such types would follow the pattern of the *insular species* discussed earlier. Subsequently some non-edaphic factor may enforce the restriction of these narrow endemics. Preliminary studies by the author, as yet unpublished, suggest that this "non-edaphic factor" may be some aspect of competition, acting on non-serpentine soils in such a way as to prevent the spread of endemics from serpentine outcrops.

Of course, this is but one of several ways in which to account for the origin of serpentine endemics. It is presented here as one logical interpretation of the serpentine-tolerance tests with serpentine and non-serpentine strains of the preponderantly serpentine species, *Streptanthus glandulosus*.

SUMMARY

In California, soils derived from serpentine rock support a unique flora, many species of which are narrowly endemic on this infertile soil type. Previous soil analyses of serpentine have shown that this soil is unusually high in magnesium, chromium, and nickel. Soils derived from this ultra-basic rock are also markedly deficient in calcium, nitrogen, phosphate, and occasionally molybdenum. Although chiefly restricted to serpentine, strains of *Streptanthus glandulosus* are occasionally also found on non-serpentine soils. When grown in experimental cultures, collections of strains from non-serpentine localities showed a marked intolerance to serpentine soil, whereas collections of other strains of the same species from serpentine sites attained normal growth on serpentine soil. The distribution pattern and intraspecific differences in serpentine tolerance of *S. glandulosus* have suggested "biotype depletion" as one possible mode of origin of serpentine endemics. This species is interpreted as being on the verge of becoming a strict serpentine endemic once its few non-serpentine biotypes have been eliminated. Tests for tolerance to serpentine soil were conducted on species of other genera occurring naturally on serpentine as well as on non-serpentine soils ("bodenvag" species). As was shown for *Streptanthus*, two of these non-endemic species — *Gilia capitata* and *Achillea borealis*—could be separated into serpentine-intolerant and serpentine-tolerant races on the basis of their growth responses on serpentile soil. From a biosystematic standpoint these soil races can be thought of as edaphic ecotypes. Yet these particular physiological differences are often wholly superimposed upon a single climatic ecotype.

DEPARTMENT OF BOTANY,
UNIVERSITY OF WASHINGTON,
SEATTLE 5, WASHINGTON

LITERATURE CITED

CLAUSEN, J., D. D. KECK, AND W. M. HIESEY. 1945. Experimental studies on the nature of species. II. Plant evolution through amphiploidy and autoploidy, with examples from the Madiinae. Carnegie Inst. Wash. Publ. 564:1-174.

————, ———, AND ———. 1948. Experimental studies on the nature of species. III. Environmental responses of climatic races of *Achillea*. Carnegie Inst. Wash. Publ. 581:1-129.

GRANT, V. 1949. A genetic and systematic analysis of the *Gilia capitata* complex. Thesis (Ph. D.) University of California, Berkeley.

GREGOR, J. W. 1944. The ecotype. Biol. Rev. 19:20-30.

JOHNSON, C. M., AND E. EPSTEIN. 1948. Methods of chemical analysis for Soil Science 113. Mimeographed.

KRUCKEBERG, A. R. In manuscript. An experimental inquiry into the nature of serpentine endemism.

MASON, H. L. 1946. The edaphic factor in narrow endemism. II. The geographic occurrence of plants of

Fig. 6. Variation of rosette leaf size for one serpentine and three non-serpentine strains of *Achillea borealis* grown on serpentine soil. Some non-serpentine strains (S-218) are uniformly dwarfed on serpentine while within other non-serpentine strains (CIW and S-161) some plants produce rosette leaves as large as those of serpentine strains.

highly restricted patterns of distribution. Madroño 8: 241-257.

MORRISON, J. L. 1938. Studies in the genus *Streptanthus* Nutt. I. Two new species in the section Euclisia Nutt. Madroño 4:204-208.

————. 1941. A monograph of the section Euclisia Nutt., of *Streptanthus* Nutt. Thesis (Ph.D.) University of California, Berkeley.

STEBBINS, G. L., JR. 1942. The genetic approach to problems of rare and endemic species. Madroño 6:241-272.

TALIAFERRO, N. K. 1943. The Franciscan-Knoxville problem. Bull. Amer. Assoc. Petroleum Geologists 27:109-219.

TURESSON, G. 1922. The genotypical response of the plant species to habitat. Hereditas 3:211-350.

UNGER, F. 1836. Über den einfluss des Bodens auf die Verteilung der Gewachse, nachgewiesen in der Vegetations des nordostlichen Tirols. Wien.

WALKER, R. B. 1948. A study of serpentine soil infertility with special reference to edaphic endemism. Thesis (Ph. D.) University of California, Berkeley.

THE *CLEMATIS FREMONTII* VAR. *RIEHLII* POPULATION IN THE OZARKS[1]

RALPH O. ERICKSON

Instructor in Botany, The University of Rochester
Formerly University Fellow, Henry Shaw School of Botany of Washington University

INTRODUCTION

During the latter half of the nineteenth century, the Darwinian theory of evolution by natural selection inspired a vast amount of research which was largely directed toward tracing of phylogenies and demonstrating the adaptation of organisms to their environment. However, the theory has recently been somewhat out of fashion. Its abeyance was coincident with the rise after 1900 of the new science of genetics and its companion, modern nuclear cytology. Preoccupation with the new disciplines partly accounted for the neglect of evolutionary studies. But it was partly due to the fact that the new principles which were emerging, the particulate theory of inheritance and the DeVriesian mutation theory, seemed to contradict some of the premises of Darwinism.

To-day there is a resurgence of interest in evolutionary matters. It is apparent that Darwin's theory, in its essentials, still stands. Modern genetics throws immediate light on some points which were hidden to Darwin. Gene mutation, which has now been studied in the laboratory and in the field, is seen to be the source of the omnipresent variation which Darwin pointed out but did not explain. The particulate nature of inheritance, far from being contradictory to the theory of natural selection, has been shown by Fisher ('30) to be essential to evolutionary change. A mathematical theory has been constructed, largely by Wright (for bibliography and non-mathematical summary, see Dobzhansky, '41), which permits rates of change of gene frequency to be calculated from mutation rates, the selective advantage of one gene over another, and size of population, under various systems of mating. These changes in gene frequency, when integrated for the entire genotype of the organism and over its entire population, may be said to constitute the primary steps in evolution.

The most important generalizations which Wright has made from his mathematical studies are those relating to the effect of population size, or more accurately, of what he terms "population number," upon the rate and course of evolution. In a very large, freely interbreeding population, where the number of potential mates for each breeding individual is large in relation to mutation rates, selection is strongly operative. The genotypes of the organism will then tend to cluster closely about a peak in the surface of adaptive values. The organism will be well adapted to its environment, but its over-all variability will be somewhat

---

[1] This paper is a revision of a dissertation which was prepared in partial fulfillment of the requirements for the degree of doctor of philosophy in the Henry Shaw School of Botany of Washington University.

Reprinted by permission of the author and publisher from the
ANNALS OF THE MISSOURI BOTANICAL GARDEN, **32**, 413–460 (1945).

restricted. It will adapt itself to a secular change in the environment by moving to a new adaptive peak, but it will not be able to cross an adaptive valley to reach a conceivably higher peak. In a very small population, or in one which is divided into small isolated colonies, the range of variation will be restricted locally, though there may be considerable variation from one colony to another. The phenomenon of "genetic drift" will come into play. There will be a random loss and fixation of genes resulting from the errors of sampling of the gametes which reproduce each generation, largely without regard to the adaptive value of the genes involved. As a result, the fate of an organism which is too greatly restricted in numbers is extinction. Wright considers the most favorable condition for continuing evolution to be that of a large population broken up into numerous small colonies which are connected by occasional migration. Each colony will be free to explore the field of gene combinations without the restrictive effect of too rigid selection. Differentiation within the population will be largely non-adaptive, but some of the colonies will be expected to arrive at favorable genotypes or adaptive peaks, perhaps quite different from the original one about which the population centered. Such colonies will tend to increase in numbers and to bring the remainder of the population up to their genotype through migration. This combination of non-adaptive differentiation of partially isolated local groups with intergroup selection will permit evolutionary advance without a secular change in conditions.

Wright's theory has become an important part of modern evolutionary thought. Eventually it may have the same importance and validity in the field of evolution which the publications of J. Willard Gibbs have in chemical thermodynamics. However, it is merely a theory, and it is impossible at present to judge whether it adequately accounts for evolutionary changes which are known to take place. It urgently requires testing against facts from the field. The facts required for its examination, or the examination of any other theory which attempts to explain the mechanism of evolutionary change, are of many kinds. The beauty of Wright's theory is that it indicates clearly the kinds of information which are important. Detailed information is required about life histories of various organisms, particularly the details of reproduction. Data are required on the numbers of individuals, and on their pattern of distribution, both at present and over a span of years. The pattern of differentiation must be understood in detail. Detailed information about sources of evolutionary change such as mutation, hybridization, and chromosomal changes must be obtained. Furthermore, the data on all these points must be coordinated for individual organisms. Such a body of detailed and coordinated facts scarcely exists for any organism, but is of first importance in any discussion of evolution.

The present study of *Clematis Fremontii* var. *Riehlii* was undertaken with the object of working out a picture of the features of its population structure which are of evolutionary importance, and if possible of making an estimate of evolutionary trends within the population. The pattern of distribution has been worked out in some detail. Biological factors such as method of pollination, seed dissemination, seed germination and longevity have been examined. Variation in flower and leaf characters has been studied. An attempt has been made to obtain quantitative data where possible, but many of the present conclusions are based on subjective judgment; the difficulties are many.

Clematis Fremontii var. *Riehlii* is a member of the section VIORNA, subsection INTEGRIFOLIAE of *Clematis* (Erickson, '43a). Besides the Eurasian *C. integrifolia*, which probably should be placed in the subsection, it includes four closely related species and one or two varieties. They are comparatively well-marked and uniform entities, contrasting with such polymorphic species as *C. Pitcheri*. All except *C. ochroleuca* are of restricted distribution, characteristically occurring on rocky barrens. *C. albicoma* and the recently proposed *C. albicoma* var. *coactilis* (Fernald, '43) occur on the Devonian shale barrens of the Appalachians of West Virginia and Virginia (Wherry, '30, '31). *C. viticaulis*, also a shale barren plant, has been collected at a single locality. *C. Fremontii* is a secondary species in the *Andropogon scoparius* habitat of the mixed prairie of north-central Kansas. There it is usually limited to the upper slopes above the brows of hills where there is an outcrop of Fort Hays Limestone or Smoky Hill Chalk (Albertson, '37, '42).

C. Fremontii var. *Riehlii* is restricted to an area of somewhat more than 400 sq. mi. in Jefferson County and portions of two adjacent counties in east-central Missouri. A distribution map and a discussion of the limits of its distribution have been published (Erickson, '43b). The plant is wholly restricted to glades, rocky barrens which occur on south- and west-facing slopes of otherwise wooded ridges. The glades occur on outcrops of the thin-bedded dolomite of several formations of the Canadian Series, particularly the Cotter and Powell. Their distribution follows the outcrop belt of these formations; glades and the similar bald knobs of south-central Missouri encircle the Ozark dome. On a smaller scale, their occurrence is determined by the presence of sufficient local relief in conjunction with the outcrop of thin-bedded dolomite. They are characterized by a thin soil cover, which is slightly acid and fairly high in organic matter, and by an extreme set of environmental conditions: saturation to the point of seepage in late fall and early spring, and desiccation during the summer months (Erickson, Brenner and Wraight, '42). The glade habitat appears to be an edaphic climax, rather than a stage in the succession to upland forest, or a product of a biotic influence, such as grazing by cattle. The red cedar, *Juniperus virginiana*, is the most characteristic tree associated with the glades; the glades can be recognized from a distance by the contrast which the dark green of the cedars offers to the surrounding broad-leaved forest. The red cedars occasionally form an open cover, but usually occur as scattered individuals and may even be absent. The dominant plant is clearly the bluestem, *Andropogon scoparius*, though there are other grasses, and several other species make a conspicuous seasonal show of flowers, such as *Leavenworthia uniflora*, *Houstonia angustifolia*, and particularly, *Rudbeckia missouriensis*. Many of the plants have xeromorphic characteristics. Flor-

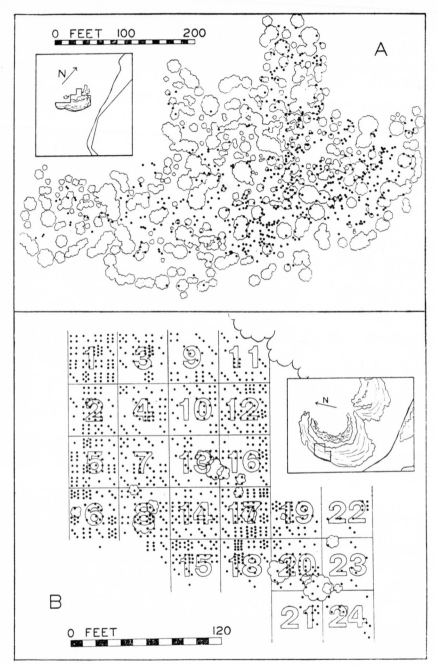

Fig. 1. Distribution of *C. Fremontii* var. *Riehlii* on greater part of small glade at R.2E, T.42N, S.10C (A); and on portion of larger glade at R.6E, T.39N, S.4-0 (B). Inserts show relation of area studied to glade as a whole. Small black dots represent *Clematis* plants, irregular outlines, trees. Domino effect in B is due to the fact that plants were counted in each 10-ft. quadrat, not plotted as they were for A. Numbered 40-ft. quadrats are referred to on p. 443 *et seq.*

istically, the glades are related to the shale barrens of the Appalachians (Wherry, '30), to the cedar glades of the Nashville Basin in Tennessee (Freeman, '33), to portions of the prairies of Kansas and Nebraska (Albertson, '37), and to glade-like grassy areas in the Arbuckle Mountains of Oklahoma and the Edwards Plateau of Texas.

Distribution Pattern

Because of its striking appearance, *Clematis Fremontii* var. *Riehlii* is a conspicuous member of the glade community, but in numbers it is subordinate. Its distribution on a number of glades has been studied in some detail. Figure 1 shows the distribution on the greater part of a small glade and a portion of a larger one that are not so much representative as illustrating approximately two extreme situations in which the plant is found. The maps were prepared from data obtained by laying out 10-ft. quadrats on the glades and plotting or counting the plants in each quadrat. On several other glades (fig. 2) the distribution has been studied by laying out 10-ft. transects of contiguous 10-ft. quadrats, usually at 250-ft. (50-pace) intervals, and normal to the "contour lines" formed by outcropping rock ledges.

Erickson and Stehn ('45) have published a statistical analysis of these data. They have pointed out that the data cannot be regarded as representing random (Poisson) distributions. Field observations suggested that the departure from randomness has its basis in a lack of uniformity of different portions of the glades as a habitat for *Clematis*. The data have been fitted by calculating two Poisson distributions for each glade, an "economic distribution," corresponding to suitable portions of the glade, and an "adventitious distribution," whose mean is small, representing unsuitable portions. The mean of the former is regarded as equivalent to Elton's ('32, '33) economic density.

The results of this statistical analysis should be considered in the light of field observations of conditions on the glades. The density counts are summarized in Table I. As contrasted with the tenfold variation in uncorrected, mean density, m_0, the economic densities, m_1, show a better agreement. The economic means of 1.02 and 1.10 plants per 100 sq. ft. are both for small glades; the rest, with means clustering around three or four plants per 100 sq. ft., apply to larger glades. The small glade at R.2E, T.42N, S.10C ($m_1 = 1.02$) is remarkable for its inaccessibility, and for the large size and number of red cedars. The data of line 6 in Table I ($m_1 = 1.10$) were obtained by combining data from two similar, adjacent glades in R.5E, T.40N, S.13. Both are small glades, though without such a conspicuous cover of red cedars as glade No. 1. The fact that the data appear to fall into two groups on the basis of economic density values is a reflection of the tendency, not recognized in the earlier field work, to select the larger, more "typical" glades for study. If more representative data were at hand, it would probably be found that the economic density is somewhat a function of the size of the glade, reaching an optimum value of three to four plants per 100 sq. ft. on large glades, and being smaller on smaller glades. It is thought that the conditions

TABLE I

DISTRIBUTION OF *CLEMATIS* ON GLADES
IN FRANKLIN CO. AND JEFFERSON CO., MO.

(Glade numbers correspond with those of fig. 2)

No.	Location	Area (acres)	Est. number of *Clematis*	Mean density (m_0)	Economic density (m_1)
1	R. 2E, T. 42N, S. 10C	2.8	1,140	0.57	1.02
2	R. 2E, T. 42N, S. 15B	13.4	6,780	1.16	3.61
3	R. 3E, T. 41N, S. 25	23.3	3,880	0.41	2.98
4	R. 4E, T. 40N, S. 15B	14.9	5,580	0.86	3.87
5	R. 4E, T. 40N, S. 15D	14.8	13,230	2.05	4.07
6	R. 5E, T. 40N, S. 13A	5.4	830	0.34	1.10
7	R. 5E, T. 40N, S. 13E	20.7	32,000	3.69	2.51
8	R. 6E, T. 39N, S. 4-0	24.3	11,300	2.85	3.76

of winter saturation and summer desiccation, etc., referred to by Erickson, Brenner and Wraight ('42), are developed to the extreme only on the largest glades, being somewhat ameliorated on smaller glades more closely surrounded by forest. *Clematis* may be limited to glades not because of its special adaptation to their physical environment, but because it finds competition from other species too severe elsewhere, as Salisbury ('29) has found to be the case for other plants of barrens, such as *Ranunculus parviflorus*. If that is so, *Clematis* would be expected to reach its optimum density on the large glades where biological competition is presumably least severe.

The implication of this statistical treatment, that the glades can be divided into two portions on the basis of their suitability for *Clematis*, deserves some amplification. A prominent physical characteristic of the glades is the occurrence at intervals of parallel outcrops of more massive rock than the thin-bedded dolomite which forms the glade proper. On the aerial photographs of the region, which were studied as a preliminary to the field work, these outcrops give the appearance of contour lines, and aid greatly in recognition of the glades. In the field the ledges are found to vary greatly in distinctness. *Clematis* characteristically occurs just below such a ledge of rock, though it is by no means strictly limited to such places. This and the fact that it seems to be more abundant near the lower edge of a glade suggest that one of the factors determining its presence is the amount of seepage water available during the spring. The unsuitable portions of the glade, or "blanks," are of at least three kinds: the exceedingly barren areas just above a ledge of massive rock, which are strewn with chert fragments and occupied almost exclusively by a sparse growth of the small grass, *Sporobolus heterolepis;* very grassy portions, where *Clematis* would presumably meet severe competition with *Andropogon;* and small clusters of trees, *Juniperus virginiana, Bumelia lanuginosa, Cornus florida,* etc., which occur at intervals on the glades, often where a gully has developed.

It is apparent then that the distribution of *C. Fremontii* var. *Riehlii* on individual glades is characterized by considerable aggregation. The *aggregates* of plants are not well delimited, as can be seen by reference to fig. 1, but they do exist. They vary considerably in area, and they may include a few plants to a few hundred.

While the aggregates of plants are undoubtedly important in breaking up the population into local groups, the *glades* themselves, by their greater definiteness of outline and more complete isolation, must also be significant. On the distribution map (Erickson, '43b, fig. 2), about 15 negative records were plotted within the distribution area of the *Clematis*, with 160-odd positive records, indicating that roughly 87 per cent of the glades support some plants. Furthermore, the plant has never been found except on a glade, and it is probably justifiable, as a first approximation, to regard glades and *colonies* of plants as equivalent in examining the organization of the population. Those which have been carefully studied (Table I) vary in area from 2.8 to 24.3 acres, and in estimated number of plants from 830 to 32,000. However, it has been pointed out above that the sampling involved has not been satisfactory. Between 200 and 250 glades have been visited more briefly, and some impressions gained from that experience should be pertinent. The glades vary in area from about 80 acres (large glade two miles north of Plattin) to small grassy areas which scarcely merit the name. In R.3E, T.41N, S.1–18, the total area in glades was measured by placing the tracings of the aerial photographs over a piece of paper ruled in small squares and counting the squares covered by glade outlines. Sixty glades were counted with a total area of 123 acres. Here, then, the average glade measures very nearly two acres in area. The number of plants per glade varies greatly, and probably corresponds only roughly with the area of the glade. Several glades of considerable area have been visited on which only one or a very few plants could be found. The upper limit in size of a colony is indicated by the figures in the fourth column of Table I, and the average size of a colony appears to be about 970, as calculated on page 422.

An impression of the degree of isolation between separate glades ($=$ colonies) can be gained by examining fig. 2 and the larger scale map (fig. 3). On the whole, there is little difficulty in defining separate glades. It is apparent that the glades are not randomly distributed. No attempt has been made to treat this matter statistically, but obvious relations of the glades to the drainage pattern can be seen, as, for example, at R.4E, T.40N, S.11 and 14 (fig. 3) where the glades are ranged on either side of "branches" of Cotter Creek. Such topographically determined *clusters* of glades must also have significance in the subdivision of the population into local groups.

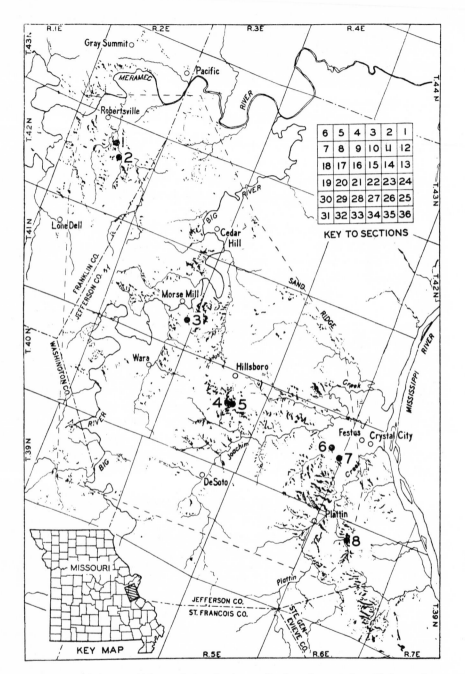

Fig. 2. Glades at which population density studies have been made. Glade numbers correspond with those of Table I.

Fig. 3.   Two clusters of glades in R.4E, T.40N, S.10, 11, 14, 15, 22 and 23, illustrating their relationship to the drainage pattern.   Figure is a reduction of tracings of aerial photographs.   Width of figure is two miles.

The next higher category of organization is seen in fig. 2 as a tendency for the entire distribution range to fall into four *regions* of glade concentration: (A) south of Robertsville, (B) about Morse Mill, (C) south of Hillsboro and (D) about Plattin. Scattered glades occur outside these regions of concentration. It is probable that the factors responsible for this large-scale grouping of the glades are variations in thickness of the determining strata of thin-bedded dolomite and the amount of local topographic relief. The four regious appear to be about equivalent in total glade area, but one has the impression from field work that the plant is most abundant on the glades about Plattin, and least abundant in the vicinity of Morse Mill, with the Robertsville and Hillsboro regions intermediate.

TABLE II

HIERARCHY OF SUBDIVISIONS OF THE *CLEMATIS* POPULATION
(Compare with fig. 4)

Subdivision	Number	Total area (sq. mi.)	Glade area		Number of *Clematis*
			(sq. mi.)	(acres)	
Distribution range	1	436	7.0	4,460	1,500,000
Regions	4	100	1.5	980	300,000
Clusters of glades	50	------	0.09	60	30,000
Colonies (= glades)	1,450	------	------	2 (0.1–80)	970 (1–32,000)
Aggregates	15,000	------	------	0.2	97

It is thus seen that the distribution of *C. Fremontii* var. *Riehlii* falls naturally into a hierarchy of subdivisions, reminiscent of the hierarchy of subdivisions of the population of *Linanthus Parryae* which Wright ('43) devised for statistical reasons, but differing in that they have a natural basis and show no approach to equality in size. Some speculative calculations can be made of the relative size and number of the subdivisions (Table II). The estimate made in a previous paper (Erickson, '43b) of the total area over which *Clematis* is distributed stands; while several new records could now be added to the map, none are beyond the limits shown there. The calculations made in that paper of the total number of plants have been revised to include all the density data used in compiling Table I. The total was found to be 2,191,000, in gratifying agreement with the previously quoted estimate of 2,200,000 (rounded off from 2,197,000). However this figure has been reduced arbitrarily to 1,500,000, since the density counts weighted large glades too heavily. The estimate of the total number of glades, 1450, has been calculated by assuming that the 60 glades counted in the 18 sq. mi. at R.3E, T.41N, S.1–18, can be considered representative of the entire area. The average number of plants per glade, 970, has been obtained by dividing the number of glades into the total number of plants for the entire area. Similar calcula-

Fig. 4. Diagram to illustrate organization of the distribution range of *C. Fremontii* var. *Riehlii* into a hierarchy of subdivisions: regions of glade concentration; clusters of glades; glades; and aggregates of *Clematis* on glades. Compare with Table II.

tions, with liberal rounding-off of numbers, have given the other values in the table.   An indication of the variation in numbers of plants has been given in parentheses for the glades.   The other subdivisions also vary greatly in area and number of plants.   The organization of the population into a hierarchy of sub-divisions is illustrated diagrammatically in fig. 4.

On purely geographical grounds, then, C. Fremontii var. Riehlii can properly be described as a large population broken up into partially isolated groups.   The partially isolated groups of greatest evolutionary significance are probably the aggregates of plants found to occur on each glade, difficult as they are to define in terms of area or number of plants.   However, the concept of partial isolation applies equally well to the larger categories, the glades, the clusters of glades, and regions.

CONSTANCY OF NUMBERS

Great fluctuations in population size are known to occur in many organisms. Elton ('42, and other publications) has shown this to be the case for many northern mammals, and it is true of some species of Drosophila (see, for example, Spencer, '41).   Linanthus Parryae, an annual plant which has been the subject of a population study, is reported to vary greatly in numbers from year to year (Epling and Dobzhansky, '42).   Since the smallest size to which a population may be reduced largely determines its effective size for evolutionary purposes, the possibility of such fluctuations in this Clematis population must be considered. Albertson ('42) states that many plants of C. Fremontii in Kansas were killed during the years of drought from 1933 to 1939.   The late drought, however, was not so severe in the Ozarks, which adjoin the Mississippi embayment, as it was on the prairies.   This study was not begun long enough ago to have permitted any first-hand observations, but Anderson ('43) states that the drought of 1936 did not greatly harm many of the glade plants.   Its main effect was to check Andropogon scoparius, so that other species which are normally held back by competition with it showed an unusually large display of flowers in the im-mediately following years.   No specific observations of C. Fremontii var. Riehlii were made, but Anderson's opinion is that whatever damage it suffered during the drought was more than balanced by the release of competition from Andro-pogon.   It might also be added that the habit of Riehlii of completing its growth by the middle of June probably contributes to its ability to withstand drought.

The influence of grazing on the numbers of Clematis is manifested in a similar way.   The leaves, besides being very leathery when mature, are exceedingly acrid (Greshoff, '09, reports the presence of hydrocyanic acid in C. Fremontii), and cattle avoid them.   The only evidence of disturbance by livestock is an occasional young shoot which has been nipped off when an inch or so above ground, presum-ably by error, and flowers which are occasionally removed without disturbance to the leaves.   Grazing, however, keeps back the grasses, such as Andropogon, and the ultimate effect is to allow Clematis to increase both in numbers and in the size of individual plants. This is strikingly seen in some cases where a fence divides a glade into a grazed and ungrazed portion. The plants on the grazed portion are noticeably larger, and flower somewhat earlier than those on the ungrazed part. Another biotic factor may be mentioned. The plant is subject to sporadic attacks by blister beetles, *Epicauta marginata,* which devour the leaves. Their attacks, however, are merely an annoyance to the investigator. They occur too late in the season, and are not frequent enough, to influence the population size of the plant seriously.

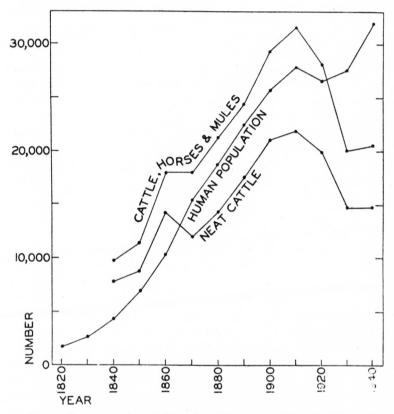

Fig. 5. Data on numbers of livestock and human population in Jefferson Co., Mo., from U. S. Census.

It is presumed that *Clematis* has increased in numbers since the white settlement of the country. United States Census data (fig. 5) show that the livestock population of Jefferson County reached a maximum in 1910, with a considerable decline until a minimum was reached in 1930, since when there has been an increase. Because the numbers of plants is believed to have varied roughly in proportion to the severity of grazing of the glades, it may be concluded that the population size of *Clematis* has increased considerably since 1800, and that it now has reached relative stability, subject to fluctuations in relation to general economic conditions and changes in the management of individual farms. It is thought that the perennial habit of the plant may serve to damp such influences. Unfortunately, no direct evidence is at hand. A study of the old records of collection of the plant (Erickson, '43b) makes it seem probable that no conspicuous extension or restriction of range has occurred since the 1880's. Certainly no large-scale fluctuation in numbers has occurred in the four years during which the author has observed the plant. On the whole, the size of individual colonies appears remarkably stable as compared with the spectacular fluctuations which are known to occur in some other organisms.

The apparent constancy in size of this *Clematis* population at present does not, of course, imply that there have been no restrictions or extensions of its range in geological time. The presence of the very closely related *C. Fremontii* in Kansas suggests that it and *C. Fremontii* var. *Riehlii* must at one time have had a continuous distribution. A study of the distributions of other glade plants, particularly *Oenothera missouriensis*, suggests that the two *Clematis* populations may have been connected by way of the Edwards Plateau of Texas (unpublished maps prepared by Edgar Anderson). The separation into two populations may have occurred during the semi-arid period of late Pleistocene, or, in view of the importance of competition from grasses, during the warmer, moister period which followed (Sears, '35).

LIFE HISTORY

Clematis Fremontii var. *Riehlii* is a herbaceous perennial with a woody stem and remarkably coriaceous, prominently veined leaves, which have inspired the common name, "leatherleaf." It flowers during the last week of April and the first week of May, though it was seen flowering sporadically in September, 1941, a month of unusually high rainfall. Growth is completed within three weeks or a month after flowering, and the plants remain green for eight or ten weeks, turning brown during July. Because of their woody nature, many of the stems remain in place until February or March of the following year, the leaves by that time having become skeletonized and weathered to attractive gray laceworks of veins. However, some of the plants have been blown free of their moorings by October. A large plant forms a roughly spherical mass of rigid stems and leaves, and when it is freed, it may be carried for some distance over a glade as a tumbleweed.

The persisting structure is a woody caudex (fig. 6), provided with a mass of brown fleshy roots, in which the reserve food is starch. Two or four lateral buds are formed in the fall at the lower nodes of the old stem, one or more of which unfolds the next spring to form a new shoot. This process, over a period of years, gives rise to a certain amount of branching of the caudex, the older portions of which are torn apart by the growth of the roots. A large plant may consist of perhaps 20 shoots, arising from four or five separate caudices. Branching of the

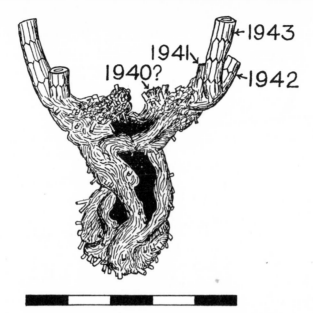

Fig. 6. Caudex of *C. Fremontii* var. *Riehlii,* which supported two shoots in 1943. It was collected in June, and lateral buds had not yet developed. Fleshy roots have been removed. Scale in centimeters.

caudex apparently does not provide a very efficient means of vegetative propagation. Morphological variation from plant to plant is sufficient to permit genetic individuals to be distinguished with some certainty. In a careful examination of perhaps 200 plants for evidences of clonal reproduction, only one case was found in which two separate plants appeared to belong to the same clone. They were about one foot apart, and there was evidence that the separation was accidental, caused by the fall of a tree trunk over the original clump. Three or four clumps were found which were actually two plants. In the population density studies reported above, each plant (or clump) old enough to have flowered has been scored as an individual regardless of its size or number of shoots.

In most species of *Clematis* the achenes are provided with conspicuous plumose tails, presumably well adapted to wind dispersal (fig. 7). In *C. Fremontii* var. *Riehlii,* however, the achene-tails are naked for the greater part of their length, though their basal portions and the apices of the achenes are silky (fig. 8). They are not suited for wind dispersal in the usual sense. Dispersal by the fur of a mammal is hard to visualize, and no evidence has been seen of their use as food by a bird or mammal. Some dissemination is probably achieved by the tumbleweed habit of the largest plants, but most of the achenes merely fall to the base of the parent plant. Dispersal of the achenes over a single glade is probably adequate, but the transportation of achenes from one glade to another must be a rare occurrence.

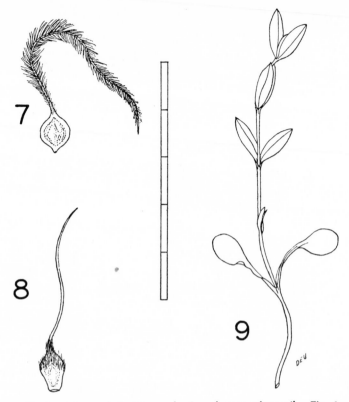

Fig. 7. Achene of *C. Viorna*, showing plumose achene-tail. Fig. 8. Achene of *C. Fremontii* var. *Riehlii*, showing naked achene-tail. Fig. 9. Seedling of *C. Fremontii* var. *Riehlii*, perhaps one month after germination. Scale in centimeters.

Attempts to germinate seeds under greenhouse conditions have been largely unsuccessful. Of about 600 seeds planted, three have germinated. Better success would perhaps be had by layering, but the experiments have not been carried out. Indications are that the percentage of germination of seed in the field is also low. The seedlings escaped detection in the early field work, because of their minute size (fig. 9). Many small sterile plants were found, but examination of the caudex always showed them to be two or more years old. When the seedlings were finally recognized, little trouble was had in finding them on any glade where careful search was made. They are not abundant. Presumably achenes are dropped in the vicinity of every large plant every fall; groups of seedlings can be found in such places in perhaps one case in 100. The conditions required for germination are not well understood, but adequate shade appears to be one of them. Germination takes place in the spring. Seedlings have not been found in September and October, though these months are often characterized by warm rainy weather, similar to that of April.

Growth of the plants seems to be quite slow, four or five years apparently being required from germination until the first flower is produced. Young, sterile plants (fig. 10) have been found on all the glades which have been studied. At R.4E, T.40N, S.15D, 61 of the 528 plants counted, or 8.7 per cent, were such plants. The conclusion that four or five years are required before flowering is based on examination of the caudices of many sterile plants, and of young plants which have produced a single flower. It is more difficult to estimate the age of larger clumps, since the older portions of a caudex are badly fragmented, and annual rings in the wood of the caudex are quite indefinite. Deduction from the size of the plant and of the caudex places the age of large clumps, such as illustrated in fig. 11, at 15 or 20 years, though there is no reason for thinking that they may not be indefinitely older.

POLLINATION

Since vegetative reproduction and seed dispersal are quite inefficient, pollen transportation must be looked to as the principal means of gene exchange from one glade to another, and perhaps also from one portion of a glade to another. The flowers are insect-pollinated. They are protogynous, as will be seen from fig. 12, and produce nectar at the base of the stamens. In view of these facts, cross-pollination would seem to be the rule, and more will be said about that below. However, the filaments elongate after the anthers have dehisced, and in an old flower the inner anthers are in contact with the style-tips, so that self-pollination is at least mechanically possible. Glassine bags have been placed over a number of flowers before anthesis to determine the seed-set in enforced self-pollination. The results have been nearly inconclusive. In the first attempts the bags were fastened around the peduncles of flowers, and with one exception failed to stay in place. When the bags were placed over several leaves as well as the flower, the plant and bag were blown over in the wind, became wet, and in most cases molded. Of 106 bags which were placed and later collected, three contained a full head of achenes, and three a few seeds each. The failures to set seed are attributed to the injury done the plant by enclosing it. Normally seeds are set by all the flowers except the smallest ones which occur late in the season on weak branches. Tentatively it is perhaps safe to assume that a plant will be self-pollinated if cross-pollination does not occur first.

Clematis is visited by a variety of insects while it is in flower. An insect net was carried for seven days during April, 1943, and as many as possible of the insects found on the flowers were captured. The specimens have been identified by Mr. Harold I. O'Byrne, and Mr. Richard Froeschner, with the exception of some smaller Hymenoptera. The data are presented in Table III. The most frequently found insects are four species of Pentatomidae. They are typically found lurking at the base of a flower, often with the proboscis inserted into one of the fleshy sepals. It is doubtful whether they are concerned in pollination, since they rarely venture to the opening of the flower, and apparently do not move from one plant to another often. The most conspicuous visitors, in order of the

TABLE III

INSECTS COLLECTED ON *CLEMATIS* FLOWERS

Order Family Species	Number of specimens		
	♂	♀	Total
Homoptera			
Cicadellidae			
Oncometopia lateralis (Fab.)		1	1
Hemiptera			
Pentatomidae			
Euschistus variolarius (Beauv.)	19	3	22
Eu. euschistoides (Voll.)	4	1	5
Thyanta custator (Fab.)	2	2	4
Peribalus limbolarius Stål.		1	1
Neididae			
Neides muticus (Say)	2	2	4
Lepidoptera			
Papilionidae			
Papilio ajax Linn.	1	1	2
P. troilus Linn.		2	2
P. philenor Linn.	1	1	2
Lycaenidae			
Strymon melinus Hbn.	1		1
Everes comyntas (Godt.)	1	1	2
Hesperiidae			
Proteides clarus (Cram.)	2	1	3
Thorybes pylades (Scud.)		1	1
Th. bathyllus (Ab. & Sm.)	3		3
Erynnis brizo (Bdv. & Lec.)	1		1
Sphingidae			
Hemaris diffinis (Bdv.) form tenuis Grote	5	6	11
Coleoptera			
Dermestidae			
Cryptorhophalum picicorne Lec.			1
Melyridae			
Collops vicarius Fall	1		1
Hymenoptera			
Bombidae			
Bombus impatiens Cresson		2	2
B. americanorum (Fab.)		3	3
Apidae			
Apis mellifica Linn.			1
Unidentified			
Hymenoptera (5 species ?)			12
Arachnida, Thomisidae			15

frequency with which they have been seen on the flowers, are the hawk moth, *Hemaris diffinis,* the bumblebees, *Bombus impatiens* and *B. americanorum,* and the swallowtails, *Papilio ajax, P. troillus* and *P. philenor.* They alone of the insects captured have proboscides long enough to reach the nectaries from the opening of the flower, a distance of about two cm. It is doubtful whether *Hemaris* or the *Papilio* species are involved in pollination to a considerable extent. The manner in which they cling to the recurved tips of the sepals while obtaining nectar suggests that they may be able to visit many flowers without picking up

Fig. 10. Plant of *C. Fremontii* var. *Riehlii* estimated to be four years old. Scale in centimeters. Fig. 11. Mature plant of *C. Fremontii* var. *Riehlii* probably 15 years old or older. Scale in centimeters. Fig. 12. Flower of *C. Fremontii* var. *Riehlii*. Note that styles are exserted. Anthers have not yet dehisced.

[Vol. 32

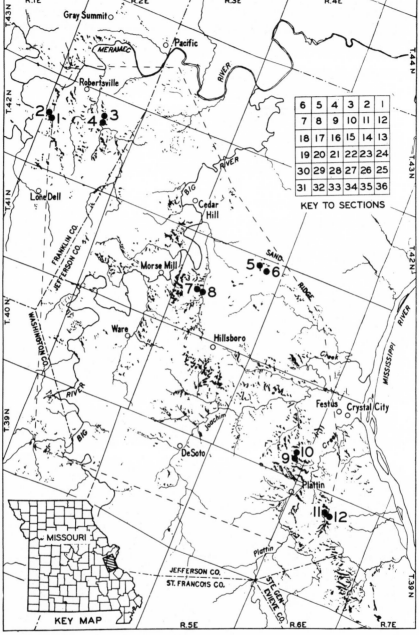

Fig. 13. Glades at which frequency of colored sepal tips has been determined. Glade numbers correspond with those of Table IV.

much pollen. No pollen grains have been detected on the pinned specimens with a hand lens. The bumblebees are undoubtedly queens who have recently come out of hibernation. In late April, they have just begun the establishment of nests (Frison, '27), and are engaged in collecting nectar rather than pollen. This is borne out by the fact that the corbiculae of all the specimens are empty. However, some pollen has been found clinging to the hairs of the head and the prothoracic legs of all of the pinned specimens. It is easy to understand how the bumblebees pick up this pollen. Their behavior at the flowers is much cruder than that of the hawk moths and the swallowtails. Instead of hanging daintily from the sepal tips and probing discretely for nectar, a bumblebee appears to be struggling in an attempt to ram its entire head into the flower as far as possible. The visits of the smaller butterflies of the Lycaenidae and Hesperiidae were puzzling at first. It was obvious that they are unable to reach the nectar by the normal route. Closer observation of several individuals showed that they insert their proboscides at the base of the flower, between the valvate margins of two sepals. By this means, of course, they completely avoid contact with the pollen. Old flowers, from which the sepals are about to drop, often swarm with black ants. The ants undoubtedly come in contact with pollen, but it is doubtful whether a single ant visits many flowers in a short period of time, or visits flowers which are young enough to have receptive styles. The honeybee specimen, *Apis mellifica,* and several of the unidentified smaller bees are well loaded down with pollen. They and the bumblebees are certainly the most important pollinators of this *Clematis.* Other species listed in Table III are probably accidental visitors; they could have been collected more efficiently by sweeping. An interesting sidelight on the insect relations of *Clematis* concerns the crab spiders (Thomisidae), of which 15 specimens were obtained. The writer was fascinated on one occasion to watch a *Hemaris* hovering before a flower, and to see it attacked and killed by a spider which had been waiting at the base of the flower.

During the 1942 season some notes were taken on the frequency of insect visits to the flowers. The observations were made without the disturbance caused by attempts to capture the visitors, and were incidental to other work. In an estimated 15 hours on seven different glades, during which an average of perhaps 20 plants were under close enough observation to insure detection of a pollinating insect, nine bumblebees were observed to visit a total of 24 flowers, two honeybees visited one flower each and flew out of sight, one small bee was observed on a single flower, five *Papilios* visited a total of 17 flowers, four *Hemaris* were observed, and one visit by an unidentified smaller butterfly was made. In all of the observations of insects, the writer has been impressed with the great variation from one glade to another. For instance, few hawk moths were recorded in 1942, while in 1943, when other glades were visited, they appeared to be the most frequent visitors, mainly because of the large numbers encountered on a single glade at R.2E, T.42N, S.15B. If any reliance can be placed on the crude estimates made above, it would seem that there is ample provision for the cross-

[VOL. 32

pollination of a plant within two days of anthesis. Actually, the frequency of pollination is probably higher; the smaller bees were not recorded because their visits failed to attract the writer's attention from other activities and no observations of nocturnal insects were made. Since the bumblebees and the honeybees are reputed to forage over wide areas, the occasional transport of pollen from one glade to another seems quite probable. While working on a single glade, the bumblebees do not systematically go from one flower to its nearest neighbor, but may fly several yards between visits. In a large colony of *Clematis* it seems probable that the circle of possible mates for a given plant may well include a few hundred individuals.

PATTERN OF DIFFERENTIATION

Data on the distribution of gene frequencies within a population provide the most useful information for evaluating the relative roles of selection and random differentiation. However, the collection of such data presupposes a basic fund of knowledge of the genetics of an organism which exists in relatively few cases. Lacking that for *Clematis,* a careful examination of many plants has been made for a morphological character which can at least be scored as present or absent, in the hope that eventually it might turn out to have a simple genetic basis. There is considerable variation in flower color, the outer surfaces of the sepals ranging from the blue and purple of the manuals, to practically white. Most flowers in anthesis are nearly white, with considerable variation in the distribution of the small amount of color which is present. It is suspected that true albino flowers exist, but they cannot be distinguished with certainty from those in which the pigment is very dilute.

The inner (adaxial) surfaces of the recurved sepal tips, however, show a discrete variation in color which is suggestive of a simple mode of inheritance, and a number of plants have been scored for presence or absence of color (pink or blue) at this place. A collection of 36 or fewer flowers was made on each of 12 glades, so selected that they could be arranged in pairs. The two glades of a pair are on adjacent ridges (fig. 13) about 0.35 mi., or 1850 ft., apart on the average. Two pairs of collections, 4.1 mi. apart on the average, were made in each of three regions. Glades 1–4 in the Robertsville region are about 28.5 mi. from glades 9–12 in the Plattin region, and glades 5–8, in the Morse Mill region, are midway between. The number and proportion of flowers with colored sepal tips in each collection, in each pair of collections, and in each region are shown in Table IV. The proportions for the three regions, 0.36, 0.11, and 0.05, suggest a "cline" (Huxley, '38), the frequency of colored sepal tips being greatest in the Robertsville region and decreasing toward the southeast.

In examining the data statistically, the assumption that the population is really uniform in proportion of colored sepal tips has first been tested by the χ^2 test. Theoretical frequencies of colored sepal tips have been calculated by multiplying the total number of flowers in each collection by the over-all proportion,

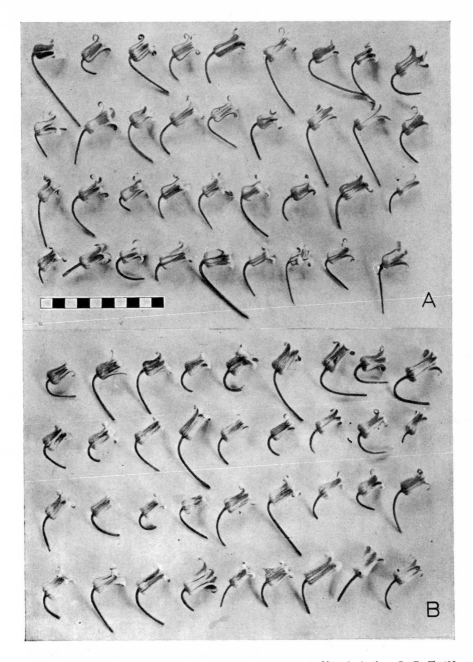

Fig. 14. Two collections of flowers of *C. Fremontii* var. *Riehlii*, obtained at R.2E, T.42N, S.18H (A), and at R.6E, T.39N, S.4P (B), to illustrate nature of morphological variation. Scale in centimeters.

[Vol. 32

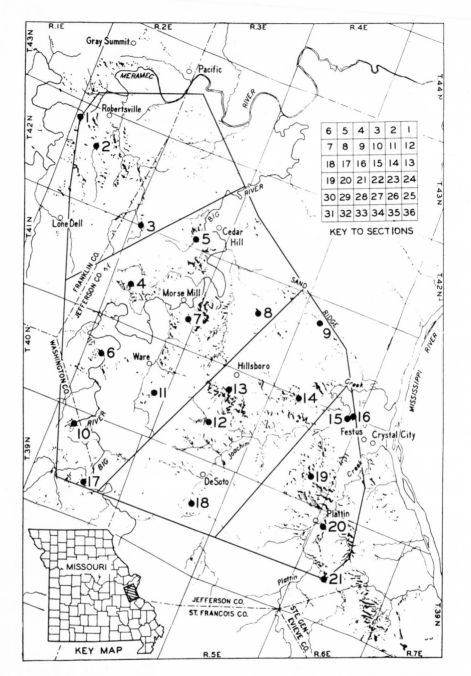

Fig. 15. Glades at which measurements have been made of sepal length, sepal width, margin width, and sepal coil. Glade numbers correspond with those of Table V.

TABLE IV

FREQUENCY OF COLORED SEPAL TIPS

(Glade numbers correspond with those of fig. 13)

No.	Location	Number of flowers			Number and proportion with colored tips			Significance of difference between proportions			
								Betw. glades		Betw. pairs	
		Glade	Pair	Region	Glade	Pair	Region	x	2P	x	2P
1	R. 2E, T. 42N, S. 18D	31	67		11–0.36	26–0.39		0.52	0.61		
2	R. 2E, T. 42N, S. 18H	36		139	15–0.42		50–0.36			0.67	0.50
3	R. 2E, T. 42N, S. 10E	36	72		11–0.31	24–0.33		0.52	0.62		
4	R. 2E, T. 42N, S. 10K	36			13–0.36						
5	R. 4E, T. 41N, S. 2E, F	18	54		3–0.17	7–0.13		0.57	0.58		
6	R. 4E, T. 41N, S. 2G	36		93	4–0.11		10–0.11			0.81	0.42
7	R. 4E, T. 41N, S. 20D	14	39		2–0.14	3–0.08		1.16	0.25		
8	R. 4E, T. 41N, S. 20E	25			1–0.04						
9	R. 5E, T. 40N, S. 25F	36	72		2–0.06	3–0.04		0.59	0.56		
10	R. 5E, T. 40N, S. 25B	36		144	1–0.03		7–0.05			0.39	0.70
11	R. 6E, T. 39N, S. 4P	36	72		3–0.08	4–0.06		1.03	0.30		
12	R. 6E, T. 39N, S. 4S	36			1–0.03						

Significance of difference between proportions, between regions:
Betw. glades 1–4 and 5–8: $x = 4.30$; $2P = 1.6 \times 10^{-5}$
Betw. glades 1–4 and 9–12: $x = 6.52$; $2P = 1.1 \times 10^{-10}$
Betw. glades 5–8 and 9–12: $x = 1.72$; $2P = 8.6 \times 10^{-2}$
Betw. glades 1–4 and 5–12: $x = 7.05$; $2P = 2.0 \times 10^{-12}$

0.178. Carrying through the calculation gives a χ^2 value of 43.9, with 8 degrees of freedom. The probability for a higher χ^2 value is less than 0.001, which rules out the possibility that the population is uniform in this character. (In this statistical analysis, and the succeeding ones, the methods and orthography of Rider ('39) have been followed except in the analysis of covariance on p. 446 *et seq.*)

For a more detailed analysis of the data, calculations have been made of the significance of the difference between the proportions for each pair of glades, for the two pairs of glades in each region, and for the three regions. There is no significant difference in proportion of colored sepal tips between any two adjacent glades (Table IV, third column from right), nor between the two pairs of glades in each region (Table IV, last column). The difference in proportion between the Robertsville and Morse Mill regions, between Robertsville and Plattin, and between

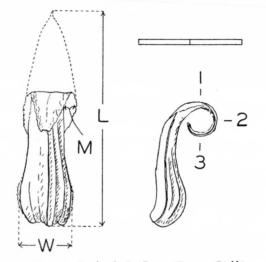

Fig. 16. Sepal of *C. Fremontii* var. *Riehlii*. Drawing at left illustrates manner in which measurements of sepal length, L, sepal width, W, and margin width, M, were made. Drawing at right illustrates method of scoring "sepal coil" in quadrants. Scale in centimeters.

the Robertsville region and the remaining glades, however, is highly significant (Table IV, bottom). Whether there is a real difference between the Morse Mill and Plattin regions is doubtful. The northwest–southeast differentiation in this character may be described as a cline, but its most significant feature is the deviation of the plants of the Robertsville region.

The flowers were brought to one place so that they could be studied at one time and photographed. Examination of the flowers indicated that the differentiation in proportion of colored sepal tips is correlated with similar differentiation in the color of the entire sepal. Perhaps it is merely an expression of the latter.

The flowers also show evident differences in a number of continuously varying characters, as illustrated in fig. 14. Measurements of four such characters have been made on another series of glades. The 21 glades at which measurements, usually of 35 flowers, were made are indicated in fig. 15. They are scattered throughout the distribution range. Measurements of the distance between each of the 210 pairs of glades have been made with dividers on a map (scale: $\frac{1}{4}$ in. = 1 mi.), averaged, and the average converted to miles. This yields an average distance between the glades of 12.8 mi.

In making the flower measurements, care was taken to select flowers only from the primary shoots of mature clumps. The flowers which terminate the primary shoots of a single clone are remarkably similar in size, coloration, and general aspect. Those which terminate secondary branches are often smaller, later in anthesis, and darker in color. None of the latter have been included in the measurements. The sampling scheme has been to select flowers from a re-

TABLE V

MEASUREMENTS OF FLOWERS

Means and Standard Deviations for Glades

(Glade numbers correspond with those of fig. 15)

No.	Location	N	Sepal length, mm.		Sepal width, mm.		Margin width, mm.		Sepal coil quadrants	
			$\bar{X}$	σ *	$\bar{X}$	σ *	$\bar{X}$	σ *	$\bar{X}$	σ *
1	R. 2E, T. 42N, S. 7A	45	33.56	2.93	8.84	0.54	2.03	0.47	3.29	1.05
2	R. 2E, T. 42N, S. 17B	37	34.08	3.86	9.51	1.04	2.46	0.57	3.41	1.12
3	R. 3E, T. 42N, S. 31D	35	37.54	4.92	10.00	0.98	1.87	0.70	3.06	0.88
4	R. 3E, T. 41N, S. 20A	35	34.20	3.95	9.31	0.93	1.74	0.51	3.46	0.98
5	R. 3E, T. 42N, S. 35B	35	33.09	4.10	9.31	1.07	1.70	0.43	3.31	0.80
6	R. 3E, T. 40N, S. 17A	35	34.20	3.47	10.11	0.97	1.73	0.41	2.74	0.79
7	R. 3E, T. 41N, S. 25D	35	34.66	2.92	9.83	1.19	1.89	0.42	3.69	0.55
8	R. 4E, T. 41N, S. 15B	35	33.14	3.38	10.11	1.15	2.00	0.42	3.20	0.60
9	R. 5E, T. 41N, S. 8B	32	29.72	5.92	9.06	1.08	1.69	0.47	3.34	0.84
10	R. 3E, T. 39N, S. 5D	35	32.91	4.02	9.54	1.39	1.66	0.60	2.97	0.79
11	R. 3E, T. 40N, S. 24B	35	34.46	3.72	9.34	1.03	2.06	0.64	2.63	0.87
12	R. 4E, T. 40N, S. 22C	35	35.06	3.10	10.14	1.28	1.76	0.43	3.11	0.84
13	R. 4E, T. 40N, S. 10E	35	34.37	4.06	9.80	0.97	1.70	0.41	2.80	0.69
14	R. 5E, T. 40N, S. 5D	35	33.80	3.34	9.54	1.19	1.67	0.49	2.77	0.87
15	R. 5E, T. 40N, S. 1B	35	32.37	2.74	9.37	1.28	1.89	0.41	2.89	0.95
16	R. 5E, T. 40N, S. 1C	35	32.66	3.73	9.49	1.09	1.90	0.53	2.71	0.90
17	R. 3E, T. 39N, S. 22B	35	34.60	3.59	10.26	1.21	2.14	0.55	3.00	1.00
18	R. 4E, T. 39N, S. 14A	35	36.57	3.40	10.23	1.48	2.09	0.55	3.17	0.96
19	R. 5E, T. 40N, S. 26B	35	33.89	7.02	9.69	1.96	1.74	0.53	2.71	1.17
20	R. 6E, T. 39N, S. 6J	35	35.97	4.00	9.49	4.09	2.01	0.44	3.14	0.99
21	R. 6E, T. 39N, S. 20B	35	33.34	2.89	9.31	1.12	1.64	0.43	2.97	0.83
Total		744	34.02	4.18	9.63	1.28	1.88	0.53	3.07	0.94

stricted portion of each glade, rather than to sample the entire population of the glade. Usually the measurements were begun at a point where the plants were abundant, and a roughly spiral course was followed, during which a flower from each mature plant encountered was measured. No records were kept of the location on the glade of the plants selected. A sepal was removed from each flower, and the measurements indicated in fig. 16 were made with a celluloid rule. The length of the sepal was measured to the nearest mm., after straightening the recurved tip, but no attempt was made to flatten the thick base. Width was

TABLE VI

MEASUREMENTS OF FLOWERS

A. Analysis of Variance for Glades

CHARACTER	Sum of squares of deviations	Degrees of freedom	Mean square deviation	w	P
SEPAL LENGTH					
Within glades	11,271.14	723	15.59	5.51	$<$ 0.0001
Among glades	1,717.64	20	85.88		
Total	12,988.78	743			
SEPAL WIDTH					
Within glades	1,158.92	723	1.603	3.60	$<$ 0.0001
Among glades	115.46	20	5.773		
Total	1,274.38	743			
MARGIN WIDTH					
Within glades	202.65	723	0.2803	5.52	$<$ 0.0001
Among glades	30.96	20	1.5480		
Total	233.61	743			
SEPAL COIL					
Within glades	658.84	723	0.9113	3.16	$<$ 0.0001
Among glades	57.66	20	2.8833		
Total	716.50	743			

B. Analysis of Variance for Regions

CHARACTER	Sum of squares of deviations	Degrees of freedom	Mean square deviation	w	P
SEPAL LENGTH					
Within regions	12,906.32	740	17.44	1.58	0.20
Among regions	82.46	3	27.49		
Total	12,988.78	743			
SEPAL WIDTH					
Within regions	1,257.78	740	1.700	3.26	0.020
Among regions	16.60	3	5.533		
Total	1,274.38	743			
MARGIN WIDTH					
Within regions	224.85	740	0.3039	9.61	$<$ 0.0001
Among regions	8.76	3	2.9200		
Total	233.61	743			
SEPAL COIL					
Within regions	705.44	740	0.9533	3.87	0.0089
Among regions	11.07	3	3.6887		
Total	716.50	743			

measured, to the nearest mm., at the widest point, quite near the base of the sepal, without any attempt to flatten it. The width of the expanded sepal margin was measured to the nearest 0.5 mm., at its widest point, usually quite near the tip of the sepal. The degree to which the tip of the sepal is recurved, "sepal coil," was scored by noting the number of quadrants through which the tip has moved in anthesis. Thus, if the sepal tip has turned through 360°, as has the one illustrated, it is scored as 4. The mean and standard deviation of each series of measurements are given in Table V. Because of the relative coarseness of the scale used for three of the measurements (width, margin and coil), Sheppard's correction has been applied in calculating the standard deviations.

Inspection of the table discloses differences in means from one glade to another in each of the characters. In order to determine whether the variation in these characters from one glade to another is greater than that on a single glade (in

TABLE VII

MEASUREMENTS OF FLOWERS

A. Means and Standard Deviations for Regions

Region	N	Sepal length, mm.		Sepal width, mm.		Margin width, mm.		Sepal coil, quadrants	
		$\bar{X}$	σ *	$\bar{X}$	σ *	$\bar{X}$	σ *	$\bar{X}$	σ *
Robertsville. Glades 1, 2, 3	117	34.90	4.41	9.40	1.24	2.12	0.62	3.26	1.03
Morse Mill. Glades 4, 5, 6, 7, 8, 10, 11, 17	280	33.91	3.72	9.73	1.19	1.86	0.53	3.13	0.88
Hillsboro. Glades 9, 12, 13, 14, 18	172	33.98	4.18	9.77	1.29	1.78	0.50	3.03	0.87
Plattin. Glades 15, 16, 19, 20, 21	175	33.65	4.57	9.47	1.38	1.84	0.49	2.89	0.99
Total	744	34.02	4.18	9.63	1.28	1.88	0.53	3.07	0.94

B. Tests of Significance of Differences between Means for Regions

Between Regions	Sepal length, mm.		Sepal width, mm.		Margin width, mm.		Sepal coil, quadrants	
	t	$2P$	t	$2P$	t	$2P$	t	$2P$
Robertsville and Morse Mill	2.28	0.023	−2.46	0.015	4.15	< 0.0001	1.12	0.26
Morse Mill and Hillsboro	−0.18	0.86	−0.33	0.74	1.64	0.10	1.06	0.29
Hillsboro and Plattin	0.70	0.48	2.08	0.038	−1.04	0.30	1.49	0.14
Robertsville and Hillsboro	1.79	0.075	−2.40	0.017	5.09	< 0.0001	1.65	0.10
Morse Mill and Plattin	0.67	0.50	2.13	0.033	0.55	0.58	2.68	0.0077
Robertsville and Plattin	2.32	0.021	−0.42	0.67	4.32	< 0.0001	2.64	0.0088

other words, whether these samples must be regarded as representing a number of separate populations or as portions of a single statistical population), the data have been subjected to an analysis of variance. The results are presented in Table VI, A. In each of the four flower characters the probability that the 21 series of measurements can be regarded as portions of the same statistical population is very low, clearly beyond the threshold of significance. This excess of variance among glades over that within individual glades is evidence of considerable local differentiation. It may be ascribed to the partial isolation of the glades, which has been discussed above.

It is also of interest to inquire whether these data demonstrate a cline, or regional differentiation of any sort, in any of the characters. In view of the local differentiation, it has not been possible to find evidence of differentiation on a regional scale by examining the means of individual glades, or by studying a series of ideograms, such as Anderson ('36) prepared from his data on *Iris*. The sampling scheme used in selecting these glades leaves a good deal to be desired when it comes to investigating the question of regional differentiation. Nevertheless, the data for the 21 glades have been combined into four groups as shown in fig. 15 and Table VII, A. The four groups correspond approximately with the Robertsville, Morse Mill, Hillsboro and Plattin regions, described above. An analysis of variance has been carried out for each of the four sepal measurements (Table VI, B). It indicates that the excess of variance from one region to another over that within regions is significant for margin width and sepal coil, perhaps so for sepal width, and not for sepal length. In other words, there appears to be significant regional differentiation in two (or three) of the four measurements.

It is then worth while to compare the means for each of the regions. Means and standard deviations for each of the measurements have been entered in Table VII, A. The t value for the difference between each pair of means has also been determined. In this calculation the variance of the difference has been estimated separately for each pair of means. The probability corresponding to each t value has been found from a table of "Student's" distribution (Table VII, B). In sepal length, the plants from the Robertsville region are perhaps significantly higher than those of the other three regions, while there are no significant differences among the latter. The Robertsville, and perhaps the Plattin, plants have significantly narrower sepals than do those of Morse Mill and Hillsboro. The valvate margin of the sepal is wider in the Robertsville region than in the other three regions, and this difference is highly significant. As in sepal length, the differences in margin width among the Morse Mill, Hillsboro and Plattin regions are not significant. The sepals are most strongly recurved in the Robertsville region and least so around Plattin. The differences in this character between adjacent regions are on the border-line of significance, but the differentiation becomes significant from one end of the range to the other.

In summary, there is significant regional differentiation in each of the four flower measurements. In only one case, sepal coil, can the differentiation be described as a cline, in the sense of a consistent geographical trend. The most striking feature of the differentiation in these characters is the difference between the Robertsville plants and those of the other portions of the population. The same conclusion was drawn above from the analysis of the data on proportion of colored sepal tips (Table IV).

It has been shown above that there is greater differentiation in the flower measurements from one glade to another than on single glades. It may also be inquired whether there is local differentiation from one portion to another of a single glade. To answer this question it is necessary to obtain data on the location on a glade of the plants studied. Such data were not obtained for the plants whose flowers were measured. Laying out quadrats such as those used in population density studies is time-consuming, and it would not have been feasible during the flowering period of *Clematis* to have obtained both flower measurements and accurate locality data for any large number of plants.

On several glades, however, a leaf was collected from each plant plotted during the population density study. The leaves on a single plant vary in size and shape, though those at corresponding positions on different shoots of a single clone are closely similar. To obtain leaves from different plants which would be comparable, one leaf of the pair which subtends the first flower of the plant, or of the most vigorous shoot of a clone, was taken. The leaves of this pair are usually the longest, and comparatively, the widest ones on a shoot. On young sterile plants, however, the apical pair of leaves is usually small, and from such plants a leaf of the largest pair was taken, which was usually at the third or fourth node from the apex. The quadrat in which each leaf was collected was noted on the leaf with wax pencil, or on a small label attached to the leaf with Cellophane tape. Since the leaves are leathery in texture, it was not felt necessary to press them.

Two of the leaf collections have been subjected to measurement and statistical analysis. One of these was obtained over a continuous portion of the large glade at R.6E, T.39N, S.4-O (Glade no. 8 in fig. 2 and Table I). The entire area was laid out in 10-ft. quadrats (fig. 1, B), and a leaf was removed from each plant. Somewhat more than 1,000 leaves were collected. In some cases the label indicating the quadrat in which the leaf was obtained was lost, so that 983 leaves were available for study. Measurements of the dry leaves were made to the nearest mm. with a celluloid rule, some time after collection. Length was measured on the adaxial surface, from the tip to the point of attachment to the stem. Width was measured at the widest place, usually in the proximal half of the leaf. Many of the leaves are not plane, the adaxial surfaces sometimes being markedly concave, and rarely saddle-shaped. In all cases the rule was bent to follow the curvature of the leaf surface. (The author is indebted to John R. Melin, A. S., a U. S. Navy V-12 student, for the measurements, and for assistance in the calculation.)

It may first be inquired whether there are significant differences in the absolute length and width measurements from one portion of the area studied to another. This may be answered, as for the flower measurements discussed above, by carrying out an analysis of variance. For the purpose of the analysis, the area has been subdivided in three ways. The 10-ft. quadrats have first been combined by fours into a total of eighty-eight 20-ft. quadrats, which include an average of 11.17 measured leaves each. The number of leaves in each 20-ft. quadrat varies from 2 to 27 in a non-Poisson manner (see p. 417). Secondly, the 20-ft. quadrats have been combined by fours, with slight irregularities, into a total of twenty-four 40-ft. quadrats, which include an average of 40.96 leaves each, ranging from 9 to 80. The arrangement of the 40-ft. quadrats, and the numbers which have been assigned to them are shown in fig. 1, B. Finally, the entire area has been divided into three strips 80 ft. wide. They consist of the 40-ft. quadrats numbered 1–8, 9–18 and 19–24, and include 435, 435, and 113 leaves respectively. These strips will be referred to as 80-ft. quadrats.

For each of the three schemes of subdivision, calculations have been made of: the sums of squares of the deviations of the length and width of each leaf from

TABLE VIII

MEASUREMENTS OF LEAVES AT R.6E, T.39N, S.4-0

Analysis of Variance and Covariance

A

	Σx^2	Σxy	Σy^2	Degrees of freedom
Within 20-ft. quadrats	249,046.89	186,367.06	199,118.64	895
Among 20-ft. quadrats	77,572.11	71,742.80	76,685.39	87
For variance in length, $n_1 = 87$, $w = 3.20$, $P < 0.0001$				
For variance in width, $n_1 = 87$, $w = 3.96$, $P < 0.0001$				
Within 40-ft. quadrats	279,040.46	210,952.56	226,036.68	959
Among 40-ft. quadrats	47,578.54	47,157.30	49,767.36	23
For variance in length, $n_1 = 23$, $w = 7.11$, $P < 0.0001$				
For variance in width, $n_1 = 23$, $w = 9.18$, $P < 0.0001$				
Within 80-ft. quadrats	314,033.96	244,203.24	260,436.61	980
Among 80-ft. quadrats	12,585.04	13,906.62	15,367.42	2
Total	326,619.00	258,109.86	275,804.03	982
For variance in length, $n_1 = 2$, $w = 19.64$, $P < 0.0001$				
For variance in width, $n_1 = 2$, $w = 28.91$, $P < 0.0001$				

B

	Sum of squares of deviations	Degrees of freedom	Mean square deviation	w	P
Within 20-ft. quadrats:					
Average regression	139,462.41	1	139,462.41		
Regression differences	6,060.80	87	69.66	1.05	0.28
Residuals	53,595.43	807	66.41		
	(199,118.64)	(895)			
Among 20-ft. quadrats:					
Regression of means	66,351.55	1	66,351.55		
Residuals	10,333.84	86	120.16	1.81	< 0.0001
	(76,685.39)	(87)			
Total	275,804.03	982			
Within 40-ft. quadrats:					
Average regression	179,478.60	1	179,478.60		
Regression differences	2,419.41	23	105.19	1.53	0.050
Residuals	64,138.67	935	68.60		
	(226,036.68)	(959)			
Among 40-ft. quadrats:					
Regression of means	46,739.87	1	46,739.87		
Residuals	3,027.48	22	137.61	2.01	0.0034
	(49,767.35)	(23)			
Total	275,804.03	982			
Within 80-ft. quadrats:					
Average regression	189,900.55	1	189,900.55		
Regression differences	1,075.38	2	537.69	7.56	0.0005
Residuals	69,460.68	977	71.10		
	(260,436.61)	(980)			
Among 80-ft. quadrats:					
Regression of means	15,366.98	1	15,366.98		
Residuals	0.44	1	0.44	161.8	0.062
	(15,367.42)	(2)		$(n_1 = 977)$	
Total	275,804.03	982			

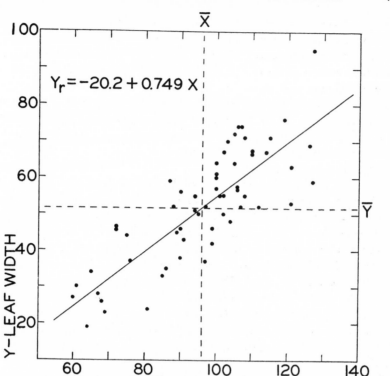

Fig. 17. Length and width measurements of 58 leaves of *C. Fremonti* var. *Riehlii* collected in 40-ft. quadrat no. 8 of fig. 1, B (R.6E, T.39N, S.4-0). Line of regression of width on length has been fitted to the data.

the mean length and width for the quadrat in which the leaf was collected (Table VIII, A, "within quadrats" rows), the sums of squares of deviations of the mean length and width for each quadrat from the over-all mean length and width ("among quadrats" rows), and the sums of squares of deviations of the length and width of each leaf from the over-all means ("total" row). Corresponding sums of products of the length and width deviations have also been determined. By the usual methods of analysis of variance, it is found that there is significantly greater variance among 20-ft. quadrats, 40-ft. quadrats, and 80-ft. quadrats, than within such quadrats, in both the length and width measurements (see the w and P values listed in Table VIII, A).

It is apparent in the field that the size of a leaf is greatly dependent on the general vigor of the plant. Presumably it is strongly influenced by environmental factors, and measurements of absolute length and width cannot be considered of much value in investigating the possibility of genetic differentiation from one portion of a glade to another. It might be supposed that the shape of a leaf is less strongly influenced by environmental variables. It is then of interest to investigate whether these data yield any information about local differentiation in shape. One aspect of leaf shape is the relationship between width and length. One way in which this relationship might be expressed for a series of leaves is by the mean width:length ratio. When the width of each leaf is plotted against its length for a portion of the area studied, however, it appears that width and length are correlated, and that it may be justified to fit a regression line to the data (fig. 17). While the relationship between width and length may be regarded as approaching a linear one in the range of sizes at hand, the straight line fitted to the data does not pass through the origin. In other words, the width:length ratio does not tend to remain constant for leaves of varying length, but tends to increase with increasing leaf length.

Because of this circumstance, it is thought that the coefficient of linear regression of width on length is a more satisfactory index of the relationship between width and length than is the mean width:length ratio. It may be calculated by fitting an equation of the form $Y_r = a + bX$ (where $Y =$ leaf width, $X =$ leaf length, $a =$ intercept on the Y-axis and $b =$ regression coefficient) to the data for a series of leaves by the method of least squares. This has been done for the data plotted in fig. 17. (The fact that the regression line does not pass through the origin, of course, indicates that it does not fit the data entirely adequately. The relationship between width and length is undoubtedly expressed properly by a curved line passing through the origin. Nevertheless, the coefficient of linear regression is regarded as adequate for the purposes of this statistical study.)

The problem of determining whether there is local differentiation in the relationship between leaf width and length from one portion of this area to another can then be restated as the statistical problem of determining whether the regression coefficients calculated for leaves from different portions of the area are significantly different. This could be done by calculating the coefficients, and applying Student's t test to the differences between pairs. It is possible to do this more efficiently, however, by carrying out an analysis of covariance.

The total variance in width has been divided above (Table VIII, A) into two portions, that within and that among quadrats. The analysis of covariance requires that it be subdivided further. It has been suggested above that there is a significant regression of width on length within at least one of the 40-ft. quadrats (fig. 17). The variance in width within each quadrat could then be subdivided into two portions: the variance of the regression line about the quadrat mean width, and the variance of the individual width measurements about the regression line. The sum of squares of deviations in width can then be written $\Sigma (Y - \overline{Y})^2 = \Sigma (Y - Y_r)^2 + \Sigma (Y_r - \overline{Y})^2$ (where $Y =$ width of an individual leaf, $\overline{Y} =$ mean leaf width for a quadrat, and $Y_r =$ theoretical width for a leaf calculated by substituting its length into the regression equation for the quadrat). If the length and width measurements for a quadrat are put in terms of deviations from the quadrat mean length and width, so that $x = X - \overline{X}$ and $y = Y - \overline{Y}$, the three terms of this equation can be rewritten: $\Sigma (Y - \overline{Y})^2 =$

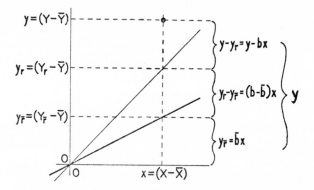

Fig. 18. Diagram to illustrate manner in which deviation in width of a leaf from its quadrat mean has been divided into three portions in the analysis of covariance. Further explanation in text.

Σy^2, $\Sigma (Y - Y_r)^2 = \Sigma y^2 - (\Sigma xy)^2/\Sigma x^2$, and $\Sigma (Y_r - Y)^2 = (\Sigma xy)^2/\Sigma x^2$, as shown in any general treatise on statistics. The equation for the regression line can also be rewritten $y_r = bx$ (where $b = \Sigma xy/\Sigma x^2 =$ regression coefficient for the quadrat).

The regression line for a quadrat, whose equation is written in this way, passes through the origin, that is, through the point which corresponds with the quadrat mean length and width. The regression lines for each of the quadrats can then be visualized as radiating from a common origin. An average regression line for a series of quadrats, which passes through the same origin, can also be considered. Its equation can be written $y_{\bar{r}} = \bar{b}x$. In fig. 18 are shown a regression line for one quadrat (lighter line) and the average regression line for a series of quadrats (heavier line). The deviation from the quadrat mean of a single measurement, y, can be seen to be made up of three portions: (1) the theoretical deviation from the quadrat mean, calculated by substituting the length deviation of the leaf into the average regression equation $(y_{\bar{r}})$; (2) the difference between the theoretical deviation calculated from the quadrat regression equation and that calculated from the average regression equation $(y_r - y_{\bar{r}})$; and (3) the difference between the actual width deviation and the theoretical deviation calculated from the quadrat regression equation $(y - y_r)$. It can be shown that the corresponding sums of squares of deviations in width for all the leaves over a series of quadrats are given by the following formulae:

(1) Sum of squares attributable to the average regression $= (\Sigma\Sigma xy)^2/\Sigma\Sigma x^2$;

(2) Sum of squares attributable to differences between the quadrat regressions and the average regression $= \Sigma[(\Sigma xy)^2/\Sigma x^2] - (\Sigma\Sigma xy)^2/\Sigma\Sigma x^2$; and

(3) Sum of squares attributable to deviations of the separate width measurements from the regression within each quadrat, or "within-quadrats residuals" $= \Sigma\Sigma y^2 - \Sigma[(\Sigma xy)^2/\Sigma x^2]$. (In each case, the first sign of summation, Σ, indicates summation over a series of quadrats, the second, summations for the series of

leaves within quadrats.)

By centering each of the quadrat regression lines at the origin, differences among the mean widths and lengths for each quadrat have been ignored. The variance in width arising from these differences has been shown to be significantly greater than that within quadrats (Table VIII, A), and it is of interest to subdivide it into two portions. The among-quadrats sum of squares of width deviations consists of:

(4)   Sum of squares attributable to regression of the quadrat means, calculated most easily by substituting among-quadrats values from Table VIII, A, into an expression of the form $(\Sigma xy)^2/\Sigma x^2$; and

(5)   Sum of squares attributable to deviations of quadrat mean widths from their regression, or "among-quadrats residuals," obtained by subtracting (4) from the among-quadrats sum of squares of deviations in width.

If N is the total number of leaves over the area studied, and k the number of quadrats into which the area is divided, the number of degrees of freedom to be ascribed to each of the five sums of squares is: (1) average regression,1; (2) regression differences, $k-1$; (3) within-quadrats residuals, $N-2k$; (4) regression of means, 1; (5) among-quadrats residuals, $k-2$; totalling to $N-1$.

The within-quadrats residual mean square is to be regarded as the "error" mean square, with which other mean squares should be compared. The mean squares of interest in investigating leaf shape differences from one quadrat to another are: that attributable to regression differences (2), and the among-quadrats residual mean square (5). If the population were statistically uniform in the width to length relationship expressed by the regression coefficient, neither of these mean squares should be significantly greater than the within-quadrats residual mean square. (Dr. Donald R. Charles has given generously of his time in developing this scheme of analysis, in clarifying for the author the concepts involved, and in aiding in interpretation of the results of the analysis. The author, however, is responsible for this exposition of the method.)

The analysis of covariance of this leaf collection is summarized in Table VIII, B. A separate analysis has been made for each of the three schemes of subdivision of the area. It will be seen that the regression differences are not statistically significant from one 20-ft. or 40-ft. quadrat to another, but are significant among the 80-ft. quadrats. The among-quadrats residuals are significantly greater than the within-quadrats residuals from one 20-ft. or 40-ft. quadrat to another, but not among the three 80-ft. quadrats. In other words, there is statistically significant local differentiation in leaf shape from one portion of the area to another. This differentiation appears at the 20-ft. and 40-ft. levels of subdivision as significant deviations of the quadrat means from their regression, and at the 80-ft. level as differences among the within-quadrats regressions.

It may then be inquired whether this local differentiation in leaf shape, and in absolute length and width, follows any discernible pattern. For this purpose the outlines of the 40-ft. quadrats shown in fig. 1, B, have been redrawn (fig. 19). Within each quadrat outline have been placed the number of the quadrat (Q),

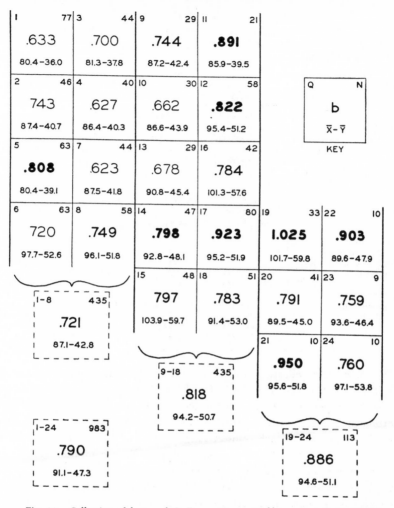

Fig. 19. Collection of leaves of *C. Fremontii* var. *Riehlii* made at R.6E, T.39N, S.4-0. Compare with fig. 1, B. Squares are 40-ft. quadrats. Number in center of each square is coefficient of regression of leaf width on length. Largest coefficients in heavy figures, intermediate coefficients in medium figures, and smallest ones in light figures. Further explanation in text.

the number of leaves measured from it (*N*), the regression coefficient of width on length for the leaves within the quadrat (*b*), and the mean length and width of the leaves ($\overline{X}$ and $\overline{Y}$). When the mean lengths and widths and the regression coefficients are compared, it is seen that the leaves of the upper-left portion of the diagram (embracing, perhaps, the nine quadrats numbered 1, 2, 3, 4, 5, 7, 9, 10 and 11, and a total of 394 leaves) are smaller and relatively narrower, than those from the remainder of the area. This grouping, however, is not without inconsistencies.

TABLE IX

MEASUREMENTS OF LEAVES AT R. 2E, T. 42N, S. 15B

Analysis of Variance and Covariance

A

	Σx^2	Σxy	Σy^2	Degrees of freedom
Within transects	90,868.35	69,857.32	76,752.97	256
Among transects	6,022.65	5,499.18	7,092.97	8
Total	96,891.00	75,356.50	83,845.94	264

For variance in length, $n_1 = 8$, $w = 2.12$, $P = 0.034$

For variance in width, $n_1 = 8$, $w = 2.96$, $P = 0.0036$

B

	Sum of squares of deviations	Degrees of freedom	Mean square deviation	w	P
Within transects:					
Average regression	53,704.56	1	53,704.56		
Regression differences	1,389.25	8	173.66	1.98	0.080
Residuals	21,659.16	247	87.69		
	(76,752.97)	(256)			
Among transects:					
Regression of means	5,021.13	1	5,021.13		
Residuals	2,071.84	7	295.98	3.38	0.0028
	(7,092.97)	(8)			
Total	83,845.94	264			

The second leaf collection which has been studied was obtained on a glade at R.2E, T.42N, S.15B (Glade no. 2 in fig. 2 and Table I). Nine transects, 10 ft. wide, were laid out at 250-ft. intervals across the glade, as illustrated in fig. 20. Collection of a leaf from each plant encountered yielded 265 leaves for measurement. The numbers for each transect range from 7 to 74. The analysis of variance and covariance described above was applied to these data also. There is significantly greater variance among transects than within in the absolute measurements of width, and perhaps of length (Table IX, A). The differences among the regressions of width on length for separate transects are not significant, but there are significant deviations of the transect means from the among-transects regression (Table IX, B). As before, this can be taken to indicate that there is statistically significant local differentiation in leaf shape from one portion of the glade to another.

In an attempt to determine whether the differentiation on this glade falls into any pattern, the transect regression coefficients have been entered near each transect in fig. 20. When the values of the coefficients are compared, it is seen that they can be arranged in two groups, those of transects 1, 3, 6, 8, and 9 being lower than those of transects 2, 4, 5 and 7. The leaves within each of these two groups of transects are statistically uniform in shape, as shown by an analysis of covariance applied to each. The glade can perhaps be thought of as divided into seven portions which have alternately wider and narrower leaves. These seven

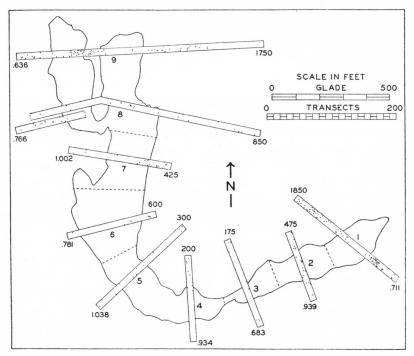

Fig. 20. Glade at R.2E, T.42N, S.15B, showing arrangement of nine transects, and distribution of plants (small dots) within transects. Length and width of a leaf from each plant have been measured. Transects have been enlarged for clarity. The fractional numbers near each transect are coefficients of regression of leaf width on length, the larger numbers have been obtained by multiplying the number of measured leaves from the transect by 25. Further explanation in text.

portions of the glade can perhaps be delimited by lines drawn midway between the transects, as has been done in fig. 20. A crude estimate of the number of plants represented by a transect is obtained by multiplying the number of leaves studied by 25, since the transects are 10 ft. wide and 250 ft. apart. These numbers have also been entered in fig. 20. If this picture of the pattern of differentiation is a true one, the differentiation appears to be effective between groups of plants numbering a few hundred.

An alternative picture of the differentiation pattern on this glade is to regard it as divided into three portions, embracing, respectively, transect 1, with an estimated 1850 plants ($b = 0.711$), transects 2–7, with 2175 plants ($b = 0.987$), and transects 8–9, with 2600 plants ($b = 0.676$). In favor of this grouping is the fact that an analysis of covariance for transects 2–7 shows no significant differentiation in shape among the five transects. If this is the true picture, the differentiation would appear to be effective between groups of plants numbering about two thousand. It does not appear possible from these data to make a choice between the two alternatives.

No information about the factors responsible for the local differentiation in leaf size and shape can, of course, be obtained from these data. The differentiation may be merely a result of differences in environmental conditions from one portion of a glade to another, or it may have a genetic basis. The glades are not believed to be a uniform habitat for *Clematis*. This topic has been discussed on pp. 418 and 419. This non-uniformity of the glades may give rise to the local differentiation in leaf size and shape merely by inducing environmental fluctuations in a population which is essentially homogeneous genetically. On the other hand, the distribution of *Clematis* on a glade is characterized by significant aggregation (p. 419). The degree of isolation between aggregates may be such as to allow a certain amount of random genetic differentiation. It should be pointed out that, on at least one of the two glades studied, the differentiation in leaf size and shape appears to be effective over a radius including a few hundred plants. Other lines of evidence, such as the distribution pattern, and observations of pollination, have suggested an effective population size of a few hundred.

The question of an environmental, as opposed to a genetic, basis for the demonstrated local differentiation, can also be directed at the results of the analysis of flower measurements (Tables VI and VII). It appears much less probable that the differences in flower measurements from one glade or region to another are environmental fluctuations than that the leaf differences discussed above can be so accounted for. There appears to be greater variation in physical conditions from one portion to another of a single glade than between separate glades taken as wholes. Furthermore, there is undoubtedly a good deal of truth to the systematists' principle that flower and fruit characters are more "stable" than are the characters of vegetative organs such as leaves. Subjective study in the field of variation within and among clones leads one to believe that the principle holds for differences among plants as well as for differences among species.

A number of subjective observations of variation have been made, which consistently point to the existence of a considerable amount of local differentiation. The glade at R.3E, T.42N, S.31D (Glade no. 3 in fig. 15) is small and relatively isolated. It supports 75 to 100 plants. The flowers strike one immediately by their lack of color and unusual proportions. The sepals are longer (one of them measured 51 mm.), and exceed the stamens much more than usual. Perhaps one-third of the plants share these characteristics, and, in other respects as well, show a resemblance which suggests close relationship. At R.2E, T.42N, S.18H (Glade no. 2 in fig. 13) a fairly large glade with a population of 1,000 or 2,000, 15 or so plants were seen which resemble each other in that the sepals are rolled back so as to expose about half the length of the stamen mass. This peculiarity was subsequently seen on a near-by glade, but has not been noticed elsewhere. Two monstrous plants, in which the leaves are irregularly coalesced and incised, and otherwise distorted, were seen among the estimated 600 plants at R.5E, T.40N, S.13A. No teratological specimens have been seen elsewhere, though an occasional ternate shoot has been found in the midst of a decussate-leaved clone. Exploration of the large glade at R.4E, T.41N, S.2F (Glade no. 5, fig. 13) disclosed only eight plants in a small area at one end. The six which were in flower at the time of the visit were remarkably alike in flower color and form and in general habit. The resemblance suggested that of sibs rather than of portions of a clone. Similar "family resemblances" of plants which are growing fairly close together have been seen less distinctly in many other instances.

Examination of the aerial photograph tracings and field experience both indicate that the glades are, on the whole, smaller and more isolated in the Robertsville region at the northwestern end of the range than they are farther southeast. The difference is more pronounced than the distribution map (fig. 13) suggests. An impression has grown during the field work that this difference in size and degree of isolation of separate colonies is reflected in a difference in the degree of variability in different parts of the range. The plants of the Robertsville region strike one as displaying more variation in the amount of color and pattern of color distribution in the sepals; in the width, texture, and degree of crisping of the expanded margin of the sepal; in the size, shape, and general aspect of the leaves. In general, there is a larger proportion of "queer-looking" plants than among the more uniform population of the Plattin region.

Sources of Variation

Gene mutation is generally regarded as the ultimate source of evolutionary change, and it would be desirable in studying the evolution of any organism to begin with information about the rate and direction of mutation of its genes. However, such information has been obtained for relatively few genes in a very few organisms which are favorable genetic material. Needless to say, no data whatever on this point are available for *Clematis*, and the plant is not favorable material for genetic study, because of the long period required before it reaches flowering age.

Chromosomal changes such as ploidy, inversion, and translocation have been demonstrated to be responsible for evolutionary change in several organisms. Polyploidy is practically non-existent in the genus *Clematis*. All the reported species are normal diploids ($n = 8$), with the exception of two tetraploid cultivated forms (Meurman and Therman, '39, Gregory, '41). The author has found the haploid number, $n = 8$, in several plants of *C. Fremontii* var. *Riehlii*. Examination in the field of the first division of the microsporocytes of about 75 plants has disclosed no chromatin bridges; in these plants at least, there were no conspicuous inversions.

Hybridization between species and varieties of higher plants is of rather frequent occurrence, and appears to be an important factor in the evolution of many forms. Anderson and Hubricht ('38) have studied a case of introgressive hybridization between two species of *Tradescantia*. Mangelsdorf and Reeves ('39) regard probable hybridization with *Tripsacum* as an important factor in the evolution of maize. Wide crosses are known to occur in the genus *Clematis*. *C. integrifolia*, which is fairly closely related to *C. Fremontii* var. *Riehlii*, has given rise to *C. Durandi* by a cross with *C. Jackmani,* one of the large-flowered oriental hybrids. A hybrid of *C. integrifolia* with *C. Flammula,* one of the small-, paniculate-flowered species, is also known, and instances of hybridization between other species can be multiplied (Rehder, '40). The fact, then, that *C. Pitcheri,* which is a member of the same section (VIORNA) of the genus as *C. Fremontii* var. *Riehlii,* occurs in the vicinity of the glades makes hybridization between the two species seem at least a possibility. Transfer of pollen between the two species appears possible but must be a rare occurrence. *C. Pitcheri* often occurs in the woods just below a glade, and bumblebees, at least, visit both species (Robertson, '28). However, they are separated by a difference in flowering period. *C. Fremontii* var. *Riehlii* has finished flowering by the second week of May, and *C. Pitcheri* does not come into flower until the middle of June. It continues to flower for some time, and it would probably be in anthesis when *C. Fremontii* var. *Riehlii* flowers sporadically in September.

Five plants have been found which strongly suggest that hybridization does occur. One of the plants (fig. 21, fig. 22, C) appears to be the F_1 progeny of a cross between the two forms. It grows on a glade at R.2E, T.42N, S.14H, about 3.4 mi. southeast of Robertsville. A graded farm-to-market road, surfaced with gravel, crosses the lower edge of this large glade. The supposed hybrid is rooted in the gravel embankment at the down-slope side of the road. The glade above the road is well populated with *C. Fremontii* var. *Riehlii,* a few plants persisting in the gravel at the edges of the road. A number of rather small plants of *C. Pitcheri* occur in the 300-ft. strip of woods between the road and Little Calvey Creek. The site of the hybrid is suggestive, since other species hybrids have often been reported to occur in disturbed habitats.

On the basis of morphological characters, it is impossible to regard the presumed hybrid as a member either of *C. Fremontii* var. *Riehlii* or of *C. Pitcheri,* variable as the latter species is. It appears to show pronounced hybrid vigor. Making allowances for that, it appears roughly intermediate between the two parental forms in the characters which have been examined. It has the ascending habit of *C. Pitcheri,* but the stems are considerably stouter. It appears intermediate in degree of compounding of the leaves between *C. Fremontii* var. *Riehlii,* with simple leaves, and *C. Pitcheri,* whose leaves are compound or decompound, though this character is difficult to evaluate. Its leaflets appear as thick and coriaceous as the leaves of *C. Fremontii* var. *Riehlii,* contrasting with the much thinner leaflets of *C. Pitcheri.* In *C. Fremontii* var. *Riehlii* the flowers are solitary, terminating the vegetative branches; in *C. Pitcheri* single flowers are borne on axillary peduncles, each with one pair of simple floral leaves. In the supposed hybrid both conditions occur (fig. 21). The flowers are intermediate in size between those of the putative parents. The sepals are less recurved, and their valvate margins narrower, than in *C. Fremontii* var. *Riehlii;* in these two characters the plant approaches *C. Pitcheri.* Its flowering period is a week or two later than that of *C. Fremontii* var. *Riehlii,* and earlier than that of *C. Pitcheri.* The clusters of

Fig. 21. Plant which is presumed to be the F₁ progeny of a cross between *C. Fremontii* var. *Riehlii* and *C. Pitcheri*. Note the old flower terminating the primary stem from which sepals and stamens have fallen. Scale in centimeters.

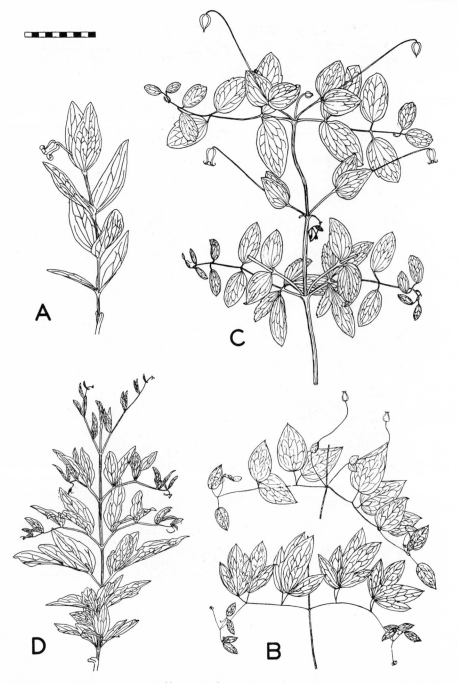

Fig. 22. *C. Fremontii* var. *Riehlii, C. Pitcheri* and two plants which are presumed to be the result of hybridization between them. A. Tracing of a photograph of a young plant of *C. Fremontii* var. *Riehlii*. B. Tracing of two pressed fragments of a large plant of *C. Pitcheri*. C. Tracing of a portion of a pressed plant, which is presumed to be the F₁ hybrid between *C. Fremontii* var. *Riehlii* and *C. Pitcheri*. Another shoot of the same clone has been illustrated in fig. 21. D. Tracing of a photograph of a plant which is presumed to have resulted from back-crossing of the F₁ to *C. Fremontii* var. *Riehlii*. Scale in centimeters.

achenes, and the achenes themselves, are larger than in either of the supposed parents. The achene-tails are naked as in both *C. Fremontii* var. *Riehlii* and *C. Pitcheri*.

It has not been possible to compare the plant with a *C. Fremontii* var. *Riehlii* × *C. Pitcheri* hybrid of known parentage.

The evidence at hand indicates that the supposed hybrid is fertile, though the crucial test of germinating the seeds has not been made. Several full heads of achenes have been seen, and the seeds appear viable on examination. The pollen appears normal in the microspore stage. Five microsporocytes at metaphase I have been analyzed completely. In each of them there appear to be eight normal bivalents. A larger number of cells at this stage have been examined more briefly, and all appear normal. Chromatin bridges have been seen in two microsporocytes out of about 50 at late anaphase I. These observations suggest that there may be one or more inversions differentiating the parents of the supposed hybrid, but that pairing is sufficiently normal to allow formation of good seed.

The supposition that the hybrid between *C. Fremontii* var. *Riehlii* and *C. Pitcheri* is fertile, is consistent with finding of the four other aberrant plants. They all resemble *C. Fremontii* var. *Riehlii* more closely than does the supposed F_1 plant discussed above, but are clearly outside the normal limits of variability of the former. They are not uniform among themselves, and can be arranged in a series according to the degree in which they resemble *C. Fremontii* var. *Riehlii*. Of these four plants, one found at R.2E, T.42N, S.7A and one at R.2E, T.42N, S.15B resemble the F_1 most closely. Next in order is a second plant found at R.2E, T.42N, S.7A (fig. 22, D), and the plant found at R.3E, T.41N, S.1D is nearest to *C. Fremontii* var. *Riehlii*. They suggest a series of backcrosses of the F_1 to *C. Fremontii* var. *Riehlii*.

If these suppositions are correct, some introgression of *C. Pitcheri* genes into the *C. Fremontii* var. *Riehlii* population presumably occurs. It is estimated that the number of plants which have been seen at close enough range to detect such aberrant forms as the five described above is of the order of 10,000. These figures indicate, to a first approximation, the frequency of the presumed introgression. The five plants discussed above appear to have a considerable amount of *C. Pitcheri* germ-plasm; it might also be expected that a larger number of plants would exhibit the presence of a smaller amount. It is not known, of course, in what way small amounts of *C. Pitcheri* germ-plasm might be evidenced. The most striking difference between the two species is the contrast between the simple leaves of *C. Fremontii* var. *Riehlii* and the compound leaves of *C. Pitcheri*. Occasionally a plant is seen which departs from the norm in a coarse toothing of the larger leaves, which are usually entire. It may be that this is evidence of some *C. Pitcheri* genes.

It might also be expected that introgression occurs in the converse direction. The fact that *C. Pitcheri*, *C. Fremontii*, and *C. Fremontii* var. *Riehlii* are the only plants in the genus lacking plumose achene tails is suggestive of exchange of genes between the species over a long period of time.

Another possible source of variability deserves mention. The data on frequency of colored sepal tips (Table IV), the measurements of sepal characters (Table VII), and subjective field observations lead to the conclusion that the plants of the Robertsville region diverge more greatly from the norm for the entire population than do those of the other three regions. The Robertsville glades as a group are relatively isolated, as can be seen by reference to one of the maps, (*e. g.*, fig. 2). It may be that this relative isolation is sufficient to account for the singularity of the Robertsville plants. One is inclined, however, to speculate on the possibility that the population of *C. Fremontii* var. *Riehlii*, limited as it is, may at one time have consisted of two smaller groups. One would suppose that the two groups were centered near Plattin and near Robertsville, since *Clematis* appears most abundant in these regions at present. Their merger may have taken place rather recently, in view of the presumed increase in numbers since white settlement of the Ozarks. This possibility has great evolutionary importance. If the population were at one time divided into two wholly isolated groups, considerable divergence between them would presumably have occurred. The hybridization resulting from their reunion would provide a source of variation of greater magnitude than that provided by gene mutation governed by the statistical mechanism which Wright hypothesizes, and of somewhat different nature than that provided by introgression of *C. Pitcheri* genes.

The variation which is seen in this *Clematis* population could well be the resultant of these three factors. Introgressive hybridization with *C. Pitcheri* is likely. It probably does not occur with great frequency, but genes of adaptive value in the glade habitat may occasionally be introduced into the population by this means. Isolation of the Robertsville region has allowed it to evolve to some extent along its own course, whether one considers the partial isolation of the present, or the possibly complete isolation of some past period. The supposition that some random differentiation of partially isolated groups of plants on separate glades or portions of glades occurs by the mechanism which Wright has described, is consistent with the pattern of distribution of the plant, and with the statistical pattern of variation in several morphological characters. Since it is probable that the effective population size is comparatively large, the fate of individual genes is probably not wholly a random matter, but is under some selective control.

The concept of this *Clematis* population which emerges is not that of an "old" endemic in which evolutionary change has ceased and which is doomed to extinction, though its restricted range may suggest such a picture to some minds. It is rather that of a population which has undergone marked changes in range and in numbers, and which appears to be increasing in numbers at present; one in which evolutionary changes of several sorts are occurring, though perhaps not as rapidly as in many organisms. *C. Fremontii* var. *Riehlii*, because of its presumably low competitive vigor, is probably doomed to restriction to the glade habitat. Its breeding structure is neither that of approximate panmixia which leads to extreme specialization, nor of extreme restriction in numbers which leads to wholly non-adaptive differentiation. This being so, it may be expected to continue to thrive on the glades, and perhaps to extend its range, though the colonization of new glades will probably be slow.

SUMMARY

Clematis Fremontii var. *Riehlii*, which is wholly restricted to dolomitic barrens, or glades, in an area of about 400 sq. mi. in east-central Missouri, has been studied in the field with particular attention to features of its distribution, biology, and pattern of variation, which are of evolutionary importance.

The population, estimated at 1,500,000, is organized into a hierarchy of natural subdivisions: *regions* of glade concentration; *clusters* of glades; *colonies* of the plant, which correspond approximately with glades; and *aggregates* of a very few, to perhaps a thousand, plants on each glade. There is great inequality in number of plants from one *colony* or *aggregate* to another. Both types of subdivision exhibit partial isolation, of a degree which is regarded as favorable for continuing evolution. The plant appears to be remarkably stable in numbers, but there is indirect evidence that it has increased since the white settlement of the Ozarks.

Inefficient seed dispersal and the longevity of the plants are factors which probably tend to promote a high degree of inbreeding. Counteracting them is the pollination of the plant by wide-ranging insects, which tends to promote cross-breeding.

Statistical study of morphological variation shows significant local differentiation at three levels of the distributional hierarchy: from one region to another, in five flower characters; from one glade to another, in four flower characters; and from one portion of a glade to another, in leaf shape. The most significant feature of the regional differentiation is the singularity of the plants near Robertsville, at the northwestern end of the range.

The pattern of distribution; the biological factors of pollination, seed dispersal and germination, and longevity; and the nature of variation in leaf shape are consistent in suggesting that the effective population size is a few hundred.

There is evidence that introgressive hybridization with *C. Pitcheri* occurs. This, together with differentiation on a regional scale, and local differentiation of a moderately random nature appear to be the most significant evolutionary processes occurring in the population.

REFERENCES

Albertson, F. W. (1937). Ecology of mixed prairie in west central Kansas. Ecol. Monogr. 7:481–547.

————, (1942). Letter of May 25.

Anderson, Edgar (1936). The species problem in *Iris*. IV. Intraspecific differentiation in the northern blue flags. Ann. Mo. Bot. Gard. 23:485–498.

————, (1943). Letter of April 8.

————, and Leslie Hubricht (1938). Hybridization in *Tradescantia*. The evidence for introgressive hybridization. Am. Jour. Bot. 25:396–402.

Dobzhansky, Th. (1941). Genetics and the origin of species. 2nd ed. New York.

Elton, Charles (1932). Territory among wood ants *(Formica rufa* L.) at Picket Hill. Jour. Animal Ecol. 1:69–76.

————, (1933). The ecology of animals. London.

————, (1942). Voles, mice and lemmings. Oxford.

Epling, Carl, and Th. Dobzhansky (1942). Genetics of natural populations. VI. Microgeographic races in *Linanthus Parryae*. Genetics 27:317–332.

Erickson, Ralph O. (1943a). Taxonomy of *Clematis* section VIORNA. Ann. Mo. Bot. Gard. 30:1–62.

————, (1943b). Population size and geographical distribution of *Clematis Fremontii* var. *Riehlii*. *Ibid.* 30:63–68.

————, Louis G. Brenner and Joseph Wraight (1942). Dolomitic glades of east-central Missouri. *Ibid.* 29:89–101.

————, and John R. Stehn (1945). A technique for analysis of population density data. Amer. Midl. Nat. 33:781–787.

Fernald, M. L. (1943). Virginian botanizing under restrictions. Rhodora 45:357–413.

Fisher, R. A. (1930). The genetical theory of natural selection. Oxford.

Freeman, Chester P. (1933). Ecology of the cedar glade vegetation near Nashville, Tennessee. Jour. Tenn. Acad. Sci. 8:143–228.

Frison, Thodore H. (1927). Experiments in rearing colonies of bumblebees (Bremidae) in artificial nests. Biol. Bull. 52:51–67.

Gregory, Walton C. (1941). Phylogenetic and cytological studies in the Ranunculaceae. Trans. Am. Phil. Soc. 31:443–522.

Greshoff, M. (1909). Phytochemical investigations at Kew. Kew. Bull. Misc. Inf. 1909:397–418.

Huxley, Julian (1938). Clines: an auxiliary taxonomic principle. Nature 142:219–220.

Mangelsdorf, P. C., and R. G. Reeves (1939). The origin of Indian corn and its relatives. Texas Agr. Exp. Sta. Bull. 574:1–315.

Meurman, O., and Eeva Therman (1939). Studies on the chromosome morphology and structural hybridity in the genus *Clematis*. Cytologia 10:1–14.

Rehder, Alfred (1940). Manual of cultivated trees and shrubs. New York.

Rider, Paul R. (1939). An introduction to modern statistical methods. New York.

Robertson, Charles (1928). Flowers and insects; lists of visitors of four hundred and fifty-three flowers. Carlinville, Illinois.

Salisbury, E. J. (1929). The biological equipment of species in relation to competition. Jour Ecol. 17:197–222.

Sears, Paul B. (1935). Glacial and postglacial vegetation. Bot. Rev. 1:37–51.

Spencer, Warren P. (1941). Ecological factors and *Drosophila* speciation. Ohio Jour. Sci. 41:190–200.

Wherry, Edgar T. (1930). Plants of the Appalachian shale-barrens. Jour. Wash. Acad. Sci. 20:43–52.

————, (1931). The eastern short-stemmed leatherflowers. *Ibid.* 21:194–198.

Wright, Sewall (1943). An analysis of local variability of flower color in *Linanthus Parryae*. Genetics 28:139–156.

POPULATION DIFFERENTIATION IN *AGROSTIS TENUIS* SIBTH

I. MORPHOLOGICAL DIFFERENTIATION

By A. D. BRADSHAW

Department of Agricultural Botany, University College of North Wales, Bangor

(*Received* 24 *May* 1958)

(With 3 figures in the text)

SUMMARY

In order to investigate the pattern of population differentiation in *Agrostis tenuis*, sixty tillers were collected from each of thirty-three areas mainly in central Wales. These were grown under garden conditions in Aberystwyth. In a subsequent experiment five of these areas were sampled again by tillers, and at the same time sampled by seed. These samples were grown under garden conditions in Bangor.

Numerous differences between these population samples were recorded. The main conclusions are as follows:

(i) The environment is the dominating factor in determining population differentiation.

(ii) Although the distribution is continuous, distances of about 50 m or less are sufficient to effectively isolate populations from one another.

(iii) Thus the species is able to evolve under the influence of natural selection in response to very local variations in environment.

(iv) Since the environment is a graded patchwork of different conditions, the pattern of differentiation is similar.

(v) It is, therefore, not possible to classify effectively such intraspecific variation.

(vi) It is likely that this situation is to be found in most other outbreeding continuously distributed plant species occupying a wide range of habitats.

INTRODUCTION

Investigations of natural plant populations have disclosed a new wealth of information which has been used extensively by the taxonomist, geneticist and ecologist and, at the same time, has become a study in itself. The natural population is the basic unit of a species. An individual cannot exist by itself unless it be habitually self-fertilized. Natural selection acts only by altering the frequencies of individuals within populations. Thus the study of plant populations is likely to yield information concerning all the factors that affect a plant, whether they be internal or external, genetical or ecological.

After the initial investigations of Turesson (1922, 1925) in which the amount of differentiation occurring within a species was appreciated for the first time, subsequent authors (Clausen, Keck and Hiesey, 1940, 1948) and others have continued in greater detail. These later workers assumed the same natural hierarchy of hereditary types as Turesson. Though they narrowed his definition they were content to recognize the ecotype as the fundamental unit. 'Regional differentiation may be expressed either as a series of ecotypes belonging to one species, or as a series of closely related ecospecies, or more commonly by both.' However, investigations of *Plantago maritima* (Gregor, Davey and Lang, 1936) showed that the pattern of variation was not really so simple. In a general survey Gregor (1946) concludes that it is not possible to resolve all intra-specific variation into discrete units and that any attempt to resolve it is a reflection of taxonomic undercurrents. This view is elaborated later (Gregor and Watson, 1954) and shared by Böcher (1949).

In order to study this problem, and that of evolution within a species, further, it is necessary first to consider briefly the various factors which are likely to be significant.

(i) *Availability of adaptive variation.* The amount and type of genetic variation will clearly exert an overriding effect. Without genes of adaptive value being present in, or available to the population, it will not be able to evolve under the influence of natural selection. *Melandrium dioicum, Ranunculus acris* and other species do not develop populations adapted to montane conditions in the Alps. This is only explicable by a lack of the necessary genes which would allow them to build up adapted populations under the influence of natural selection (Turesson, 1925). *Festuca ovina* (Wilkins, 1957) and *Agrostis tenuis* (Bradshaw, 1953) have been able to evolve populations resistant to lead contamination in soils. Other species, which in other respects seem adapted to growing on similar soils, are unable to. Presumably this is only because they do not possess the genetic variation which would enable them to resist the contamination.

(ii) *Genetic basis of the variation.* Although in the past there has been considerable attention paid to oligogenic inheritance, it is now clear that nearly all characters of importance to a plant are polygenically controlled and continuously varying. Clausen (1951) has recently reported the results of a large number of crosses made between ecotypes of *Potentilla glandulosa* and other species, and in no case is there evidence of clear-cut oligogenic inheritance.

(iii) *Breeding system.* Baker recently (1953) has considered the likely effects of different reproductive methods on the pattern of variation. While outbreeding will prevent the formation of discontinuities and population differences, by allowing gene flow, inbreeding will not do so, and discontinuities may well develop as in *Thlaspi arvense* (Riley, 1956). However, if inbreeding is the primary cause of such discontinuities, it must be complete, and there are very few species in which this is so. It is only in apomictic plants that discontinuities develop to any considerable extent.

(iv) *Pattern of distribution of the species.* The spatial distribution of the species whether continuous or otherwise, will have a profound effect on the pattern of differentia-tion. Discontinuities of distribution, whatever their cause, by preventing gene flow will permit the evolution of genetically distinct populations. This has been considered by Mayr (1942) (1947) and Stebbins (1950) with reference to the evolution of species, but it applies equally to the evolution of ecological races. A subsidiary aspect of the distribu-tion of the species is the random genetic drift which may occur in small populations (Wright, 1940). However, Fisher and Ford (1947) have recently shown that random genetic drift is unlikely to occur in populations of more than about 1000 breeding individuals, and will only have appreciable effects in populations of less than 100.

(v) *The pattern of the environment.* The final factor affecting the pattern of differentiation, and perhaps the most important one, is the pattern of the environment, that is, of the selection pressure itself. The evolution of the plant population is likely to be dominated by the selection exerted on it. Thus the pattern of differentiation might well be expected, if the other factors are not important, to follow closely the pattern of the environment. If the environment changes only gradually with distance, then so will the plant type of the species occupying it. If there are sudden discontinuities in the environment, these are likely to cause related discontinuities of plant type. If there are no environmental differences between two areas, then it is likely that there will be no differences of plant type.

METHOD

In order to investigate the inter-relation of these factors, the common 'Bent' grass, *Agrostis tenuis* Sibth., was studied in the region round Aberystwyth in central Wales. *A. tenuis* is a wind-pollinated outbreeding plant, functionally diploid, with no apparent cytological races. Its distribution is more or less continuous in the area studied, since it is abundant in the natural and semi-natural grassland of the region. It is a plant easy to cultivate since it is a perennial, spreading only slowly by rhizomes, and can therefore be studied over a period of years.

A variety of populations were each sampled by collecting sixty tillers at random within an area about 30 m across. These were put in boxes and grown on for 3 months before being planted out into an experimental plot. Each population was divided into six groups, each of ten plants. All the populations were laid out together in a randomized block arrangement with six replicates, individual plots consisting of a group of ten plants. The plants were spaced separately so that they could be measured individually, though the results have been calculated from plot means. After planting the plants were never cut back or disturbed in any way.

In a few of the populations some plants were found to be infected with the fungal parasite 'choke', *Epichloe typhina*. In nearly all cases this prevents inflorescence production by attacking inflorescence primordia. As a result tiller production is increased. These plants, though part of the populations concerned, have not, therefore, been included in any of the calculations. This has meant that in some cases the plot means are from less than ten plants. The significance of *E. typhina* in these populations will be discussed in a subsequent paper.

Tillers rather than seeds were taken for two reasons. Firstly, tillers are samples of what is actually present, established in the sward, after the intervention of natural selection. Secondly, because seed is difficult to obtain in a region that is heavily grazed, biased sampling may occur if only one or two panicles which have escaped grazing are picked, since these are likely to belong to prostrate plants. There is also a tendency, when panicles are scarce, to collect them from parts not really representative of the area being studied, e.g. the margins instead of the centres of fields. The results quoted in this paper show that this could be a very real source of inaccuracy.

To minimize any environmental modifications, transitory phenotypic changes, which might be introduced into the experiment, the following precautions were taken:

(*a*) Standard sized tillers were taken from all localities.

(*b*) The size of all plants was equalized on planting out.

(*c*) Careful notes of the characteristics of the plants were made in the first year and in subsequent years when they could have been considered to have grown out of their original modified state. The result of this showed that population differences were small in the first year and only became definite later on, the reverse of what would be expected in the case of modifications.

369

An experiment designed to test the validity of the sampling method is described in the paper.

ECOLOGY OF THE SITES

The region is ecologically fairly simple. The underlying rock is almost entirely Ordovician shales and mudstones which weather to a poor loam deficient in bases. In the lowlands, where the rainfall is about 40 in., the land is mainly arable but there are numerous fields of permanent grass, usually *Agrostis-Festuca* or *Lolium-Agrostis*, all heavily grazed. Where the land is steep, there is usually rougher pasture. Further inland, with increasing altitude, the amount of permanent grass increases. On some of the steeper slopes, e.g. those on the sides of the valley of the river Rheidol, there are extensive woodlands of *Quercus petrea*. Again some regions are heavily grazed, others are rough and under-grazed. Further inland, as a result of still higher altitudes and rainfall, there is no arable land and the *Agrostis-Festuca* grassland begins to give way to rough upland grazing dominated by *Nardus*. This continues to the highest point, Plynlymon (2468 ft). In these hill regions the ground and the vegetation is variable. In the wetter regions *Molinia* and *Eriophorum* are found, but for the most part the rolling, gently sloping ground is sufficiently well drained to permit a *Nardus-Festuca-Agrostis* grassland. This is quite well grazed by sheep, even though the rainfall is about 100 in. and the soil strongly podsolized. Thus the picture is one of a gently rising, undulating countryside predominantly grass covered, poor and rather exposed, with an overall climatic trend from low to high altitude, but within this quite a variable pattern of environment (Stapledon, 1936).

DESCRIPTION OF SITES

Except for those sites not in the mid-Wales area, details of position, altitude and rainfall for individual sites are to be found on the maps (Figs. 1 and 2). All pastures are permanent and natural unless otherwise stated.

1. *Dale cliff.* Very exposed west-facing Atlantic sea cliff at West Dale, Pembroke-shire (O.S. grid ref. 12/799059). Isolated, lightly grazed, tufted plants, accompanied by *Festuca rubra, Armeria maritima, Plantago maritima*, etc. Altitude 100 ft, rainfall 38 in.

2. *Morfa coast.* Moderately exposed west-facing sea cliffs at Morfa Mawr, Cardi-ganshire (O.S. grid ref. 22/499658). Covered with continuous cover of *Agrostis tenuis* and *Festuca rubra* heavily grazed by sheep. Altitude 15 ft, rainfall 35 in.

3. *Ynyslas ungrazed.* Scattered pioneer plants in ungrazed, partially fixed sand dunes dominated by *Ammophila arenaria*.

4. *Ynyslas grazed.* Very heavily rabbit-grazed sward of *Agrostis tenuis, Festuca rubra* and *Poa pratensis* at back of sand dunes. 110 m from (3).

5. *Pen Dinas foot.* Rough grazing at foot of steep hill facing sea but 200 m from it and protected from strong winds by the slope behind. Typical *Agrostis-Festuca* pasture.

6. *Pen Dinas top.* Thin pasture on top of hill, very exposed to sea winds. *Festuca rubra* sward with only occasional plants of *Agrostis tenuis, Plantago maritima* and *Armeria maritima*. 90 m from (5).

7. *Pen Dinas back.* Rough grazing at back of hill, protected from sea winds. Typical *Agrostis-Festuca* pasture. 40 m from (6).

8. *Dale pasture.* Very protected pasture at Dale, Pembrokeshire, above Milford Haven (O.S. grid ref. 12/811063). Rough grassy slope on fertile soil in good climate.

370

Typical *Lolium-Agrostis* sward, but little grazed. 1 km from (1). Altitude 60 ft, rainfall 38 in.

9. *Borth dry*. Rough sheep grazing on dry rocky knoll in middle of Borth bog. Thin and poor *Festuca ovina* sward.

10. *Borth wet*. Good sheep grazing at foot of knoll on edge of bog. Damp thick matted *Agrostis tenuis*, *Festuca rubra* and *Holcus lanatus*. 40 m from (9).

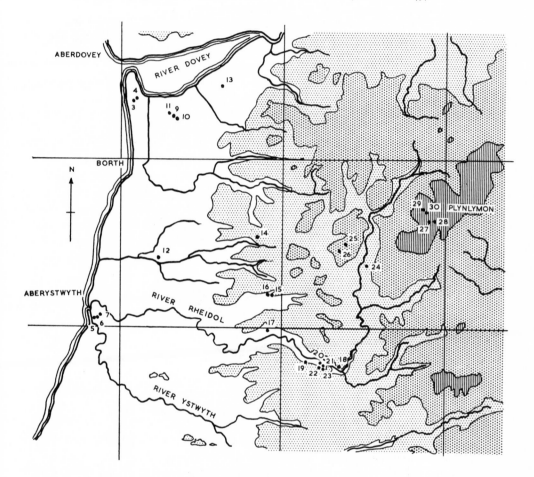

Fig. 1. Map of Aberystwyth region showing sampling sites.

Key to populations.

3. Ynyslas ungrazed	13. Hen Hafod weeds	22. Rheidol pasture
4. Ynyslas grazed	14. Llety pasture	23. Rheidol hillock
5. Pen Dinas foot	15. Goginan rough	24. Hirnant pasture
6. Pen Dinas top	16. Goginan mine	25. Disgwylfa north
7. Pen Dinas back	17. Neuadd wood	26. Disgwylfa south
9. Borth dry	18. Devil's Bridge wood	27. Plynlymon Nardetum
10. Borth wet	19. Rheidol lower wood	28. Plynlymon flush
11. Borth bog	20. Rheidol upper wood	29. Plynlymon scree
12. Bow Street pasture	21. Rheidol wood edge	30. Plynlymon summit

11. *Borth bog*. Isolated plants of *Agrostis tenuis* growing with *A. canina* in predominantly acid *Molinietum*. Although not collected near to (10) it is effectively an outlier of it. 200 m from (9).

12. *Bow Street pasture.* Old lowland pasture. Mainly *Agrostis tenuis* and *Holcus lanatus.*

13. *Hen Hafod weeds.* Weeds at edges of arable fields on good silt.

14. *Llety pasture.* Good inland pasture, typical *Agrostis-Festuca.* Close to farm buildings, and therefore has always been heavily grazed.

15. *Goginan rough.* Rough inland pasture on steep but fertile slope. Typical ungrazed *Agrostis-Festuca.* Not easily accessible to sheep, and some scrub developing.

16. *Goginan mine.* Isolated plants growing on old lead-mine workings and waste, accompanied by little other vegetation. These plants are markedly resistant to lead toxicity (Bradshaw, 1953). 100 m from (15).

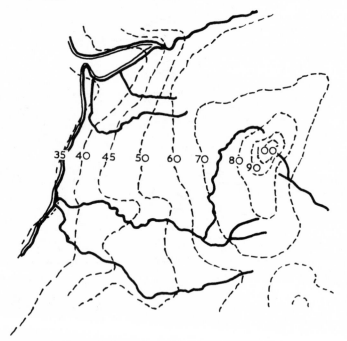

Fig. 2. Isohyets (in.) of the Aberystwyth region.

17. *Neuadd wood.* Isolated plants in *Quercus petrea* woodland with mosses and *Festuca ovina.* Sometimes grazed.

18. *Devil's Bridge wood.* Isolated plants in steep south-facing *Quercus petrea* woodland with bracken, etc. Area subject to drought in summer owing to considerable drainage.

19. *Rheidol lower wood.* Isolated plants in steep north-facing *Q. petrea* woodland on opposite side of valley. Damp, occasionally sheep grazed, with *Anthoxanthum* and mosses.

20. *Rheidol upper wood.* Exactly as (19) but further up valley.

21. *Rheidol wood edge.* Upper edge of wood where borders on grazed *Agrostis-Festuca* pasture. More continuous sward, 70 m from (20).

22. *Rheidol pasture.* Heavily grazed good upland permanent *Agrostis-Festuca* pasture, 100 m from (21).

23. *Rheidol hillock.* Rough rocky exposed hillock. Lightly grazed *Agrostis-Festuca* with some *Calluna vulgaris.* 80 m from (21).

24. *Hirnant pasture.* Poor *Agrostis-Festuca* pasture adjoining upland sheep farm in hill region. (Sample of thirty plants only.)

25. *Disgwylfa north.* Poor thin *Nardetum* on hillside facing north-east. Considerable amount of lichen in sward. Sheep grazed.

26. *Disgwylfa south.* *Nardetum* on hillside facing south-west. More herbage than in (25) and more *Agrostis*, no lichen. Sheep grazed. 200 m from (25).

27. *Plynlymon Nardetum.* *Nardetum* on hillside facing south similar to (26) but at higher altitude. Sheep grazed.

28. *Plynlymon flush.* A small area about 10 m square of flushed *Agrostis tenuis* grassland, very heavily grazed in the middle of *Nardetum*. (Sample of thirty plants only.)

29. *Plynlymon scree.* Scattered single plants on loose scree just below summit.

30. *Plynlymon summit.* Very exposed, thin grazed *Festuca ovina* with scattered *Nardus* and *Agrostis* only in more protected parts.

31. *Lakenheath Warren.* From Grassland E. (Watt, 1940) on Lakenheath Warren, Suffolk, in the Breckland (O.S. grid ref. 52/753818). Very acid, very sandy *Agrostis-Festuca* grassland. Altitude 60 ft, rainfall 23 in.

32. *Richmond Park.* Damp lightly grazed *Agrostis* grassland with *Nardus*, *Molinia*, *Holcus lanatus* on acid sandy soil in Richmond Park, Surrey (O.S. grid ref. 51/202717). Altitude 150 ft, rainfall 25 in.

33. *Ruislip Wood.* Damp oakwood on acid clay near Ruislip, Middlesex. Isolated trailing plants with *Holcus mollis*, etc., ungrazed (O.S. grid ref. 51/094885). Altitude 170 ft, rainfall 25 in.

The last three populations, being collected outside the mid-Wales region, are intended to provide a contrast with the other populations. Three other populations were collected outside mid-Wales at Port Meadow, Pixey Mead, and Waterperry Wood, near Oxford, and one other on the Rheidol meadows near Aberystwyth. In these hybrids with *Agrostis stolonifera* were found (Bradshaw, 1958) and so they have been omitted from the analysis. Another population, at Llety-Evan-Hen near Talybont, Cards., was found to contain hybrids with *A. gigantea* and therefore was also omitted.

CHROMOSOME NUMBERS OF POPULATIONS

The chromosome number of $2n = 28$ is the only one reported for *A. tenuis* (Jones, 1956). However, the chromosome numbers of twenty-two plants from twelve extreme populations were kindly determined by K. Jones of the Welsh Plant Breeding Station. No aberrant chromosome numbers were discovered. The only aberrant numbers found were plants with $2n = 35$ in the population already referred to from Llety-Evan-Hen corroborating the presence of hybrids involving *A. gigantea* ($2n = 42$).

THE CHARACTERISTICS OF THE POPULATIONS

A number of measurements were made, all on individual plants, and these are given in Fig. 3 as population means with their appropriate standard errors. These will be commented on separately. A number of general observations on other characters were made which will also be given. The measurements were made at appropriate times during 1951-53, sometimes being repeated in successive years. Analyses of variance were made on all characters. In all cases population differences were highly significant, the variance ratios having probabilities of less than o.1 %. The analyses are not given, but the standard errors of each character are given in Fig. 3.

Inflorescence height

Since each plant has many inflorescences, the height was measured to the top of the main mass of inflorescences.

The coastal populations are conspicuously the shortest, in particular those nearest to the sea, on sea cliff and sand dune, where the exposure to high wind is greatest. The Pen Dinas populations further away are not so short, but even so contrast with those further inland. Amongst the inland populations there is a small but clear relation to grazing intensity. Thus Rheidol hillock is significantly taller than the adjoining Rheidol pasture, and clearly has affinities with Goginan rough to which it is ecologically very similar. Goginan mine, by contrast, is very small which is in keeping with all its other characteristics. In the upland there is a general tendency to decrease in height. However, Hirnant pasture is conspicuously tall. Although for geographical reasons this population is included in the upland group, ecologically it is lowland and it is to this group, although it is rather taller, that it shows its affinities. It is curious for other reasons which will be discussed later. Further afield Lakenheath Warren is distinctly short, interestingly similar to the sand-dune populations with which it has other affinities. This confirms earlier work (Philipson, 1937).

Vegetative height

The height was measured to the top of the main mass of vegetative tillers excluding any odd longer tillers.

At first sight there seems to be little variation in this character. But closer examination shows the variation is on a local and not a regional basis. The heavily grazed pastures, e.g. Llety pasture and Hirnant pasture are distinctly shorter than their ungrazed counterparts, even when the populations are only a very short distance apart, e.g. Rheidol pasture and Rheidol top. The same dwarfness is found on Pen Dinas where there is less grazing but severe exposure. In contrast to this, Dale cliff, which is subject to very severe exposure and no grazing, is not particularly dwarf. This population adopts a spreading but dense cushion type of growth habit which is quite distinct from all the other populations. It would appear, by comparison with other cushion maritime plants such as *Armeria maritima*, that in the absence of grazing this is a more successful growth habit for resistance to strong winds. The overall smallness of Goginan mine is again shown. The upland populations appear to be anomalous on first examination. As a group they are all quite tall, yet they occupy severe and poor conditions. However, the vegetation in which these populations grow is dominated by *Nardus* and *Molinia*, relatively tall tufted plants. The height of the *Agrostis* is therefore clearly correlated with this, with the microclimate and competition of the surrounding vegetation, and not with the overall climate. Lakenheath Warren is very short, again similar to the sand-dune population. This would appear to correlate with the combination of poor conditions and heavy grazing of the area similar to the poor conditions and coastal exposure in sand dunes.

Diameter of plants

Since individual plants were rather irregular in shape, the average diameter was measured. It is probable that the plants of larger diameter should have scores rather higher than those recorded owing to the hoeing necessary to keep the plants weed free.

Populations from damp lowland habitats have clearly the greatest diameter. In these conditions the ability of *A. tenuis* to spread is paramount if it is to survive the strong vegetative competition of other grasses. In fact it is probably the ability of *A. tenuis* to spread laterally that contributes to its success in so many grasslands. In lowland

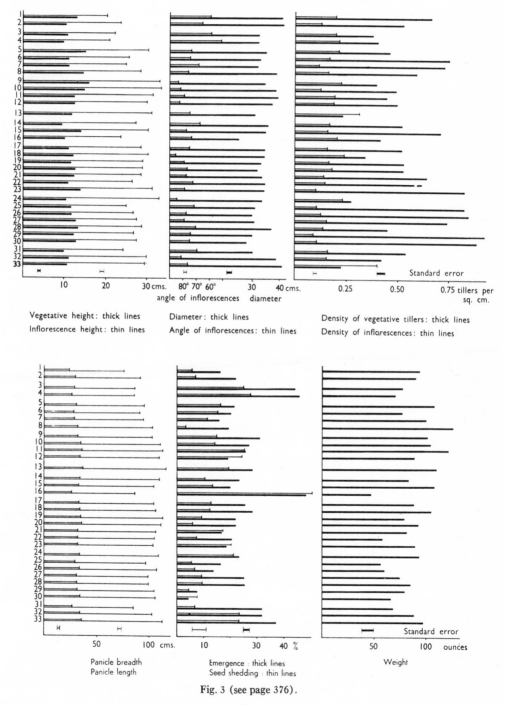

Vegetative height: thick lines
Inflorescence height: thin lines

Diameter: thick lines
Angle of inflorescences: thin lines

Density of vegetative tillers: thick lines
Density of inflorescences: thin lines

Panicle breadth
Panicle length

Emergence : thick lines
Seed shedding : thin lines

Weight

Fig. 3 (see page 376).

areas where conditions are less favourable to grass growth, such as sand dunes, lead mine and dry heathland, the populations do not possess such powers of spreading. Hen Hafod weeds is another lowland population with relatively low ability to spread, which initially is surprising since it is found on good moist arable land. But as its density score shows, it is a population in which the greatest part of the growth of the plant is devoted to seed production. The foregoing arguments therefore cannot apply to it. The upland populations in general have low values for spread. The plants are in fact distinctly tufted, but when grown as single plants they tend to flop outwards and give rather higher values than they might under more natural conditions. Taken in conjunction with the values for vegetative height, it is clear that the upland populations have a distinct growth habit. This confirms earlier work (Prendergast, 1948), and correlates in more ways than one with the growth habit of the surrounding vegetation. It is interesting, however, that where the upland conditions are markedly different, a distinctly different population is found, e.g. Plynlymon flush.

Density of inflorescences

This was determined by counting the number of inflorescences in an area 1 cm × 20 cm, formed by two wires 1 cm apart inserted through the plant. The length of sampling area ensured that the sample was representative of all parts of the plant, and therefore only one sample was necessary for each plant.

Two populations outstanding for their density of inflorescences are Ruislip wood and Devil's Bridge wood. *A. tenuis* is not a true woodland plant in the strict sense, and occupies marginal and open areas of woods. Such intermittently open habitats are occupied characteristically by species with high seed output (Salisbury, 1942). It would appear that these populations have evolved under the influence of such selection, increase in panicle number being a very simple way in which seed output is increased. Devil's Bridge wood has recently been felled, and the colonization of bare ground by *A. tenuis* was comparable to that which can occur by *Digitalis purpurea*. The status of the Neuadd and Rheidol wood populations is not so explicable. It is, however, significant that in these woods which are more permanent, *Agrostis tenuis* grows as if it were a true woodland plant. Such plants have low seed rates (Salisbury, op. cit.).

The weed population of Hen Hafod is equally outstanding. More tillers are devoted

Fig. 3. The characteristics of the populations of *Agrostis tenuis* (expressed as population means with appropriate standard errors). Sites are numbered as below:

1. Sea cliff: ungrazed	Dale cliff	19. inland wet	Rheidol lower
2. grazed	Morfa coast		wood
3. Sand dune: ungrazed	Ynyslas ungrazed	20. inland wet	Rheidol upper
4. grazed	Ynyslas grazed		wood
5. Coastal grassland: protected	Pen Dinas foot	21. wood edge	Rheidol wood edge
6. exposed	Pen Dinas top	22. grazed pasture	Rheidol pasture
7. protected	Pen Dinas back	23. grazed hillock	Rheidol hillock
8. ungrazed very protected	Dale pasture	24. Upland: pasture	Hirnant pasture
9. Lowland grassland: dry	Borth dry	25. exposed Nardetum	Disgwylfa north
10. wet	Borth wet	26. protected Nardetum	Disgwylfa south
11. bog	Borth bog	27. protected Nardetum	Plynlymon Narde-
12. grazed	Bow Street pasture		tum
13. Arable weeds	Hen Hafod weeds	28. grazed flush	Plynlymon flush
14. Inland grassland: grazed	Llety pasture	29. exposed scree	Plynlymon scree
15. ungrazed	Goginan rough	30. summit grassland	Plynlymon summit
16. lead mine	Goginan mine	31. Heathland: dry and poor	Lakenheath
17. Woodland: lowland	Neuadd wood		Warren
18. inland dry	Devil's Bridge	32. damp	Richmond Park
	wood	33. Woodland	Ruislip Wood

to inflorescence production than vegetative growth, and the population provides an interesting example of a 'commercial' type of grass in the agronomic sense. Hirnant pasture is curious, remarkably different from populations related to it. It is, however, possible that the pasture from which it was taken was reseeded with commercial seeds at one time, including some *A. tenuis*, and that this has left its effect on the population with regard to this character.

The remaining populations show relatively straightforward trends. Those populations occupying dry and difficult habitats, in which survival by seed is important, have high values, while those in habitats in which survival by vegetative growth is important have low values. Examples of the former are Ynyslas grazed and ungrazed, Borth dry and Goginan mine; of the latter Morfa coast, Borth wet, Plynlymon summit.

Density of vegetative tillers

This was measured in the same manner as the inflorescences.

This character is the most variable of all the characters differentiating the populations, the highest values differing from the lower by a factor of four. It is a character of great adaptive significance. In many respects the values are reciprocal to those of inflorescences. Total tiller number is, however, by no means the same for all populations and therefore vegetative tiller density must be considered an independent variable. It is likely to be related to the same factors as affect inflorescence density, but in a reciprocal manner.

The highest values are those of the tufted upland populations whose whole growth habit is very distinct. Plynlymon flush, already noted to have a greater spread, is distinct from these. On the other hand Rheidol hillock, subject to conditions approaching to those of Disgwylfa, is similar to them. The lowland populations occupying habitats in which vegetative growth is important have high values, e.g. Borth wet, Goginan rough. This applies particularly to the extremely exposed populations such as Dale cliff, where it would appear that the close packing prevents mechanical damage of individual tillers (cf. *Armeria maritima*). Populations in dry and difficult conditions have low values, e.g. Ynyslas grazed and ungrazed, Borth dry.

Panicle length and breadth

These figures show, on inspection, a marked correlation and therefore will be considered together as panicle size. They can vary independently, since *Agrostis stolonifera* possesses a panicle which is longer and narrower than *A. tenuis* to which it is closely related. That the two measures do not vary independently within *A. tenuis* suggests there is no selective value of difference in shape, but only of differences in size.

The coastal populations are all quite distinct from the others in the smallness of their panicles. The extreme is Dale cliff, which occupies the most wind-exposed habitat. Nearly all the other populations are remarkably similar. The exceptions are Goginan mine and Lakenheath Warren, both of which are small in all respects, an adaptation to the difficult conditions of their habitats. It is interesting to note that grazing has no effect. This is understandable, since panicle size could scarcely be considered to be an adaptive character in relation to grazing. It is wind that is the significant factor, since the natural delicacy of *A. tenuis* panicles lays it open to wind damage.

Angle of inflorescences

In most populations the inflorescences are more or less vertical. But the inflorescences of the four most coastal populations are distinctly inclined. In combination with the small size of the inflorescences of these populations, this provides a considerable measure of protection for the panicles from the wind, and is clearly adaptive. Morfa coast is not so extreme as Dale cliff, which is to be expected. Ynyslas grazed is the most extreme, differing from the nearby Ynyslas ungrazed. In this case this must be an adaptation to very heavy rabbit grazing, and not wind exposure. In the original habitat the small prostrate inflorescences of the plants are often almost hidden from view in the turf and therefore escape grazing. The soil is so dry and the density of the grass cover sufficiently low that the panicles do not rot. In populations which have larger inflorescences and grow in damper situations, such prostration would not allow the panicles to escape grazing and would also cause them to become tangled in the damp grass and rot. Despite this, there is a small but fairly clear relation to grazing, similar to that shown by inflorescence height.

Emergence and seed maturation

Emergence was determined by scoring the plants at a single date after it had begun. Plants were classified: 0 = no emergence, 1 = panicle half emerged, 2 = panicle fully emerged, 3 = panicle open, 4 = anthesis occurring. Actual flowering dates were not determined but they correlate with the values for emergence closely, plants scoring one flowering about 10 days later than those scoring four. The values obtained were subsequently converted into percentages.

When seeds of *Agrostis* become mature they are shed. So at a time towards the end of the summer (mid-August) the percentage of seed shed was determined by eye.

Earlier workers record that plants from higher altitudes flower and mature their seeds more rapidly than do those from lowlands. There is no clear indication of such an adaptation occurring in *Agrostis*; in general the upland populations are later than those from the lowland. However, it is a general tendency in grasses for perennial types originating from extreme pasture conditions to be late, and those from hay conditions to be early, e.g. *Dactylis glomerata* (Stapledon, 1926). Furthermore, types adapted to very dry or continental regions tend to be even earlier, e.g. *Lolium rigidum* (Cooper, 1951). This would seem to provide the explanation of the differences that are found both in emergence and seed maturity, between both the extreme and the less extreme populations. The situation is then remarkably similar to that in *L. perenne* (Gregor and Watson, 1954).

In upland habitats the growing season is short, accumulated temperatures for Plynlymon for March to May being less than one-third that for the lowlands. It is therefore understandable that in late seasons complete failure of seed setting occurs in *Agrostis tenuis* growing in natural habitats above 2000 ft. But it remains not easy to understand why a more rapidly maturing type has not been favoured which overcomes this, unless it is because in such situations, where propagation is predominately vegetative, sufficient seed is produced in good seasons.

Yield

At the end of the experiment, during the third season, all plants were cut to ground level and fresh weights determined. The values are therefore for total growth in the absence of cutting or grazing over 3 years. No comparisons of seasonality of growth were made except by eye. These did not indicate any difference whatever in time of onset or period of active growth. Clearly the values given are not a complete record of the growth of the plants, since it is possible that they would give different yield under grazing conditions. This is, however, not usually the case.

There is a considerable variation in this character. It is immediately possible to point out that populations coming from regions ungrazed, or of high fertility, have the highest yields, e.g. Dale pasture and Goginan pasture. Those from regions of heavy grazing, or low fertility, have the lowest yield, e.g., Ynyslas grazed, Goginan mine, Disgwylfa and Plynlymon. The effects of exposure seem to be similar to those of grazing though not so great. The differences occur even between populations only a short distance apart, e.g. Pen Dinas foot and Pen Dinas top, and Rheidol upper wood and Rheidol pasture. The population with the highest yield, Dale pasture, comes from a habitat which is fertile ungrazed, and well protected. The population with the lowest yield, Disgwylfa north, comes from a habitat which is very infertile, well grazed and exposed.

These correlations deserve some consideration. A plant, if it is to be adapted to its habitat, must be adapted in all ways. One important way is the demands which it makes upon that habitat for nutrients, etc. Such demands will be affected by the growth of the plants. So throughout world vegetation formations, plant growth shows a correlation with habitat potential. It is clear that this applies on a smaller scale to evolution within a species.

The effect of grazing, or lack of it, can be explained in a similar manner. A plant will be well adapted to grazing conditions only if it evades grazing. This adaptation can be obtained by slow growth resulting in a dwarf habit. A plant will be well adapted to lack of grazing only if it can compete satisfactorily with the other plants of the sward. Such adaptation can only be obtained by rapid, voluminous, tall growth. Clearly, in rough ungrazed pastures, slow-growing small plants are soon eliminated. This is a principle well known to agronomists dealing with swards containing mixtures of species. It seems reasonable that it should apply also to evolution within a species.

Mode of growth and spread

Eye examination of the populations show that they differ in their mode of spread. In some populations plants spread mainly by rhizomes, while in others plants spread mainly by stolons; and in some aerial tillers are produced in quantity, while in others all tillers arise at ground level. An extensive analysis of these characters was not possible. But in eight populations one plant characteristic of each population was taken and subject to careful analysis. To determine mode of growth, all the tillers of the inner third of the plant were counted and subdivided into two groups: (i) basal, arising at ground level, (ii) aerial, arising from above ground level. To determine mode of spread, all the tillers in the outer third of the plant were counted and subdivided in three groups: (i) rhizomatous, arising out of the ground, (ii) stoloniferous, arising from the surface of the ground, (iii) aerial, arising from above the ground.

The values converted into fractions of 10 are given in Table 1. They show that these populations are very different in their characters. The populations from ordinary grassland spread predominantly by stolons, but those from dry sandy areas and from extreme upland predominantly by rhizomes. Ordinary grassland populations tend to produce a number of aerial tillers, while those from sandy and upland areas do not. The production of aerial tillers allows *A. tenuis* to exert considerable competitive effects on other grasses particularly in ungrazed areas. The greatest proportion of aerial tillers is produced by Dale cliff. This explains the mode of origin of the high value for tiller density of this population whose adaptive significance has already been discussed. The smallest proportion of aerial tillers is produced by Plynlymon summit. Since this population suffers the severest exposure, and under actual conditions always dies back over winter, it would appear that aerial tillers would be too vulnerable, and so all tillers arise basally. Therefore, although its value for tiller density is similar to that of Dale cliff, its life form is entirely different.

Table 1. *Mode of growth and spread of eight extreme populations*

Population	Mode of growth			Mode of spread				
	Basal	:	aerial tillers	Rhizomatous	:	stoloniferous	:	aerial tillers
Dale cliff	5	:	5	1	:	6	:	3
Ynyslas grazed	10	:	0	6	:	4	:	0
Pen Dinas foot	8	:	2	1	:	8	:	1
Dale pasture	5	:	5	0	:	8	:	2
Plynlymon Nardetum	8	:	2	0	:	10	:	0
Plynlymon summit	10	:	0	9	:	1	:	0
Lakenheath Warren	9	:	1	8	:	2	:	0
Ruislip Wood	6	:	4	0	:	7	:	3

COMPARISON OF SAMPLING BY SEED AND BY TILLERS

An experiment designed to test the validity of the method of sampling was carried out subsequent to the main experiment. Plants raised from seed from various sites already sampled were compared with those raised from tillers taken from original plants of the same populations growing in the main experiment. Twelve populations were laid out in randomized blocks with six replications on the University College of North Wales farm at Aber, Caernarvonshire. The plants were planted in the autumn of 1953 and measured 2 years later. Unfortunately, the trial had to be discontinued prematurely and the results are therefore only for height of vegetative growth and inflorescence.

The populations chosen were Pen Dinas foot and top, Ynyslas grazed and ungrazed and Goginan rough and mine. Due to an error the seed sample of Goginan rough was omitted from the trial and was replaced by a new seed sample, Goginan mine foot. This was taken from the Goginan lead mine, but in a large area of lead-rich ore grindings at the foot of the main mine, about 300 m from the previous sample. It will be commented on separately.

Table 2. *Characteristics of twelve populations in sampling experiment*

Site	Vegetative height (cm)	(Values from main trial)	Inflorescence height (cm)	(Values from main trial)
Pen Dinas foot (tillers)	9.85	14.7	30.7	30.3
(seed)	9.97		31.9	
Pen Dinas top (tillers)	8.62	11.1	26.4	25.6
(seed)	8.42		27.1	
Ynyslas ungrazed (tillers)	8.48	10.8	23.4	22.3
(seed)	8.30		23.7	
Ynyslas grazed (tillers)	6.68	9.8	18.6	20.9
(seed)	7.62		21.6	
Goginan mine (tillers)	7.53	10.2	24.2	23.8
(seed)	7.73		24.5	
Goginan rough (tillers)	10.32	14.1	30.2	30.3
Goginan mine foot (seed)	9.70		31.7	
Standard error	0.78		2.07	

The analysis of variance for the twelve populations (not given) gave a highly significant variance ratio for population differences. Table 2 gives the population means and standard errors. It shows that there is a remarkably good agreement between the values for populations sampled by seed and tillers. This is borne out by an analysis of variance of the first five pairs of populations. The variance ratio for sampling is nowhere near significance level for either measurement (Table 3). There is also good agreement between these values and those obtained previously in the main experiment at Aberystwyth, although differences in soil, etc., do not allow any critical comparison to be made.

The similarity of the values for populations sampled by seed and tillers permits one other important deduction to be made. The amount of gene flow between the populations must be very small. Otherwise the genetic constitution of the seed would differ from that of the established populations in the direction of the surrounding populations. For this seed, being collected from the natural populations *in situ*, could have arisen by cross pollination with the adjoining populations. A certain small amount of gene flow cannot, however, be precluded by this experiment. The discrepancy between Ynyslas grazed (seed) and (tiller) is in the direction that suggests that it could be due to gene flow. But further more detailed work would be necessary to prove this.

Table 3. *Analysis of variance for the five paired populations of sampling experiment*

(i) Vegetative height

	N	s.s.	m.s.	F.
Sites	4	51.731	12.933	8.03***
Sampling	1	0.368	0.368	n.s.
Site/sampling	4	2.181	0.545	n.s.
Replicates	5	17.507	3.501	2.17 n.s.
Error	45	72.475	1.1611	
Total	59			

(ii) Inflorescence height

	N	s.s.	m.s.	F.
Sites	4	827.00	206.75	17.29***
Sampling	1	17.93	17.93	1.50 n.s.
Site/sampling	4	16.23	4.06	n.s.
Replicates	5	203.18	40.64	3.40*
Error	45	538.22	11.96	
Total	59			

If we now examine the two remaining population samples we find that Goginan rough (tillers), though it cannot be compared with a seed equivalent, shows a satisfactory relationship with the value obtained in the main experiment. Goginan mine foot (seed) on first examination appears remarkable. Although it was taken from a different region of the mine from that of the original Goginan mine sample, it could well be expected to be similar to it. But it is in fact quite different and is instead indistinguishable from Goginan rough. The lead mine, therefore, does not possess a uniform population over it. The higher, drier and poorer areas have a dwarf population, the lower and damper areas a much taller population. Both areas are heavily contaminated with lead, so the dwarfness of the original Goginan mine population cannot be correlated directly with soil lead content but with a complex of environmental factors. These facts are confirmed by unpublished data of Mr. D. Jowett, who is analysing the situation further.

DISCUSSION

The relative importance of the various factors causing differentiation

If we now return to our starting-point it would appear that the situation in *A. tenuis* exemplifies the interplay of all the factors discussed in the introduction. *A. tenuis* is outbreeding. All the characters observed show continuous variation which suggests that they are determined by polygenic systems. As a result these characters show smooth gradations in all directions substantiating the suggestion of Baker (1953). There is no evidence of discontinuities due either to the isolation imposed by inbreeding or to the effects of oligogenes.

The effects of the availability of suitable adaptive genes are clear in the special ability of *A. tenuis* to produce a population able to grow on lead-mine waste. It is difficult to make comment about other characters without knowledge of other species for comparison. But the apparent lack of a broad-leaved, lax, woodland ecotype such as in *Dactylis glomerata* could be due to this.

In general the distribution of *Agrostis tenuis* in the Aberystwyth region is continuous for it is a plant which can be found in almost every community. At first sight, therefore, isolation of populations from one another by distance would not appear to apply except over the greater distances. But it was pointed out in an earlier paper (Bradshaw, 1954) that the integrating effects of gene flow must always be equated with the differentiating effect of different levels of natural selection. Providing differences in natural selection are great enough they can maintain differences between populations between which there is considerable gene flow. This has recently been demonstrated experimentally in populations of *Drosophila* (Thoday, 1958). The other point to be considered is that recorded values for gene flow in wind pollinated plants are much less than might be expected. In *Lolium perenne* (Griffiths, 1952), although exact values depend on various factors, in conditions comparable to those existing in natural populations the amount of cross pollination recorded is under 4% at distances of 50 ft. This is supported by the agreement between the values for populations of *Agrostis tenuis* sampled by seed and tillers.

Such small gene flow will enable differences in natural selection to maintain differences between populations only very small distances apart. It seems reasonable to suppose that in *A. tenuis* such distances need be no more than 50 m. As a result population differentiation could occur in relation to very local variations in environment.

The data shows exactly this. Local variations in habitat such as in the Ynyslas, Pen Dinas and Rheidol regions have different populations associated with them. In fact, local variations in environment assume as great an importance in determining the characteristics of populations as do regional variations. This is well shown in the values for tiller and inflorescence density.

From a study of spot distribution in the butterfly *Maniola jurtina*, Dowdeswell and Ford (1953) reach the same conclusions concerning the importance of isolation in population differentiation. Small geographically isolated island populations of *M. jurtina* tend to occupy one habitat only and therefore are able to evolve in response to natural selection in one direction. Large continuous populations, however, occupy several habitats and being, therefore, subject to natural selection in several different directions do not show any marked evolutionary change. In *Agrostis tenuis* isolation by distance automatically breaks up its continuous distribution into local populations, equivalent to island populations in *Maniola jurtina*, sufficiently to allow each population to be adapted to its own local environment. In no case can these populations be small enough to permit genetic drift.

The same situation is to be found in the snail *Cepea nemoralis* (Sheppard, 1952). Here the lack of mobility of the individual snails results in populations which appear to be isolated to the same degree as those of *Agrostis tenuis* and therefore show the same pattern of differentiation.

It would seem likely that such patterns of local differentiation are to be found in nearly all plant species, for all are subject to the same degree of restricted gene flow. This will be in contrast to the situation in most animal species where mobility of individuals results in extensive gene flow and consequent lack of any marked ecological differentiation.

The amount of the variation between populations recorded in *A. tenuis* is considerable. But a species which is not the dominant member of a climax community does not determine its own environment, and is therefore subject to many more different selective influences (Sinskaja, 1931). *A. tenuis* is such a species, since its natural habitats are a variety of sub-climax communities. In addition these communities are usually closed communities subject to strong biotic effects. There are therefore likely to be strong selective pressures. Marked population differences are therefore to be expected.

The strongly tufted growth habit of *A. tenuis* in upland habitats is interesting to note. Although in most habitats the factors determining the morphology of *A. tenuis* are those such as grazing intensity, exposure, soil moisture and fertility, in upland habitats the significant factor must be the particular competitive effect of other plants. *Nardus*, *Molinia*, and the various large mosses, which are the other main constituents of upland grasslands, all possess tufted growth habits. The tufted growth habit of *Agrostis tenuis* is clearly in relation to this, and is a good example of adaptation to phyto-social factors analogous to those occurring in *Camelina sativa* and other species (Sinskaja, 1931).

With all this considered, it is clear that the environment is the dominating factor in the development of population differences in *Agrostis tenuis*. The inter-relation of the other factors is such that the environment has the greatest influence. It is the environment, even its local variations, which determines the pattern of the differentiation. So where there are sharp changes in environment, e.g. from the foot to the top of Pen Dinas, there are sharp correlated changes in the populations. Where there are gradual changes in environment, e.g. from the foot of Pen Dinas to the summit of Plynlymon, the population changes are equally gradual. Where in such gradients there are sudden local variations, e.g. Goginan mine, there are sudden population changes.

The concept of variation within a species being limited to major differences of the nature of ecotypes cannot therefore be held in *A. tenuis*. This is likely to be so in other similar plant species. The environment by its selective pressure imposes its own pattern on the differentiation of species. The differentiation within a species will be as complex and as varied as the pattern of the habitats it occupies. While by examining a few extreme habitats we will discover a few extreme ecotypes, more detailed examination will give a more detailed picture.

Recently, however, doubt has been cast on the validity of much work on plant populations (Harberd, 1957). It is clear that any conclusions about the adaptive significance of differences that are found between populations can only be tentative. This is true especially of those morphological characters whose adaptive value cannot easily be tested by experimental cultivation under natural conditions. Such characters are those commonly used in population studies. But any alternative approach is not without its pitfalls. Mathematical correlations between population means and environmental factors are suggested, but these are no more valid as evidence of the effects of natural selection than direct observational inferences concerning the adaptive value of population differences. Correlations can be made between observations which have no causal connection. Only actual demonstration of adaptive values can indicate unequivocally the significance of any character.

But even when the adaptive values of population differences are not demonstrable or deduceable, the discovery of similar patterns of differentiation by different authors in different species is not without significance. The correspondence of the pattern of emergence in *A. tenuis* to that in *Lolium perenne* (Gregor and Watson, 1945) would suggest the conclusions drawn concerning the selective value of the character are valid.

All explanations of the origin of observed differences must be considered but in most cases it is unnecessary to postulate the effects of anything other than natural selection. Where population type appears to be unrelated to the environment, it is perfectly possible that our assessment of the environment is faulty. For failure to demonstrate a relationship between the characteristics of a population and its environment is no indication that such a relationship does not exist. Firstly, the selective effect of a particular environment may not be what we imagine. The particular factor of the environment that we consider important may not be at all significant to the characters in question, and another factor that we do not even notice may be much more significant. Secondly, the conditions that we observe now may not have been operating earlier. This is very likely in the natural and semi-natural habitats which are often sampled, especially at the present day when there are considerable changes in the pattern of land use. Thus apparently anomalous results in *Festuca ovina* (Harberd, 1957) may be intelligible after a further examination of the original environments.

The repeated isolation of single genotypes as a source of error (Harberd, 1958) must constantly be guarded against. In the collection of *Agrostis tenuis* the sampling area was always relatively large. No figures were collected for the amount of reduplication. But in populations of the sterile hybrid *A. tenuis* × *stolonifera* in conditions where reduplication could have been expected to be very frequent, a negligible amount was found (Bradshaw, 1958) using the same sampling method. So it is unlikely that any apparent anomalies in the findings in *Agrostis tenuis* are due to this cause.

Taxonomy

The pattern of differentiation in *A. tenuis* immediately raises the problem of its classification, and of the classification of intraspecific variation in general. It would seem reasonable to expect that the pattern of differentiation in *A. tenuis* is to be found in most outbreeding species with a fairly continuous distribution.

The pattern shows that it is clearly not possible to delimit ecotypes, ecodemes or any other units in *A. tenuis* without being subjective. Since there are no discontinuities it is utterly impossible to decide where one unit begins or ends.

As a result, although it would be perfectly possible to delimit different taxonomic units, as has been done in the past (Philipson, 1937), any system of classification would be a source of confusion. It would, as in *Cepea nemoralis* (Cain, 1952), hide the true pattern of the variation, since it would imply the existence of units which have no objective reality. It would only be of value if it were specifically indicated that the units were not natural, but were arbitrary parts of a continuous range.

It would be interesting to discover how far this applies to other species studied previously. It seems reasonable to believe that the ecotypes in various species described by Clausen, Keck and Hiesey (1940, 1948) are really parts of a continuous range. The same is likely to apply to many of the ecotypes described by Turesson (1925). From observations on *Prunella vulgaris* and *Plantago maritima* Böcher (1949) and Gregor (1946) subscribe to this view.

In two situations, however, the delimitation of units may have some objective reality. Firstly, when a species has a discontinuous distribution, it will fall immediately into units, though whether these will all be sufficiently distinct to be considered separate units in the taxonomic sense, is another matter. In *Agrostis tenuis* the distribution being more or less continuous, such examples are not forthcoming.

Secondly, the habitats occupied by the species may be so distinctive and separate that the populations occupying those habitats may be classified as different ecotypes. It was in this sense that the term ecotype was first envisaged (Turesson, 1925). But such ecotypes often themselves contain locally distinct populations. In the cases where the habitat of the populations concerned is very distinct, e.g. the sand dunes in the *A. tenuis* series, this need not cause any difficulties in classification since a general ecotype can still be defined. In other regions, however, sand dunes are to be found which change quite gradually into more normal habitats. In these cases, an objectively separable sand-dune ecotype is unlikely. This is well exemplified by the upland populations of *A. tenuis*; although by examination of only one upland population it would be possible to define an upland ecotype, examination of other populations shows that it is not objectively separable. A very similar situation is recorded in *Deschampsia caespitosa* (Lawrence, 1945).

The concept of the cline (Huxley, 1938) does not help this problem very much. Although there are distinct gradients, both in the environments and in the characteristics of the populations, these are not simple. There are many different clines in different directions, in relation to different ecological factors. The individual factors do not themselves necessarily form regular gradients, complicating the situation still further.

For these reasons no attempt has been made to categorize the variations found in *Agrostis tenuis*. It is seemingly sensible only to record the differences between individual population samples as they occur.

ACKNOWLEDGMENTS

I am much indebted to Professor T. J. Jenkin of the Welsh Plant Breeding Station and Professor P. T. Thomas for their encouragement and hospitality for the main part of the investigation, which was carried out with a Research Studentship of the Agricultural Research Council, and to Professor R. Alun Roberts for his encouragement over the latter part. I am also indebted to Mr. A. R. Beddows and other members of the Grass Breeding Department of the Welsh Plant Breeding Station for their unstinted help and advice, to Dr. Keith Jones for his cytological examination of some of my material, and to Dr. J. W. Gregor who originally stimulated my interest in the subject.

REFERENCES

BAKER, H. G. (1953). Race formation and reproductive method in flowering plants. *Symp. Soc. Exp. Biol.*, 7, 114.

BÖCHER, T. W. (1949). Racial divergences in *Prunella vulgaris* in relation to habitat and climate. *New Phytol.*, 48, 285.

BRADSHAW, A. D. (1952). Populations of *Agrostis tenuis* resistant to lead and zinc poisoning. *Nature, Lond.*, 169, 1098.

BRADSHAW, A. D. (1958). Natural hybridization of *Agrostis tenuis* Sibth. and *A. stolonifera* L. *New Phytol.*, 57, 66.

BRADSHAW, A. D. (1954). Local population differences in *Agrostis tenuis*. *Proc. 9th Internat. Genet. Cong. Caryologia Vol. suppl.*, 1026.

CAIN, A. J. (1952). Local evolution and taxonomy in very polymorphic species. *Proc. Leeds Phil. Soc.*, 6, 47.

CLAUSEN, J. (1951). *The Evolution of Plant Species*. Ithaca, New York.

CLAUSEN, J., KECK, D. D. & HIESEY, W. M. (1940). Experimental studies on the nature of species I. *Carnegie Inst. of Washington Publ.*, 520.

CLAUSEN, J., KECK, D. D. & HIESEY, W. M. (1948). Experimental studies on the nature of species III. *Carnegie Inst. of Washington Publ.*, 581.

COOPER, J. P. (1951). Studies on growth and development in *Lolium* II. Pattern of bud development of the shoot apex and its ecological significance. *J. Ecol.*, **39**, 228.

DOWDESWELL, W. H. & FORD, E. B. (1953). The influence of isolation on variability in the butterfly *Maniola jurtina* L. *Symp. Soc. Exp. Biol.*, **7**, 254.

FISHER, R. A. & FORD, E. B. (1947). The spread of a gene in natural conditions in a colony of the moth *Panaxia dominula* L. *Heredity*, **1**, 143.

GREGOR, J. W. (1946). Some reflections on intra-specific ecological variation and its classification. *Trans. Bot. Soc. Edin.*, **34**, 377.

GREGOR, J. W., DAVEY, V. McM. & LANG, J. M. S. (1936). Experimental taxonomy I. Experimental garden technique in relation to the recognition of the small taxonomic units. *New Phytol.*, **35**, 323.

GREGOR, J. W. & WATSON, P. J. (1954). Some observations and reflections concerning the patterns of intra-specific differentiation. *New Phytol.*, **53**, 291.

GRIFFITHS, D. J. (1952). The liability of seed crops of perennial rye grass (*Lolium perenne*) to contamination by wind borne pollen. *J. Agric. Sci.*, **40**, 19.

HARBERD, D. J. (1957). The within population variance in genecological trials. *New Phytol.*, **56**, 269.

HARBERD, D. J. (1958). A spurious significance in genecological trials. *Nature, Lond.*, **181**, 138.

HUXLEY, J. S. (1938). Clines: an auxiliary taxonomic principle. *Nature, Lond.*, **142**, 219.

JONES, K. (1956). Species differentiation in *Agrostis* II. The significance of chromosome pairing in the tetraploid hybrids of *Agrostis canina* isubsp. *montana* Hartm., *A. tenuis* Sibth. and *A. stolonifera* L. *J. Genet.*, **54**, 377.

LAWRENCE, W. E. (1945). Some ecotypic relations of *Deschampsia caespitosa*. *Amer. J. Bot.*, **32**, 298.

MAYR, E. (1942). *Systematics and the origin of species.* New York.

MAYR, E. (1947). Ecological factors in speciation. *Evolution*, **1**, 263.

PHILIPSON, W. R. (1937). A revision of the British species of the genus *Agrostis* Linn. *J. Linn. Soc.*, **51**, 73.

PRENDERGAST, J. J. (1948). The Genus Agrostis in Ireland. M.Sc. Thesis, University College, Dublin.

RILEY, R. (1956). The influence of the breeding system on the genecology of *Thlaspi alpestre* L. *New Phytol.*, **55**, 319.

SALISBURY, E. J. (1942). *The reproductive capacity of plants.* London.

SHEPPARD, P. M. (1952). Natural selection in two colonies of the polymorphic land snail, *Cepea nemoralis*. *Heredity*, **6**, 233.

SINSKAJA, E. N. (1931). The study of species in their dynamics and inter-relation with different types of vegetation. *Bull. Appl. Bot., Gen., Plant Breed.*, **25**, 1.

STAPLEDON, R. G. (1926). Cocksfoot grass (*Dactylis glomerata*. L.): Ecotypes in relation to the biotic factor. *J. Ecol.*, **16**, 71.

STAPLEDON, R. G. (1936). *A Survey of the Agricultural and Waste Lands of Wales.* London.

STEBBINS, G. L. (1950). *Variation and Evolution in Plants.* New York.

THODAY, J. M. (1958). The effects of disruptive selection: the experimental production of a polymorphic population. *Nature, Lond.*, **181**, 1124.

TURESSON G. (1922). The genotypical response of the plant species to the habitat. *Hereditas*, **3**, 211.

TURESSON, G. (1925). The plant species in relation to habitat and climate. *Hereditas*, **6**, 147.

WATT, A. S. (1940). Studies in the ecology of the Breckland IV. The grass heath. *J. Ecol.*, **28**, 42.

WILKINS, D. A. (1957). A technique for the measurement of lead tolerance in plants. *Nature, Lond.*, **180**, 37.

WRIGHT, S. (1940). The statistical consequences of mendelian heredity in relation to speciation. *The New Systematics*, Oxford.

DELPHINIUM GYPSOPHILUM, A DIPLOID SPECIES
OF HYBRID ORIGIN

HARLAN LEWIS AND CARL EPLING

Department of Botany, University of California, Los Angeles

Received February 11, 1959

The purpose of this paper is to examine evidence that *Delphinium gypsophilum* had its origin by hybridization at the diploid level without change in chromosome number and by a more direct process of recombination than that ordinarily referred to as introgression. This hypothesis was first stated in an abstract (Lewis and Epling, 1946), and was discussed later by Epling (1947) and by Stebbins (1950) after more data were at hand. We shall now discuss the total evidence that has accrued since our abstract appeared.

The genus *Delphinium* is mostly associated with plant communities that have been derived during later Cenozoic time from the Arcto-Tertiary Geoflora of the New and Old Worlds. The species we have studied are associated with present derivatives of the Madro-Tertiary Geoflora: the oak woodland, chaparral, and to some extent, the shrubby communities of the Sonoran desert. They have generally independent ranges with a considerable overlap in some cases, and some are included within the ranges of others. Whether their ranges overlap or are included, the species that grow in the same vicinity generally occupy ecologically different sites. Repeated observations indicate a considerable restriction of migration from colony to colony, either by pollen or by seeds. For example, blue or white flowered colonies of the same species persist unchanged for indefinite periods within short distances of each other and in similar habitats (Epling and Lewis, 1952). Thus, each colony has a considerable permanence of its adaptive attributes.

The colonies of two species are sometimes contiguous and may be composite, providing ample opportunity in either case for gene exchange between them. The vectors of pollen are bees, especially *Bombus*. There is no apparent selectivity on their part for flower color or conformation, and visits from plant to plant in mixed populations appear to be at random. The species with which we shall deal are self compatible, but the behavior of the bees results mostly in cross pollination because of protandry. Barriers to interspecific hybridization are often lacking, not only because of the pollinating process, but also for genetic causes. A full seed set occurs after most first crosses. The seeds are viable for the most part and generally produce normally developed and vigorous F_1 plants. The fertility of F_1's when selfed is sometimes high and sometimes low but is reasonably consistent for each interspecific cross. The seed set is generally higher after backcrossing. Even though fertility is low for a particular cross, some individuals, even triploids, will set occasional viable seeds.

With these opportunities for gene exchange one might expect to find hybrid swarms wherever two species intermix. This is seldom the case. On the contrary, hybrid individuals in flower are few and seldom seen. Mixed colonies are mostly divisible into two taxa of which neither differs substantially from its relatives throughout their main ranges. Nevertheless, a considerable number of hybrid plants may be present in the vegetative state in these colonies and reach flowering only in response to particular conditions (Epling and Lewis, 1952). These hybrids can and do persist without flower-

Reprinted by permission of the authors and publisher from
EVOLUTION, **13**, 511–525 (1959).

ing for many years in virtue of root dormancy by which the adaptive potentials that each genotype carries are stored, so to say, against the rainy day when each may flower and fruit.

This dormancy is a characteristic of the *Delphinium* species that occur in Madro-Tertiary environments. It rests on the capacity of the roots to become dormant and remain so for an indefinite period during which they are brittle, chalky within, and apparently lifeless. With the onset of dormancy, the flowering shoot dies back to the crown regardless of whether the flowers or seeds have matured. This response is induced by periods of seasonal drought that characterize these environments. With the advent of the winter rains the roots again become fleshy and active. Whether a rosette of leaves will form at the crown and how long it will function before withering; whether a flowering shoot will form and remain alive long enough to mature the seeds; whether the seeds will germinate during the following winter or remain dormant in the soil: all these apparently depend on the responses of individual genotypes to particular environments. Resumption of the yearly cycle of development is seemingly invoked by the conditions of weather acting on each local soil type. The result is that a flowering colony will consist in one year of hundreds or even thousands of individuals, and in the following year it may have only tens or perhaps none. In some years, some species, such as *D. gypsophilum*, seem to be geographically continuous in their areas even though locally concentrated. The spacing and grouping of individuals from year to year also varies (Epling and Lewis, 1952). The effect of root dormancy on these differences of population structure and density and gene exchange is crucial for understanding the dynamics of a mixed population. This effect would be particularly important for the establishment of genetic variants that might be harbored in the colony for long periods, especially when one takes into account the more or less rhythmic long range fluctuations of climate which may become critical for the persistence of taxa in the Madro-Tertiary environments they occupy.

COMPARISON OF THE SPECIES

We shall be primarily concerned in this discussion with three species: *D. recurvatum, D. hesperium pallescens* and *D. gypsophilum* (Lewis and Epling, 1954). We shall refer to the second simply as *D. hesperium*. All are diploid (n = 8) but *D. gypsophilum* has a tetraploid race that is indistinguishable from the diploid in external morphology. We shall refer only to the diploid.

These taxa grow primarily in the foothills that border the western and southern parts of the central valley of California (fig. 1). Their ecological preferences are as readily distinguished as their morphology. *Delphinium recurvatum* occurs chiefly in saline areas on the lower slopes of the foothills that are dominated by *Atriplex,* and extends into the valley itself along salty streams in association with *Allenrolfia.* It occupies one of the most drastic and arid habitats, climatically and physiologically, to which the genus is adapted. It is closely related to, but distinct from, a desert species, *D. parishii,* to which we shall refer. *Delphinium hesperium,* on the other hand, occupies the oak woodland which is the most mesic of present day derivatives of the Madro-Tertiary Geoflora in this region. This woodland occurs on the higher, well drained slopes that surround the valley. Because of topography it frequently approaches the valley bottom. In the western foothills it consists chiefly of *Quercus douglasii* associated locally with occasional individuals or small groves of *Q. lobata. D. gypsophilum* occupies a habitat that is intermediate between these two extremes. It is abundantly distributed throughout a narrow zone of grassland along the western and southern borders of the valley. The original cover of this

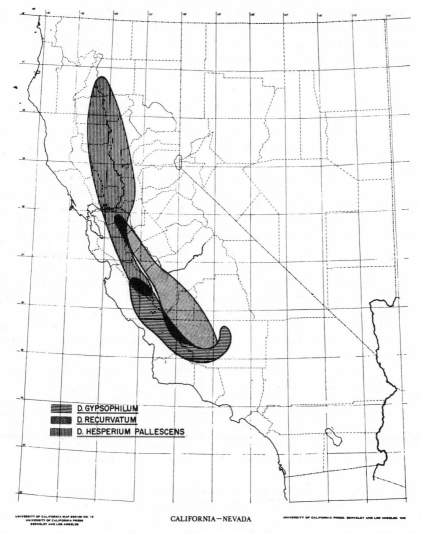

FIG. 1. Approximate geographic range of the two probable parental species and their hybrid species, *D. gypsophilum*.

zone was doubtless bunch grass, dominated by species of *Stipa,* together with many small perennial herbs and annuals. The perennial grasses are now largely replaced by mediterranean annuals, in genera such as *Avena* and *Bromus.*

There can be no doubt that the habitats of the species of *Delphinium* we shall refer to have been modified by man's occupation during the last century, particularly by grazing. Thus, many colonies of *D. hesperium* are found only along roads outside of fences and not so much in the grazed woodland within them. We have estimated that some of the individuals we have found may be fifty years old or more, suggesting that these present limited habitats probably represent their original ranges fairly well. At their closest points of contact, *D. hesperium* and *D. recurvatum* are separated now by several miles and by a considerable ecological barrier. This does not preclude the possibility that they were once within pollinating range during recent time. Both species overlap at some points with *D. gypsophilum.*

D. recurvatum, D. gypsophilum and *D. hesperium* are instantly determinable throughout their respective ranges by the summation of characters contrasted in table 1. Most of these characters are complex, such as leaf habit and the conformation of the flower. Taken individually, their expression overlaps in the different species, but the modes are quite distinct. We have been able to treat quantitatively some other characteristics, such as internode number and flower number; but they also overlap, partly because of individual responses in development. Others, such as the presence or absence of pubescence or glaucousness, and the nature of the seed coat, are sharply differentiated in both wild and cultivated specimens. All are determined by multiple genetic factors, and to judge from segregations in F_2 progenies are more or less independently determined. However, glabrousness and glaucousness, on the one hand, and pubescence and nonglaucousness, on the other (the first being a characteristic of *D. recurvatum* and *D. gypsophilum,* the second of *D. hesperium*), are linked to an appreciable extent, sufficient for them to show strong positive correlations in segregation. We have not been able to measure linkage precisely because of the high frequency of gametic and zygotic elimination of genotypes and our inability to determine the degree of its randomness with respect to any given phenotypic expression.

The associations of characters represented in each column of table 1 are the result of careful analysis of hundreds of individuals, both wild and cultivated. The fairly uniform association of these characters over wide areas that are ecologically differentiated, and the probable persistence of these associations for the long period of geological time that their distribution suggests, argue strongly that each species is genetically integrated throughout its range. Each species is a well defined mode of evolution. The contrast between each character of *D. recurvatum* and *D. hesperium* is sharp, but it will be noted that the characters of *D. gypsophilum* are a composite; some of its attributes resemble the corresponding ones of *D. recurvatum,* some are intermediate, and some resemble those of *D. hesperium.* The first point of our argument is that, taken as a whole, *D. gypsophilum* is intermediate between *D. recurvatum* and *D. hesperium* in its character associations (fig. 2).

The differentiating traits of each spe-

TABLE 1.   *Comparison of the more conspicuous morphological traits of* D. gypsophilum *with those of* D. hesperium pallescens *and* D. recurvatum

	D. hesperium pallescens	*D. gypsophilum*	*D. recurvatum*
plant height	tall	tall	short
no. of internodes between inflorescence and rosette	many	many	few
stem pubescence	puberulent	glabrous	glabrous
stem surface	non-glaucous	glaucous	glaucous
stem color	green	intermediate	red
stem thickness	stout	stout	slender
leaf segments	broad	intermediate	narrow
leaf venation	prominent	inconspicuous	inconspicuous
inflorescence	dense	intermediate	lax
flower number	many	many	few
flower conformation	cupped	rotate	reflexed
sepal color	white	white	lavender
sepal shape	broad	intermediate	narrow
seed coat	adhering	loose	loose

390

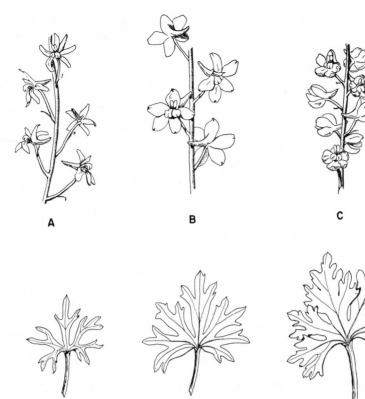

FIG. 2. Outline drawings of the habit of flower, inflorescence and leaf of A) *D. recurvatum,* B) *D. gypsophilum,* and C) *D. hesperium pallescens.*

cies vary to some extent from colony to colony. Two examples will illustrate the scope of this variance. The leaf segments of *D. recurvatum* from population 542 (table 2) when grown under uniform garden conditions, were consistently broader and fewer in number than those of population 413, when both were compared in a given year. In the same manner, plants of *D. gypsophilum* from population 545 were stockier than those of population 411. The wild colonies from which such transplant populations were made are generally fairly uniform; but the progenies from selfing these transplants are usually more variable than the colony from which their parents were obtained. This would be expected of a highly heterozygous normally outcrossed species

when grown under less rigorous conditions than prevail in the wild.

CULTURE AND SCORING

Stocks to be used as parents for experimental crosses were transplanted from wild colonies (table 2). The transplants were made sometimes during the growing period and sometimes after the plants had become dormant. Transplants were grown in 4-inch pots sunk in wood shavings out of doors. When in bud or flower they and experimental hybrids were moved into an insect free screenhouse in which the pollinations were made. Flowers to be crossed were emasculated before the stigmas became receptive. In crossing hybrid and nonhybrid individuals, the hybrid was used as the female parent unless otherwise indicated. The seeds set by each cross were counted and sown in 4-inch pots in the autumn. Germination frequencies were obtained the following spring by counting the seedlings in each pot. Those desired for further study were allowed to become dormant and were separated and planted in individual pots the following autumn prior to the winter rains. Because of small size, yearlings were seldom scored or used for hybridization. Normal size is attained in the second year during which most crosses were made and the characters scored. These included the size and conformation of the uppermost rosette leaf, the amount and kind of pubescence on the leaves and stem, the presence or absence and distribution of glaucousness on the stem, the number of flowers, the size, shape, and color of the sepals, and the conformation of the flower. Color was recorded by using *A Dictionary of Color* (Maerz and Paul, 1930).

Fertility was measured primarily by the proportion of seed set per follicle and the frequency of germination (tables 3 and 4). We also ascertained the proportion of visibly good pollen, but found it of little use in estimating fertility because the percentage of good pollen is highly variable, even among individual wild transplants. Most individuals of *D. recurvatum* and *D. hesperium pallescens* have better than 75 per cent good pollen, but some may be as low as 30–35 per cent.

TABLE 2. *Collections of* Delphinium gypsophilum *(diploid only)*, D. hesperium pallescens, *and* D. recurvatum *transplanted to the experimental garden and used as parents for hybridization studies. All localities are in California*

	Accession number	Locality	Collector	Date
D. gypsophilum	411	1 mile north of McKittrick, Kern County	Mehlquist	1940
	431	10 miles east of King City, Monterey County	Lewis and Mehlquist	1941
	531	U. S. Highway 399, 5 miles south of Maricopa, Kern Co.	Epling and Lewis	1944
	545	Same locality	Epling and Miles	1945
D. hesperium pallescens	444	Marsh Creek Road, 2.3 miles west of Byron, Contra Costa County	Lewis and Mehlquist	1942
	445	East margin of Antioch Golf Course, Contra Costa County	Lewis and Mehlquist	1942
	446	5.4 miles north of Marsh Creek road on the road to Antioch, Contra Costa County	Lewis and Mehlquist	1942
	449	2.8 miles south of the entrance to Pinnacles National Monument, San Benito County	Lewis and Mehlquist	1942
	450	0.5 mile south of Paicines, San Benito County	Lewis and Mehlquist	1942
	586	1.0 mile south of Marsh Creek Road on the road to Livermore, Contra Costa County	Epling	1945
	589	Same locality	Epling and Lewis	1945
D. recurvatum	412	7.2 miles north of Coalinga, Fresno County	Mehlquist	1941
	413	13.6 miles north of Coalinga, Fresno County	Mehlquist	1941
	453	Same locality as 412	Lewis and Mehlquist	1942
	542	5 miles west of State Highway 120 on the road to Byron Hot Springs	Epling and Miles	1945

TABLE 3. *Seed set and germination of the* Delphinium *crosses indicated.*
Female parent is listed first

	Number of com- binations	Mean seed set per follicle	Number of seeds planted	Number germi- nated	Per cent germi- nation
hesperium × *hesperium*	14	15.3	707	405	57
hesperium × self	23	14.7	1578	508	32
hesperium × *recurvatum*	6	5.2	295	143	48
recurvatum × *recurvatum*	19	16.7	1029	570	55
recurvatum × self	11	17.8	1528	511	33
recurvatum × *hesperium*	6	15.2	615	231	38
recurvatum × *gypsophilum*	5	13.4	125	87	70
gypsophilum × self	6	24.4	630	258	43
gypsophilum × *hesperium*	1	22.0	25	15	60
gypsophilum × *recurvatum*	1	35.0	25	14	56

The scoring of traits in successive years is influenced by environmental modifications and comparisons between parents and their progeny is open to error for this reason. Even though the conditions of culture are "uniform," the weather differs from year to year and the composition of the soil in the pots changes. Thus, it is not surprising that some traits chosen for study have been found to vary to some extent from year to year. For example, the uppermost rosette leaves on a given plant of *D. variegatum* may show greater variation in shape from one year to the next, than the range in one year of variation of the entire sample (Lewis, 1947). Comparisons of vegetative traits of this sort must, therefore, be treated with caution. Those we have made for the purposes of this paper have been drawn from contemporary progenies as far as possible.

FERTILITY

We have estimated fertility within and between species by the number of seeds set per follicle, of which there are three in each flower, and the germination of each class in the following spring after they were exposed in four inch pots to the prevailing temperatures and the winter rains. The frequencies of germination were reasonably consistent and representative although they may not represent the total capacity of the seeds to germinate, inasmuch as an occasional seed was found to hold over until the following year, perhaps because of a different reaction to external conditions. Most follicles in nature are well filled and the normal seed numbers for each species are about the same as those shown in the second column of table 3, where wild transplants were crossed or selfed. The seed set of *D. gypsophilum* is definitely higher than that of *D. recurvatum* or *D. hesperium*. Seed set in the F_1 crosses of the species we have worked with, including those listed above, generally approximates that of the parental species. A noteworthy reduction was found, however, in the initial cross between *D. recurvatum* and *D. hesperium* when the latter was used as the female parent. Seed germination of the crosses in either direction was not substantially different, but was somewhat lower than that of the wild parents.

Regardless of the direction of the cross, the fertility of the selfed or backcrossed F_1 hybrids between *D. recurvatum* and *D. hesperium* is low, compared with the normal seed set of the species or with that of the first crosses (table 4). The seed set from backcrossing was higher than from selfing, and seed germination was much higher. But of particular interest, the cross of *D. gypsophilum* to the

F_1 was higher on the average, than backcrosses to either parent. In contrast to the evident reproductive barrier between *D. recurvatum* and *D. hesperium, D. recurvatum* and *D. gypsophilum* are highly interfertile. This sharp difference is probably caused primarily by the different chromosome architecture of the species involved.

The haploid chromosome complement of *Delphinium* consists of 8 chromosomes including two long metacentrics, five shorter subequal acrocentrics and a shorter metacentric (Lewis *et al.*, 1951). We have found no evidence of structural heterozygosity in wild individuals of either *D. recurvatum* or *D. gypsophilum,* nor in the F_1 hybrids from crossing different transplants of these species. The case of *D. hesperium* is different. In the first place, it is itself structurally variable and second, F_1 hybrids we produced between *D. hesperium* and *D. recurvatum* were heterozygous for at least two paracentric inversions and a large reciprocal translocation between the two large chromosomes.

Two transplants of *D. hesperium pallescens* from among those of five localities were found to have the meiotic irregularities that are characteristic of structural heterozygosity. A bridge and fragment were found, for example, in 1 to 2 per cent of anaphase cells in one plant, indicating a paracentric inversion, and a second plant, from another population showed a high degree of delayed separations between one pair of the larger chromosomes. Several cells of the latter had a micronucleus at telophase which probably resulted from chromosome exclusion because of the delayed separation. This phenomenon has been observed in several species of *Delphinium* (Lewis *et al.,* 1951) and may indicate a difference in homology along the length of the paired chromosomes. Structural differences of this sort could arise from introgression and our studies of this species group show clearly that introgression occurs between *D. hesperium* and *D. varie-*gatum (Epling and Lewis, 1952). We shall refer to this later.

One would expect an appreciable reduction in fertility in the hybrid between *D. hesperium* and *D. recurvatum* from the segregation of the translocated chromosomes because they frequently form two independently segregating pairs, and when a ring is formed it often separates with adjacent chromosomes going to the same pole. The structural heterozygosity we have observed is probably only a part of the total because many other structural differences could be concealed by the low chiasma frequency, which is usually one per bivalent for the six short chromosomes and two per bivalent in the two long ones (Mehlquist, Blodgett, and Bruscia, 1943; Lewis *et al.*, 1951). This inference that much or perhaps all of the sterility of the *recurvatum-hesperium* cross is the result of structural differences is strengthened by comparison with an allotetraploid from this cross, which we induced by colchicine. When selfed, this allotetraploid produced about 10 seeds per follicle in contrast to an average of one seed in the diploid hybrid. Their germination (15 per cent) was comparable to that of the seeds of the selfed diploid hybrid. The allotetraploid was not as fertile as either parent but the reason was apparent from an examination of meiosis where it could be seen that the chromosomes frequently did not pair autosyndetically. Rings of 4 or chains of 3 or 4 involving the rearranged large chromosomes of the genome were frequent, and association as great as a ring of eight was observed. In addition, fertility may have been reduced by crossing over within heterozygous inversions because seven out of 135 first telophase cells examined showed a bridge, usually accompanied by a fragment.

VARIATION

Interspecific hybrids generally have a narrow range of variation in the first generation (Anderson, 1949). We have found, however, that the F_1's of *D. re-*

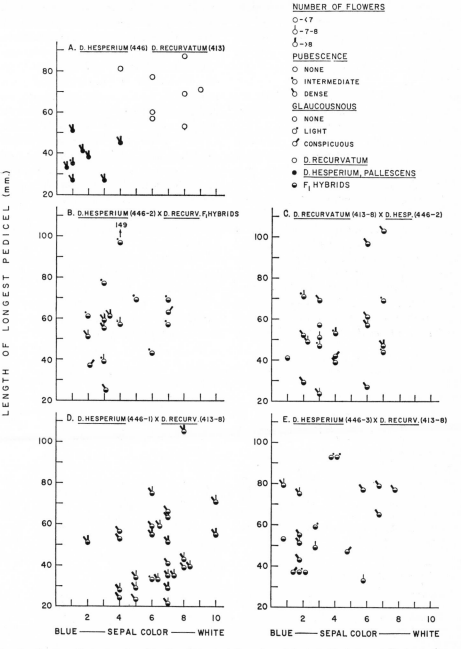

FIG. 3. Scatter diagrams showing the characteristics of certain hybrids between *D. hesperium pallescens* and *D. recurvatum*.

curvatum × *hesperium* are remarkably variable, approaching the variance to be expected in an F_2 progeny and exceeding by far that found in the progenies of intraspecific crosses. This variance is illustrated in figure 3. The abscissa of these scatter diagrams records the differences in sepal color from the white of

D. hesperium to the blue of *D. recurvatum,* following Maerz and Paul, and the ordinate records the length of the longest pedicel. Other characters are recorded by the whiskers on each ideograph, according to the legend: flower number, pubescence, and glaucousness. These are the more easily contrasted traits of these species. In the examples shown, one plant of *D. recurvatum* (413-8) was used in making crosses with three plants of *D. hesperium* from the same colony (446-1, 2, 3).

The range of variation of the F_1 hybrids of this cross clearly exceeds that of the parents. Inasmuch as the same plant of *D. recurvatum* was used in each case, the differences between crosses must have come from the different individuals of *D. hesperium,* and it seems likely that part of the concealed variability arose from previous introgression of another species, *D. variegatum,* with our parental

population. *Delphinium hesperium* and *D. variegatum* are partly sympatric and are known to hybridize when in contact with each other. A clue to this introgression is found in the differences in pubescence graphed in figure 3. All of the individuals in one of the hybrid progenies had pubescent stems; whereas some individuals in the other three had glabrous stems. Since hybrids between *D. recurvatum* and *D. hesperium* characteristically have pubescent stems whereas hybrids between *D. recurvatum* and *D. variegatum* consistently have glabrous stems, the segregating F_1 progenies strongly suggest that the *D. hesperium* parents were introgressants with *D. variegatum* although such introgression was not evident from the morphology of the parents.

Among 374 F_1 *D. hesperium* × *D. recurvatum* plants examined, some were found that closely approached *D. gypso-*

TABLE 4. *Fertility of the F₁ hybrids indicated.* Female parent is listed first except in original crosses

	Number of plants pollinated	Number of carpels pollinated	Mean seed set per follicle	Seeds sown	Seeds germinated	Per cent germination
D. recurvatum × *D. hesperium**						
F_1 × self	125	1829	1.0	1710	178	10
× F_1	93	676	.7	371	78	21
× *recurvatum*	38	321	1.9	534	222	42
× *hesperium*	30	243	2.0	310	94	30
× *gypsophilum*	14	138	3.2	286	149	52
recurvatum × F_1	6	60	7.7	502	183	36
D. recurvatum × *D. gypsophilum***						
F_1 × self	27	261	19.7	2900	607	21
× F_1	25	225	23.1	1000	380	38
× *recurvatum*	14	126	19.8	628	270	43
× *gypsophilum*	4	36	23.5	570	250	44
D. gypsophilum × *D. hesperium****						
F_1 × self	2	27	1.5	32	2	6
× *hesperium*	1	9	6.0	50	30	60

* F_1's from 9 combinations including reciprocal crosses.
** F_1's from 6 combinations including reciprocal crosses.
*** F_1's from 1 cross.

philum in respect to particular traits such as leaf shape or flower conformation but differed conspicuously from that species in other traits. However, one individual (2196-1) from the cross *hesperium 445-4 × recurvatum 413-8* was indistinguishable from *D. gypsophilum* even after a careful comparison. It proved to be a triploid with two genomes of *D. recurvatum* and one of *D. hesperium*. No progeny were obtained from it.

The F_2, backcross, and subsequent generations produced a vast array of variants, some recombining parental traits and others combinations unlike those of either parent. Some individuals were dwarfs, others commenced flowering in the rosette, some had 6-merous or otherwise abnormal flowers, or abnormal branching in the inflorescence. Some backcrosses were scarcely distinguishable from one parent or the other, and some crosses between *recurvatum*-like individuals produced progenies of which most if not all would have passed for this species in a wild population. When selfed, some individuals of such progenies would betray their hybrid origin, just as one might expect of naturally produced introgressants.

The hybrid derivatives of greatest interest to our study were 35 individuals that very closely resembled or were not separable from *D. gypsophilum* as it occurs over a wide geographic area. The progenies that produced these individuals are shown in table 5. Most were obtained by backcrossing to *recurvatum*, mostly 413. None was obtained from backcrossing to *D. hesperium*. The fertility of these *gypsophilum*-like plants, measured by seed set, was variable but was often as high as that of either parental species and in some instances as high as that of *D. gypsophilum*. The inference is reasonable that some of the hybrids recovered genomes structurally comparable to those of *D. recurvatum* after backcrossing to it. Progenies from *gypsophilum*-like individuals showed a limited amount of segregation around a *gypsophilum*-like mode,

TABLE 5. *The derivation of individuals closely resembling* Delphinium gypsophilum *from hybrids between* D. recurvatum *and* D. hesperium- pallescens

	Number of plants	Number closely resembling *D. gypsophilum*
Hybrids		
F_1	374	1*
F_2	238	0
$F_2 \times F_1$	36	0
F_3	128	5
F_4	506	0
$F_2 \times recurvatum$	37	0
$F_2 \times hesperium$	36	0
$(F_2 \times recurvatum) \times$ self	46	0
$F_3 \times (F_2 \times recurvatum)$	16	0
Backcrosses to *D. recurvatum*		
B_1	417	3
$B_1 \times$ self	41	0
$B_1 \times B_1$	120	11
$B_1 \times F_2$	56	9
B_2	43	5
$B_2 \times$ self	331	1
B_3	205	0
Backcrosses to *D. hesperium*		
B_1	70	0
$B_1 \times$ self	146	0
$B_1 \times B_1$	27	0
B_2	230	0

* Triploid, see text.

but it seems not unlikely that a sufficient number of trials would have produced a true breeding race, had we made them.

DISCUSSION

From relatively few initial crosses between two strongly differentiated species, *Delphinium hesperium* and *D. recurvatum*, we have obtained a series of hybrid individuals that so strongly resemble a third wild species that they can be differentiated from it only after careful detailed comparisons or not at all. The parental species are not only morphologically distinct; they occupy quite different environments and are associated with plant communities which themselves have long and different histories. They have doubtless been independent lines of evolution for a long period.

The species do not now grow within pollinating distance of each other, but because of the variable and changing landscape of the western cordillera during Cenozoic time, coupled with a fluctuating and changing climate, we find little reason to doubt that they may once have been in contact. Even today, being separated by only five miles at their closest point, the parental species are still doubtless within the range of seed transfer. We have no direct evidence that the seeds of either of these species will germinate within pollinating range of the other. We know from experiment, however, that this is possible with other species (Epling and Lewis, 1952). The terrain and habitats around most colonies are diverse and broken. One can surmise that a seed of one species might find lodgment in a tolerable habitat near a colony of the other even though the latter might occupy a very different environment. With a favorable season it might germinate and, given sufficient time and the protective trait of root dormancy, a series of hybrids might be formed and their seeds in turn might be transported to an environment in which natural selection might then develop a stable taxon. We can visualize the origin of *D. gypsophilum* in that way. No substantial reduction of fertility between it and its parents was required for its formation and the principal deterrents to present gene exchange are distance and habitat preference. Its formation was made possible, in fact, *because gene exchange between its parents was possible.*

We do not regard this process of rapid reticulate speciation as an isolated or unique event in *Delphinium*. The example described is one in which the process has reached a definitive stage and the derived species is a widespread integrated taxon. We are acquainted with what may have been its incipient stages by several examples of hybridization between other species that are similarly connectant (fig. 4).

D. parishii and *D. parryi,* for example, are two species as sharply defined as *D. hesperium* and *D. recurvatum.* The former chiefly inhabits communities found on the alluvial outwashes from the mountains that ring or are contained within the deserts of southern California and Arizona. The second is confined to the more arid aspects of the coastal vegetation of southern California, particularly the chaparral. The whole cycle of seasonal development is different in the communities in which each species finds its place. Because of variable topography and weather these communities frequently interdigitate and may produce fairly broad ecotones at some places. When they do so, *D. parishii* and *D. parryi* may be found in sufficiently close proximity to each other to exchange genes. We know of two areas, in Riverside and Ventura Counties, in which highly variable intermediate populations, or hybrid "swarms," indicate current or recent hybridization. In addition, we know of three areas in which uniform intermediate populations occur. The fact is of importance to our hypothesis that although these uniform populations are all derivatives of the same parental pair of species, they are measurably different from each other and recognizable. They represent three independent pools of interspecific recombination and resemble in different ways progeny we have obtained from hybridizing *D. parishii* and *D. parryi,* as well as individuals found in hybrid swarms elsewhere. Each occurs in an ecotone or marginal area, and their morphological uniformity shows that each has become fairly well stabilized. One is found in San Diego County in a small area along the Banner grade, east of Julian, where the chaparral is marginal to the Sonoran vegetation. This taxon has been formally described as *D. subglobosum* Wiggins. It resembles *D. parryi* more than *D. parishii.* It is a single population as far as we know. The second has a more extensive range at low elevations along the western margin of the Colorado desert in San Diego

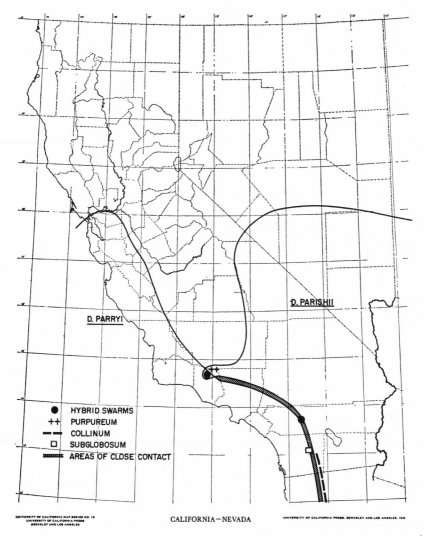

Fɪɢ. 4.   Approximate geographic ranges of *D. parryi* and *D. parishii,* together with the positions of the hybrid swarms and stabilized taxa referred to in the text.

County and adjacent Baja California. It has been described as *D. collinum* Ewan. It resembles *D. parishii* more than *D. parryi,* and occurs in a habitat which more closely resembles that of *D. parishii.* It grows associated with desert shrubs at the base of the mountains, particularly near the mouths of canyons, where large colonies are found intermittently for a distance of more than fifty miles. The third occurs in Cuddy and Lockwood Valleys in southern Kern and northern Ventura counties. Minor differences dis-

tinguish the colonies in Cuddy Valley from those in Lockwood Valley but both are morphologically more similar to *D. parishii* than to *D. parryi.* In both areas they are growing with sagebrush (*Artemisia tridentata sensu lato*) adjacent to pinon-juniper woodland.

For taxonomic convenience we have grouped these three stabilized intermediate populations under *D. parishii.* Those from San Diego County (*D. subglobosum* and *D. collinum*) we have referred to subsp. *subglobosum* and those from Kern and Ventura counties to subsp. *pur-pureum* (Lewis and Epling, 1954).

We believe that these hybrid swarms and stabilized intermediate populations between *D. parryi* and *D. parishii* may very well illustrate stages that occurred in the evolution of *D. gypsophilum*. The colony of *D. subglobosum* only rarely comes into flower and frequently does not even appear as rosettes. We were fortunate one year in getting a considerable series of transplants. They proved to be remarkably uniform. But the colony is very restricted and may not occur elsewhere. With expected changes in topography and climate, it may be extinguished; or should these changes (and the new plant associations that would follow) extend its habitat, it might then increase its range. *D. collinum* has apparently done this and, as we believe, *D. gypsophilum* also. The habitat of the latter is assuredly intermediate between those of the oak woodland and the saline playas in which its parents grow.

Few will doubt that the process we describe is one of evolution. New, well defined, and adaptively different taxa have been formed by hybridization without change of chromosome number and have multiplied and spread in newly evolving habitats. One might regard this process as a component of phyletic evolution (Simpson, 1944) because *Delphinium* and the closely related genus *Aconitum* represent a very ancient, distinct, and morphologically circumscribed phylad that has not greatly transcended certain environments of the northern hemisphere. So far as we can judge from crosses made by Professor G. A. L. Mehlquist and by us, interspecific fertility is commonly present in *Delphinium,* giving thus the possibility of repeatedly producing new taxa in nature of the sort we have described. These data, combined with our observations of natural populations, show clearly that interspecific sterility has not developed between many well defined and ancient taxa. The fact that interspecific hybridization can result in the formation of new species by amphiploidy is no longer novel. The importance of our data is to indicate that genetic recombination and a new synthesis may also come rapidly at the diploid level. The rapidity of the adaptive spread of a population of hybrid origin and its establishment and genetic integration as a species would depend on the then prevailing rates of environmental change, which might be either local or general.

Opinion may be less than unanimous that this process results in speciation, inasmuch as final barriers seem seldom to have arisen in *Delphinium*. By this criterion, *Delphinium* would appear to be a long continued anastomosing phylad within which species are approached but seldom realized. Nevertheless, well integrated and independent lines of evolution are formed that may persist for long periods without distintegration even though they may frequently be in contact and interfertile. We regard them as species.

We believe, therefore, that *Delphinium gypsophilum* has good claim to specific rank in spite of its interfertility with other members of its alliance, and that it was formed by interspecific hybridization without change of chromosome number, in the manner described.

SUMMARY

Delphinium gypsophilum is a well defined, wide spread species found at lower elevations in the foothills of the coastal and cross ranges that border the central valley of California. It is morphologically intermediate between two other widespread species and occupies a habitat that is geographically and ecologically intermediate. Evidence is discussed that suggests that *D. gypsophilum* had its origin by a rapid sequence of hybridizations and fixations of a limited number of hybrid genotypes, without change of chromosome number. Other evidence indicates that the process of reticulate anastomosing speciation represented by this example is a general attribute of *Delphinium,* because the barriers to interspecific gene exchanges are seldom absolute and are commonly moderate. Our criterion for speciation is the persistence for indefinite periods of well defined, recognizably stabilized taxa, even though they may frequently be in sufficient contact to exchange genes abundantly.

LITERATURE CITED

ANDERSON, E. 1949. Introgressive Hybridization. New York. Wiley & Sons, Inc.

EPLING, C. 1947. Actual and potential gene flow in natural populations. Am. Nat., 81: 104–113.

—— AND H. LEWIS. 1952. Increase of the adaptive range of the genus *Delphinium*. EVOLUTION, 6: 253–267.

LEWIS, H. 1947. Leaf variation in *Delphinium variegatum*. Bull. Torrey Bot. Club, 74: 57–59.

—— AND C. EPLING. 1946. Formation of a diploid species of *Delphinium* by hybridization. (Abstract). Amer. Jour. Bot., 33: 21s–22s.

—— AND ——. 1954. A taxonomic study of Californian delphiniums. Brittonia, 8: 1–22.

——, ——, G. A. L. MEHLQUIST AND C. G. WYCKOFF. 1951. Chromosome numbers in California Delphiniums and their geographical occurrence. Annals Mo. Bot. Gard., 38: 101–118.

MAERZ, A., AND M. R. PAUL. 1930. A Dictionary of Color. New York. McGraw Hill. 1st Edition.

MEHLQUIST, G. A. L., O. BLODGETT AND L. BRASCIA. 1943. Colchicine induced tetraploidy in *Delphinium cardinale*. Jour. Hered., 34: 187–192.

SIMPSON, G. G. 1944. Tempo and Mode in Evolution. New York. Columbia University Press.

STEBBINS, G. L., JR. 1950. Variation and Evolution in Plants. New York. Columbia University Press.

INTROGRESSION OF *SALVIA APIANA* AND *SALVIA MELLIFERA*

EDGAR ANDERSON
Missouri Botanical Garden and Washington University
AND BURTON R. ANDERSON

Salvia apiana and *Salvia mellifera* are two common species of sage in coastal California. Over much of their overlapping ranges they give little or no indication that they can (and frequently do) hybridize and that their hybrids are quite fertile. These significant facts were called to scientific attention by Epling. After monographing these and other Salvias taxonomically (Epling, 1938), he studied them experimentally in the field and in the breeding plot. He demonstrated (Epling, 1947) that they hybridize readily when artificially cross-pollinated and that the resulting hybrids are fertile enough to yield variable F-2's and back-crosses. Though these two species grow closely intermingled over thousands of square miles he found little evidence that hybridization did take place except under disturbed conditions. This he interpreted as due to a complex of internal and external barriers. One of the most important is the different adaptive mechanisms for insect pollination in the two species, *S. apiana* being pollinated largely by bumble bees and *S. mellifera* by small solitary bees.

The problem seemed such an interesting one that the senior author has studied it repeatedly and intensively in the field for somewhat over a decade and has used these two species as field and laboratory material for a summer school course. Population samples from critical areas were pickled for laboratory study, and with the help of the junior author an exhaustive analysis of variation in pubescence, calyx shape, corolla shape, and inflorescence branching was undertaken. This confirms and extends Epling's experimental and field studies. It analyzes a little more precisely the conditions under which the barriers break down between the two species. Thanks are due to Carl Epling, to Harlan Lewis, and to E. G. Anderson for assistance in making the collections.

In addition to the various facts collected by Epling, careful study of two quite different matters seemed necessary before we could interpret the hybridization dynamics of these two species: (1) a more complete morphological analysis of the two species and their intermediates; (2) a precise investigation of the disturbed habitats in which intermediates were common.

MORPHOLOGICAL ANALYSIS OF SPECIES DIFFERENCES

If one is effectively to analyze the variation pattern in populations where hybridization is known or suspected, the first *desideratum* is a thorough understanding of the nature of the differences between the hybridizing entities. *Salvia apiana* and *Salvia mellifera* are well-differentiated species, distinguishable at a glance, but if we are to use this difference as a yardstick in measuring what is happening in populations, we must refine our understanding of it to the point where we can distinguish *S. mellifera* with eight ancestors out of eight belonging to

or less on the contour) from the road up the Santa Anita Canyon. Less in-
field studies were carried on at several other locations. In this area the slope
mountains is prevailingly toward the south. It is so steep as to approximate
ch of a church roof, and the thin soil is stony with rock particles. As re-
by Epling, though the two species frequently grow intermingled, *Salvia*
showed a preference for the drier sites. Along the steepest and jutting ridges,
in almost pure stands, while in shadier and moister spots along sections of
il only *Salvia mellifera* was represented. The trail is one much used for
ional purposes and the vegetation along it has suffered repeated incursions
he public. Beer cans dot the landscape, particularly near the road. Half-
side-trails are common, and the shrubs and larger perennials bear the scars
ated vandalism. The site had been subject to disturbances for some decades,
flora as a whole was largely native. Out-and-out weeds were rare and the
(at first glance) did not seem to have mongrelized at all. There were no
t hybrids, and the casual impression was that for these two species one had
except typical specimens of *Salvia mellifera* and of *Salvia apiana*. The
pecies, to be sure, is extremely variable, but the variations all tend in the
n of *Salvia apiana* var. *compacta* (see below) and seemingly have nothing
ith *S. mellifera*.

er plant-by-plant inspection did not quite bear out this conclusion. In
he gullies, close to the point at which the path left the road, the vegetation
e scars of intensive vandalism. Here there were a number of plants of
era which varied more from plant to plant than is typical for this species.
examination demonstrates (see below) that this variation (in so far as it
rable) is all *in the direction of* S. apiana and presumably represents slight
ssion from that species. A meticulous examination of every plant along
indicated that introgression from *S. apiana*, so slight as scarcely to be
even to the experienced eye, had taken place at several points along the

ne point, however, there had been much introgression, and this area was
ntensively. There were a few plants obviously intermediate between the
ies, and others which were more or less like S. apiana or like S. mellifera
color patterns, growth habits, corolla shapes, and inflorescences which
rly atypical. It was not until the area had been repeatedly visited that it
vident that the hybrids and introgressants formed a compact population
to a distinct area, only one corner of which abutted on the trail.
from the first examination it was evident that this area was at the point
e trail came down the farthest from the mountain side, to a spot once
by oaks. Gradually it was realized that the variants were confined to a
ere some years ago the oaks had been cut and a small grove of olives had
ated. The olives had been abandoned but had continued to grow, and
getation had spread in around them. The upper corner of this area, which
ed by the trail, had been used repeatedly for camping and some of the

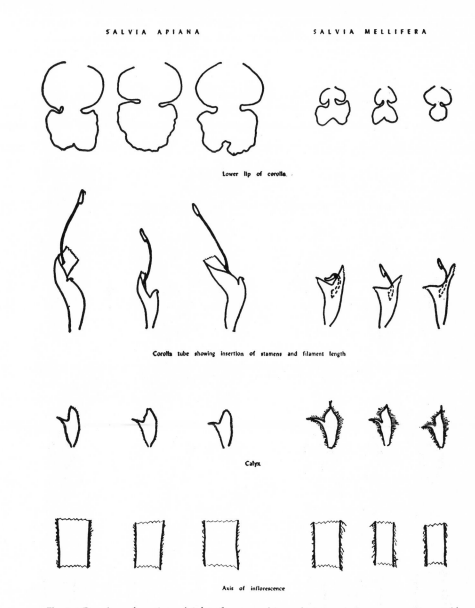

Fig. 1. Drawings of portions of *Salvia* flowers used in analyzing variation pattern. Comparable portions of three plants of *Salvia apiana* and three of *Salvia mellifera* were drawn to scale with camera lucida. Upper row ($\times$ 2); second row ($\times$ 2) showing filament lengths and position of stamen insertion in corolla tube; third row, calyx $\times$ 2), showing length of terminal spine and length of pubescence; bottom row ($\times$ 8), view from the side showing length and direction of pubescence.

INTERMEDIATE   SUB-MELLIFERA

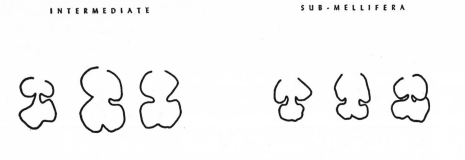

Lower lip of corolla

Corolla tube showing insertion of stamens and filament length

Calyx

Axis of inflorescence

Fig. 2. Camera lucida drawings of three hybrids and three plants of probable hybrid ancestry from the "Olives" population; same scale and same portions of the flower as in fig. 1. Note the intermediacy of the plants at the left compared to those in fig. 1. The plants to the right, when compared with the examples of S. *mellifera*, are typical of the variation pattern produced by introgression. Note that though all three are similar to normal S. *mellifera*, they are more variable, and their slight departures from the average are mostly *in the direction of S. apiana*.

---

that species, from a second back-cross seven of whose ance one from S. *apiana*. Species (and subspecies) characteristical a species difference seen as a whole is compounded of m 1954). Differences in proportion are more common than size, while differences in change of proportion with size are e Pubescence *patterns* are as important as pubescence and co portant as differences in color. One needs to define in as exa totality of this difference so that it can be used with precisior There are other Salvias in southern California besides S. *apia* need to understand the difference between S. *apiana* and S. that we can unhesitatingly distinguish between introgressic and introgression of either of them with S. *clevelandii*, for job well requires repeated and exhaustive examination. come with labels on them; as Linnaeus said long ago, "Th you find them." A slipshod examination of the difference better than a slipshod interpretation of the population dyna

The characters eventually used (see fig. 1) were as foll

(a) *The length of the lower lip of the corolla, measur meter.*—This is precisely the character used by Epling.

(b) *Point of insertion of the stamens.*—In S. *mellifera* on the corolla well inside the tube; in S. *apiana* well outsid scored in the following grades: well inside tube, barely in or tube.

(c) *Pubescence of calyx.*—Salvia *mellifera* has coarse l ticularly along the veins. The pubescence of S. *apiana* is so does not look like hairs at all, except under high magnificati longest hairs on the calyx was measured to the nearest milli

(d) *Length of terminal spines on calyx.*—The calyx l tipped with long weak spines; in S. *apiana* the spines are so invisible. This character was scored by measuring the spines lobes to the nearest millimeter.

(e) *Pubescence on the axis.*—Both S. *apiana* and S. *m* pubescence on the axis of the inflorescence. In S. *mellifer* downwards; in S. *apiana* they point upwards. They were grades: downward, outward, upward.

(f) *Length of filament*, measured to nearest millimeter.

FIELD STUDY

Hybridization between the two species was studied on San Gabriel Mountains above Arcadia, California. This sit not for any special features but because (for the laboratory was working) it was the closest spot at which the two Sal profusion. They were studied mainly along a footpath w

trees had been cut. It was in this doubly disturbed spot that most of the strangest-looking hybrids were found, but the entire area in among the abandoned olives, in so far as it had any Salvias, had nothing but atypical ones. Some of them were so grossly atypical as to be readily demonstrable as such in the pictorialized diagram (fig. 3) which takes account of only six measured characters. Some were so similar to *Salvia mellifera* that to demonstrate their introgressive origin would require careful scoring of such evanescent characters as flower color pattern and the angles at which the stamens are held.

ANALYSIS OF VARIATION

Collections were made from every plant abutting on the trail and from the area in among the olives. These were treated as two population samples, "path" and "olives." The data are presented as pictorialized scatter diagrams and as frequency distributions for a hybrid index based on these diagrams in figs. 3 and 4. Drawings to scale are shown in figs. 1 and 2 for a few representative plants. It will be seen that the population along the path is mostly composed of plants of the two species which show little or no indication of introgression but that a few of the *S. mellifera* showed slight introgression from *S. apiana*, about as much as we would expect in a second back-cross (i.e. in plants with seven ancestors from *S. mellifera* and one from *S. apiana*). The "Olives" population is clearly mongrel. Off-type plants are in the majority. Seen as a whole they represent the kind of criss-crossing recombinations of intermediate characters so typical of hybrid populations whether natural or artificial. In the area of the abandoned olive orchard such mongrels are clearly in the majority; had it been possible to score such characters as color pattern it would probably have been possible to demonstrate that they make up virtually the entire population.

DISCUSSION

This example of introgression between *S. apiana* and *S. mellifera* is in some ways the most illuminating of the numerous examples of hybridization in natural populations which have been reported in recent years. Let us summarize the main points. Two species easily hybridized in the experimental plot do not ordinarily hybridize in the field, though they grow intermingled over wide areas. However, in a strange habitat (or collection of strange habitats) adjacent to their natural range, hybrids and their mongrel descendants press in to the virtual exclusion of the parental species. There are several important inferences which can be drawn from this example. The abundance of hybrids in the field, once a habitat is provided in which they are at an advantage, demonstrates that there is no barrier (as such) to hybridization between these species. Hybrids are virtually absent, not because they are not being produced but because when they do occur there is no place for them. The association of which these two Salvias are a part has been through the sieve of natural selection. All kinds of species in it have been continuously selected for getting on with each other; they form a multi-dimensional

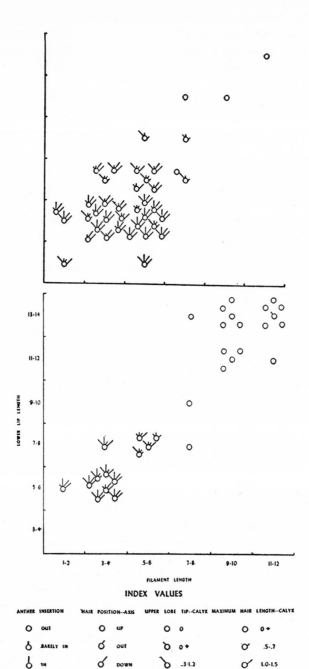

Fig. 3.   Pictorialized scatter diagrams of two populations of *Salvia*; above "Olives" population, below "Path" population.   Each circle illustrates a single plant.   Lengths of filament and of corolla are measured and diagrammed the same in both populations, though indicated only in the lower example.

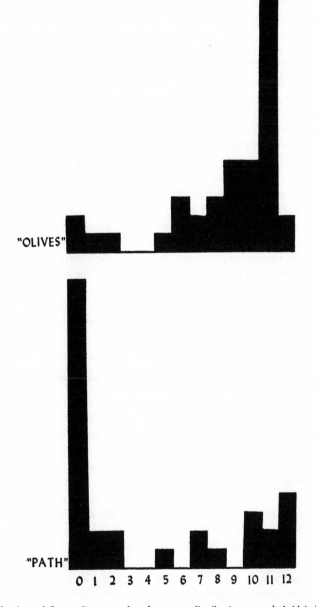

Fig. 4. The data of fig. 3, diagrammed as frequency distributions on a hybrid index which has values running from 0 for "good" *mellifera* to 12 for "good" *apiana*. Further explanation in the text.

jig-saw puzzle the pieces of which fit tightly together. There is no place in this closed association for an intermediate between any two species, or even for minor variants. It is not until a new ecological dominant, like man (Sauer, 1952), comes along and makes a set of radically new habitats that the hybrids can even demonstrate their presence readily. When this happens not only can they grow and persist but among their mongrel and variable descendants are various new recombinations, some of which are at a selective advantage in the relatively open associations produced by man.

By reference to only two of the most obvious physical variables, soil and sunshine, one can demonstrate what radically new habitats are presented by the olive orchard. Previously there had been dry sunny hillsides with pockets of soil, and shady oak woods with black woods soil. Cutting down the oaks and planting the olives produced pockets of sun, shade, and semi-shade on top of black woods soil. Planting out olives introduced an alien tree which, however, had been selected for such Mediterranean climates. On the other hand, the young trees were spaced out away from each other and from woody vegetation in a way quite unlike anything in the native woody flora. It was in these highly peculiar habitats that the variable progeny of the original hybrids had been at a selective advantage. Though we have no proof of the assumption, it seems likely that the hybrid progeny growing there are but a small and highly selected representation of the offspring originally seeded into the area.

It was Darlington (1939) who first pointed out clearly that the short-range and long-range effects of natural selection are almost diametrically opposed and that evolutionary systems which manage somehow to meet both these needs tend to be favored. The immediate need of the next generation is to conserve the adaptation already achieved. In a mature association this means producing offspring as much like the successful parent as possible. In such an association any surviving organism has fitted well into a particular niche; its offspring to succeed as well should have the same characteristics. The long-time need of the species, however, is for enough variability so that when changes arise in the physical and biological environment, the species is at length able to fit into a new niche, or even into new niches. Darlington pointed out how the side-by-side operation of apomictic and sexual reproductive systems in various plant genera allowed the successful individuals to produce, apomictically, offspring which were exact copies of the successful parent, though still retaining the capacity (by sexual reproduction) to produce variable descendants some few of which might be at a selective advantage in a changed or changing environment.

As more and more cases of introgressive hybridization have been analyzed, it has become increasingly clear that such genera as *Salvia* provide an almost ideal solution for this seemingly insoluble dilemma. It has been demonstrated repeatedly (and with increasing clarity) that hybrids and back-crosses are rare in natural populations not because of strong sexual barriers but because in mature associations of plants and animals which have evolved in each other's presence the whole association is closed. It is a complex interlocking system of mutually accommodating niches. Hybrids and back-crosses are absent not because they cannot arise but because when they do there is no place for them. Let man arrive and throw the whole association out of balance; let mammalian herbivores (as in New Zealand) be unleashed upon a vegetation with no previous experience of such beasts, and mongrel populations press into the new niches which have been created and themselves take part in building up a new interlocking system. Those genera, therefore, are at an over-all selective advantage which can build up complex barrier systems of exterior agents (in the wide sense) that protect the successful adaption from change so long as the association of which it is a part goes along its old ways, and yet can spawn hybrids and back-crosses in direct proportion to the breaking up of the old association. Genera with very strong internal barriers (such as complete hybrid sterility between well-differentiated taxa) would eventually perish under such changes and doubtless have.

SUMMARY

1. Introgression between *Salvia apiana* and *Salvia mellifera* (previously studied in the field and in the breeding plot by Epling) was studied intensively in the San Gabriel Mountains.

2. As previously noted by Epling, the two species, though highly interfertile, intergrade only slightly or not at all, even when growing intermingled over very wide areas.

3. Extensive introgression was discovered in a small localized area. It proved to be an abortive olive orchard established some years ago among live oaks adjacent to the mountain side where the Salvias were native. Among these olive trees hybrids and back-crosses between these two species grew in abundance and even formed the bulk of the population.

4. The evolutionary significance of these facts is briefly discussed.

BIBLIOGRAPHY

Anderson, E. (1954). Efficient and inefficient methods of measuring specific differences. Chapt. 6, in Kempthorne, O. et al. Statistics and Mathematics in Biology. Iowa State College Press. Ames, Iowa.

Darlington, C. D. (1939). The Evolution of Genetic Systems. Cambridge University Press.

Epling, Carl C. (1938). The Californian Salvias. A review of *Salvia*, Sect. *Audibertia*. Ann. Mo. Bot. Gard. 25:95–188.

————, (1947). Natural hybridization of *Salvia apiana* and *Salvia mellifera*. Evolution 1:69–78.

Sauer, Carl O. (1952). Agricultural origins and dispersals. Am. Geogr. Soc., Bowman Memorial Lectures Ser. II., New York.

MECHANICAL ISOLATION OF *SALVIA APIANA* AND *SALVIA MELLIFERA* (LABIATAE)

KAREN A. GRANT AND VERNE GRANT

Rancho Santa Ana Botanic Garden, Claremont, California

Accepted October 25, 1963

In recent years a number of cases have been described of plant species which grow together, bloom at the same time, are more or less interfertile, yet do not hybridize freely in nature because of mechanical isolation. Examples are found in such genera as Aquilegia, Sarcostemma, Penstemon, Mimulus, Pedicularis, Ophrys, and Stanhopea (these cases have been reviewed by Grant [1963, p. 355–359] and will be discussed in a later section of this paper). In each case the species involved possess complex floral mechanisms adapted to a relatively narrow range of different animal pollinators. These mechanical differences, operating at the stage of pollination, serve to partially or wholly exclude pollinators other than those to which each plant species is adapted (Grant, 1949, 1963).

Salvia apiana and *S. mellifera* (section Audibertia) are two closely related and widespread perennial species of sage in the California sage community. This pair of species, and the breeding relationships between them, have been studied by Epling (1947a, b) and by Anderson and Anderson (1954), and some aspects of the case are therefore well known to plant evolutionists now. Although the two interfertile species occur sympatrically over a wide area in southern California, natural hybridization is restricted by a combination of isolating mechanisms. However, heretofore, the part played by mechanical isolation in the separation of the two species has not been clarified. In particular, the role of the respective insect pollinators of *S. apiana* and *S. mellifera* in reproductive isolation has not been understood.

The purpose of the present paper is to describe the mechanical isolation existing between *S. apiana* and *S. mellifera* and some consequences of the habits of their insect pollinators. The present study based on observations of pollinators made since 1959 thus sheds new light on some aspects of the relationship between *S. apiana* and *S. mellifera*, as well as adding another case to the theory of mechanical isolation in angiosperms.

GENERAL RELATIONSHIPS BETWEEN *SALVIA APIANA* AND *SALVIA MELLIFERA*

Salvia mellifera and *S. apiana* occur sympatrically over a large portion of their respective distribution areas, as shown in fig. 1. In the area of their overlap in coastal southern California, they frequently grow side by side. In these areas of contact, ecological differences between the two species are slight, as judged by the many localities in which no apparent preference for habitat is exhibited. Earlier workers have emphasized the more xeric nature of *S. apiana*. Epling (1947a) noted, "When in contact, the colonies tend to border each other, or one may be enclosed by the other, *S. apiana* usually occurring on the drier sites."

Anderson and Anderson (1954) studied the two species on the lower slopes of the San Gabriel Mountains along the Santa Anita Canyon Road north of Arcadia. With regard to the ecological preferences of *S. apiana* and *S. mellifera* they stated: "In this area the slope of the mountains is prevailingly toward the south. It is so steep as to approximate the pitch of a church roof, and the thin soil is stony with rock particles. As reported by Epling, though the two species frequently grow intermingled, *Salvia apiana* showed a preference for the drier sites. Along the steepest

Reprinted by permission of V. Grant and the publisher from
EVOLUTION, **18**, 196–212 (1964).

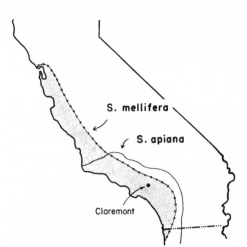

FIG. 1. Geographical distribution of *Salvia apiana* and *S. mellifera*. The present study was carried out in the Claremont area where the two species occur sympatrically. Redrawn from Epling (1947a).

and jutting ridges, it grew in almost pure stands, while in shadier and moister spots along sections of the trail only *Salvia mellifera* was represented."

The present authors studied the ecological relations of the two species in the San Gabriel Mountains north and northeast of Claremont. Here, there are many localities where both species grow side by side, and in such areas, ecological preferences of the two species are most difficult to determine. However, in these same mountains, we found that *S. apiana* attains its fullest populational development, to the virtual exclusion of *S. mellifera*, in the sandy soils of the washes and outwash plains, while *S. mellifera*, on the other hand, is best developed typically on the thin rocky soils of the steep, sunbaked slopes of the chaparral zone. On the lower slopes and at the base of the foothills there are few localities where one species may be found to the exclusion of the other. In this area, *S. apiana* and *S. mellifera* often grow intermingled or in adjacent colonies. Thus, although the two species have definite habitat preferences, their range of tolerance is widely overlapping, and in such areas of contact, ecological isolation is at best a weak barrier to natural hybridization.

Both *Salvia* species are perennial soft-wooded shrubby plants which die back to a certain extent in the winter and produce new growth in the spring, a life form shared by other plant species of the California sage community. *Salvia mellifera* is a densely branched subshrub with dark green leaves and typical mint flowers. Pale blue or lavender to white flowers are produced in dense capitate distantly placed whorls, forming an interrupted spike. *Salvia apiana* produces each spring erect branches clothed at the base with woolly whitish leaves and terminating in one to several panicled inflorescences. White to lavender flowers are situated in small branching clusters on either side of the main branch. The flowers of *S. apiana* are atypical of labiates in their corolla conformation, and are in a class by themselves in the genus.

The most definitive taxonomic characteristics separating *S. apiana* and *S. mellifera* are those of floral morphology (see Abrams, 1951), as is the usual case in plant species adapted to specialized modes of pollination by different animal pollinators (Grant, 1949). The gross differences in floral conformation exhibited by the two species are shown in fig. 2.

The species overlap in their blooming seasons, *S. mellifera* beginning to flower a month or so earlier than *S. apiana*, with both species in bloom simultaneously for a period of one to several weeks, though the exact times of initial bloom and duration of overlap vary with the locality and season (Epling, 1947a). Thus, in 1962 in the Claremont area, *S. mellifera* began to bloom in early April, *S. apiana* in early May, with an overlap in blooming seasons of a week or more. In 1963 in this same area, although the initial blooming dates of both species were several weeks later than in 1962, the sequence and pattern of overlap remained the same. Thus in 1963 as in 1962, *S. apiana* began to flower about a month later than *S. mellifera*, but the two species were in bloom together for a week or more.

Both species have the same chromosome

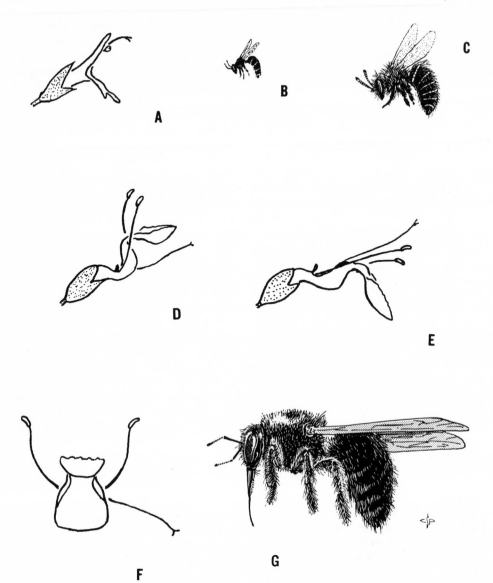

Fig. 2. The flowers of *Salvia mellifera* and *S. apiana*, and some typical insect pollinators of each plant species. All drawings × 2.

A. *Salvia mellifera.*

B. *Chloralictus* sp., a small-sized solitary bee which pollinates *S. mellifera.*

C. *Anthophora* sp., a medium-sized bee pollinator of *S. mellifera.*

D. *Salvia apiana* flower in untripped position.

E. Same, in tripped position.

F. Same, front view, in untripped position.

G. *Xylocopa brasilianorum*, a pollinator of *S. apiana.*

number ($n = 15$) and structurally similar genomes (Epling, Lewis, and Raven, 1962) and can be crossed readily in the experimental garden (Epling, 1947a). Epling (1947a) found that in nature, after open pollination, about 50% of the nutlets of the F_1 individuals developed, but in most cases the embryo shriveled and did not reach maturity. The proportion of viable seed was very low (ca. 2%) but these produced vigorous offspring. The second generation hybrids set a similar percentage of seed, of which about 30–40% was viable (Epling, 1947a).

Epling, Lewis, and Raven (1962) examined meiosis in three naturally occurring hybrids of *S. apiana* and *S. mellifera*. One individual, apparently an F_1, showed 15 chromosome pairs at first metaphase, but at anaphase a bridge and chromosome fragment appeared in a high proportion of the cells examined, evidencing heterozygosity for at least one paracentric inversion. These workers suggested that this inversion may be characteristic of the genomes of both parental species, as inversion heterozygotes had not been detected in either *S. apiana* or *S. mellifera* nor in any other species of the genus. The other two individuals examined had the phenotypic appearance of F_1's, but may have been later generation hybrids. However, neither of these plants gave evidence of inversions; one possessed an asynaptic chromosome pair, the other showed no meiotic irregularities. Epling et al. (1962) concluded that the genomes of the species pair are structurally very similar.

There is then evidence of an internal barrier to hybridization between *S. apiana* and *S. mellifera,* although this barrier seems to be relatively weak. We will have more to say about this question later in this paper.

In the areas where they grow intermingled, natural hybridization between *S. apiana* and *S. mellifera* is not infrequent (Epling, 1947a; Anderson and Anderson, 1954). The establishment of the hybrid forms, however, appears to be limited, in general, to areas of disturbed habitat, often of a man-made nature (Epling, 1947a; Anderson and Anderson, 1954). Epling (1947a) and Anderson and Anderson (1954) recognized the importance of the differently adapted floral mechanisms of *S. apiana* and *S. mellifera* as a barrier to hybridization. However, Anderson and Anderson (1954) emphasized the lack of suitable habitats in which the hybrids can grow as a restrictive factor to natural hybridization, concluding: "The abundance of hybrids in the field, once a habitat is provided in which they are at an advantage, demonstrates that there is no barrier (as such) to hybridization between these species. Hybrids are virtually absent, not because they are not being produced but because when they do occur there is no place for them."

Epling (1947a) analyzed a number of colonies of *S. mellifera*, both within the area of sympatry with *S. apiana* and in areas beyond the range of *S. apiana*, with regard to several floral and vegetative characteristics, to determine the influence of possible past hybridization with *S. apiana*. He found that *S. mellifera* showed no influence of contamination by *S. apiana* over any widespread area, and that the effect of natural hybridization between the two species was severely limited to the immediate site of hybridization.

The evidence accumulated by Epling (1947a) indicates that pollen dispersal is restricted within a short radius of the plants. He found that pure colonies of *S. mellifera* occurred only 0.2 miles on either side of a mixed colony of *S. mellifera* and *S. apiana* on Sunset Boulevard, Los Angeles. In addition, he found a mixed colony of *S. mellifera* and *S. apiana* in Topanga Canyon near Santa Monica. Progenies of ten *S. mellifera* individuals along a 100-yard transect leading away from *S. apiana* individuals were grown. Character analysis of these progenies indicated that the effects of hybridization were confined well within this distance.

Epling (1947a, b) concluded that de-

spite the potentiality for gene flow between
S. apiana and *S. mellifera*, the two species
are kept under equilibrium conditions of
competition in the community by a combination of factors—primarily by spatial,
ecological, seasonal, and mechanical isolation. The restriction of the effects of natural hybridization within a short radius of
the hybridizing individuals he attributed to
short-range dispersal of pollen and seed.

Other peculiarities in the pattern of
location and frequency of intermediate
forms were noted (Epling, 1947a). Although the hybrids generally observed
were judged to be probable F_1 individuals
(Epling, 1947a), hybrid swarms were also
found (Epling, 1947a; Anderson and Anderson, 1954). The intermediate forms
generally occurred in the vicinity of *S.
mellifera*, suggesting that pollen transfer
was a one-way affair with *S. mellifera* most
often functioning as the female parent
(Epling, 1947a). In addition, backcross
types in the direction of *S. mellifera* were
frequent, whereas those to *S. apiana* were
rare. Epling (1947a) interpreted the
greater similarity of the F_1 corolla form to
S. mellifera than to *S. apiana* as constituting a partial barrier to backcrossing with
the latter parent. Thus the habits of the
pollinating insects were implicated in a
number of ways.

With regard to the pollinators, Epling
(1947a) observed chiefly honeybees and
Bombus, and noted the improbability of *S.
apiana* being pollinated by any but the
larger bees; Anderson and Anderson (1954)
stated that *S. apiana* was largely pollinated
by bumblebees, *S. mellifera* being pollinated by small solitary bees.

THE PALMER CANYON COLONY

Sympatric populations of *Salvia apiana*
and *S. mellifera* and a number of hybrid
individuals were observed in Palmer Canyon in the spring of 1962. This mixed
stand is located in the chaparral on the
lower slopes of the San Gabriel Mountains
north of Claremont. The site is one of
man-made disturbances in habitat, in that

the hillside is cut by the Palmer Canyon
Road, and the native live oaks above the
road have largely been replaced by a now-
abandoned olive grove. *Salvia mellifera*
occurred, for the most part, on the sharply
descending slopes below the road and along
the roadside. A few plants grew above the
road. *Salvia apiana* grew intermixed with
S. mellifera below the road and above the
road and within the olive grove. The intermediate forms, or presumed hybrid
types, were confined to the roadside and
the olive grove, in a fashion similar to the
introgressive variants described by Anderson and Anderson (1954) in an olive grove
in Santa Anita Canyon farther west. Most
of the intermediates grew along the lower
side of the road; a few occurred on the
bank of the upper side of the roadcut, but
a single hybrid individual grew in the olive
grove within a stand of *S. apiana*.

In 1962 *S. mellifera* in Palmer Canyon
began to bloom the first week of April,
reaching full bloom the third week in April.
Salvia apiana began to bloom the second
week of May, when *S. mellifera* was de-
clining in bloom, and reached its peak
about the first of June. The hybrid individuals varied greatly among themselves
in date of initial bloom, but considered
together were intermediate between the
parental species in blooming season, as also
noted by Epling (1947a) for F_1 plants.
The first date of bloom of the hybrids occurred in the last week of April, which was
the time of full bloom of *S. mellifera*, and
peak of bloom of the hybrids occurred in
mid-May, when *S. apiana* was beginning to
flower. The blooming seasons of *S. mellifera* and *S. apiana* thus overlapped by a
week or more. Fig. 3 shows the blooming
seasons of the two species and their intermediates.

Most of the *S. mellifera* individuals were
observed to commence flowering within a
short time of one another, as noted by
Epling (1947a). Much variation in initial
date of bloom was observed for the intermediate forms, as noted above, and for
individual plants of *S. apiana*. The latter

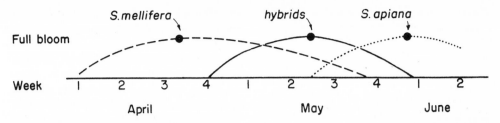

Fig. 3. The time and duration of the blooming periods of *Salvia mellifera*, *S. apiana*, and their intermediates in the Palmer Canyon colony, 1962.

was also extremely variable among colonies in time of first bloom, even when these were very close together and at comparable elevations.

The hybrid forms were intermediate between the parental species in both vegetative and floral characteristics, as described by Epling (1947a). The leaves were more similar to *S. mellifera* in shape, but intermediate in color. The influence of *S. apiana* was apparent in the increased number of whorls and in the tendency of the flowers to be clustered on either side of the main shoot. Corolla conformation was, in general, intermediate between that of *S. apiana* and *S. mellifera*. Thus, the upper lip appeared shortened and the lower lip extended and sometimes contorted, as compared with *S. mellifera*. Both stamens and style were elongated, as compared with *S. mellifera*, but the style was not deflexed to one side of the corolla as in *S. apiana*.

The intermediate forms were construed to be, for the most part, F_1's and backcross types in the direction of *S. mellifera*. However, the single hybrid individual growing in the olive grove was judged to be a backcross type to *S. apiana*. As stated above, this plant grew within a stand of *S. apiana*, *S. mellifera* being absent in the immediate vicinity, and was intermediate between the parental species in date of first bloom.

Pollen samples were collected from seven hybrid individuals, stained with aniline blue, and counted as to number of well-stained and presumably viable grains. The pollen fertility of the intermediate forms proved considerably lower than the 99% count obtained from a *S. mellifera* individual in the Cobal Canyon colony, a

locality where no intermediates occurred. The percentage of good pollen from each hybrid individual sampled was as follows: 96, 88, 87, 75, 72, 72, and 68. The three highest percentages correspond to individuals judged to be backcross types to *S. mellifera*. However, one of these plants bore mostly flowers with abortive anthers; hence its 88% pollen fertility is misleading. The pollen fertilities in the lower range are from probable F_1 individuals.

No observations on seed set of the hybrids was made, as the entire area was burnt in a brush fire in August, 1962. However, dispersal of hybrid individuals within any but a narrow radius via seed transport seems improbable. No specialized mechanism for seed disbursement is present in either species. Rather, desiccation of the capsule and wind appear to gradually dislodge the seed, which then must drop very close to the parent plant. Plants of *S. apiana* in Claremont retained a great many seed in December, 1962, and seed was still to be found within the capsules the following March.

In the spring of 1963, a single intermediate individual, apparently an F_1, was found growing in another mixed stand of *S. apiana* and *S. mellifera* in Padua Hills several hundred feet from the site of the Palmer Canyon stand and adjacent to the burn of the previous year. A narrow footpath ran between this colony and the burnt area, the F_1 individual growing alongside the path. Both *S. apiana* and *S. mellifera* grew adjacent to the hybrid plant. The pollen fertility of this probable F_1 individual was 80%.

The relatively high pollen fertility of

TABLE 1. *Seed set on a hybrid of* Salvia apiana × S. mellifera *under various conditions of pollination. Further explanation in text*

	No. of capsules counted	Total no. of seed	Average no. of seed per capsule
S. mellifera, open pollination	20	69	3.45
S. apiana, open pollination	20	68	3.40
F₁, open pollination	20	28	1.40
F₁ ♀ × S. mellifera ♂, artificial pollination	22	48	2.18
F₁ ♀ × S. apiana ♂, artificial pollination	17	34	2.00

presumed F₁ hybrids, in the range of 68 to 80%, stands in marked contrast to the rather low seed fertility of 2% reported by Epling (1947a) for open pollinated plants. This apparent discrepancy between pollen fertility and the seed fertility of open pollinated hybrids raised the question whether the seed set might be reduced by lack of pollination in addition to hybrid sterility.

Honeybees were frequent visitors to the flowers of the hybrid plant in Padua Hills, but were not observed to contact anthers and stigma while feeding. A number of test crosses were then made with this F₁ hybrid serving as the maternal parent, to determine whether the low seed set is a result of sterility or failure of pollination or both. Twenty-two flowers of the F₁ were emasculated and the stigmas heavily dusted with pollen of S. mellifera. A similar number of flowers were emasculated and dusted with pollen of S. apiana. The number of seeds per capsule produced by each species and by the F₁ individual after open pollination were counted and compared with the seed set produced by the above crosses.

As shown in table 1, the average seed set per capsule resulting from the artificial crosses F₁ ♀ × S. mellifera ♂ and F₁ ♀ × S. apiana ♂ was less than that obtained from either parental species after open pollination, but greater than that obtained from the F₁ after open pollination. Thus, lack of pollination of F₁ hybrids is indicated as a factor in their low observed seed

set following open pollination, but is not the only factor involved.

Hybrid inviability is also indicated as an internal barrier to hybridization. Embryo development was examined in a small sample of the seed resulting from each of the artificial crosses involving the F₁ individual, and from the F₁, S. mellifera, and S. apiana after open pollination. The seed from both parental species contained fully developed normal embryos. Seed produced by the F₁ after open pollination and following the artificial crosses with both parental species possessed shriveled embryos.

Thus, both failure of pollination of F₁ hybrids and hybrid inviability are involved in the low number of viable seeds produced by hybrid plants. However, controlled hybridization experiments are needed for a more precise determination of the nature of the internal barrier to hybridization.

POLLINATION

Observations of the pollinators of *Salvia apiana* and *S. mellifera* were made at a number of colonies in the Claremont area throughout the spring seasons of 1961, 1962, and 1963.

As mentioned previously, and shown in fig. 2, the corolla form of *S. mellifera* is that of a typical labiate flower. The upper lip of the corolla is long and somewhat laterally recurved at the tip, the lower lip projecting downwards. The diameter of the entrance to the floral chamber is about 2 mm across and 3 mm high. The corolla tube, measured from its base to the cleft of the upper and lower corolla lips, is 5–8 mm long.

The two stamens are inserted in the corolla throat and appressed to the upper lip, the anthers included within the lip or exserted slightly beyond it. The style lies between and behind the stamens, placing the stigma slightly higher than the anthers (about 12 mm from the base of the corolla tube). The flowers are markedly protandrous, the anthers ripening and shedding pollen before the style attains its full length. Only as the anthers shrivel does the style elongate and the stigma become receptive; the stigma may remain receptive even as the corolla shrivels and turns brown.

On a warm sunny day when *S. mellifera* is in full bloom, the fragrance of the flowers and leaves permeates the air, and many insects may be seen about the flowers. Casual visitors (Nitidulidae, Coccinellidae, Raphidiidae, and various Lepidoptera and Hemiptera) may be observed both on the flowers and foliage, as well as insect pollinators.

The insect pollinators generally alight on the whorl of flowers or on the lower corolla lip, and then thrust their proboscides into the nectar chamber, or crawl into the flowers in search of nectar and pollen. Pollen may be dusted on their heads and backs, or adhere to the hairs of their legs, depending on the size and type of insect visitor. Subesequent visits to other flowers may result in pollination when the region of the insect's body carrying the pollen contacts a receptive stigma.

The most frequently observed insect visitors to *S. mellifera* are the introduced honeybees, which undoubtedly account for much pollination of this species in this area. Native solitary bees of a similar size, which are both frequent visitors and effective pollinators include *Anthophora* sp., *Diadasia* sp., and *Osmia* sp. These insects are of a size such that they are able to force only their heads into the corolla tube. Their proboscis lengths (4–5 mm) are well suited for obtaining nectar from *S. mellifera*. These insects carried a heavy dusting of *S. mellifera* pollen about the head region.

Infrequently observed visitors to *S. mellifera* in this same size category include *Evylaeus* sp., *Melecta* (subgen. *Melectomorpha*) sp., and *Ceratina* sp., all of which are probably effective as pollinators.

Small-sized solitary bees which crawl in and among the flowers include *Ceratina arizonensis, Halictus* (subgen. *Seladonia*) sp., *Chloralictus* sp., and *Dialictus* sp. These insects are all effective pollinators of *S. mellifera,* and carried pollen of this species on the hairs of their ventral and dorsal surfaces and on their legs.

Dr. Charles D. Michener informs us (personal communication) that *Ashmeadiella salviae,* a small-sized bee, probably obtains all of its pollen from *S. mellifera.* Although the present authors did not collect this bee on *S. mellifera* in the Claremont area, Dr. Michener did find it on this species in Altadena (Los Angeles County) and other localities.

Fig. 2 shows the corolla conformation of the flowers of *S. mellifera* and small- and medium-sized solitary bees which pollinate it.

Xylocopa tabaniformis and *Bombus vosnesenskii*, both large-sized bees, were seen on rare occasions to visit *S. mellifera.* Although these bees can effectively pollinate *S. mellifera,* they infrequently visit that species and thus are not significant as pollinators.

Among the flies which visit *S. mellifera,* two species of *Bombylius* are both frequent visitors and effective pollinators, carrying pollen on their heads and about their mouths. Syrhpid flies of various kinds are very frequent visitors to *S. mellifera,* especially early in the season and in the cooler parts of the mornings. However, *Eristalis tenax,* which carried a heavy dusting of pollen on the hairs of its body, is the only syrphid judged to be an effective pollinator of *S. mellifera.*

Various species of Lepidoptera were on occasion seen to visit the flowers of *S. mellifera.* Although these insects carry a small quantity of pollen on their proboscides, they are probably not of great significance as pollinators, being both sporadic and not greatly effective.

Other insects which visit the flowers of *S. mellifera* but are ineffective as pollinators include wasps (Sphecidae, Ichneumonidae), beetles (Nitidulidae, Coccinellidae), and Hemiptera.

The Anna hummingbird (*Calypte anna*) often visits *S. mellifera* to obtain nectar. One bird was observed to feed on more than 40 flowers of a single plant in rapid succession. It is probable that some pollination of *S. mellifera* is brought about by hummingbirds, as the anthers and stigma are in a position where they can contact the bird's bill.

The flower visitors and pollinators of *S. mellifera* are listed in table 2 and annotated according to the frequency of their visits and their effectiveness as pollinators. Although not noted in the table, certain insect pollinators of *S. mellifera* were observed in one year only. This inconsistency is probably a result of the observations having been made at different localities in different years; in 1961 a number of colonies in the Claremont area were observed; in 1962 observations were concentrated on the Palmer Canyon colony; and in 1963 observations were conducted, for the most part, at the Padua Hills colony.

Salvia apiana, on the other hand, differs greatly from *S. mellifera* in both floral morphology and flora mechanism. Each spring *S. apiana* produces long, erect flowering shoots which project several feet above the leafy portion of the plant. Pale lavender to white flowers are produced in clusters at either side of the inflorescence axis.

The corolla form of *S. apiana* is strikingly different from that of *S. mellifera* and other labiates, as shown in fig. 2. The upper corolla lip is so reduced as to appear as a small lobe, whereas the lower corolla lip is very long and much folded, obstructing the entrance to the corolla chamber. Two long (14–17 mm), erect stamens protrude at a divergent angle from their insertion on the lower lip. The style protrudes 13–15 mm beyond the lower lip and is sharply deflexed to one or the other side of

TABLE 2. *Insects and birds observed visiting and pollinating the flowers of* Salvia mellifera *and* Salvia apiana *during the blooming seasons of 1961–1963*

The following list is based on observations of several colonies of *S. apiana* and *S. mellifera* in the Claremont area and on the lower slopes of the San Gabriel Mountains north of Claremont. Visitors and pollinators are annotated according to observed frequency of visits and efficacy in pollination. All pollinators and frequent visitors to the flowers are included; infrequent incidental visitors judged to be ineffective as pollinators are omitted. The insects collected during the present study are preserved at the Rancho Santa Ana Botanic Garden.

Pollinators and visitors	Frequency of visits	Effectiveness as pollinators
I. *Salvia mellifera*		
BEES		
Halictidae		
Halictus (subgen. *Seladonia*) sp.	occasional	effective
Evylaeus sp.	occasional	effective
Dialictus sp.	frequent	effective
Chloralictus sp.	frequent	effective
Megachilidae		
Osmia sp.	frequent	effective
Apidae		
Anthophorinae		
Anthophora sp.	frequent	effective
Diadasia sp.	frequent	effective
Melecta (subgen. *Melectomorpha*) sp.	rare	effective
Xylocopinae		
Ceratina arizonensis	frequent	effective
Ceratina sp.	occasional	effective
Xylocopa tabaniformis	rare	effective
Apinae		
Bombus vosnesenskii	rare	effective
Apis mellifera	frequent	effective
BEETLES		
Nitidulidae		
Carpophilus pallipennis	frequent	ineffective

TABLE 2. (*Continued*)

Pollinators and visitors	Frequency of visits	Effectiveness as pollinators
FLIES		
Syrphidae		
Syrphus sp.	frequent	ineffective
Eristalis tenax	frequent	effective
Volucella esuriens	frequent	ineffective
Bombyliidae		
Bombylius, 2 spp.	frequent	effective
BUTTERFLIES AND MOTHS		
Nymphalidae		
Vanesa carye	occasional	somewhat effective
Euphydryas chalcedona	occasional	somewhat effective
Riodinidae		
Apodemia morino virgulti	occasional	somewhat effective
Lycaenidae		
Glaucopsyche lydamus australis	occasional	somewhat effective
Pieridae		
Pieris rapae	rare	somewhat effective
Noctuidae		
Autographa californica	rare	somewhat effective
HUMMINGBIRDS		
Trochilidae		
Calypte anna	frequent	probably effective
II. *Salvia apiana*		
BEES		
Apidae		
Xylocopinae		
Xylocopa tabaniformis	frequent	effective
Xylocopa californica	rare	effective
Xylocopa brasilianorum	frequent	effective
Apinae		
Bombus vosnesenskii	occasional	effective
Apis mellifera	frequent	ineffective
HUMMINGBIRDS		
Trochilidae		
Calypte anna	frequent	probably ineffective

the corolla. The corolla tube is 6–8 mm long. The flowers of *S. apiana* are protandrous, but to a less degree than those of *S. mellifera*. The stigma becomes receptive while the pollen is still being shed, and remains receptive for a period after the shriveling of the anthers.

The grotesque appearance of the *S. apiana* flowers is yet more enigmatic when considered from the standpoint of pollinators. What type of insect is capable of pollinating these strangely formed flowers with their extremely long stamens and style and widely spread anthers and stigma? On closer examination it becomes apparent that the floral mechanism involves a trigger action. When pressure is brought to bear on the lower corolla lip, the entire lip unfolds, permitting free entrance to the corolla chamber. Concomitantly, the stamens, being inserted on the lower lip, move downward and inward, and the style undergoes a similar movement. It is evident that only a very large insect would have sufficient body weight to trip this floral mechanism.

In 1959 in San Antonio Canyon, San Gabriel Mountains, one of the present authors (V. G.) observed carpenter bees (Xylocopa) working the flowers of *S. apiana*. Later observations indicate that in the Claremont area and in the San Gabriel Mountains north of Claremont, *S. apiana* is chiefly pollinated by three species of carpenter bees (*Xylocopa brasilianorum*,

X. tabaniformis, and *X. californica*), and on occasion by *Bombus vosnesenskii*.

The outer lobe of the lower corolla lip serves as a landing platform on which the bees alight. Tripping of the floral mechanism is effected by the weight of the bee, and the downward and inward movement of the stamens and style place the anthers and stigma in a position where they readily contact the wing region and the sides of the body of the feeding insect. Thus, pollen is dusted and transported mainly on the wings and about the bases of the wings, and on the outer sides of the legs of the insect visitors. Subsequent visits to other plants and contact of the body parts carrying pollen with the stigma bring about cross-pollination. Examination of the large bees captured while feeding on *S. apiana* revealed a heavy dusting of pollen of that species on the lower cells of the wings and on the hairs about the wing bases and legs, and scattered on the back of the head.

Successful pollinators of *S. apiana*, must, then, first be of sufficient weight to trip the floral mechanism. Secondly, as a correlate, they must be of large enough body size to contact anthers and stigma when the flower is in a tripped position (see fig. 2). The three species of Xylocopa and *Bombus vosnesenskii* meet these requirements.

The two most frequently observed pollinators of *S. apiana* were weighed soon after being captured. Their fresh weights were: *Xylocopa brasilianorum*, 840 mg, and *X. tabaniformis*, 360 mg.

Apis mellifera, although a frequent visitor to *S. apiana*, is unsuccessful as a pollinator of that species because its body weight (92 mg, an average of the weights of 5 fresh specimens) is insufficient to trip the floral mechanism. Some of the honeybees investigated the flowers, but were unsuccessful in their attempts to obtain nectar and soon flew away. Others had learned to gain illegitimate entry into the floral chamber, most often by alighting on the landing platform, hind end towards the corolla tube, and then turning upside down

to force their proboscis and most of their body into the floral chamber. When their movements were such as to cause a slight inward movement of the stamens and style, the insects were often seen to grasp a stamen or style with a hind leg in an apparent effort to hold it down and out of the way. Anthers and stigma, however, were yet held too far out to contact the body of the bee. Only when a bee virtually crawled up the stamen did it receive a dusting of pollen. It is doubtful that any pollination whatsoever is effected by honeybees in their visits to *S. apiana*. The same may be said with regard to other small solitary bees which on rare occasions were seen to investigate the flowers of this species, and which of course are even lighter in weight than *Apis*.

In comparison with the great number of insects attracted to *S. mellifera*, insect activity on *S. apiana* is slight. *Salvia mellifera* has a heavy, permeating fragrance; *S. apiana* is but slightly fragrant. When in full bloom, insects swarm about *S. mellifera*. *Salvia apiana*, on the other hand, was often completely devoid of insect activity when in full bloom. On other occasions, large numbers of honeybees were observed visiting the flowers. Other than honeybees, the most frequently observed visitors to *S. apiana* were the carpenter bees. These pollinators, however, were never seen feeding on the flowers of *S. apiana* in any high frequency, as compared with the feeding activity of the pollinators of *S. mellifera*. An indication of the frequency of their visits is given by the fact that in many hours of observation, never more than a single carpenter bee was seen working an individual plant of *S. apiana* at any one time, and on many occasions no insect pollinators were seen at all.

Dawson (1923, vol. 2, p. 950) reported that the Costa hummingbird was a frequent visitor to *S. apiana* in desert and chaparral regions, feeding on the flowers as well as gathering leafy bracts of the plants for nest building. In the Claremont area, *S. apiana* is regularly visited by the Anna hummingbird and is probably visited by the Costa hummingbird. The bird has no apparent difficulty in thrusting its beak into the corolla tube, and may be seen visiting flower after flower on one or several individual plants in a single flight. Pollination by hummingbirds seems improbable, however, for even if the bird were to receive pollen about its beak and head, contact with the deflexed stigma is unlikely.

A list of the visitors and pollinators of *S. apiana* appears in table 2.

Since each species of *Salvia* has its array of native pollinators and the insects which regularly visit one species wander only rarely to the other, interspecific pollinations are rare. When these do occur, they are apparently brought about by the normal pollinators of *S. apiana* visiting *S. mellifera*. On several occasions *Bombus vosnesenskii* and *Xylocopa tabaniformis* were seen feeding on *S. mellifera*. Examination of specimens captured while feeding on *S. mellifera* revealed a heavy dusting of pollen on their heads. Head pollination probably occurs in the transfer of *S. apiana* pollen to *S. mellifera*, as these insects receive some pollen on the head region in their visits to *S. apiana*, and contact the anthers and stigma of *S. mellifera* with their heads. As *Bombus vosnesenskii* was seen to visit *S. apiana*, and *Xylocopa tabaniformis* was a frequently observed pollinator of *S. apiana*, it is reasonable to conclude that these insects are responsible, at least in part, for the interspecific pollinations of *S. apiana* and *S. mellifera*. And the fact that *Xylocopa tabaniformis*, at least, is a regular visitor to *S. apiana*, but only occasionally visits *S. mellifera*, suggests that pollen is more often transferred from *S. apiana* to *S. mellifera* than vice versa. This, in turn, would explain the preponderance of instances in which *S. mellifera* serves as the maternal parent in interspecific crosses.

Although the role of ethological isolation in the separation of the two *Salvia* species cannot be stated quantitatively, the behavior of the pollinating insects strongly suggests that ethological as well as mechanical isolation is involved. The carpenter bees, as already mentioned, regularly visit *S. apiana*, but only rarely wander to *S. mellifera*. The normal pollinators of *S. mellifera* (with the exception of honeybees) are still more rarely seen to visit *S. apiana*, and when they do they are unable to obtain nectar. The relatively short duration of overlap in blooming seasons of the two species further reduces the chance of interspecific pollinations. If, however, pollen *is* carried by insects from one species to the other, it is generally from *S. apiana* to *S. mellifera*; and pollination *may or may not* be effected when these insects visit *S. mellifera*. Interspecific pollinations must occur, under normal conditions in nature, at a very low frequency.

Observations of the pollination of the intermediate forms were made in the Palmer Canyon colony in 1962 and in the Padua Hills colony in 1963. The backcross types in the direction of *S. mellifera*, which closely resemble that species in corolla conformation, were regularly visited and pollinated by the normal pollinators of *S. mellifera*. However, little insect activity was evident on the F_1 individuals, the insects working for the most part on the still-flowering *S. mellifera*. The insect visitors to the F_1 plants were among the normal visitors and pollinators of *S. mellifera*, namely, *Apis mellifera*, *Anthophora* sp., *Diadasia* sp., *Bombylius* sp., *Syrphus* sp., and *Eristalis tenax*.

Successful pollination of the hybrids depends to a large extent on the relative position of the style and stamens in any particular individual. In many of the hybrids, the intermediate nature of the corolla conformation places the anthers and stigma in a position mostly inaccessible to the insects which were observed visiting them. The hybrid corolla lacks the folded lower corolla lip which provides a trigger mechanism in the *S. apiana* parent. Stamens and style are intermediate in length, but similar to *S. mellifera* in their position relative to the corolla tube. Thus, in many of the hybrid flowers, the excessive length places anthers and stigma too far out to regularly contact the body of the observed insect visitors. The corolla conformation of one hybrid individual, judged on phenotypic appearance to be an F_1, will suffice as an example of a floral form ill-adapted to pollination by the insects which visit it. The flowers of this individual had widely spread stamens of an intermediate length inserted on the lower corolla lip as in *S. apiana*. The style was longer than the stamens, but not deflexed to one side. The lower corolla lip was longer than that of *S. mellifera*, but not folded as in *S. apiana*. Thus no trigger mechanism was present. Honeybees were observed to alight on the lower corolla lip and feed, without contacting either anthers or stigma—both being held above the body of the feeding insect. Insect visitors did, however, pick up some pollen from other hybrid individuals.

None of the insects visiting the hybrid forms, other than *Apis mellifera*, were seen to visit *S. apiana*. Although *Apis mellifera* is a frequent visitor to *S. apiana*, it is unsuccessful as a pollinator of that species, and therefore, if *Apis mellifera* carries pollen of the hybrid forms to either parental species, effective pollinations would occur only with *S. mellifera*. The high frequency of backcross types to *S. mellifera* and the disproportionate lack of backcross types to *S. apiana* can be explained as a result of visitation of *S. mellifera* and the intermediate forms by the same insects.

The insects responsible for the rare backcrosses in the other direction, that is, to *S. apiana*, are yet unknown. Presumably, only one of the large pollinators of *S. apiana* could successfully transfer hybrid pollen to the stigma of that species. Either *Bombus vosnesenskii* or *Xylocopa tabaniformis*, both of which were seen to visit *S. mellifera*, or another of the large pollinators of *S. apiana*, may on rare occasion, backcross the hybrid forms to *S. apiana*.

The Anna hummingbird was seen to visit both *S. mellifera* and *S. apiana*, and also the backcross types to *S. mellifera*. It is

possible that hummingbirds effect pollinations bewteen *S. mellifera* and *S. mellifera*-like intermediates. But *Calypte anna* is an improbable agent of interspecific pollinations, on the basis of its probable inability to pollinate *S. apiana*, as noted earlier.

DISCUSSION

Salvia apiana and *S. mellifera* provide another instance of plant species which grow together, bloom at the same time, are more or less interfertile, but do not hybridize to any great extent in nature. The pair of species is mechanically isolated; *S. apiana* is adapted to pollination by large carpenter bees and bumblebees, whereas *S. mellifera* is pollinated by smaller-sized solitary bees and by beeflies and certain syrphids.

Although the two species have floral forms adapted to different sets of insect pollinators, some of the pollinators of *S. apiana* are not incapable of pollinating *S. mellifera*. That they do not do so more frequently suggests that ethological isolation may also be involved. The floral characters of the two species may play a role in inducing the insect pollinators to visit chiefly the species which they normally pollinate. The pollinators of *S. apiana* very rarely wander to *S. mellifera*, and those of *S. mellifera* (with the exception of *Apis mellifera*) are even more rarely seen on *S. apiana*. Interspecific pollinations are accordingly an exceptional event.

It is perhaps desirable at this point to clarify the usage of "mechanical isolation" and "ethological isolation" in the present paper. We are following here the system of classification of floral isolating mechanisms into mechanical and ethological components proposed by Grant (1949). That earlier discussion was in turn an attempt to relate the phenomena of floral isolation in the angiosperms to the previously analyzed phenomena of mechanical and ethological isolation in the animal kingdom as treated by Dobzhansky, Mayr, and other authors.

Mechanical isolation can be said to occur in flowering plants when interspecific pollinations are prevented primarily by structural differences of the flowers. Ethological isolation is involved when interspecific pollinations do not occur due to the constancy of the pollinators to one species of flower. In the latter case, recognition signals presented by the plants—scent, color, and distinctive form of the flowers—induce flower-visiting behavior by the pollinators such as to oppose the transfer of pollen from one plant species to the other. The floral isolation of *Salvia apiana* and *S. mellifera* appears to be primarily mechanical, although ethological factors are also involved.

The seasonal differences in the blooming periods of the two species may also be a component of the character complex adapting the two species to different classes of pollinators. *Salvia mellifera* blooms in early spring, and the flowering period of this species is coordinated with the early season activity of the small- and moderate-sized native solitary bees which visit it. *Salvia apiana*, on the other hand, begins to bloom in late spring and flowers through early summer, and its blooming period coincides with the flight period of the carpenter bees which pollinate it. Xylocopa is a tropical group of bees, and its representatives in the Claremont area are active during the warm season from late spring to early fall. The periods of activity of the two groups of bees overlap in late spring, as do the blooming seasons of *S. mellifera* and *S. apiana*.

However, once hybridization between *S. apiana* and *S. mellifera* has taken place, the seasonal isolation between the two species breaks down to some extent. As the backcross types in the direction of *S. mellifera* begin to bloom several weeks later than the pure *S. mellifera* individuals, the period of overlap in blooming seasons between these backcross types and *S. apiana* is extended by several weeks. Thus a greater opportunity for interspecific pollinations is present. This partial breakdown

in the seasonal isolation between the two *Salvia* species would be expected to counterbalance the factors restricting hybridization between them.

Mechanical isolation has been recorded in a number of other plant families. In the Asclepiadaceae, Robertson in 1887 reported pollination of three species of *Asclepias* (*A. sullivantii, A. verticillata*, and *A. longifolia*) by the same bumblebees. However, different body parts of the bumblebees pick up pollen and touch the stigmatic chambers in the different *Asclepias* species (see Holm, 1950). In Mexico, various sympatric species of *Sarcostemma* are apparently also mechanically isolated (Holm, 1950).

In the Ranunculaceae, Grant (1952) described mechanical isolation between *Aquilegia formosa* and *A. pubescens* in the Sierra Nevada of California. *Aquilegia formosa* is a pendant red-flowered columbine pollinated by hummingbirds, *A. pubescens* is pale yellow and erect and pollinated largely by hawkmoths.

Several cases of mechanical isolation have been described in the family Scrophulariaceae. *Mimulus cardinalis* and *M. lewisii* occur sympatrically in the Yosemite Valley region of California, and are, respectively, pollinated by hummingbirds and bees. Although these two species are interfertile, hybrids do not occur in nature (Nobs, 1954). Straw (1956) described mechanical isolation of three species of Penstemon in California. *Penstemon centranthifolius* is pollinated by hummingbirds, *P. grinnellii* by carpenter bees, and *P. spectabilis* by the wasp, *Pseudomasaris vespoides. Pedicularis groenlandica* and *P. atollens* in the Sierra Nevada of California are pollinated by the same species of *Bombus*, but venter pollination occurs in the former species, head pollination in the latter (Sprague, 1962).

Among the orchids, *Ophrys lutea* and *O. fusca* are apparently kept apart entirely by mechanical isolation. Near Algiers, Stebbins and Ferlan (1956) found a great number of individuals of both species growing together with but a few intermediate forms. Pseudocopulatory pollination is performed by male bees of the genus *Andrena*. *Ophrys lutea* is pollinated by *A. senecionis*, *O. fusca* by *A. fulvicrus*, *A. trimmerana*, and *A. nigroaenea*. *Andrena nigro-olivacea* was seen to visit both orchid species but it is not known whether it is capable of pollinating both species (see Stebbins and Ferlan, 1956; see also Kullenberg, 1961, p. 289, etc.). In Ecuador along the western slopes of the Andes in the region of Quevedo, *Stanhopea tricornis* and *S. bucephalus* occur sympatrically. Dodson and Frymire (1961) found that both species were pollinated by male bees of the genus *Eulaema*, the former by *E. meriana*, the latter by *E. bomboides*. Although these two species are highly interfertile, hybrids between them are not found in nature (Dodson, personal communication).

Both *S. apiana* and *S. mellifera* possess complex floral mechanisms adapted to a different set of insect pollinators. The precision of the floral mechanism in each case resides in a fine adjustment of a combination of characters. That the underlying gene combination controlling the floral mechanism is not a tightly linked system in either species is evidenced by the recombination of the floral characteristics of both parental species in the hybrids. It is not surprising that the recombination products of two species with differently adapted floral mechanisms possess a corolla conformation not well adapted to any particular insect pollinator which visits the flowers frequently.

As with *S. apiana* and *S. mellifera*, the mechanical isolation existing in the genera mentioned above is not always completely effective. The pair of *Aquilegia* species (*A. formosa* and *A. pubescens*) described by Grant (1952) achieve only partial isolation through floral adaptations to different pollinators. In the southwestern United States *A. chrysantha* and *A. longissima* are pollinated by hawkmoths. Both species have pale yellow erect flowers with long slender spurs. In the Sierra Nevada of California, *A. pubescens*, a short spurred member of the *A. chrysantha* group, is pollinated by both hawkmoths and hummingbirds (Grant, 1963, pp. 356–358). In this area, *A. pubescens* hybridizes freely with *A. formosa*, a red-flowered, short-spurred, hummingbird pollinated species, and the effects of hybridization and introgression are evident in the short spurs of *A. pubescens*. Mechanical isolation in these columbines is most pronounced in the southwestern species which are not hybridizing. In the Sierras, hybridization between *A. formosa* and *A. pubescens* does occur, and mechanical isolation is weakly effective. *Aquilegia formosa* remains a hummingbird pollinated species, whereas *A. pubescens* is facultatively pollinated by hummingbirds and hawkmoths.

Nobs (1954) found that hybrids between *Mimulus cardinalis* and *M. lewisii* produced by artificial pollination in the experimental plot had an intermediate corolla conformation such that neither pollinator of either parental species nor any other insect visiting them could effect pollination. Only three types of F_2's proved reproductively successful—those that closely resembled one parent or the other and could be pollinated by the normal pollinators of *M. cardinalis* and *M. lewisii*, and a rare recombinant type which was self-fertilizing. Thus, even if interspecific pollinations occurred in nature, the F_1's would first be restricted by lack of pollinators. Given pollinators, selection would favor F_2 types resembling either parent and introgression would take place. The only favorable prospect for the establishment of hybrids between *M. cardinalis* and *M. lewisii* in nature lies in the rare self-fertilizing recombination type.

SUMMARY

Natural hybridization between *Salvia apiana* and *S. mellifera* is restricted by ecological, seasonal, mechanical, and ethological isolation, and by partial sterility barriers which are not yet fully understood.

Mechanical isolation plays a key role in this combination of isolating mechanisms.

The small flowers of *S. mellifera* are similar in corolla form to many other mint flowers, and are well suited for pollination by the small- and medium-sized insects which visit them. A wide array of insects is capable of pollinating the flowers of *S. mellifera*; in the present study 13 species of bees, one syrphid fly, two species of beeflies, six species of Lepidoptera, and the Anna hummingbird were observed visiting and pollinating the flowers. The flowers of *S. apiana*, on the other hand, are unique in the genus. The corolla form of this species is atypical of labiate flowers in the much reduced upper corolla lip, the greatly extended and folded lower corolla lip, and the extremely long and wide set stamens and style. In contrast to the many effective insect pollinators of *S. mellifera*, only four species of very large bees were observed to be capable of pollinating *S. apiana*.

The mechanical isolation existing between the two *Salvia* species is based on their differently formed flowers; and each plant species is, with rare exception, visited by insects belonging to its own respective set of pollinators. The normal pollinators of *S. mellifera* are incapable of pollinating *S. apiana*, and the corolla conformation of *S. apiana* constitutes a barrier to pollination by any insects which visit the flowers with the exception of very large bees. However, the mechanical isolation between the two species breaks down to the extent that at least two of the smaller pollinators of *S. apiana* (*Xylocopa tabaniformis* and *Bombus vosnesenskii*) can, and on occasion do, pollinate *S. mellifera*.

The smaller of the carpenter bee pollinators, *Xylocopa tabaniformis*, is probably the chief agent of interspecific pollinations, for it was frequently seen to visit *S. apiana*, and on rare occasions to visit *S. mellifera*. Pollen is mainly transferred from *S. apiana* to *S. mellifera* in interspecific pollinations, and *S. mellifera* thus generally serves as the maternal parent in these crosses. The intermediate nature of the corolla conformation of F_1 individuals is a barrier to pollination in itself. As the insects which do visit the F_1 types are among the normal pollinators of *S. mellifera*, backcrossing takes place largely in the direction of this parental species. Such backcross types in the direction of *S. mellifera*, closely resembling that parent in corolla form, are regularly pollinated by the normal pollinators of *S. mellifera*.

Thus *S. apiana* and *S. mellifera* are separated by a combination of isolating mechanisms, yet hybridization is not infrequent in areas where the ecological isolation between them is ineffective and the two species grow side by side. Once hybridization has taken place, introgression is favored by the disintegration of the seasonal isolation between the two species. The backcross types in the direction of *S. mellifera* bloom several weeks later than pure *S. mellifera* individuals, and thus extend the period of simultaneous bloom with *S. apiana*, increasing the opportunities for interspecific pollination. On the other hand, reproduction of F_1 individuals is restricted by their reduced fertility, low seed viability, and their floral form which is not well adapted for pollination by the insects which visit them. Although natural hybridization is promoted by factors working in opposition to the mechanisms isolating the two species, the effects of hybridization are severely restricted to the immediate vicinity of the hybridizing individuals by short-range pollen and seed dispersal.

ACKNOWLEDGMENTS

For identifications of insects the authors are deeply indebted to Mr. P. H. Timberlake of the University of California, Riverside; Mr. Lloyd Martin of the Los Angeles County Museum; and Dr. David P. Gregory, formerly of the Rancho Santa Ana Botanic Garden. Mr. Charles S. Papp of Riverside prepared the illustrations. This study was aided by a research grant (no.

9962) from the National Science Foundation.

LITERATURE CITED

ABRAMS, L. 1951. Illustrated flora of the Pacific states. Vol. 3. Stanford Univ. Press, Stanford.

ANDERSON, E., AND B. ANDERSON. 1954. Introgression of *Salvia apiana* and *Salvia mellifera*. Anns. Mo. Bot. Gard., **41**: 329–338.

DAWSON, WM. L. 1923. The birds of California. Vol. 2. South Moulton Co., San Diego, Los Angeles, and San Francisco.

DODSON, C. H., AND G. P. FRYMIRE. 1961. Preliminary studies in the genus Stanhopea (Orchidaceae). Anns. Mo. Bot. Gard., **48**: 137–172.

EPLING, C. 1947a. Natural hybridization of *Salvia apiana* and *S. mellifera*. EVOLUTION, **1**: 69–78.

——. 1947b. The genetic aspects of natural populations. Actual and potential gene flow in natural populations. Amer. Nat., **81**: 104–113.

——, H. LEWIS, AND P. H. RAVEN. 1962. Chromosomes of Salvia: section Audibertia. Aliso, **5**: 217–221.

GRANT, V. 1949. Pollination systems as isolating mechanisms in angiosperms. EVOLUTION, **3**: 82–97.

——. 1952. Isolation and hybridization between *Aquilegia formosa* and *A. pubescens*. Aliso, **2**: 341–360.

——. 1963. The origin of adaptations. Columbia Univ. Press, New York.

HOLM, R. W. 1950. The American species of *Sarcostemma* R. Br. (Asclepiadaceae). Anns. Mo. Bot. Gard., **37**: 477–560.

KULLENBERG, B. 1961. Studies on Ophrys pollination. Zool. Bidrag (Uppsala), **34**: 1–340.

NOBS, M. A. 1954. Genetic studies on Mimulus. Carnegie Inst. of Wash. Year Book No. **53**: 157–159.

SPRAGUE, E. F. 1962. Pollination and evolution in Pedicularis (Scrophulariaceae). Aliso, **5**: 181–209.

STEBBINS, G. L., AND L. FERLAN. 1956. Population variability, hybridization, and introgression in some species of *Ophrys*. EVOLUTION, **10**: 32–46.

STRAW, R. M. 1956. Floral isolation in Penstemon. Amer. Nat., **90**: 47–53.

ADDITIONAL REFERENCES

ALSTON, R. E., and B. L. TURNER. 1963. Biochemical systematics. Prentice-Hall, Englewood Cliffs.

ANDERSON, E. 1949. Introgressive hybridization. John Wiley & Sons, New York.

BENSON, L. 1962. Plant taxonomy. Ronald Press, New York.

CAIN, S. 1944. Foundations of plant geography. Harper & Bros., New York.

CARLQUIST, S. 1961. Comparative plant anatomy. Holt, Rinehart & Winston, New York.

CLAUSEN, J. 1951. Stages in the evolution of plant species. Cornell University Press, Ithaca.

DAVIS, G. L. 1966. Systematic embryology of the angiosperms. John Wiley & Sons, New York.

DAVIS, P. H., and V. H. HEYWOOD. 1963. Principles of angiosperm taxonomy. Oliver & Boyd, Edinburgh.

EAMES, A. J. 1961. Morphology of the angiosperms. McGraw-Hill Book Co., New York.

HESLOP-HARRISON, J. 1956. New concepts in flowering-plant taxonomy. Harvard University Press, Cambridge.

SOKAL, R. R., and P. H. A. SNEATH. 1963. Numerical taxonomy. W. H. Freeman, San Francisco.

STEBBINS, G. L. 1950. Variation and evolution in plants. Columbia University Press, New York.

STEBBINS, G. L. 1966. Processes of organic evolution. Prentice-Hall, Englewood Cliffs.

SWAIN, T., ed. 1966. Comparative phytochemistry. Academic Press, New York.